D1423170

CHEMISTRY OF CARBON COMPOUNDS

SOLE DISTRIBUTORS FOR THE U.S.A. AND CANADA:
ELSEVIER PRESS INC., 402 LOVETT BOULEVARD, HOUSTON (TEXAS),
AND 155 EAST 82ND STREET, NEW YORK 28 (N.Y.)
FOR THE BRITISH COMMONWEALTH EXCEPT CANADA:
CLEAVER-HUME PRESS, LTD., 42A SOUTH AUDLEY STREET, LONDON, W.1

Printed in The Netherlands

CORRIGENDA TO VOLUME IIA

Page 24: line 14, delete "two molecules of".

Page 34: line 6*, for dicarbocylic read dicarboxylic.

Page 40: line 14, for 2:3-Diphenylcyclopropane- read 2:3-Diphenylcyclopropene-.

Page 67: line 6, for dl-cis-*caryophyllenic acid* read dl-cis-*norcaryophyllenic acid.*

Page 106: delete double bond leading to hydroxyl group in formula for Reductic acid.

Page 115: line 9*, for CH·CONHEt read C·CONHEt.

Page 139: line 16, for "see p. 10" read "see p. 133".

Page 168: line 13, for cyclohexanetetrol read cyclohexanehexol.

Page 169: line 7, for aee read see.

Page 189: reference opposite Cyclohexa-1:3-dienealdehyde (eight up from bottom of table) should be 12, not 2.

Page 255: line 2*, for 3-bromocyclohex-3-ene read 3-bromocyclohex-1-ene.

Page 235: lines 16 and 17, for "ethylene, trimethylene and tetramethylene" read "tetramethylene, trimethylene and ethylene".

Page 246: line 16, for -2:4-dione- read -2:5-dione-.

Page 307: formula 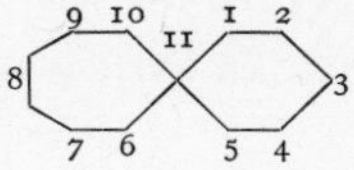 at top of page should be 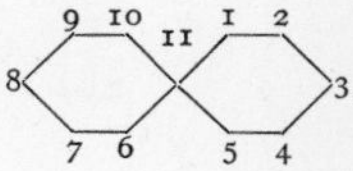 .

* denotes from bottom.

CHEMISTRY OF CARBON COMPOUNDS

ADVISORS

CHEMISTRY
of
CARBON COMPOUNDS

VOLUME I

GENERAL INTRODUCTION
ALIPHATIC COMPOUNDS

*

VOLUME II

ALICYCLIC COMPOUNDS

*

VOLUME III

AROMATIC COMPOUNDS

*

VOLUME IV

HETEROCYCLIC COMPOUNDS

*

VOLUME V

MISCELLANEOUS
GENERAL INDEX

*

CHEMISTRY
of
CARBON COMPOUNDS

A modern comprehensive treatise

Edited by

E. H. RODD, A.C.G.I., D.I.C., D.SC., F.R.I.C.

VOLUME II PART A

ALICYCLIC COMPOUNDS

ELSEVIER PUBLISHING COMPANY

AMSTERDAM HOUSTON LONDON NEW YORK

1953

CONTRIBUTORS TO THIS VOLUME

R. G. R. Bacon, *Belfast*, PH.D., A.R.C.S.

L. Crombie, *London*, B.SC., PH.D.

R. E. Fairbairn, *Manchester*, B.SC., PH.D., A.R.I.C. (Index)

R. F. Hunter, *Birmingham* (formerly *Port Sunlight*), D.SC., PH.D., D.I.C., A.R.C.S.

R. A. Raphael, *Glasgow*, PH.D., D.SC., A.R.C.S.

PREFACE TO VOLUME II

This second volume of "Chemistry of Carbon Compounds", presenting the chemistry of the non-aromatic carbocyclic compounds, is planned on simple lines. The opening chapter discusses theoretical aspects of the structure and stability of saturated carbon rings, after which eight chapters are devoted to the chemistry of the different types of alicyclic compounds, from those containing single rings of all sizes to the more complex spiro, fused ring and bridged ring compounds. The foundation is thus laid for the understanding of the chemistry of the large groups of increasingly complex substances of natural origin of alicyclic type, especially the terpenoid and steroid compounds and their relatives. For better or worse these adjectives have become nouns and we speak of the "terpenoids" and "steroids". The group of naturally occurring polyene compounds known as "carotenoids" has been given a separate chapter. Certain of the carotenoids and terpenoids are, indeed, aliphatic, having no closed rings in their structure but, because of their close affinity with their more numerous cyclic relatives, they are discussed in this volume. For a similar reason the discussion of rubber and related compounds was not included in Volume I but was postponed for inclusion in the same volume as the terpenoids. So much of our detailed knowledge of the chemistry of rubber has been gained from technological studies that no excuse need be offered for the somewhat technical flavour of Chapter XI. This chapter also offered a convenient place for a discussion of the subject of the polymerisation of olefinic compounds for which no place had been found in Volume I.

Many natural products have, in this volume, been discussed as members of one of the chemical types to which they structurally belong; for example the pyrethrins and the acids related to chaulmoogric acid appear in the chapter dealing with cyclopentane derivatives. For many reasons it was not considered wise to present the terpenoids in this way and the historical practice of presenting them separately has been followed. In discussing the chemistry of the terpenoids and steroids, moreover, the writers have, for didactic reasons, not adhered to the formal order of discussion used in the earlier chapters, i.e. starting with hydrocarbons and finishing with carboxylic acids. The steroids have been given what may be considered unusually full and detailed treatment for a treatise of this kind. The elucidation of their structures, in all their stereochemical complexity, and the successes which have attended efforts to synthesise members of the group, constitute some of the most brilliant achievements of organic chemists. For these reasons, and because of their extraordinary biological importance and the probability that their study will for many years be a major activity, the space allotted to them would appear to be justified.

April, 1953 E. H. RODD

CONTENTS

ALICYCLIC COMPOUNDS

Chapter IV. Cyclopentane Group

by R. A. Raphael

Chapter V. Cyclohexane Group

by R. A. Raphael

Chapter VI. Cycloheptane, Cyclo-octane and Macrocyclic Groups

by R. A. RAPHAEL

Chapter VII. Polynuclear Alicyclic Compounds with Separate Ring Systems and Spiro Compounds

by R. A. RAPHAEL

Chapter VIII. Polynuclear Alicyclic Compounds

Condensed Cyclic Systems

by R. A. RAPHAEL

Chapter IX. Bridged Ring Systems

by R. A. Raphael

Chapter X. The Carotenoid Group

by R. F. Hunter

Chapter XI. Open-chain and Cyclic Polymers Derived from Olefinic Compounds; Rubber and Rubber-like Compounds, Natural and Synthetic, and Their Derivatives

by R. G. R. Bacon

For Contents of Vol. II B, see next page

VOLUME IIB

will contain the following chapters:

LIST OF PERIODICALS

The figure in brackets after the title is the first ascertainable year of publication

Acta Chem. Scand.	Acta Chemica Scandinavica (1947)
Acta Phytochim. Japan	Acta Phytochimica, Japan (1922/23)
Adv. Carb. Chem.	Advances in Carbohydrate Chemistry (1945)
Adv. Colloid Sci.	Advances in Colloid Science (1942)
Angew. Chem.	Angewandte Chemie (1887)
Ann.	Annalen der Chemie, Justus Liebigs (1832)
Ann. Chim.	Annales de chimie, before 1914 Annales de chimie et de physique, before 1816 Annales de chimie ou recueil de Mémoires etc. (1789).
Ann. Physik	Annalen der Physik (1799)
Ann. Rev. Biochem.	Annual Review of Biochemistry (1932)
Ann. Suppl.	Annalen der Chemie, Supplement (1861)
Annual Reports	Annual Reports on the Progress of Chemistry, London (1904)
Arch. Biochem.	Archives of Biochemistry (1943). Changed in 1951 to Archives of Biochemistry and Biophysics
Arch. Exp. Path.	Archiv für experimentelle Pathologie und Pharmakologie unter Mitwirkung der deutschen pharmakologischen Gesellschaft, Naunyn-Schmiedeberg's (1873)
Arch. Pharm.	Archiv der Pharmazie, Berlin (1822)
Arch. Rubbercultuur	Archief voor de Rubbercultuur in Nederlandsch-Indië (1917)
Australian J. Science	Australian Journal of Science (1938)
Ber.	Berichte der deutschen chemischen Gesellschaft (1868), since 1947 Chemische Berichte
Biochem. Z.	Biochemische Zeitschrift (1906)
Biokhimiya	Biokhimiya U.S.S.R. (1936)
Brennstoff-Chem.	Brennstoff-Chemie (1926)
Brit. chem. Abstr.	British Chemical Abstracts, London (1926) since 1945, British Abstracts
Bull. Acad. roy. sci. Belg.	Bulletin de l'académie royale des sciences de Belgique (1832)
Bull. Acad. Sci. Petrograd	Bulletin of the Academy of Science Petrograd (1835)
Bull. Acad. Sci. U.R.S.S.	Bulletin de l'académie des sciences de l'U.R.S.S., Classe des sciences mathématiques et naturelles (1931)
Bull. Acad. Sci. U.R.S.S., Sér. biol.	Bulletin de l'académie des sciences de l'U.R.S.S. Série biologique (1925)

Bull. chem. Soc. Japan	Bulletin of the Chemical Society of Japan (1926)
Bull. Classe sci. Acad. roy. Belg.	See Bull. Acad. roy. sci. Belg.
Bull. Soc. chim. Belg.	Bulletin de la société chimique de Belgique et Recueil des travaux chimiques belges (1887)
Bull. Soc. chim. Fr.	Bulletin de la société chimique de France (1859)
Bull. Soc. Sci. Nancy	Bulletin de la société des sciences de Nancy, formerly Bulletin mensuel de la société des sciences de Nancy (1936)
C.A.	Chemical Abstracts (1907)
Canad. J. Res.	Canadian Journal of Research (1922)
Chem. Ber.	See Ber.
Chem. Eng. News	Chemical and Engineering News (1923)
Chem. and Ind.	Chemistry & Industry (1923)
Chem. Reviews	Chemical Reviews (1924)
Chem. Weekbl.	Chemisch Weekblad (1903)
Chem. Ztbl.	Chemisches Zentralblatt (1830, from 1945–1949 two competing editions were published in the Eastern and Western zones of Germany which were combined in 1950)
Chem.-Ztg.	Chemiker-Zeitung (1877)
Chim. et Industr.	Chimie et Industrie (1918)
Coll. Czech. chem. Comm.	Collection of Czechoslovak Chemical Communications (1929)
Compt. rend.	Comptes rendus hebdomadaires des séances de l'académie des sciences, Paris (1835)
C.r. Acad. Sci. U.R.S.S.	Comptes rendus (Doklady) de l'académie des sciences de l'U.R.S.S. (1922)
Curr. Sci.	Current Science, Bangalore (1932)
Dict. appl. Chem.	Thorpe's Dictionary of Applied Chemistry
Endeavour	Endeavour, London (1942)
Experientia	Experientia, Bazel (1945)
Faraday Soc. Discussions	Discussions of the Faraday Society (1947)
Fortschr. chem. Forschg.	Fortschritte der chemischen Forschung (1949)
Gazz. chim.	Gazzetta chimica italiana, Roma (1871)
Gomma	Gomma (discontinued in 1943) (1937)
Helv.	Helvetica Chimica Acta (1918)
Ind. Eng. Chem.	Industrial and Engineering Chemistry, before 1923 Journal of . . . . (1909)
Ind. Eng. Chem. Anal. Ed.	Industrial and Engineering Chemistry, Analytical Edition (1929)
India Rubber World	India Rubber World and Electrical Trades Review (1889)
J. Amer. chem. Soc.	Journal of the American Chemical Society (1879)
J. Amer. pharm. Assn	Journal of the American Pharmaceutical Association, Scientific Edition (1912)
J. biol. Chem.	The Journal of Biological Chemistry (1905)
J. chem. Educ.	Journal of Chemical Education (1924)
J. chem. Phys.	Journal of Chemical Physics (American Institute of Physics) (1933)

J. chem. Soc.	Journal of the Chemical Society, London (1849)
J. gen. Chem. U.S.S.R.	Journal of General Chemistry U.S.S.R. (1931)
J. Indian chem. Soc.	Journal of the Indian Chemical Society, vols 2–4 The Quarterly Journal of . . . . (1924)
J. Indian Inst. Science	Journal of the Indian Institute of Science (1914)
J. org. Chem.	Journal of Organic Chemistry (1936)
J. Pharm. Chim. Paris	Journal de pharmacie et de chimie, Paris (1815)
J. pharm. Soc. Japan	Journal of the Pharmaceutical Society of Japan (1881)
J. phys. Chem.	Journal of Physical Chemistry (U.S.S.R.) (1930/31)
J. Polymer Sci.	Journal of Polymer Science, New York (1946)
J. pr. Chem.	Journal für praktische Chemie (1834)
J. Res. Nat. Bur. Stand.	Journal of Research of the National Bureau of Standards, formerly Bureau of Standards Journal of Research (1928)
J. Rubb. Res. Inst. Malaya	Journal of the Rubber Research Institute of Malaya (1929)
J. Sci. Food and Agric.	Journal of the Science of Food and Agriculture (1950)
J. Soc. Chem. Ind.	Journal of the Society of Chemical Industry (1881)
J. Soc. chem. Ind. Japan	Journal of the Society of Chemical Industry (1898). Continued in 1948 as Journal of the Chemical Society of Japan, Industrial Chemistry Section
J. Soc. phys.-chem. Russe	Journal of the Russian Physical-chemical Society (1869/70, discontinued 1930)
Kautschuk	Kautschuk (1925). In 1943 name changed to Gummi-Zeitung und Kautschuk
Kemijski Vjestnik	Vol. 15–17 of Arhiv za Kemiju (1927)
Klin. Wochschr.	Klinische Wochenschrift (1922)
Kolloid-Z.	Kolloid-Zeitschrift (1906/07)
Malay. agric. J.	The Malayan Agricultural Journal (formerly Agricultural Bulletin of the Federated Malay States) (1912)
Monatsh.	Monatshefte für Chemie und verwandte Teile anderer Wissenschaften (1880)
Nature	Nature, London (1870)
Naturwiss.	Die Naturwissenschaften, Berlin (1913)
Org. Reactions	Organic Reactions, New York (1946)
Org. Synth.	Organic Syntheses, New York (1921)
Öst. Chem.-Ztg.	Österreichische Chemiker-Zeitung (1898)
Pharm. J.	Pharmaceutical Journal (1841)
Pharm. Weekbl.	Pharmaceutisch Weekblad (1864)

Phil. Mag.	Philosophical Magazine, London (1798)
Proc. Koninkl. Nederland. Akad. Wetenschap.	Proceedings of the Koninklijke Nederlandsche Akademie van Wetenschappen (formerly Proceedings of the Royal Academy of Sciences of Amsterdam (1898)
Proc. roy. Soc.	Proceedings of the Royal Society of London (1885)
Proc. Rubber Tech. Conf.	Proceedings of the Rubber Technology Conference
Pyrethrum Post	Pyrethrum Post, London (1949)
Quart. J. Rubb. Res. Inst. Malaya	Quarterly Journal of the Rubber Research Institute of Malaya (1929)
Quart. J. Sci.	Quarterly Journal of Science, Literature and Arts, London (1816)
Quart. Reviews	Quarterly Reviews, London (1947)
Rec. Trav. chim.	Recueil des travaux chimiques des Pays-Bas (1882)
Research	Research, London (1947/8)
Science	Science, Washington (1883)
Svensk Kem. Tidsk.	Svensk Kemisk Tidskrift (1889)
Trans. Faraday Soc.	Transactions of the Faraday Society (1905/06)
Trans. Instn. Rubb. Ind.	Transactions of the Institution of the Rubber Industry (1925/26)
U.S. Pub. Health Service Bull.	United States Public Health Service. Hygienic Laboratory Bulletin (1900)
Z. anal. Chem.	Zeitschrift für analytische Chemie (1888)
Z. angew. Chem.	Zeitschrift für angewandte Chemie, see Angewandte Chemie (1888)
Z. anorg. Chem.	Zeitschrift für anorganische und allgemeine Chemie (1892)
Z. Elektrochem.	Zeitschrift für Elektrochemie und angewandte physikalische Chemie (1894/5)
Z. Naturforsch.	Zeitschrift für Naturforschung (1946)
Z. phys. Chem.	Zeitschrift für physikalische Chemie (1887)
Z. physiol. Chem.	Hoppe-Seyler's Zeitschrift für physiologische Chemie (1877)

OFFICIAL PUBLICATIONS

B.P.	British Patent
Dutch P.	Dutch Patent
F.P.	French Patent
G.P.	German Patent
U.S.P.	United States Patent
B.I.O.S.	British Intelligence Objectives Sub-Committee Reports, H.M. Stationery Office, London
F.I.A.T.	Field Information Agency. Technical Reports of U.S. Group Control Council for Germany

LIST OF COMMON ABBREVIATIONS AND SYMBOLS USED

Å	Ångström units
at.	atmosphere
as	asymmetrical
b.p.	boiling point
conc.	concentrated
crit.	critical
d	density
dec. or decomp.	decomposing
deriv.	derivative
f.p.	freezing point
K	dissociation constant
kcal.	kilocalories
max.	maximum
ml.	millilitres
mm.	millimetres
mol.	molecule, molecular, mole
m.p.	melting point
M.R.	molecular refraction
mμ	10^{-6} mm.
n	refractive index
s	symmetrical
soln.	solution
T	absolute temperature
temp.	temperature (in degrees centigrade)
$[\alpha]_D$	specific rotation, sodium D line
ε	molecular extinction coefficient
μ	dipole moment
χ	magnetic susceptibility
Ac	acetyl
Bu	butyl
Et	ethyl
Me	methyl
Ph	phenyl
Pr	propyl
Tosyl	*p*-toluenesulphonyl
Trityl	triphenylmethyl

Homo- as prefix signifies next higher homologue.
Nor- as prefix signifies next lower homologue.

Optical rotations are in water unless otherwise stated.

Chapter I

Introduction

R. A. RAPHAEL

Saturated ring systems

As the term implies the description alicyclic (alternatively cycloaliphatic) is applied to those compounds the chemical constitution of which involves one or more rings of carbon atoms and the characteristic properties of which closely resemble those associated with aliphatic compounds of the same functional type (see Vol. I, p. 18). They are widely distributed in nature; representatives of the monocyclic series occur as naphthenes and naphthenic acids in petroleum, as monoterpenes in essential oils, as pyrethrins in pyrethrum flowers and as natural odorants such as jasmone, muscone and civetone. The polycyclic series are well exemplified by such important classes as the sesqui-, di- and tri-terpenes and the multitudinous members of the steroid family.

The Kekulé formulation of benzene as cyclohexatriene gave added impetus to the study of the reduction products of this ring system and up to the early 1880's the only members of the alicyclic group known were derivatives of cyclohexane; indeed it had been categorically stated that rings with less or more than six members were incapable of existence (*V. Meyer*, Ann., 1876, **180**, 192). In 1883, however, *W. H. Perkin*, against the advice of his more experienced contemporaries, began his classical and immensely fruitful investigations into this subject (cf. Pedler Lecture, J. chem. Soc., 1929, 1347). The cyclobutane ring system was first obtained (Ber., 1883, 16, 1793), rapidly followed by representatives of the three and five membered systems. Cyclopropane and cyclobutane-1:3-dicarboxylic acid had a few years previously been prepared in an impure state but their nature had not been recognized (*W. Markovnikov* and *A. Krestovnikov*, Ann., 1881, **208**, 333; *A. Freund*, Monatsh., 1882, **3**, 626).

It was apparent from the first that the different ring systems exhibited wide variations in stability. Thus, although cyclohexane and cyclopentane derivatives showed great resistance to ring fission, similarly constituted cyclopropanes and cyclobutanes proved to be extremely reactive compounds; indeed in many of its reactions cyclopropane more closely resembled ethylene than cyclohexane.

The first explanation brought forth to account for these differences was the famous Strain Theory of *A. von Baeyer* (Ber., 1885, **18**, 2277; 1890, **23**, 1275). This employed the Le Bel–van't Hoff tetrahedral model of the carbon valencies and was based on two hypotheses. The first postulated that the carbon atoms in any alicyclic ring were uniplanar. The second stated that although the four carbon valencies were normally directed to the apices of a *regular* tetrahedron (i.e. the angle subtended between any two valencies was 109° 28′), this was not a rigid arrangement, the bond angles being capable of alteration. Any such deviation from the norm of 109° 28′, however, was supposed to set up a condition of *strain* in the ring, which exhibited itself by a corresponding decrease in stability; the greater the angular deviation, the greater would be the strain involved and the greater would be the ease of ring fission. The angular deflections for the various rings, if the carbon atoms are to be in one plane, may be readily computed geometrically and are as follows.

No. of C atoms in ring	3	4	5	6	7	8	9	15
Deflection	+24°44′	+9°44′	+0°44′	–5°16′	–9°51′	–12°51′	–15°16′	–23°16′

For rings smaller than cyclohexane the size of the angular deflection does indeed parallel the reactivity of the ring system. Thus, although ethylene (which for this purpose may formally be regarded as a two membered ring possessing the maximum deflection) reacts readily with halogens and halogen acids, cyclopropane forms addition compounds with rather more difficulty whilst cyclobutane, cyclopentane and cyclohexane are inert to these reagents under normal conditions (*G. Gustavson*, Compt. rend., 1900, **131**, 273; *N. Kishner*, Chem. Ztbl., 1912, I, 2025). Again, the rate of hydrogenation decreases in the order, double bond > 3-ring > 4-ring, the 5- and 6-rings being inert; dehydrogenation under mild conditions proceeds readily with 3- and 4-rings whilst 5- and 6-rings remain unaffected. Oxidising agents (e.g. potassium permanganate, ozone) are with little effect on the medium sized rings whilst the double bond is rapidly attacked.

The Baeyer theory predicts the ready formation and stability of the five-membered ring and this was strikingly verified by the properties of the cyclopentane ring described by *Perkin* (Ber., 1885, **18**, 3246). The theory is obviously capable of extension to all ring systems of atoms which possess tetrahedrally directed valencies and, on its basis, a ready explanation is forthcoming of the stabilities of γ- and δ-lactones and succinic and glutaric anhydride.

The original strain theory was modified by J. F. Thorpe and C. K. Ingold who drew attention to the fact that the subtended bond angle would be $109^{0}28'$ (i.e. conforming to a *regular* tetrahedron) only if the four groups attached to the carbon atom were identical.

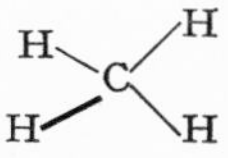

(I)

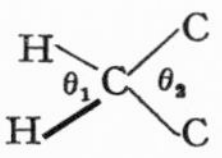

(II)

Thus in (I) the bond angles would be $109^{0}28'$ but in the case of (II) Θ_1 would be less and Θ_2 more than this value because of the increased volume of the groups subtending Θ_2. Although this conception could not be applied quantitatively, qualitatively it removed some deficiencies of the Baeyer theory and it is supported by many experimental observations. In particular it provided a basis of interpretation of the effect of substitution on the ease of formation and the stability of ring systems (*J. F. Thorpe, C. K. Ingold et al.*, J. chem. Soc., 1921, **119**, 305; 1923, **123**, 3140; 1926, 10; 1928, 1318; Annual Reports, 1925, 129; *C. L. Arcus*, Chem. and Ind., 1947, 676).

Although the Baeyer theory is in fair agreement with the facts in so far as rings smaller than that of cyclohexane are concerned it breaks down completely when employed for the interpretation of the properties of the many membered (macrocyclic) rings. Thus cyclopentadecane (muscane), with a negative valency deflection of $23^{0}16'$, might be expected to possess the same order of stability as cyclopropane with a positive valency deflection of $24^{0}44'$. In fact muscane approximates in stability to cyclohexane and the same is true of all the macrocyclic ring systems. *H. Sachse* in 1890 produced an explanation of this anomaly (Ber., 1890, **23**, 1363; Z. phys. Chem., 1892, **10**, 203) but his conceptions remained neglected until revived and elaborated by *E. Mohr* thirty years later (J. pr. Chem., 1918, [ii], **98**, 349; 1922, [ii], **103**, 316). They showed that the erroneous conclusions stemmed from the assumption that all rings must necessarily be uniplanar. This is indeed true for rings up to and including five-membered systems but from cyclohexane upwards puckered, multiplanar configurations can be envisaged which involve little or no distortion of the tetrahedral valency angles. Thus there is no theoretical barrier to the existence of macrocyclic rings as the work of L. Ruzicka, K. Ziegler, W. Hückel and many others has abundantly shown.

It must be pointed out that there is little real correlation between facility of ring formation and ease of ring fission (i.e. strain). Ring opening is powerfully influenced by steric factors and substituent effects whilst ring closure is affected by the reactivity of the reactants, by the stability of the products under the conditions of formation and, most of all, by the probability of intramolecular collision of the chain ends bearing the reactive groups. The importance of this last factor is illustrated by the poor yields of the highly stable macrocyclic compounds obtained in the earlier methods of synthesis. *Ruzicka* has expressed this probability as a "distance factor", i.e. the distance in the straight chain progenitor between the atoms which link to form the ring. This may be illustrated graphically as in Fig. 1 (Chem. and Ind. 1935, 54, 6; Helv., 1926, 9, 499).

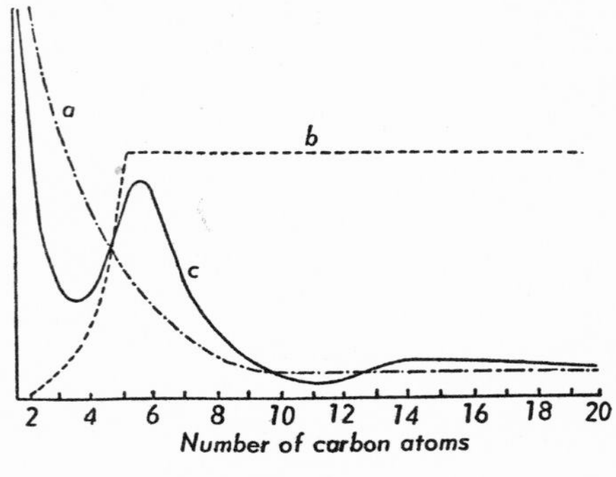

Fig. 1

Curve *a* represents the "distance factor" which, of course, leads to a decreased yield as the number of carbon atoms increases, and *b* delineates the strain factor or ease of fission, the lessening of which enhances the yield up to the first strainless ring (5) and thereafter remains constant. The combination of *a* and *b* gives curve *c* which is an approximate measure of the relative yields actually obtained under comparable preparative conditions. Modern methods of cyclisation due to M. Stoll and V. Prelog (p. 272) almost completely eliminate the "distance factor" and furnish remarkably high yields of macrocyclic compounds.

Mention should be made of the formation and stability of the unsaturated ring systems. Compounds with one double bond in the ring are known from cyclopropene upwards and, apart from their inherent ethylenic reactivity seem to possess stabilities very similar in degree to those of their saturated parent compounds. A cyclic acetylene is impossible in the smaller ring systems and attempts to obtain cycloheptyne have resulted in the formation of the cyclic allene, cyclohepta-1:2-diene (*A. Favorski*, Bull. Soc. chim. Fr., 1936, [v], 3, 727; C.A., 1936, 30, 1936). Cyclo-octyne and the higher homologues present no difficulty in preparation (*L. Ruzicka et al.*, Helv., 1933, 16, 498; *N. A. Domnin*, C.A., 1939, 33, 1282; 1940, 34, 4383; 1948, 42, 3337; *A. T. Blomquist et al.*, J. Amer. chem. Soc., 1951, 73, 5510; *idem, ibid.*, 1952, 74, 3634, 3643; *V. Prelog et al.*, Helv., 1952, 35, 1598).

Isomerism of alicyclic compounds

Position isomerism occurs in analogous fashion to that arising in the aliphatic series and lack of the elements of symmetry also results in stereoisomerism with consequent resolvability. As the three-, four- and five-membered rings are uniplanar (but see p. 76) geometrical isomerism can arise in the same manner as in the two-membered ring system (double bond), thus:

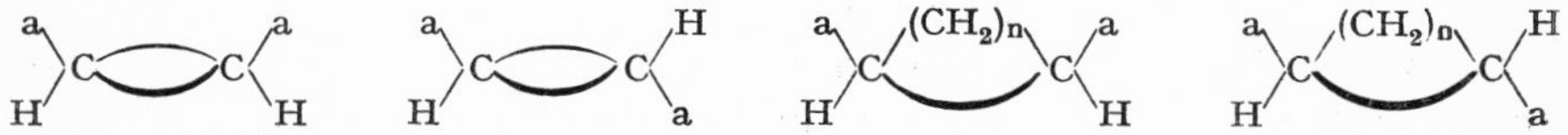

where n = 1, 2 or 3.

In the alicyclic rings more carbon atoms are available and further substitution of these leads to a large increase in the number of possible geometrical isomers. Again, since the two-membered ring inherently possesses a plane of symmetry, neither geometrical isomer is resolvable; this does not hold with the alicyclic rings where lack of the elements of symmetry with resulting resolvability is frequent. A mathematical formula for computing the number of isomers for a given alicyclic compound has been developed (*A. Morro Ramirez*, Brit. chem. Abstr., 1942, AII, 354). The detailed isomerism connected with each ring system will be discussed in its appropriate chapter but the following formulae will illustrate the points made above.

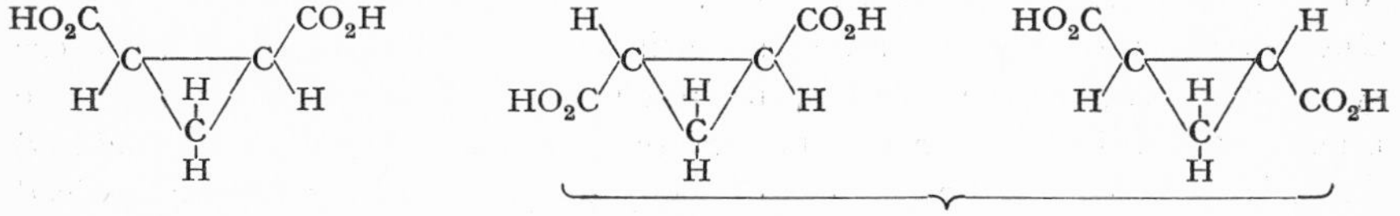

cis
non-resolvable

dl-trans
resolvable

In the case of highly substituted rings the cis(c)-trans(t) nomenclature is employed thus:

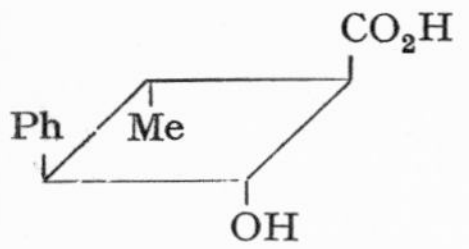

CO_2H Ph Me OH

2^c-Phenyl-3^t-methylcyclobutan-1^t-ol-4^c-carboxylic acid,

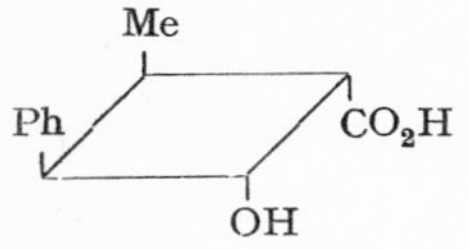

Me Ph CO_2H OH

2^c-Phenyl-3^c-methylcyclobutan-1^t-ol-4^t-carboxylic acid.

The superscripts c and t indicate the spatial position above or below the plane of the ring respectively.

Although the Sachse-Mohr concept indicates a multiplanar structure for the six-membered ring, in practice the isomers found for a *single* ring of this size conform in number to those derivable from a uniplanar structure. The reason for this will be discussed later (p. 130 ff).

Because of their uniplanar configuration the lower rings are able to replace one or both of the double bonds in unsymmetrical allene systems with the formation of alicyclic compounds which, although containing no asymmetric carbon atom, possess no element of symmetry and are therefore resolvable. This is exemplified by the substituted cyclohexane (I) (*W. H. Perkin, W. J. Pope* and *O. Wallach*, J. chem. Soc., 1909, 95, 1789) and the spiroheptane derivative (II) (*S. E. Janson* and *W. J. Hope*, Chem. and Ind., 1932, 51, 316; cf. also *H. J. Backer* and *H. B. J. Schurink*, Rec. Trav. chim., 1931, 50, 921).

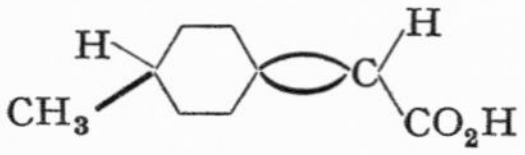

H CH_3 C H CO_2H

(I)

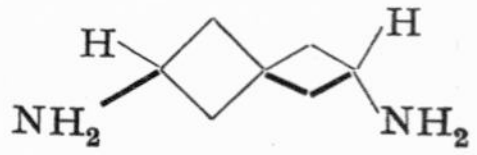

H NH_2 H NH_2

(II)

In the case of the multiplanar rings from cycloheptane upwards the terms *cis* and *trans* lose their precise significance and very little systematic study has been made of the stereoisomerism of substituted members of these systems. Stuart models are helpful in visualising the structures but care must be taken in interpreting the results too literally (cf. *C. S. Marvel* and *D. B. Glass*, J. Amer. chem. Soc., 1938, 60, 1051). It has long been recognised theoretically that geometrical isomerism could occur about a double bond in the ring if this were large enough.

H $(CH_2)_n$ C C H $(CH_2)_n$ H C C H

It was only later, however, that this supposition received practical confirmation by the preparation of *cis-* and *trans-*civetone (p. 279), and the *cis-* and *trans-*isomers of cyclo-octene (*K. Ziegler et al.*, Ann. 1950, **567**, 1, 214), cyclononene and cyclodecene (*A. T. Blomquist et al.*, J. Amer. chem. Soc., 1952, **74**, 3634, 3643; *V. Prelog et al.*, Helv., 1952, **35**, 1598). Modern work has yielded much information with regard to the spatial configurations, or "constellations" as they are termed, of the many-membered rings themselves (p. 274).

Physical properties of alicyclic compounds

The melting-point curves of the main alicyclic types (hydrocarbons, alcohols, ketones and diketones) exhibit a marked contrast to those of the corresponding aliphatic compounds. In the aliphatic series melting points rise continuously with increasing molecular size whilst the values for the homologous alicyclic compounds oscillate to a maximum and then descend to a minimum (*L. Ruzicka et al.*, Helv., 1930, **13**, 1152; 1945, **28**, 395).

A similar situation obtains in the density curves; the density of the aliphatic compounds increases steadily with the number of carbon atoms whilst that of the cycloparaffins, cyclic ketones and cyclic alcohols reaches a maximum and then slowly falls off, the final values approaching those of the aliphatic series (*L. Ruzicka et al.*, Helv., 1926, **9**, 499; 1930, **13**, 1157; 1934, **17**, 79; 1949, **32**, 256; *W. H. Carothers* and *J. W. Hill*, J. Amer. chem. Soc., 1933, **55**, 5042, 5048). An explanation of this latter point is offered by the conception of the molecules of the higher solid alicyclic compounds as arranged in long closed chains in parallel orientation reminiscent of the paraffin structure. A thermodynamic relationship between density and size of ring confirms this idea; up to C_{14} the methylene chain is regarded as occupying a roughly spherical volume whilst from C_{16} upwards the ring is stretched out in one direction with parallel sides (*M. Stoll* and *G. Stoll-Comte*, Helv., 1930, **13**, 1185). These conclusions receive further support from X-ray spectroscopic data (*J. R. Katz*, Z. angew. Chem., 1928, **41**, 329; *A. Muller*, Helv., 1933, **16**, 155) and from the properties of monomolecular films of cyclic ketones; a large ring ketone behaves as a double paraffin chain joined to the carbonyl group (*E. H. Buchner et al.*, Z. phys. Chem., 1929 (B), **5**, 327).

The molecular volumes of the alicyclic compounds are throughout smaller than those of the corresponding aliphatics; a formula for calculating the molecular volume of cyclic hydrocarbons has been proposed (*S. S. Kurtz* and *M. R. Lipkin*, Ind. Eng. Chem., 1941, **33**, 779).

The values of the parachor for cyclic compounds approach those of the corresponding aliphatic structures as the molecular size increases (*A. I. Vogel*,

J. chem. Soc., 1928, 2018; 1946, 1804, 1809; *L. Ruzicka et al.*, Helv. 1932, **15,** 8; 1933, **16,** 487; *A. Muller*, Helv., 1933, **16,** 155, 162).

The mean molecular coefficient of compressibility given by the expression $M\beta/d$ (where M = molecular weight, d = density, β = coefficient of compressibility) is nearly constant in the aliphatic series but decreases markedly with increasing size of ring in the alicyclic compounds.

The heats of combustion of the cyclic paraffins parallel the chemical stability of the systems; a direct comparison is provided by dividing the heats of combustion by the number of methylene groups (*W. Hückel*, Ber., 1920, **53,** 1277; *L. Ruzicka* and *P. Schläpfer*, Helv., 1933, **16,** 162).

Ring size	2	3	4	5	6	7	8	15	17	30	Paraffin hydrocarbon
Heat of combustion per CH_2 (kcals.)	170	168·5	165·5	159	158	158	157·8	157	157·2	156·7	158

The exaltation of molecular refraction varies from ring to ring; the three- and four-membered rings show positive exaltations whilst higher membered systems exhibit negative exaltations (*L. Ruzicka et al.*, Helv., 1930, **13,** 1162; 1931, **14,** 1323; 1934, **17,** 81; 1949, **32,** 256; *W. H. Carothers* and *J. W. Hill, loc. cit.*; *A. I. Vogel, loc. cit.*, 1948):

Ring size	3	4	5	6	7	8	9	10	11
Increment	+0·62	+0·32	−0·19	−0·15	−0·28	−0·57	−0·77	−1·58	−0·96

Ring size	12	13	14	15	16	17	18
Increment	−1·71	−0·83	−1·05	−0·95	−0·86	−0·98	−0·54

Ring closure appreciably depresses the specific exaltation of unsaturated compounds (*K. von Auwers*, Ann., 1915, **410,** 299; 1918, **415,** 98).

The maximum or minimum in the curve of physical properties of the ring homologues very frequently lies in the region between the eight-membered and twelve-membered rings. This has been demonstrated convincingly by employing the cyclic alcohol acetates as the homologous series under examination; all these compounds are liquid at ordinary temperature and thus the need for extrapolation is eliminated (*L. Ruzicka, V. Prelog et al.*, Helv., 1949, **32,** 256; J. chem. Soc., 1950, 420). These authors have furnished an explanation of the phenomenon based on modern concepts of free rotation about a single C – C bond.

$$\overset{1}{CH_2}\diagdown\underset{2}{CH_2}\diagup\overset{3}{CH_2}\diagdown\underset{4}{CH_2}$$

The results of much modern physical research have shown that, contrary to the classical conception, rotation round a simple C – C bond may tend to be hindered by virtue of the fact that the various possible configurations or "constellations" do not possess the same potential energy. If the rotation of a tetramethylene chain about the central bond ($C^2 - C^3$) be considered in this light it can be shown that the potential energy (E kcals./mol.) of the system is related to the constellation by the expression $E = -1 \cdot 7 \cos 3\varphi - 0 \cdot 5 \cos\varphi$ where φ is the angle subtented by the planes $C^1C^2C^3$ and $C^2C^3C^4$ (*H. Kuhn*, J. chem. Phys., 1947, **15**, 843; *K.S. Pitzer*, J. chem. Phys., 1940, **8**, 811). This relationship may be expressed graphically and pictorially as shown in Fig. 2; the subtending angle φ is indicated by the span of the curved arrow (• = C atoms; o = H atoms).

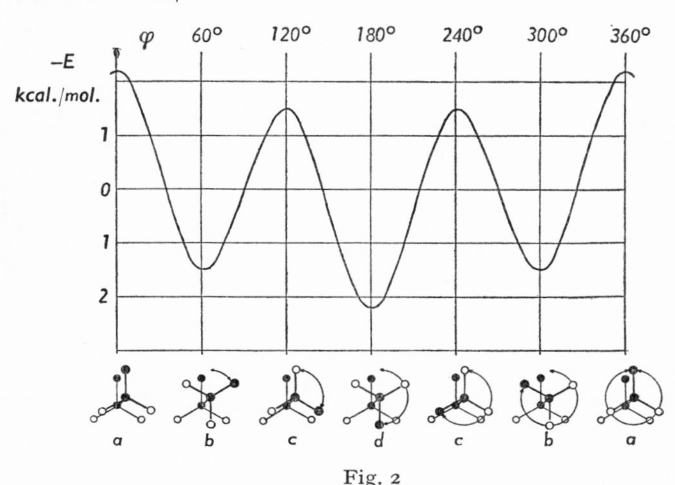

Fig. 2

From this diagram it is seen that the most favourable arrangement from an energy point of view is the zig-zag constellation *d*; such is, in fact, the molecular architecture of the highly stable straight chain paraffins. It is obvious, however, that, in the cycloparaffins, the possibility of attaining this favourable zig-zag constellation will be severely conditioned by the size of the ring. Thus the reactive nature of cyclopropane and cyclobutane might be expected in view of the fact that only the highly unfavourable constellation *a* can occur.

Pictorial representation of the alicyclic structures may be obtained by employing the known bond angles and atomic radii (either covalent or van der Waals' radii may be used according to preference, i.e., whichever fits the observer's ideas better); the so-called Stuart scale models of atoms serve this purpose admirably. If this method be applied to the medium sized rings (8–12) it becomes apparent that they can only be constituted by employing the less favourable constellations. With larger rings, however, the energetically favourable constellations *b* and *d* become possible more frequently and the molecules approximate in structure to the paraffins. This difference in constellation is paralleled by a difference in physical properties (density, molecular refraction etc.) the direction of which can be predicted on theoretical grounds.

Many of the physical properties of substituted alicyclic compounds can be employed as clues to their stereochemical configuration. Thus the so-called Auwers-Skita rule states that usually the density and refractive index of the *cis*-isomer of an alicyclic compound are higher and the molecular refraction is lower than the corresponding values for the *trans*-isomer (*K. von Auwers*, Ann., 1919, **420**, 92; *A. Skita*, Ber., 1920, **53**, 1792). In the first place this concept was established by purely empirical considerations but it has since been given a theoretical basis. In spite of this there are exceptions to the rule and caution should be used in its application. Similar considerations apply to the use of the parachor as a criterion in such cases; it is found that the parachor of the *trans*-isomer usually has a value higher than that of the *cis*- (*D. T. C. Gillespie et al.*, J. chem. Soc., 1940, 280).

A much more trustworthy method for establishing such distinctions is that associated with the name of K. S. Pitzer; this is based on thermodynamic studies involving considerations of entropy. Use of this approach has resulted in a reassessment of the compounds hitherto regarded as the *cis*- and *trans*-1:3-dimethylcyclohexanes and has shown that these appellations should be interchanged (*C. W. Beckett* and *K. S. Pitzer*, J. Amer. chem. Soc., 1947, **69**, 977). Such thermodynamic analysis of alicyclic compounds has led to much greater appreciation of the molecular fine structure in such ring systems as cyclohexane, cyclopentane, cyclohexene and cyclopentene (*K. S. Pitzer et al.*, J. Amer. chem. Soc., 1948, **70**, 4227; 1947, **69**, 2483, 2488).

The determination of the constitution of cyclic compounds, especially when an unsaturated centre is present, is often aided by consideration of the Raman spectra (*G. Dupont, P. Daure* and *J. Lévy*, Bull. Soc. chim. Fr., 1932, [v], **51**, 921; *R. Gachard*, Chem. Ztbl., 1933, II, 3269; *G. Kornfeld*, Z. angew. Chem., 1930, **43**, 393; *J. Goubeau* and *E. Köhler*, Ber., 1942, **75**, 65; *G. Chiurdoglu*, Bull. Soc. chim. Belg., 1944, **53**, 55; *J. Goubeau* and *I. Sander*, Chem. Ber., 1949, **82**, 176; *H. Gerding* and *F. Haak*, Rec. Trav. chim., 1949, **68**, 293; *Y. R. Naves et al.*, inter alia, Helv., 1949, **32**, 394); the light absorption in the ultra-violet may be employed for the same purpose (*inter al., E. A. Braude, E. R. H. Jones et al.*, J. chem. Soc., 1949, 607; *H. Bastron et al.*, J. org. Chem., 1943, **8**, 515; *W. C. Price* and *A. D. Walsh*, Proc. roy. Soc., 1941, A, **179**, 201; *I. M. Klotz*, J. chem. Educ., 1945, **22**, 328; J. Amer. chem. Soc., 1944, **66**, 88; *R. B. Woodward*, *ibid.*, 1942, **64**, 76). The infra-red spectra of alicyclic compounds are proving invaluable as a method of "finger-printing" in a unique manner each individual compound (*J. D. Bartleson et al.*, J. Amer. chem. Soc., 1946, **68**, 2513; *D. H. Whiffen* and *H. W. Thompson*, J. chem. Soc., 1948, 1420; *H. Gerding* and *F. Haak*, Rec. Trav. chim., 1949, **68**, 293; *J. M. Derfer et al.*, J. Amer. chem. Soc., 1949, **71**, 175). A recent example of the diagnostic capabilities of this new method is provided by the unequivocal confirmation of the structure of a degradation product of the antibiotic actidione as one of the optical isomers of 2:4-dimethylcyclohexanone (*E. C. Kornfeld et al.*, *ibid.*, 1949, **71**, 151).

Ring expansions and contractions

Note on structural formulae. In representing ring compounds much use will be made of simplified structural formulae in which only the bonds between the carbon atoms forming the ring are shown. The bonds may be single or double, represented by single or double lines, and carbon atoms are to be supposed situated at each point of junction. Hydrogen atoms, not shown, are assumed to be attached to each carbon atom to satisfy the valencies not engaged in carbon-carbon bonds. Thus a simple triangle represents cyclopropane, C_3H_6, a square cyclobutane, C_4H_8, a pentagon cyclopentane, C_5H_{10}, a hexagon cyclohexane, C_6H_{12} and so on. Substituent groups, OH, NH_2, CO_2H and so on are represented in the conventional manner, each such group replacing one of the unrepresented hydrogen atoms. In the formulae of terpenoid and steroid compounds alkyl groups attached to a ring may be represented in the same abbreviated fashion; thus, a single short line represents a methyl group $-CH_3$, a double line the methylene group, $=CH_2$, a zig-zag line a higher alkyl group with a carbon atom at each angle and at the free end.

Many reactions of alicyclic compounds lead to products containing a ring system of a size different from that of the starting material. At first sight this may seem to be strong evidence for the Baeyer strain theory; it may be supposed that the driving force of such transformations could spring from a tendency of strained systems towards a diminution of ring tension. Although many examples of ring expansion of the smaller rings and ring contraction of larger rings are known close examination of the subject reveals that there is no such simple correlation with the strain theory (*S. Nametkin,* Die Umlagerung alicyclische Kerne ineinander, 1926).

The oldest method for bringing about change in ring size is that due to N. J. Demjanov, involving the action of nitrous acid on cyclic primary amines. If the primary amino group is attached directly to one of the ring carbons ring contraction usually takes place (*R. Stoermer et al.,* Ber., 1927, **60**, 2566; *R. Stoermer* and *E. Asbrand,* Ber., 1931, **64**, 2793; *F. Schenk,* J. pr. Chem., 1932, **134**, 215; *D. V. Nightingale et al.,* J. org. Chem., 1952, **17**, 1017; *idem,* J. Amer. chem. Soc., 1950, **72**, 4823).

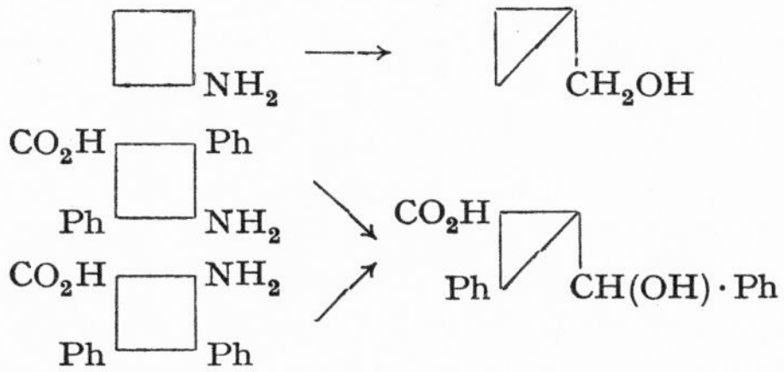

NH_2 → CH_2OH

CO_2H Ph Ph NH_2

CO_2H NH_2 Ph Ph

→ CO_2H Ph CH(OH)·Ph

It will be seen that this result is not capable of explanation on the basis of the strain theory.

If the primary amino group is situated on the first exocyclic carbon atom the action of nitrous acid produces ring expansion (*N. J. Demjanov et al.*, Chem. Ztbl., 1903, I, 828; 1904, I, 1214; 1931, II, 40; Ber., 1907, **40**, 4393; *O. Wallach*, Ann., 1907, **353**, 318; *L. Ruzicka* and *W. Brugger*, Helv., 1926, **9**, 399; *H. Barbier*, Helv., 1940, **23**, 519, 524; *M. Qudrat-I-Khuda* and *S. K. Ghosh*, J. Indian chem. Soc., 1940, **17**, 19; *Y. R. Naves* and *P. Bachmann*, Helv., 1943, **26**, 1334).

$$\text{CH}_2\text{NH}_2 \longrightarrow \text{OH} \quad [+ \quad + \quad \text{CH}_2\text{OH} \quad + \quad =\text{CH}_2]$$

Generally, as by-products, there are formed the expected primary alcohol of unaltered ring size and the dehydration products of the two carbinols. The generally accepted mechanism of this change is based on the postulate, supported by kinetic studies, that a diazonium salt is first formed which then undergoes fission into nitrogen and a carbonium ion. Rearrangement of this latter yields the expanded ring product. The formation of the alcohol of unaltered ring size may be explained by a bimolecular (S_2) replacement of $-N_2^+$ (*H. Schmid* and *G. Muhr*, Ber., 1937, **70**, 421; *W. Hückel*, Theoretische Grundlagen der Organischen Chemie, 2nd. edition, Vol. I, p. 264; *M. J. S. Dewar*, Electronic Theory of Organic Chemistry, Oxford University Press, 1949, p. 211).

$$\text{CH}_2\text{NH}_2 \longrightarrow \text{CH}_2\cdot\text{N}_2^+ \xrightarrow[-\text{N}_2]{} \text{CH}_2^+$$

$$(\text{S}_2)\ {+\text{H}_2\text{O}}\ {-\text{N}_2}: \quad \text{CH}_2\text{OH} \qquad \text{OH} \longleftarrow +$$

When cyclobutylamine is treated with nitrous acid the mixture of products formed is identical with that obtained by similar treatment of cyclopropylmethylamine. This suggests the participation of an intermediate carbonium ion $C_4H_7^+$; the structure of this entity may be very elegantly formulated by molecular orbital theory (*J. D. Roberts et al.*, J. Amer. chem. Soc., 1951 **73**, 2509, 3176, 3542, 5034; *M. J. S. Dewar*, Annual Reports, 1951, **48**, 120).

A similar type of ring expansion involves the action of nitrous acid on the substituted hydroxymethylamines obtained by reduction of the cyanohydrins or nitromethane adducts of the cyclic ketones; in this case the products are the homologous cyclic ketones.

$$\text{OH, CH}_2\text{NO}_2 \text{ or OH, CN} \xrightarrow{\text{H}_2} \text{OH, CH}_2\text{NH}_2 \xrightarrow{\text{HNO}_2} =\text{O}$$

(*B. Tchoubar*, Compt. rend., 1941, **212**, 195, 1033; 1942, **215**, 224; *L. Ruzicka et al.*, Helv., 1943, **26**, 1631; *H. J. Dauben et al.*, J. Amer. chem. Soc., 1951, **73**, 2359).

Seemingly straightforward metathetical reactions have sometimes resulted in change of ring size; both expansion and contraction of the ring have been observed in such processes. Thus cyclopropylcarbinol with hydrobromic acid furnishes some cyclobutyl bromide in addition to the expected product, whilst cyclobutylcarbinol under the same conditions gives mainly cyclopentyl bromide (*N. J. Demjanov*, Chem. Ztbl., 1914, I, 1998; Ber., 1907, **40**, 4960). Solvolysis in aqueous alcohol of either cyclobutyl chloride or cyclopropylmethyl chloride gives the same mixture of products via the cation $C_4H_7^+$.

The claim of *N. A. Rosanov* (Chem. Ztbl., 1924, I, 2426) that 1-nitro-1-methylcyclopentane is produced by the reaction of silver nitrite with cyclohexyl iodide has been refuted (*N. Kornblum* and *C. Teitelbaum*, J. Amer. chem. Soc., 1952, **74**, 3079).

The dehydration of many types of cyclic alcohol by acidic reagents such as oxalic acid or zinc chloride frequently brings about ring transformation. The following examples are typical:

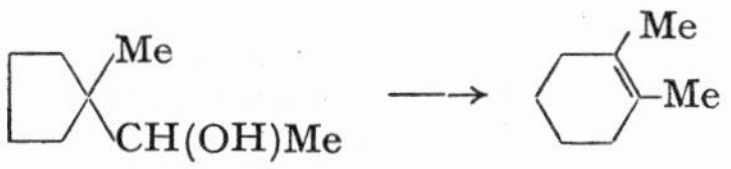

Me
CH(OH)Me
→
Me
Me

(*H. Meerwein*, Ann., 1918, **417**, 268).

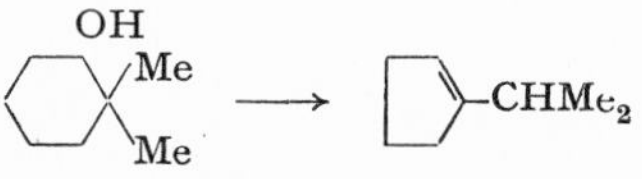

OH
Me
Me
→
$CHMe_2$

(*H. Meerwein*, Ann., 1914, **405**, 145, 151).

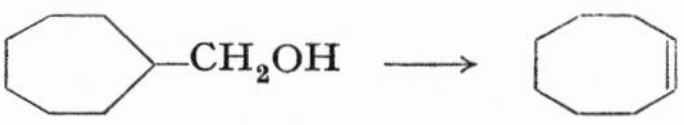

CH_2OH →

(*N. A. Rosanov*, Chem. Ztbl., 1930, II, 229).

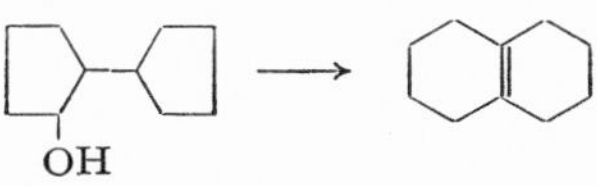

→
OH

(*W. Hückel et al.*, Ann., 1929, **474**, 121; 1930, **477**, 131).

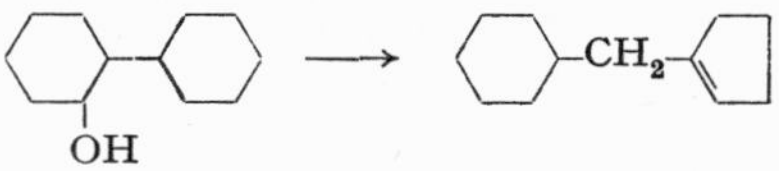

(*W. Hückel*, Ann., 1930, 477, 106).

The type of dehydration involving the grouping

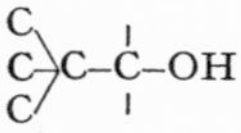

is sometimes termed the Wagner-Meerwein rearrangement (cf. Vol. IIB for its study in connection with the chemistry of the monoterpenes); it can effect either ring enlargement or ring contraction as the following example demonstrates (*H. Meerwein*, J. pr. Chem., 1922, 104, 289).

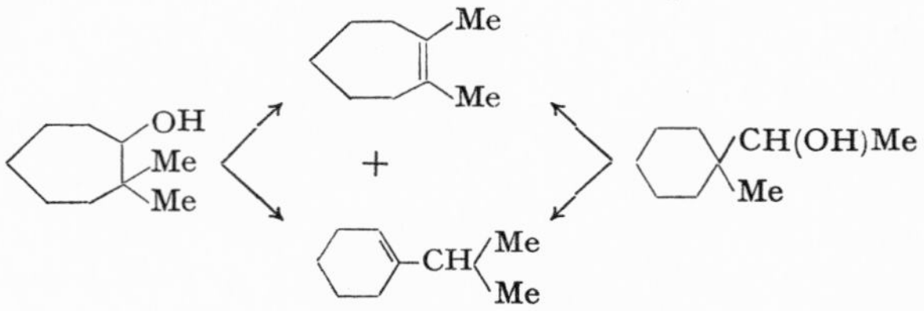

It will be noticed in each case that the production of a dehydration product of unaltered ring size has involved the migration of a methyl group.

In very similar fashion the elimination of hydrogen halide from cyclic compounds is sometimes accompanied by ring transformation (*O. Wallach*, Ann., 1905, 339, 94; *R. W. L. Clarke* and *A. Lapworth*, J. chem. Soc., 1910, 97, 11; *N. I. Schuikin*, Brit. chem. Abstr., 1945, AII, 227). The reverse of this type of reaction occurs in the well studied conversion of pinene to bornyl chloride (Vol. IIB).

Many ring transformation reactions seem to be closely related to the pinacol-pinacone rearrangement. Thus dehydration of cyclicvicinal glycols is often accompanied by change in ring size, e.g.

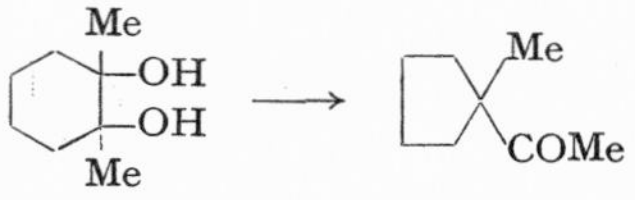

(*S. Nametkin* and *N. Delektorsky*, Ber., 1924, 57, 583); but

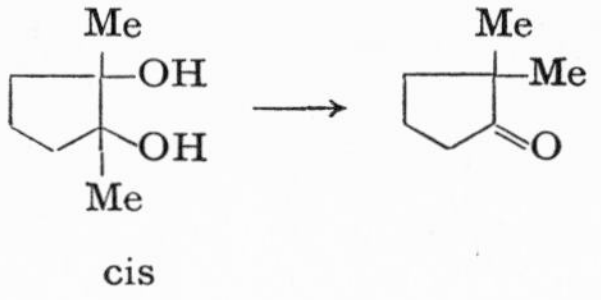

cis

(*P. D. Bartlett* and *A. Bawley*, J. Amer. chem. Soc., 1938, **60**, 2416);

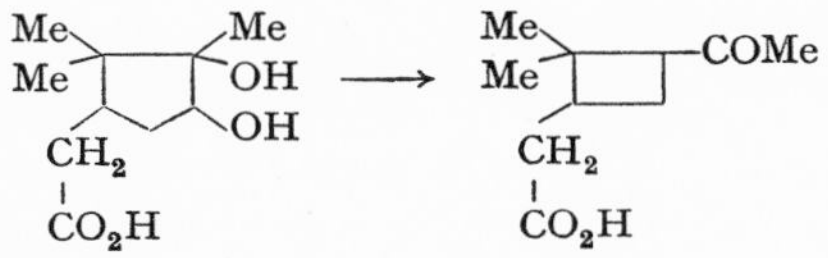

(*F. Tiemann*, Ber., 1896, **29**, 3014);

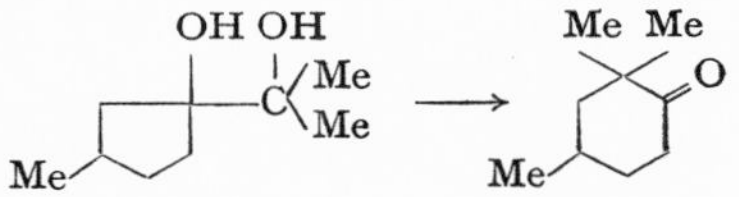

(*R. Calas*, Compt. rend., 1939, **208**, 1413; *P. J. Tarbouriech*, *ibid.*, 1913, **156**, 75);

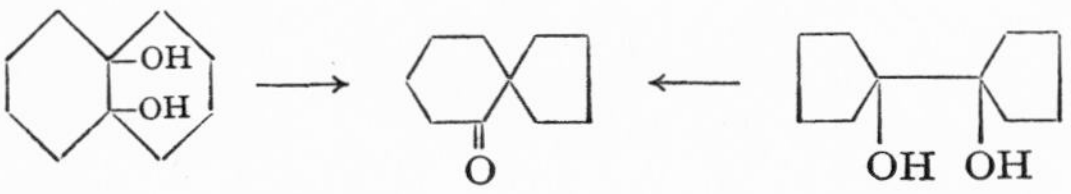

(*W. Hückel et al.*, Ann., 1929, **474**, 121; *W. Meiser*, Ber., 1899, **32**, 2049).

An interesting example is the dehydration, rearrangement and decarboxylation of the lactone shown:

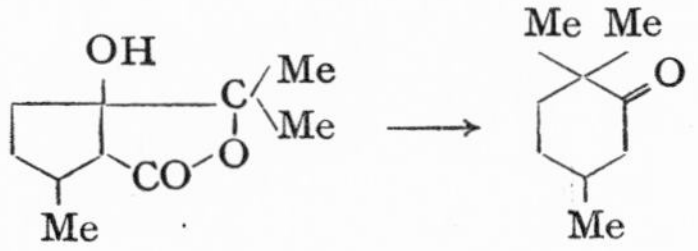

(*O. Wallach*, Ann., 1903, **329**, 83; *H. Meerwein* and *W. Unkel*, Ann., 1910, **376**, 154).

The dehydrohalogenation of cyclic halohydrins is a closely allied reaction and takes a similar course:

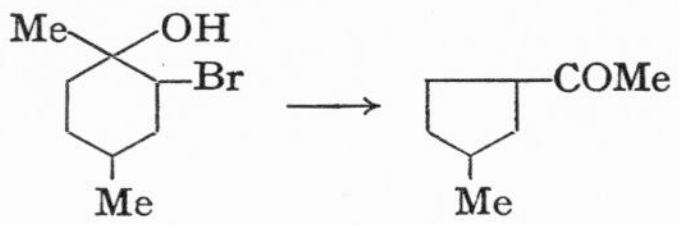

(*B. Tchoubar,* Compt. rend., 1939, **208**, 355; cf. also *M. Tiffeneau, ibid.,* 1932, **195**, 1284; *M. Le Brazidec, ibid.,* 1914, **159**, 774; *N. J. Demjanov* and *M. Dojarenko,* Ber., 1922, **55**, 2730).

The isomerisation of cyclic epoxides frequently proceeds on lines analogous to the pinacol transformation e.g.:

(*M. Tiffeneau,* Compt. rend., 1932, **195**, 1284; cf. also *J. Lévy* and *J. Sfiras, ibid.,* 1928, **187**, 45; Bull. Soc. chim. Fr., 1931, [iv], **49**, 1830).

Alkaline reagents seem to be very suitable for bringing about ring transformation; some rearrangements effected by this means are typified by the following. α-Halogenated cyclohexanones in an alkaline medium are dehydrohalogenated with concomitant ring contraction; this is sometimes termed the Favorsky reaction (see p. 200).

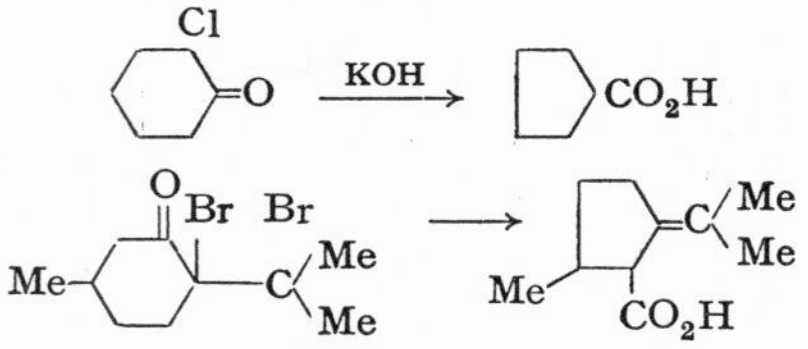

(*O. Wallach,* Ann., 1903, **327**, 147; 1903, **329**, 108; 1918, **414**, 233; *A. Favorsky* and *W. Boshovsky,* Chem. Ztbl., 1915, I, 984).

Alkali is also employed to effect an interesting benzil-benzilic acid type of rearrangement involving certain cyclic α-diketones:

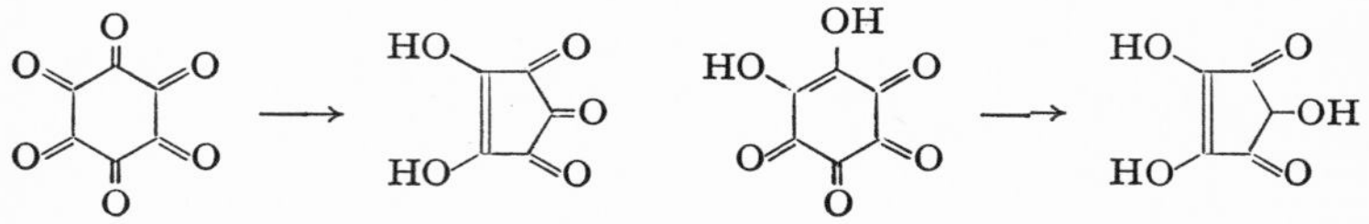

(*R. Nietzki* and *T. Benckiser,* Ber., 1885, **18**, 499, 1833; 1886, **19**, 293; 1887, **20**, 1627; 1890, **23**, 3136; cf. humulone and lupulone p. 218 ff). The transformation of purpurogallin to purpurogallone is of a similar type (*A. G. Perkin*, J. chem. Soc., 1912, **101**, 803; cf. Vol. III).

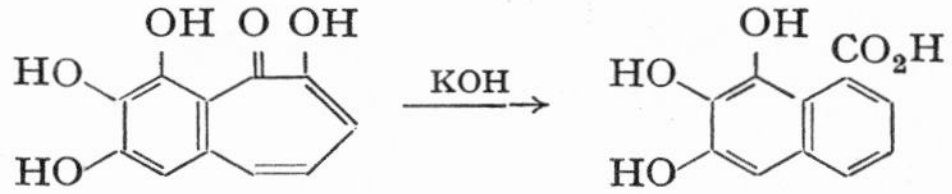

An interesting case of an alkali-catalysed *reversible* ring transformation has been reported:

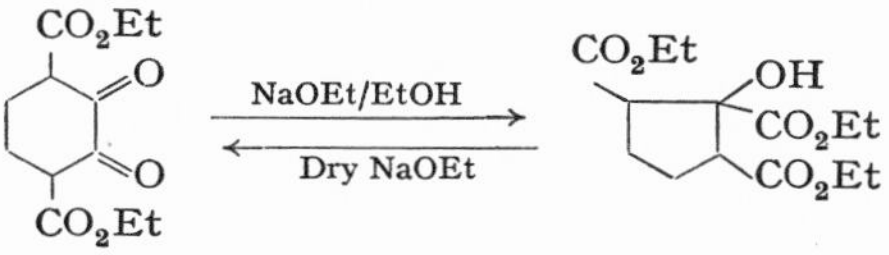

(*S. N. Naumov* and *L. S. Dedusenko*, Brit. chem. Abstr., 1940, AII, 47).

Ring isomerisations can occur during sodium ethoxide-catalysed reactions such as the Dieckmann condensation, e.g.

(*N. J. Toivonen*, Chem. Ztbl., 1928, II, 38; cf. also *W. Semmler*, Ber., 1892, **25**, 3520; *L. Ruzicka* and *H. Trebler*, Helv., 1921, **4**, 666).

Some processes of oxidation and reduction give rise to isomerisation. Use of the drastic reducing agent hydrogen iodide (alone or in the presence of phosphorus) can result in either expansion or contraction of the ring e.g.

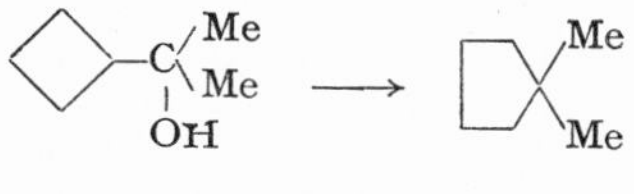

(*N. Kishner*, Chem. Ztbl., 1908, II, 1859; cf. also *N. D. Zelinsky*, Ber., 1895, **28**, 1022; 1897, **30**, 387, 1512; *W. Markovnikov*, J. pr. Chem., 1894, **49**, 409; Ann., 1898, **302**, 5, 36; 1902, **324**, 7; Ber., 1897, **30**, 1213, 1225; *F. Wreden* and *B. Znatowicz*, Ann., 1877, **187**, 163; *N. Kishner*, J. pr. Chem., 1897, **56**, 3). A remarkable transformation of this type is that of carbazole into 3:3′-dimethyldicyclopentyl (*J. Schmidt* and *A. Sigwart*, Ber., 1912, **45**, 1779).

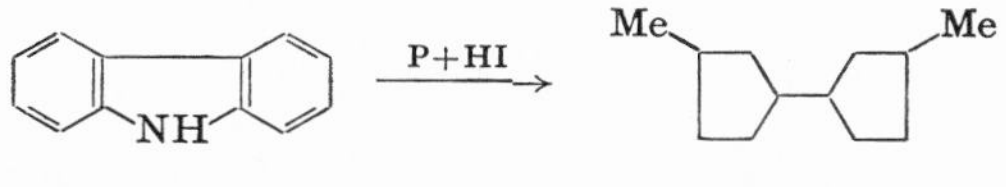

The reverse process, dehydrogenation, is particularly prone to result in rearrangement when applied to alicyclic compounds of spirane structure e.g.

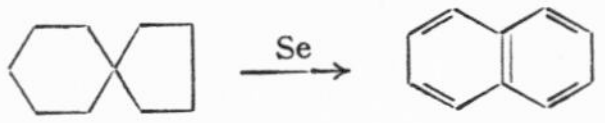

(*G. R. Clemo* and *J. Ormston,* J. chem. Soc., 1933, 352).

The results of dehydrogenation should therefore be interpreted with caution if there is a possibility of the initial compound being formulated as a spirane (*M. Levitz, D. Perlman* and *M. T. Bogert,* J. org. Chem., 1941, **6**, 105; *M. Levitz* and *M. T. Bogert,* J. Amer. chem. Soc., 1942, **64**, 1719; *C. D. Nenitzescu* and *E. Cioranescu,* Ber., 1936, **69**, 1040).

The conversions brought about by oxidation are sometimes unexpected. A relatively straightforward one is due to *W. Treibs* (Ber., 1933, **66**, 1485):

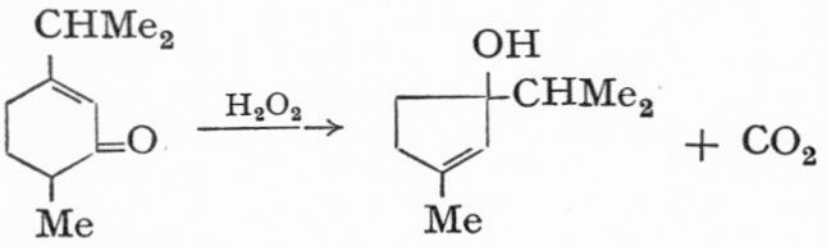

but a later example is truly spectacular:

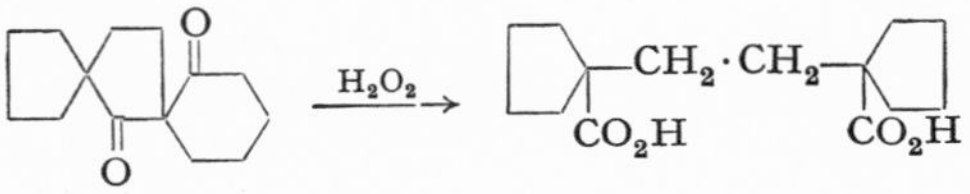

(*C. Mannich,* Ber., 1941, **74**, 1007).

Pyrogallol under the influence of many oxidising agents undergoes an oxidative coupling with concomitant ring expansion to furnish purpurogallin, a compound containing the interesting cycloheptatrienolone structure (*J. A. Barltrop* and *J. S. Nicholson,* J. chem. Soc., 1948, 116; *R. D. Haworth et al., ibid.,* 1948, 1045. For earlier formulation see *R. Willstätter* and *H. Heiss,* Ann., 1923, **433**, 17).

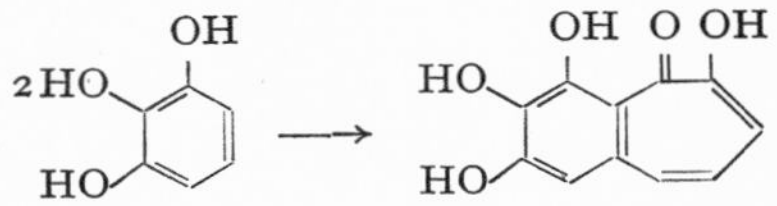

Prolonged halogenation of cyclic compounds can often give rise to a transition into a more favoured ring:

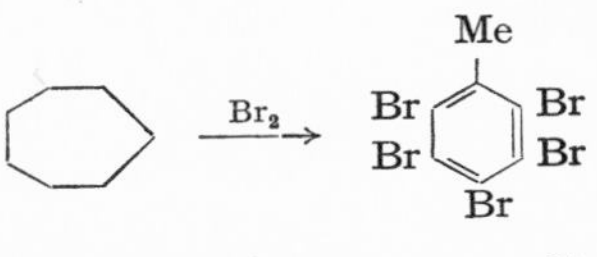

(*W. Markovnikov,* J. pr. Chem., 1894, [ii], **49**, 428);

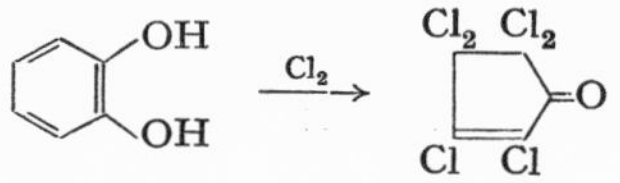

(*T. Zincke et al.*, Ann., 1897, **296**, 135; 1898, **299**, 373; 1909, **367**, 1).

Reactions with diazo- or triazo-compounds often result in ring isomerisation. The action of diazomethane on cyclic ketones furnishes the next higher ring homologue and the method is of considerable preparative value (*M. Mousseron* and *G. Manon*, Compt. rend., 1948, **226**, 1989; *E. P. Kohler et al.*, J. Amer. chem. Soc., 1939, **61**, 1057; *A. P. Giraitis* and *J. L. Bullock*, *ibid.*, 1937, **59**, 951; *E. Mosettig* and *A. Burger*, *ibid.*, 1930, **52**, 3456; *R. Robinson* and *L. H. Smith*, J. chem. Soc., 1937, 371; *D. W. Adamson* and *J. Kenner*, *ibid.*, 1939, 181) e.g.:

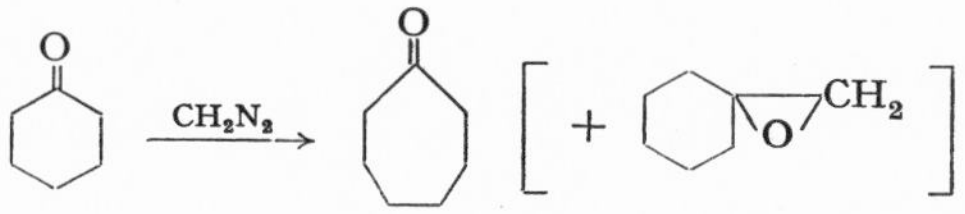

The reaction has been successfully extended to α-chloroketones (*T. R. Steadman*, J. Amer. chem. Soc., 1940, **62**, 1606). Diazoacetic ester attacks most benzenoid hydrocarbons to produce fused ring systems which in many cases are capable of isomerisation to seven-membered rings (*E. Buchner et al.*, Ber., 1901, **34**, 982; 1900, **33**, 684; 1898, **31**, 2241; 1897, **30**, 632; 1896, **29**, 106; *A. St. Pfau* and *P. A. Plattner*, Helv., 1939, **22**, 202).

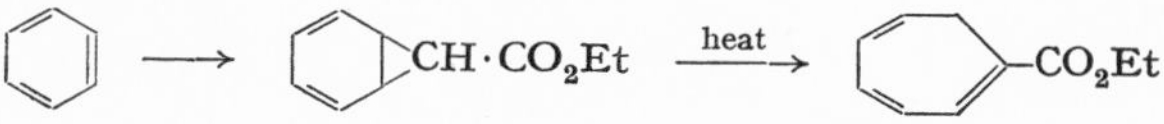

The triazole obtained by the action of phenyl azide on cycloheptene is transformed to hexahydrobenzaldehyde under the influence of acid (*K. Alder* and *G. Stein*, Ann., 1933, **501**, 1).

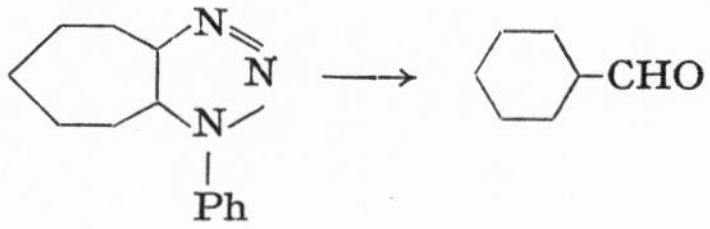

An interesting example of ring-contraction involving an aromatic diazoanhydride has been reported by *O. Süs* (Ann., 1944, **556**, 65, 85); the transformation occurs under the influence of sunlight and proceeds as follows (yield 70%):

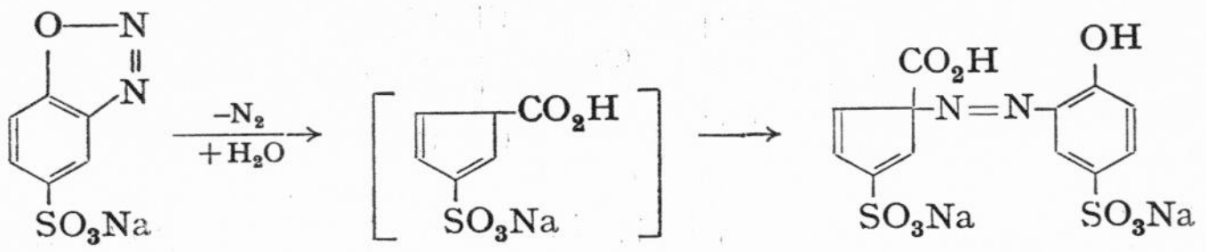

$\xrightarrow[+H_2O]{-N_2}$ [CO_2H, SO_3Na] $\longrightarrow$ CO_2H, $-N{=}N-$, OH, SO_3Na, SO_3Na

A cyclopentadienecarboxylic acid is first produced and this immediately couples with unchanged diazoanhydride.

Many of the familiar reactions employed in organic chemistry for molecular augmentation can in certain cases lead to products with altered ring size.

Grignard reaction:

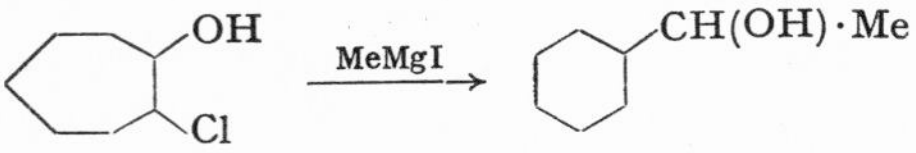

OH, Cl $\xrightarrow{MeMgI}$ CH(OH)·Me

(*M. Godchot* and *G. Cauquil*, Compt. rend., 1928, **186**, 375; *M. Vavon* and *V. M. Mitchovitch*, *ibid.*, 702).

Reformatsky reaction:

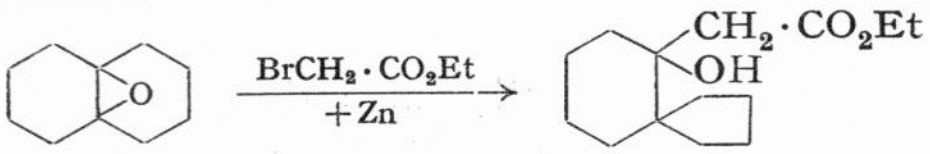

O $\xrightarrow[+Zn]{BrCH_2\cdot CO_2Et}$ $CH_2\cdot CO_2Et$, OH

(*G. R. Clemo* and *J. Ormston*, J. chem. Soc., 1932, 1778).

Friedel-Crafts reaction:

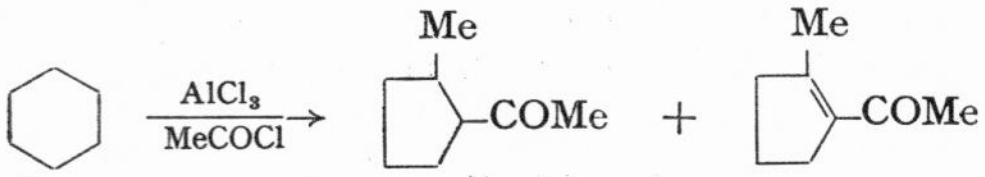

$\xrightarrow[MeCOCl]{AlCl_3}$ Me, COMe + Me, COMe

(*F. Unger*, Ber., 1932, **65**, 467; *H. Hopff*, *ibid.*, 482; *C. D. Nenitzescu* and *C. N. Ionescu*, Ann., 1931, **491**, 189).

It has been found that the Friedel-Crafts catalyst, aluminium chloride, is capable of causing ring transformation of certain cyclic hydrocarbons under relatively mild conditions; an interesting point is the reversibility of the reaction. Because of its technical implications the isomerization of cyclohexane to methylcyclopentane has been studied in great detail.

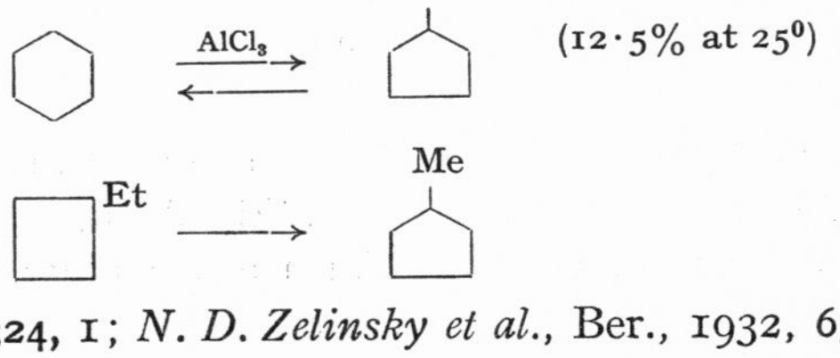

$\underset{\longleftarrow}{\xrightarrow{AlCl_3}}$ Me (12·5% at 25°)

Et $\longrightarrow$ Me

(*O. Aschan*, Ann., 1902, **324**, 1; *N. D. Zelinsky et al.*, Ber., 1932, **65**, 1173;

1930, **63**, 1584; *C. D. Nenitzescu* and *I. P. Cantuniari*, Ber., 1933, **66**, 1099; Ann., 1932, **491**, 189; *G. Chiurdoglu*, Bull. soc. chim. Belg., 1944, **53**, 55; *J. A. Arbusov*, Brit. chem. Abstr., 1945, AII, 226; *M. B. Turova-Pollak et al.*, *ibid.*, 1945, AII, 227; 1939, AII, 360; C.A., 1948, **42**, 7255; *A. L. Glasebrook* and *W. G. Lovell*, J. Amer. chem. Soc., 1939, **61**, 1717; *D. P. Stevenson* and *O. Beeck*, *ibid.*, 1948, **70**, 2890).

Also of technical importance are the catalytic methods employing high pressures and temperatures, e.g.

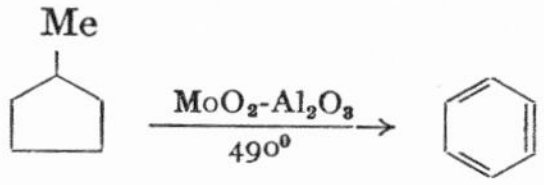

Me

MoO_2-Al_2O_3, 490°

(*R. S. Greensfelder* and *D. J. Fuller*, *ibid.*, 1945, **67**, 2171). Methylcyclohexane with MoS_2 at 400°/300 at. gives a mixture of 1:2- and 1:3-dimethylcyclopentane (*P. V. Putschkov*, Brit. chem. Abstr., 1947, AII, 220) and chlorocyclohexane with Al_2O_3–Fe_2O_3 at 300° gives a mixture of 1- and 3-methylcyclopent-1-ene (*W. I. Schuikin*, *ibid.*, 1945, AII, 227).

Under milder conditions ring isomerization can be brought about by an acid catalyst. Thus sulphuric acid at 130° converts cyclobutylformaldehyde into cyclopentanone (*E. D. Venus-Danilova*, *ibid.*, 1940, AII, 45). The reverse of this particular transformation may be effected photolytically, cyclopentanone being converted into cyclobutane and carbon monoxide (*G. B. Kistiakowsky* and *S. W. Benson*, J. Amer. chem. Soc., 1942, **64**, 80; U.S.P. 2,414,880, 1947). Another example is the conversion of hexahydrobenzaldehyde into cyclopentyl methyl ketone by H_2SO_4-$HgSO_4$ (*E. D. Venus Danilova*, Chem. Ztbl., 1936, II, 2903).

Acid catalysts, such as hydrofluoric or sulphuric acids, in the presence of alkenes effect ring enlargement with concomitant increase in molecular size (*H. Pines* and *V. N. Ipatieff*, J. Amer. chem. Soc., 1945, **67**, 1631), e.g.

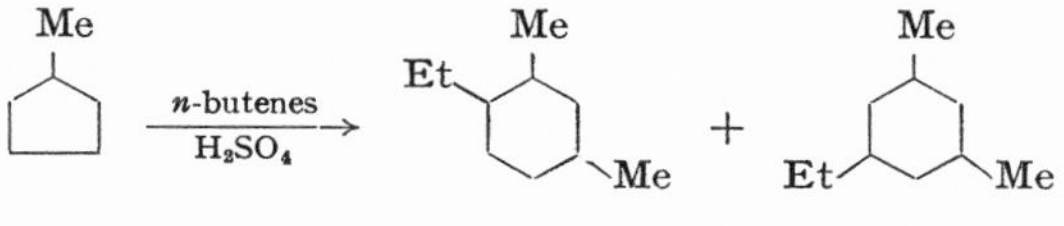

Me — *n*-butenes, H_2SO_4 → Me, Et, Me + Me, Et, Me

An intramolecular reaction of this type is exemplified by the following (*D. Davidson* and *J. Feldman*, *ibid.*, 1944, **66**, 488):

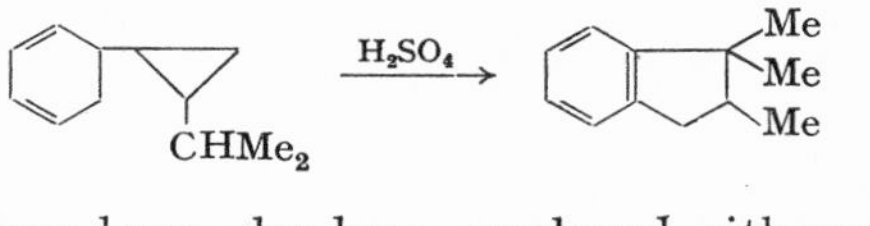

$CHMe_2$ — H_2SO_4 → Me, Me, Me

Cracking techniques have also been employed with unsaturated alicyclic hydrocarbons such as cyclohexene, which is converted at 400° by BeO into 1-methylcyclopent-1-ene (*J. A. Arbusov, N. D. Zelinsky et al.*, Brit. chem. Abstr., 1946, AII, 372; 1945, AII, 226; 1940, AII, 9; *H. Adkins* and *A. K. Roebuck*, J. Amer. chem. Soc., 1948, **70**, 4041; *H. L. Bloch* and *C. L. Thomas*, *ibid.*, 1944, **66**, 1589).

Chapter II

Cyclopropane Group

R. A. RAPHAEL

1. Occurrence, formation and properties

For long the only known occurrence of the individual cyclopropane ring in nature was in the acidic moiety of the natural insecticides the pyrethrins (chrysanthemum mono- and di-carboxylic acids; see p. 99). This monopoly has been broken by the isolation of a long-chain cyclopropane acid, lactobacillic acid, from *Lactobacillus arabinosus* and a structurally similar cyclopropene derivative, sterculic acid, from the kernel oil of *Stercula foetida* (p. 37). The cyclopropane structure is much more frequently found fused with another ring in bicyclic terpenoid compounds including sabinol, carene and thujone. Thus the great majority of cyclopropane derivatives must needs be obtained synthetically.

Preparative methods. The methods used fall into five classes.

(1) A usual method of obtaining the hydrocarbons of this series is by an intramolecular reaction of the Wurtz type on 1:3-dihalogeno-compounds (generally the dibromides) employing sodium or zinc as the dehalogenating agent, e.g.

$$CH_2\begin{cases} CH_2Br \\ CH_2Br \end{cases} \xrightarrow{Na} \triangle \qquad \begin{matrix} Me \\ Me \end{matrix}\!\!>C\begin{cases} CH_2Br \\ CH_2Br \end{cases} \xrightarrow{Zn} \begin{matrix} Me \\ Me \end{matrix}\!\!>\triangle$$

(*O. Freund*, Monatsh., 1881, **3**, 626; *R. W. Shortridge et al.*, J. Amer. chem. Soc., 1948, **70**, 946).

Zinc seems to be generally preferred as the practical reagent; it can be used either in alcohol (*G. Gustavson et al.*, J. pr. Chem., 1887, **36**, 300; 1898, **58**, 548; *R. W. Shortridge et al.*, *loc. cit.*; *J. D. Bartleson et al.*, *ibid.*, 1946, **68**, 2573) or in molten acetamide (*H. B. Hass et al.*, Ind. Eng. Chem., 1936, **28**, 1178). The yields from different types of dibromides are in the following order: primary-primary > primary-secondary > secondary-secondary; all reaction conditions involving a tertiary bromide produce olefinic compounds, but milder methods of cyclisation have now been found which overcome this limitation (*R. G. Kelso et al.*, J. Amer. chem. Soc., 1952, **73**, 287).

(2) The cyclopropane ring may be formed by intramolecular dehydrohalogenation; this reaction occurs particularly well when the initial halide possesses an active methylene or methine group in the position β to the halogen, e.g.

$$\begin{array}{l} CH_2 \\ | \quad \diagdown CH_2\cdot CO\cdot CH_3 \\ CH_2Br \end{array} \xrightarrow{KOH} \triangleright CO\cdot CH_3 \qquad \begin{array}{l} Me \\ | \\ CH \\ | \quad \diagdown CH_2CN \\ CH_2Cl \end{array} \xrightarrow{KOH} \overset{Me}{\triangleright} CN$$

(*J. B. Cloke et al.*, J. Amer. chem. Soc., 1931, **53**, 2791; 1945, **67**, 1587).

F. C. Whitmore and his co-workers have made a study of this method as applied to the preparation of substituted hydrocarbons such as 1:1:2-trimethylcyclopropane (J. Amer. chem. Soc., 1939, **61**, 1616; 1941, **63**, 124, 2633).

A modification of the reaction consists in the interaction of a γ-halonitrile and a Grignard reagent when cyclopropyl ketones are formed (*P. Bruylants*, Chem. Ztbl., 1909, I, 1859).

(3) Many carboxylic acids of the cyclopropane series may be made by the interaction of vicinal dihalides with two molecules of sodiomalonic ester. The reaction proceeds as follows:

$$\begin{array}{l} CH_2Br \\ | \\ CH_2Br \end{array} + NaCH(CO_2Et)_2 \longrightarrow \begin{array}{l} CH_2\cdot CH(CO_2Et)_2 \\ | \\ CH_2Br \end{array}$$

$$\downarrow NaCH(CO_2Et)_2$$

$$\triangleright\!\!<\begin{array}{l} CO_2Et \\ CO_2Et \end{array} \longleftarrow \begin{array}{l} CH_2\cdot CNa(CO_2Et)_2 \\ | \\ CH_2Br \end{array}$$

The last step is exactly analogous to method (2) above. Other compounds containing an active methylene group may also be employed, e.g. acetoacetic ester, cyanoacetic ester, phenylacetonitrile etc.

This type of reaction may be carried out in the reverse manner; a 1:3-disodio salt is treated with iodine, the resulting elimination of sodium iodide yielding the three-membered ring compound, e.g.:

$$CH_2\left\langle\begin{array}{l} CNa(CO_2Et)_2 \\ CNa(CO_2Et)_2 \end{array}\right. \xrightarrow{I_2} \triangleleft\begin{array}{l} (CO_2Et)_2 \\ (CO_2Et)_2 \end{array}$$

(*O. Dressel*, Ann., 1890, **256**, 171).

(4) Many pyrazolines may be readily converted by elimination of nitrogen into cyclopropane derivatives. Such pyrazolines may be prepared either by addition of aliphatic diazo compounds (diazomethane, diazoacetic ester etc.) to olefinic compounds or by the action of hydrazine on $\alpha\beta$-unsaturated carbonyl compounds, e.g.

$$\begin{matrix} CH\cdot CO_2Et \\ \| \\ CH\cdot CO_2Et \end{matrix} \xrightarrow{CH_2N_2} N\langle\begin{matrix} CH_2-CH\cdot CO_2Et \\ | \\ N\text{——}CH\cdot CO_2Et \end{matrix} \xrightarrow{-N_2} \triangleleft\begin{matrix} CO_2Et \\ \\ CO_2Et \end{matrix}$$

(*E. Buchner*, Ber., 1890, **23**, 703), or

$$Me_2CH\cdot CH{=}CH\cdot COMe \xrightarrow{N_2H_4} \begin{matrix} Me_2CH\cdot CH\cdot CH_2\cdot CMe \\ \quad | \qquad\qquad \| \\ \quad NH\text{———}N \end{matrix} \xrightarrow{-N_2} Me_2CH\!\bigtriangledown\!Me$$

(*N. Kishner*, Chem. Ztbl. 1913, II, 2133; 1916, II, 318; 1923, II, 669; 1929, II, 3011; *D. Davidson* and *J. Feldman*, J. Amer. chem. Soc., 1944, **66**, 488).

(5) A method of obtaining substituted cyclopropane tetranitriles consists in the reaction of a carbonyl compound with bromomalononitrile in the presence of potassium iodide (*S. Widequist et al.*, Brit. chem. Abstr., 1943, AII, 195; 1946, AII, 142). This interesting reaction presumably proceeds by the following mechanism:

$$\begin{matrix} R \\ R_1 \end{matrix}\rangle CO + \begin{matrix} CHBr(CN)_2 \\ CHBr(CN)_2 \end{matrix} \longrightarrow \begin{matrix} R \\ R_1 \end{matrix}\rangle C\langle\begin{matrix} CBr(CN)_2 \\ CBr(CN)_2 \end{matrix} \xrightarrow{KI} \begin{matrix} R \\ R_1 \end{matrix}\rangle C\langle\begin{matrix} CI(CN)_2 \\ CI(CN)_2 \end{matrix} \xrightarrow{-I_2} \begin{matrix} R \\ R_1 \end{matrix}\rangle\triangleleft\begin{matrix} (CN)_2 \\ (CN)_2 \end{matrix}$$

Properties of cyclopropane compounds. As has been briefly indicated (p. 2) the cyclopropane ring possesses many of the properties associated with the ethylenic double bond. Thus the ring may be hydrogenated to yield propane derivatives (*R. Willstätter* and *J. Bruce*, Ber., 1907, **40**, 4456; *R. W. Shortridge et al.*, J. Amer. chem. Soc., 1948, **70**, 946). Iodine and bromine react fairly readily to form 1:3-dihalogenopropanes; the reaction has been studied kinetically (*M. S. Kharasch et al.*, *ibid.*, 1939, **61**, 2139; *R. A. Ogg* and *W. J. Priest*, *ibid.*, 1938, **60**, 217). Halogen acids cause fission of the ring giving substituted propyl halides; the manner in which addition takes place is governed by the number and disposition of the substituent alkyl groups. The ring always opens between the carbon atoms holding the smallest and largest number of alkyl groups, the principal product being that in which the halogen is combined with the carbon atom holding the largest number of alkyl groups, i.e. the Markovnikov rule is obeyed (*N. Kishner*, C.A. 1912, 6, 2915; *E. P. Kohler* and *J. B. Conant*, J. Amer. chem. Soc., 1917, 39, 1404; *D. Davidson* and *J. Feldman*, *ibid.*, 1944, 66, 488; *M. S. Kharasch et al.*, *loc. cit.*). Organic acids in the presence of boron fluoride catalyst produce propyl esters (*J. B. Davis* and *F. J. Sowa*, *ibid.*, 1938, **60**, 358). The colour reaction with tetranitromethane characteristic of ethylenic compounds is also given by cyclopropane derivatives (*O. Filipov*, Chem. Ztbl., 1915, I, 1057). The discriminating factor between the two classes of compounds is provided by the action of potassium permanganate; cyclopropyl compounds are untouched by this reagent in the cold whereas olefines react readily. This difference is well illustrated by the following reaction (*N. J. Demjanov* and *M. Dojarenko*, Ber., 1922, 55, 2718).

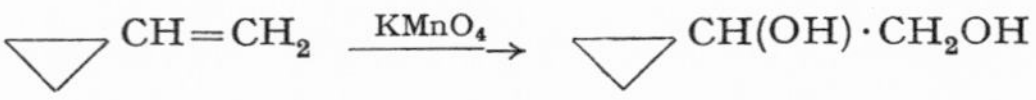

$$\triangledown\!-CH{=}CH_2 \xrightarrow{KMnO_4} \triangledown\!-CH(OH)\cdot CH_2OH$$

Ozone also has little effect on the three-membered ring.

In view of this extremely close similarity it would seem to be desirable that there should be a watertight chemical proof of the existence of a three-membered ring. This has been provided in a conclusive and elegant manner by the fission of a 1:2:3 unsymmetrically substituted cyclopropane at the three different sides of the triangular molecule (*E. P. Kohler* and *J. B. Conant*, J. Amer. chem. Soc., 1917, 39, 1404).

$$PhCHBr\begin{cases}CH_2\cdot COPh\\ C(CO_2Et)_2\end{cases} \xleftarrow{HBr} PhCH\begin{cases}CH\cdot COPh\\ C(CO_2Et)_2\end{cases}$$

$$PhCH\begin{cases}CH\cdot COPh\\ C(CO_2Et)_2\end{cases} \xrightarrow{H_2} PhCH\begin{cases}CH_2\cdot COPh\\ CH(CO_2Et)_2\end{cases}$$

$$PhCH\begin{cases}CH\cdot COPh\\ C(CO_2Et)_2\end{cases} \xrightarrow[-NH_3]{+NH_3} PhC\begin{cases}{=}C\cdot COPh\\ CH(CO_2Et)_2\end{cases}$$

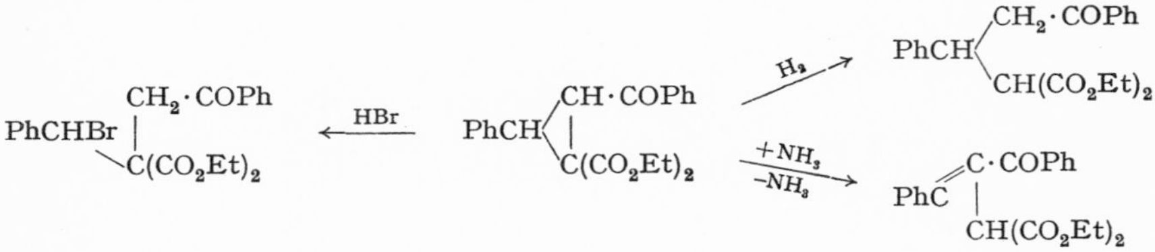

A direct comparison of two molecules, differing only in the substitution of a cyclopropane ring for a double bond, has been made by *R. C. Fuson* and *F. N. Baumgartner* (*ibid.*, 1948, **70**, 3255).

A further analogy between the two systems is seen in the ability of the cyclopropane ring to conjugate with unsaturated groupings. Thus the characteristic 1:4 addition associated with conjugated dienes has been reported to occur in the case of a compound containing an $\alpha\beta$-unsaturated cyclopropane system (*R. van Volkenburgh et al., ibid.*, 1949, **71**, 173); it has also been demonstrated that the properties of a system containing a carbonyl group attached to a cyclopropane ring are not fundamentally different from those of the corresponding $\alpha\beta$-unsaturated carbonyl compound (*E. P. Kohler* and *J. B. Conant, ibid.*, 1917, **39**, 1404). Thus the products of ring fission of cyclopropyl carboxylic acids or ketones with hydrogen bromide are the γ-bromo-substituted compounds, e.g.

$$\triangledown\text{-}CO_2H \longrightarrow CH_2(CH_2Br)\text{-}CH_2\cdot CO_2H$$

$$\triangledown\text{-}COPh \longrightarrow CH_2(CH_2Br)\text{-}CH_2\cdot COPh$$

Similarly the Michael type of addition of malonic ester to ethyl cyclopropane-1:2-dicarboxylate gives ethyl butane-1:1:4:4-tetracarboxylate:

$$\triangledown(CO_2Et)_2 \xrightarrow{NaCH(CO_2Et)_2} \begin{array}{l} CH_2\cdot CH(CO_2Et)_2 \\ | \\ CH_2\cdot CH(CO_2Et)_2 \end{array}$$

(*W. A. Bone* and *W. H. Perkin*, J. chem. Soc., 1895, **67**, 108).

This chemical similarity is paralleled by the spectroscopic properties of the three-membered ring. *I. M. Klotz* has shown that compounds incorporating a cyclopropylethylene structure exhibit maximal absorption in the ultra-violet at a wave-length (2100 Å.) considerably higher than that of a simple ethylene (1850 Å.) the value being closer to that of a conjugated diene (2150 Å.) (J. Amer. chem. Soc., 1944, **66**, 88; cf. also *R. P. Mariella et al., ibid.*, 1948, **70**, 1494; 1952, **74**, 518; *M. T. Rogers, ibid.*, 1947, **69**, 2544; *E. P. Burt* and *C. P. Carr, ibid.*, 1918, **40**, 1590; *J. D. Roberts* and *C. Green, ibid.*, 1946, **68**, 214; *L. I. Smith* and *E. R. Rogier, ibid.*, 1951, **73**, 3840). This phenomenon is well exemplified by the following hydrocarbons (*M. T. Rogers, loc. cit.*):

	λ max., Å.	ε max.
$Ph\text{-}CH_2\cdot CH_3$	2060	32000
Ph-$\triangledown$	2200	8400
$Ph\text{-}CH{=}CH_2$	2455	16000

These pseudo-conjugate properties of the three-membered ring are borne out by dipole moment data (*M. T. Rogers* and *J. D. Roberts, ibid.*, 1946, **68**, 843;

1947, **69**, 2544). They indicate that the C – C bond electrons in the three-membered ring are more weakly bound than the usual σ electrons and tend to exhibit the characteristics associated with mobile π electrons. This concept receives confirmation from the nature of the far ultra-violet spectrum of cyclopropane (*A. A. Ashdown et al., ibid.*, 1936, **58**, 850) and from the high value of the quenching cross-section of cyclopropane for cadmium resonance radiation (*E. W. R. Steacie* and *D. J. Le Roy*, J. chem. Phys., 1943, **11**, 164. This cross-section increases if mobile π electrons are present; the value for cyclopropane is intermediate between those for olefines and paraffins respectively). A π complex structure of the type (I) has in fact been suggested for cyclopropane (*A. D. Walsh*, Nature, 1947, **159**, 165, 712) but the concept has met with criticism (*R. Robinson*, Nature, 1947, **159**, 400; **160**, 162; *T. M. Sugden, ibid.*, **160**, 367; *C. A. Coulson* and *W. E. Moffitt*, J. chem. Phys., 1947, **15**, 151; *M. J. S. Dewar*, Trans. Faraday Soc., 1948, Discussion on the Labile Molecule).

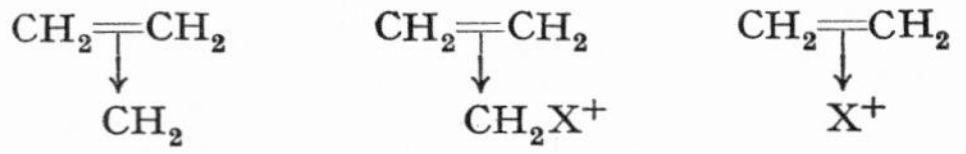

$$CH_2{=}CH_2 \rightarrow CH_2 \quad \text{(I)} \qquad CH_2{=}CH_2 \rightarrow CH_2X^+ \quad \text{(II)} \qquad CH_2{=}CH_2 \rightarrow X^+ \quad \text{(III)}$$

The geometry of the cyclopropane molecule has been investigated by many physical methods and these support the picture of a fully symmetrical planar ring with the carbon atoms at the corners of an equilateral triangle and the $C{<}^{H}_{H}$ planes bisecting the corresponding ring angle; as expected, the $C{<}^{H}_{H}$ angle is close to 120° (*H. A. Skinner*, Nature, 1947, **160**, 902; *J. M. O'Gorman* and *V. Schomaker*, J. Amer. chem. Soc., 1946, **68**, 1138; *O. Bastiensen* and *O. Hassell*, C.A., 1946, **40**, 6059; *L. Pauling* and *L. O. Brockway*, J. Amer. chem. Soc., 1937, **59**, 1223).

The correlation of the properties with the structure of cyclopropane has been considered in detail by *A. D. Walsh* (Trans. Faraday Soc., 1949, **45**, 179, where collected information concerning the infra-red absorption, Raman spectra, dipole moment data and electron diffraction data for cyclopropyl compounds is critically discussed). An interpretation in terms of molecular orbitals has been produced by *C. A. Coulson* and *E. W. Moffitt* (Phil. Mag., 1949, **40**, 1).

M. J. S. Dewar (The Electronic Theory of Organic Chemistry, Oxford University Press, 1949, p. 156) has suggested that, whatever the actual structure of cyclopropane might be, it would be expected to combine readily with cationoid reagents to form π complexes (II) of a type analogous to the well authenticated π complexes from ethylene (III). As the subsequent reactions of (II) and (III) would be expected to be comparable, the orientation of addition in substituted ethylenes and cyclopropanes should be similar. Thus the π complex should be formed by the attack of X^+ on the most negative carbon of the three-membered ring followed by the addition of the anion to the most positive carbon; this orientation (i.e. the Markovnikov rule) is, in fact, observed.

2. Saturated hydrocarbons

Saturated hydrocarbons of the cyclopropane series, with physical properties, are listed in Table 1.

TABLE 1

SATURATED HYDROCARBONS OF THE CYCLOPROPANE SERIES

Hydrocarbon	B.p.°	M.p.°	d_4^{20}	n_D^{20}	Ref.
Cyclopropane	–34·5/750	–127	d_4^{-79} 0·720		1
1-Methylcyclopropane	4–5		d_0^{-20} 0·6912		2
1-Ethylcyclopropane	35·94/760	–149·41	0·6839	1·3786	3
1:1-Dimethylcyclopropane	20·63/760	–108·96	0·6589	1·3668	4
1-*iso*Propylcyclopropane	58·7/760	–118·3	0·6889	1·3833	3
1:1:2-Trimethylcyclopropane	51·7–52·7/735		0·6853	1·3850	5
1-Methyl-1-ethylcyclopropane	64–65				6
1-Methyl-2-*n*-propylcyclopropane	92–93				6
1:1-Diethylcyclopropane	88·67	–105·91	0·7318	1·4042	4
1:2-Dimethyl-3-ethylcyclopropane	87 and 94				5
1-Ethyl-2-*n*-butylcyclopropane	140·41	–102·68	0·7559	1·4183	4
1-Phenylcyclopropane	174	–36	0·940	1·5316	7
1-Phenyl-2-methylcyclopropane	184–186		0·925	1·5237	7
1-Phenyl-2-ethylcyclopropane	203–205		0·918	1·5162	7
1-Phenyl-2-*iso*propylcyclopropane	213–216		0·899	1·5072	7
1:1:2:2-Tetraphenylcyclopropane		165·5			8

[1] *M. Trautz* and *K. Winkler*, J. pr. Chem., 1922, [ii], **104**, 37.
[2] *N. J. Demjanov*, Ber., 1895, **28**, 22.
[3] *R. van Volkenburgh et al.*, J. Amer. chem. Soc., 1949, **71**, 172.
[4] *R. W. Shortridge et al.*, *ibid.*, 1948, **70**, 946.
[5] *J. D. Bartleson, et al.*, *ibid.*, 1946, **68**, 2513.
[6] *R. Lespieau*, Compt. rend., 1931, **192**, 1395.
[7] *D. Davidson* and *J. Feldman*, J. Amer. chem. Soc., 1944, **66**, 488.
[8] *G. Fittig* and *B. Overman*, Ber., 1934, **67**, 2053.

Methods of preparation of the hydrocarbons have already been given (p. 23, methods 1 and 2). The homologues all have very similar chemical properties to those of cyclopropane.

Cyclopropane is an easily condensible gas, which has attained considerable importance by virtue of its powerful anaesthetic effect (see *C. L. Hewer*, "Recent Advances in Anaesthesia and Analgesia", J. and A. Churchill Ltd., 1948, p. 48). Because of this property much research has been undertaken to cheapen its industrial preparation from petroleum products [*H. B. Hass et al.*, B. P., 498,225 (1937); *W. A. Lott*, U.S.P., 2,261,168, (1941)].

Properties. Pyrolysis of cyclopropane at moderate temperatures (400–500°) results mainly in its conversion to propylene; at higher temperatures hydrogen, ethylene, saturated hydrocarbons and carbon are produced (*inter al.*, *S. Tanatar*, Ber., 1896, **29**, 1297; 1899, **32**, 702, 1965; *S. Z. Roginski* and *F. H. Rathmann*, J. Amer. chem. Soc., 1933, **55**, 2800. For kinetics and mechanism see *T. S. Chambers* and *G. B. Kistiakowsky*, *ibid.*, 1934, **56**, 399; *E. S. Corner* and *R. S. Pease*, *ibid.*, 1945, **67**, 2067). The temperature needed to bring about the rearrangement to propylene may be considerably reduced (100–200°) by employing a catalyst (iron, nickel, palladium, alumina). It has been stated that this reaction is reversible and that, in fact, tautomerism exists between propylene and cyclopropane but this conclusion seems doubtful. (For a full discussion see *G. Egloff*, "Reactions of Pure Hydrocarbons", A.C.S. Monograph No. 73, p. 696 *et seq.*). As has already been indicated (p. 25) cyclopropane may be catalytically hydrogenated to propane although the conditions are less mild than those used for olefines; this latter fact is the basis of a method of determining both components in cyclopropane-olefine mixtures (*E. S. Corner* and *R. S. Pease*, Ind. Eng. Chem., Anal. Ed., 1945, **17**, 564). Hydrogenation of 1:1-dialkylcyclopropanes results in fission at the bond opposite the quaternary carbon atom (*R. W. Shortridge et al.*, ref. 4, Table 1).

Bromine and iodine convert cyclopropane to 1:3-dihalogenopropanes. Thermal chlorination furnishes mainly substituted chlorocyclopropanes with a fair proportion of allyl chloride as contaminant; this impurity may be avoided by carrying out the reaction photochemically (*G. Gustavson*, J. pr. Chem., 1890, **42**, 496; 1891, **43**, 396; *J. D. Roberts* and *P. H. Dirstine*, J. Amer. chem. Soc., 1945, **67**, 1281; *P. G. Stevens*, *ibid.*, 1946, **68**, 620). Cyclopropane reacts comparatively slowly with iodine bromide and this reagent has been employed in the analysis of mixtures of cyclopropane and propene (*S. Z. Roginski* and *F. H. Rathmann*, *ibid.*, 1933, **55**, 2800). Hydrogen halides cause fission of the three-membered ring yielding propyl halides (see p. 25). Cyclopropane is inert to ozone and cold potassium permanganate solution.

3. Unsaturated hydrocarbons

Some unsaturated hydrocarbons derived from cyclopropane are listed in Table 2.

TABLE 2

UNSATURATED HYDROCARBONS OF THE CYCLOPROPANE SERIES

Hydrocarbon	B.p.°	*d*	*n*	Ref.
Cyclopropene	–36/744 mm.			1
Vinylcyclopropane	40/755 mm.	d_4^{15} 0·726	n_D^{15} 1·4172	2
1-Methyl-1-vinylcyclopropane	71–71·5	d_0^{20} 0·7523	n_D^{20} 1·4252	3
*iso*Propenylcyclopropane	70·33/760 mm.	d^{20} 0·75153	n_D^{20} 1·42550	4
1:1-Dimethyl-2-*iso*butenyl-cyclopropane	132/758 mm.	*d* 0·7677	n_D 1·4420	5
1-Methyl-1-(2-methylhex-2-enyl)-cyclopropane	160/735 mm.	d_4^{20} 0·7744		6

[1] *M. J. Schlatter*, J. Amer. chem. Soc., 1941, **63**, 1733.
[2] *N. J. Demjanov* and *M. Dojarenko*, Ber., 1922, **55**, 2718.
[3] *N. Kishner* and *W. Klavordikov*, Chem. Ztbl., 1911, II, 362.
[4] *V. A. Slabey et al.*, J. Amer. chem. Soc., 1949, **71**, 1518.
[5] *N. Kishner*, Chem. Ztbl., 1913, II, 2130.
[6] *N. Kishner*, Chem. Ztbl., 1923, III, 569.

Cyclopropene. The properties of a three-membered ring system containing a double bond have been elucidated mainly from a study of cyclopropene itself. This interesting hydrocarbon was first prepared by *N. J. Demjanov* and *M. Dojarenko* (Ber., 1923, **56**, 2200; C.A., 1930, **24**, 1848) and their findings have been confirmed (*M. J. Schlatter*, ref. 1, Table 2). It is obtained by the Hofmann elimination reaction from trimethylcyclopropylammonium hydroxide; the report of the earlier authors that it could be prepared by the zinc debromination of 1:2-dibromocyclopropane has not been confirmed. The hydrocarbon polymerises very rapidly and cannot be kept even at -78^0; with bromine it reacts normally to yield 1:2-dibromocyclopropane. 1-Methylcycloprop-1-ene was reported to be formed by the debromination of 1:3-dibromo-2-methylprop-1-ene but the evidence of its presence was only indirect (*B. Mereshkowski*, Chem. Ztbl., 1914, I, 2161).

The cyclopropylethylenic hydrocarbons are prepared in one of two ways. The alcohols obtained by the action of a Grignard reagent on a cyclopropyl alkyl ketone may be readily dehydrated; the alternative route consists in employing the Kishner hydrazine method (p. 25) on a doubly unsaturated ketone.

$$CMe_2{=}CH\cdot CO\cdot CH{=}CMe_2 \xrightarrow[KOH]{N_2H_4} CMe_2{:}CH\bigtriangledown Me_2$$

Vinylcyclopropane is obtained from cyclopropyl methyl ketoxime by reduction and exhaustive methylation followed by the Hofmann elimination. The interesting 2-*cyclopropylbuta*-1:3-*diene* (*maleic anhydride adduct* m.p. 83–84^0) is formed by the dehydration of 1-methyl-1-vinylcyclopropan-1-ol (*A. P. Golovtschanskaya*, Brit. chem. Abstr., 1942, AII, 252). The properties of the cyclopropylethylenes are analogous to those of ethylene itself; they add hydrogen and bromine and may be hydroxylated by the action of cold potassium permanganate solution.

4. Halogen derivatives

Some halogen derivatives of cyclopropane hydrocarbons are given in Table 3.

Hexafluorocyclopropane is formed by the pyrolysis of tetrafluoroethylene polymer or chlorodifluoromethane. The chloro-compounds are obtained by chlorination of cyclopropane as described on p. 30; dipole moment measurements on the 1:2-dichloro-compound indicate that it is the *dl*- and not the *meso*-isomer (*B. I. Spinrad*, J. Amer. chem. Soc., 1946, **68**, 617). The introduction of more and more chlorine atoms progressively stabilises the cyclopropane ring; thus 1:1-*dichlorocyclopropane* is unaffected by hot concentrated hydrochloric acid. Ring fission may be brought about by sulphuryl chloride in the presence of benzoyl peroxide, when polychloropropanes are formed. Side chain halogeno-compounds are generally obtained by the usual metathetical methods from the corresponding alcohols (*P. Bruylants*, Chem. Ztbl., 1909, I, 1859). 1-*Bromomethylcyclopropane*

TABLE 3

HALOGEN DERIVATIVES OF CYCLOPROPANE HYDROCARBONS

Compound	B.p.°	M.p.°	d_4^{25}	n_D^{25}	Ref.
Hexafluorocyclopropane	–29				1
1-Chlorocyclopropane	43			n_D^{20} 1·4101	2
1:1-Dichlorocyclopropane	75		1·2178	1·4377	3
1:2-Dichlorocyclopropane	87·2/757 mm.	–19·5	1·2492	1·4502	3
1:1:2-Trichlorocyclopropane	124·2/763 mm.	–36·5	1·4270	1·4782	3
1:1:2:2-Tetrachloro-cyclopropane	145·8/762 mm.	–18·5	1·5682	1·4976	3
1:2-Dibromocyclopropane	57–58/50 mm.	–1–+1			4
Bromomethylcyclopropane	106		d_{22}^{22} 1·392		5

[1] *J. D. Park et al.*, Ind. Eng. Chem., 1947, **39**, 354; U.S.P. 2,394,581.
[2] *J. D. Roberts* and *P. H. Dirstine*, J. Amer. chem. Soc., 1945, **67**, 1281.
[3] *P. G. Stevens, ibid.*, 1946, **68**, 620.
[4] *M. J. Schlatter, ibid.*, 1941, **63**, 1733.
[5] *J. A. Arvin* and *R. Adams, ibid.*, 1928, **50**, 1983.

is best prepared by the action of phosphours pentabromide on benzoylaminomethylcyclopropane, the reaction taking the following course (*J. von Braun et al.*, Ann., 1925, **445**, 201; *J. A. Arvin* and *R. Adams, loc. cit.*):

$$\triangledown CH_2NHCOPh + PBr_5 \longrightarrow \triangledown CH_2Br + PhCN + POBr_3 + HBr$$

1:2-Di-(*p*-chlorophenyl)cyclopropane has insecticidal properties approximating to those of 1:1:1-trichloro-2:2-bis-(*p*-chlorophenyl)ethane (D.D.T.) (*P. Lauger et al.*, Helv., 1944, **27**, 920).

5. Alcohols

Physical properties of some alcohols derived from cyclopropane are given in Table 4.

TABLE 4

ALCOHOLS OF THE CYCLOPROPANE SERIES

Compound	B.p.°	*d*	*n*	Ref.
Cyclopropanol	100–103	d_{20}^{20} 0·9110	n_D^{20} 1·4129	1
Cyclopropylcarbinol	123/728 mm.	$d^{17·5}$ 0·8995	n_D^{15} 1·4313	2
Cyclopropylmethylcarbinol	122/757 mm.	d_0^{19} 0·8856	n_D^{19} 1·4285	3
Cyclopropyldimethylcarbinol	123·4/760 mm.	d_4^{20} 0·8852	n_D^{20} 1·4337	4
Cyclopropylmethylethylcarbinol	141·5–143	d_0^{20} 0·8869	n_α^{20} 1·4396	5
Cyclopropylmethylvinylcarbinol	139/751 mm.			6
Cyclopropylmethylethynyl-carbinol	145–146			6
Cyclopropylethylene glycol	213–215/750 mm.	d_4^{20} 1·0677	n_D^{20} 1·4637	7

[1] *D. L. Cottle et al.*, J. Amer. chem. Soc., 1943, **65**, 1782; 1942, **64**, 484.
[2] *N. J. Demjanov* and *N. K. Fortunatov*, Ber., 1907, **40**, 4397.
[3] *N. J. Demjanov* and *S. Pinegin*, Chem. Ztbl., 1914, I, 1998.
[4] *R. van Volkenburgh et al.*, J. Amer. chem. Soc., 1949, **71**, 172.
[5] *T. A. Favorskaya*, J. gen. Chem. U.S.S.R., 1947, **17**, 541.
[6] *A. P. Golovtschanskaya*, Brit. chem. Abstr., 1942, AII, 252.
[7] *N. J. Demjanov* and *M. Dojarenko*, Ber., 1922, **55**, 2723.

Cyclopropanol was for long thought to be incapable of existence as all attempts to prepare it had resulted in the formation of allyl alcohol. Eventually, however, it was found as a by-product of the reaction between epichlorohydrin and ethylmagnesium bromide and by suitable modifications the yield may be raised to 40% (*D. L. Cottle et al., loc. cit.*). It behaves as a typical alcohol, forming a *phenylurethane*, m.p. 101·5–102°, and a 3:5-*dinitrobenzoate*, m.p. 108–109°. On repeated distillation it rearranges to propionaldehyde; with strong alkalis resins are produced but under milder conditions (e.g. with potassium carbonate) 2-methylpent-2-en-1-al is formed. The methyl, ethyl and vinyl ethers of cyclopropanol all have anaesthetic properties (*C. L. Hewer*, "Recent Advances in Anaesthesia and Analgesia", J. and A. Churchill Ltd., 1948, p. 99).

The primary exocyclic alcohols are best made by Bouveault-Blanc reduction of the corresponding esters, the secondary are obtained by reduction of the ketones (*P. Bruylants*, Chem. Ztbl., 1909, I, 1859) and the tertiary may be prepared from the cyclopropyl alkyl ketones by means of the Grignard reaction (*idem*, Bull. Soc. chim. Belg., 1927, **36**, 153). Their properties are analogous to those of their aliphatic counterparts. Cyclopropyldimethylcarbinol undergoes ring fission with hydrochloric acid to form 5-chloro-1-methylpent-2-ene; the reaction may be reversed under the influence of weak alkali (*P. Bruylants* and *A. Dewael*, Bull. Classe sci. Acad. roy. Belg., 1928, **14**, 140).

$$\begin{array}{l} CH_2 \\ | \quad \rangle CH{-}C(OH)Me_2 \\ CH_2 \end{array} \rightleftharpoons \begin{array}{l} CH_2Cl \\ | \quad \diagup CH{=}CMe_2 \\ CH_2 \end{array}$$

This interconversion may be regarded as an example of ring-chain anionotropy.

6. Amines

Amino derivatives of cyclopropane are not a very well-investigated class. **Cyclopropylamine,** b.p. 49°, d_4^{20} 0·8240, n_D^{20} 1·4210, may be obtained from cyclopropanecarboxyamide by the usual Hofmann or Schmidt procedures (*N. Kishner*, Chem. Ztbl., 1901, II, 579; 1905, I, 1704; *P. Lipp et al.*, Ann., 1932, **499**, 13; *M. J. Schlatter*, J. Amer. chem. Soc., 1941, **63**, 1733). *Phenylthiourea* deriv., m.p. 125·5°, *picrate* m.p. 149°. Nitrous acid converts it into allyl alcohol. *NN-Dimethylcyclopropylamine*, produced as a by-product in the preparation of cyclopropene (*M. J. Schlatter, loc. cit.*), has b.p. 60·1°/748 mm., d_4^{25} 0·7607, n_D^{20} 1·3999, *picrate* m.p. 196·5° (dec.), *methiodide* m.p. 274° (dec.). *Cyclopropyl-*

methylamine, b.p. 86°/758 mm., d^{16} 0·8144, n_D^{19} 1·4251, is obtained by reduction of cyclopropyl cyanide (*P. Dalle*, Chem. Ztbl., 1902, I, 913); with nitrous acid it undergoes ring enlargement to yield cyclobutanol (p. 55). *Cyclopropylethylamine* (*benzoyl* deriv., m.p.46–47°) is similarly prepared from cyclopropylacetonitrile (*J. von Braun et al.*, Ber., 1926, **59**, 1081). *α-Aminoethylcyclopropane*, b.p. 94·2–94·8°/745 mm., a_0^{23} 0·8019; n_D^{23} 1·4265, is produced by reduction of the corresponding ketoxime (*N. J. Demjanov* and *S. Pinegin*, Chem. Ztbl., 1914, I, 1999). 1-*Amino-2-phenylcyclopropane* occurs in cis- and trans-*forms*, b.p. 74–81°/1·7 mm. (*benzoyl*, m.p. 122–123·5°) and b.p. 78–80/1·5 mm. (*benzoyl* deriv., m.p. 119–120°) (*A. Burger* and *W. L. Yost*, J. Amer. chem. Soc., 1948, **70**, 2198).

7. Aldehydes and Ketones

Cyclopropanealdehyde,

$$\begin{matrix} CH_2 \diagdown \\ | \quad CH\cdot CHO, \\ CH_2 \diagup \end{matrix}$$

b.p. 99·3–99·5/771 mm., d^0 0·9473, $n_D^{15.2}$ 1·4286, 2:4-*dinitrophenylhydrazone*, m.p. 186–187·5°, *semicarbazone*, m.p. 127–128°, was first prepared by the controlled chromic acid oxidation of cyclopropylcarbinol or cyclobutanol (*N. J. Demjanov et al.*, Ber., 1908, **41**, 43; 1907, **40**, 4398) and can also be obtained by the reversible rearrangement of 2:3-dihydrofuran above 375° (*C. L. Wilson*, J. Amer. chem. Soc., 1947, **69**, 3002). With 90% sulphuric acid at 0° α-hydroxy-*n*-butaldehyde is formed and 60% sulphuric acid at 120° produces acetoin; the action of bromine yields αγ-dibromobutyric acid (*E. D. Venus-Danilova* and *V. F. Kazimirova*, Brit. chem. Abstr., 1939, AII, 265).

Cyclopropanone,

$$\begin{matrix} CH_2 \diagdown \\ | \quad CO, \\ CH_2 \diagup \end{matrix}$$

has not yet been obtained in a pure condition. It is formed from diazomethane and excess of keten in absolute ether, but all attempts at isolation result in rapid polymerisation. In the presence of water a *hydrate*, m.p. 71–72°, is produced which isomerises into propionic acid; if methanol is present a *methyl hemiacetal*, b.p. 45–46°/14 mm., is obtained (*P. Lipp et al.*, Ann., 1932, **499**, 23). These properties are reminiscent of those of keten, CH_2:C:O, and provide another analogy between the three-membered ring and the ethylenic double bond. The formation of cyclopropanone by treatment of cyclopropan-1-ol-1-carboxylic acid or cyclopropan-1-ol-1:2-dicarbocylic acid with sulphuric acid is doubtful (*C. K. Ingold et al.*, J. chem. Soc., 1921, **119**, 305; 1922, **121**, 1177; *N. J. Demjanov* and *V. V. Feofilaktov*, Brit. chem. Abstr., 1939, AII, 376).

Cyclopropyl methyl ketone, b.p. 111·2°/760 mm., f.p. –68·3°, d_4^{20} 0·8991, n_D^{20} 1·4250, *semicarbazone*, m.p. 110–112°, 2:4-*dinitrophenylhydrazone*, m.p. 149–150°, is available commercially. It is formed by hydrolysis and decarboxylation of the keto-ester from the interaction of ethylene dichloride and sodioaceto-acetic ester. It may also be obtained by the dehydrohalogenation of 5-bromo-pentan-2-one or by the action of methyl-magnesium bromide on cyclopropyl cyanide (*N. D. Zelinsky* and *E. F. Dengin*, Ber., 1922, **55**, 3360; *P. Bruylants*, Chem. Ztbl., 1927, II, 1019). With ethyl formate under the conditions of the Claisen condensation 3-keto-3-cyclopropylpropanal is initially formed but this rapidly undergoes self-condensation to 1:3:5-tricyclopropionylbenzene (*G. V. Tschelintzev*, C.A., 1947, **41**, 101). Alkyl and aryl cyclopropyl ketones are prepared in an analogous manner (*P. Bruylants*, Chem. Ztbl., 1927, II, 1019; 1928, I, 488; Bull. Soc. chim. Belg., 1927, **36**, 519; *N. Kishner*, Chem. Ztbl., 1923, III, 669; *H. Wohlgemuth*, Ann. Chim., 1915, [ix], **3**, 141; *C. F. H. Allen et al.*, Canad. J. Res., 1933, **9**, 159; *G. Haller*, Compt. rend., 1912, **154**, 1567).

E. P. Kohler et al. have made an extensive study of cyclopropyl phenyl ketones with a nitro-group attached to the cyclopropane ring (J. Amer. chem. Soc., 1919, **41**, 1379, 1644, 1697; 1922, **44**, 624; 1928, **50**, 884; 1930, **52**, 424, 1174; 1931, **53**, 1117); they are prepared by the following general method:

$$Ph{-}CH{=}CH{-}COPh \xrightarrow{CH_3NO_2} Ph{-}\underset{\displaystyle CH_2NO_2}{\underset{|}{CH}}{-}CH_2{-}COPh$$

$$\downarrow Br_2$$

$$\underset{(I)}{Ph{-}CH{-}CH{-}COPh \text{ (ring closed via } CH{-}NO_2)} \xleftarrow[-HBr]{} Ph{-}\underset{\displaystyle CH_2NO_2}{\underset{|}{CH}}{-}CHBr{-}COPh$$

An interesting property of these compounds is their extreme sensitivity to alkalis, the final product being a β-diketone, e.g. $PhCH_2{\cdot}CO{\cdot}CH_2{\cdot}COPh$ from (I) above).

8. Carboxylic acids

Some monocarboxylic acids derived from cyclopropane, with derivatives, are given in Table 5.

(*a*) *Monocarboxylic acids*

The acids are prepared by the general methods 1 and 2 (p. 23); the properties of the parent compounds will suffice to describe the whole group. **Cyclopropane-carboxylic acid** is best obtained by hydrolysis of the nitrile (*M. J. Schlatter*, ref. 1, Table 5); the decarboxylation of cyclopropane-1:1-dicarboxylic acid does not result in good yields. The compound behaves as a typical aliphatic acid and, in addition, possesses the properties conferred on it by the presence of a three-membered ring, e.g. chlorine and bromine open the ring to give the $\alpha\gamma$-dihalo-butyric acids (*N. Kishner*, Chem. Ztbl., 1909, II, 1130). An unusual reaction is the formation of the allyl ester by electrolysis of a mixture of equivalent amounts

TABLE 5

MONOCARBOXYLIC ACIDS OF THE CYCLOPROPANE SERIES

Compound	B.p.°	M.p.°	Amide m.p.°	Nitrile b.p.°	Ref.
Cyclopropane-1-carboxylic acid	80–81/13 mm.	18	125	69–70/80 mm.	1
2-Methylcyclopropane-1-carboxylic acid			99–100	145/759 mm.	2
2:2-Dimethylcyclopropane-1-carboxylic acid	100/10 mm.		177		3
2-*iso*Propylcyclopropane-1-carboxylic acid	115/15 mm.		167		3
1-Phenylcyclopropane-1-carboxylic acid		86–87	97–98	250/751 mm.	4
2-Phenylcyclopropane-1-carboxylic acid		(a) 93 (b) 106–107	190–191		5
2-Nitrophenylcyclopropane-1-carboxylic acid		197–199	225–227		6
1-Naphthylcyclopropane-1-carboxylic acid		187–189	144	m.p. 85	7

[1] *M. J. Schlatter*, J. Amer. chem. Soc., 1941, **63**, 1733.
[2] *J. B. Cloke et al., ibid.*, 1945, **67**, 1587.
[3] *G. Blanc*, Compt. rend., 1907, **145**, 78.
[4] *E. C. Knowles* and *J. B. Cloke*, J. Amer. chem. Soc., 1932, **54**, 2034.
[5] *A. Burger* and *W. L. Yost, ibid.*, 1948, **70**, 2198.
[6] *D. G. Markees* and *A. Burger, ibid.*, 1948, **70**, 3329.
[7] *J. B. Cloke* and *T. S. Leary, ibid.*, 1945, **67**, 1249.

of the acid and its potassium salt; allyl alcohol is formed as an intermediate (*F. Fichter* and *H. Reeb*, Helv., 1923, **6**, 450). The same mechanism is probably operative in the reaction of the silver salt of the acid with iodine when the *triglyceride* of *cyclopropanecarboxylic acid*, b.p. 144°/0·04 mm. is obtained (*P. Lipp et al.*, Ann., 1932, **499**, 1).

The preparation of a great many nitriles of this class has been recorded by *J. B. Cloke et al.* (J. Amer. chem. Soc., 1929, **51**, 1174; 1931, **53**, 2794; 1932, **54**, 2028; 1938, **58**, 2014; 1945, **67**, 1249, 1587).

Acids of the type $C_3H_5 \cdot CH_2 \cdot CHR \cdot CO_2H$ (where R = amyl to tetradecyl) have been prepared by condensation of cyclopropylmethyl bromide with substituted malonic esters; some of the series are bactericidal against *Mycobacterium leprae* (*J. A. Arvin* and *R. Adams*, J. Amer. chem. Soc., 1928, **50**, 1893). It has also been reported that the cyclopentyl ester of 2-*p*-chlorophenylcyclopropane-1-carboxylic acid (I) possesses insecticidal properties comparable with those of D.D.T. (*P. Lauger et al.*, Helv., 1944, **27**, 920).

Cl ... COO ...

(I)

Unsaturated acids of the cyclopropane series are obtained by the action of diazoacetic ester on dienes (*H. Staudinger et al.*, Helv., 1924, **7**, 390). The most important member of this series is chrysanthemumcarboxylic acid, the esterifying acid of one of the pyrethrins, which is discussed under pyrethrins and cinerins, p. 99.

From *Lactobacillus arabinosus K. Hoffman* and *R. A. Lucas* (J. Amer. chem. Soc., 1950, **72,** 4328; J. biol. Chem., 1952, **195,** 473) obtained lactobacillic acid, m.p. 28–30°, to which they assigned the partial formula (I; x + y = 14). Ricinoleic acid has been proposed as the biogenetic precursor of this acid and, on this basis, x would be 5 and y, 9 (*E. M. Kosower*, Science, 1951, **113,** 605). A related cyclopropene acid, *sterculic acid, ω-(2-n-octylcycloprop-1-enyl)octanoic acid* (II), m.p. 18·2° has been isolated from the kernel oil of *Stercula foetida* (*J. R. Nunn*, J. chem. Soc., 1952, 313).

$CH_3\cdot(CH_2)_x$–△–$(CH_2)_y\cdot CO_2H$

Lactobacillic acid (I)

$CH_3\cdot(CH_2)_7$–△(=)–$(CH_2)_7\cdot CO_2H$

Sterculic acid (II)

(*b*) *Hydroxycarboxylic acids*

Although a few simple hydroxy-acids are known (*N. Kishner*, Chem. Ztbl., 1911, II, 363; *C. K. Ingold*, J. chem. Soc., 1921, **119,** 305) by far the most interesting and important members of this series are the complex *3-α-hydroxybenzyl-2-phenylcyclopropane-1-carboxylic acids* obtained by degradation of α-, γ- and ε-truxillic acids and of β- and δ-truxinic acids (p. 60). The transformation is brought about by the following reactions: the monoamides of the parent dicarboxylic acids are subjected to the Hofmann degradation procedure to furnish the corresponding amino-acids, which are then treated with nitrosyl bromide; a Demjanov-type rearrangement (p. 11) occurs, and lactones containing the cyclopropane ring are formed. Finally, the lactones are hydrolysed to the hydroxy-acids.

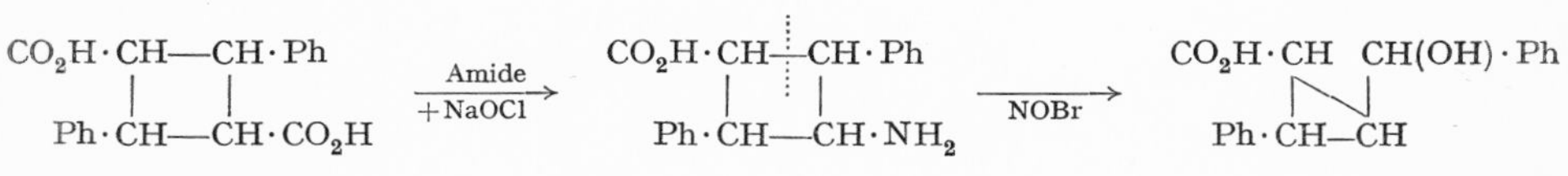

$CO_2H\cdot CH$—$CH\cdot Ph$ / $Ph\cdot CH$—$CH\cdot CO_2H$ (Truxillic acid) $\xrightarrow[+NaOCl]{Amide}$ $CO_2H\cdot CH$—$CH\cdot Ph$ / $Ph\cdot CH$—$CH\cdot NH_2$ $\xrightarrow{NOBr}$ $CO_2H\cdot CH$ $CH(OH)\cdot Ph$ / $Ph\cdot CH$—CH

Truxillic acid

$CO_2H\cdot CH$—$CH\cdot CO_2H$ / $Ph\cdot CH$—$CH\cdot Ph$ (Truxinic acid) $\xrightarrow[+NaOCl]{Amide}$ $CO_2H\cdot CH$—$CH\cdot NH_2$ / $Ph\cdot CH$—$CH\cdot Ph$ $\xrightarrow{NOBr}$ $CO_2H\cdot CH$—CH / $Ph\cdot CH$ $CH(OH)\cdot Ph$

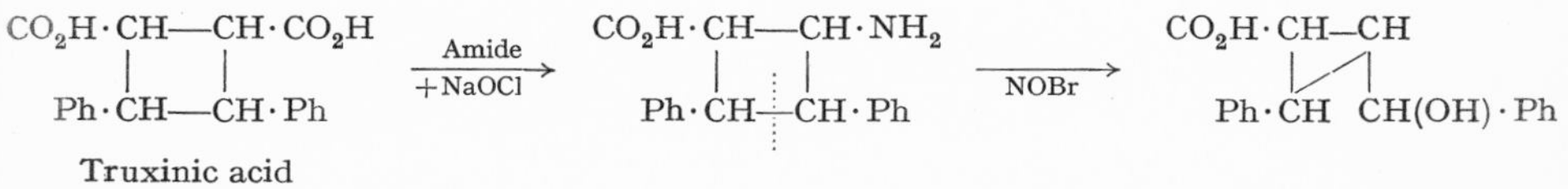

Truxinic acid

(For the interpretation of this rearrangement in terms of modern electronic theory see *H. I. Bernstein* and *E. S. Wallis*, J. org. Chem., 1942, **7,** 261; *I. S. Goldstein* and *H. I. Bernstein*, J. Amer. chem. Soc., 1944, **66,** 760). The configurations of these acids, which have been worked out by *R. Stoermer* and his collaborators illustrate well the stereochemistry associated with the cyclopropane ring (Ber.,

1927, **60**, 2573; 1928, **61**, 2312; 1931, **64**, 2785; J. pr. Chem., 1932, **134**, 230).

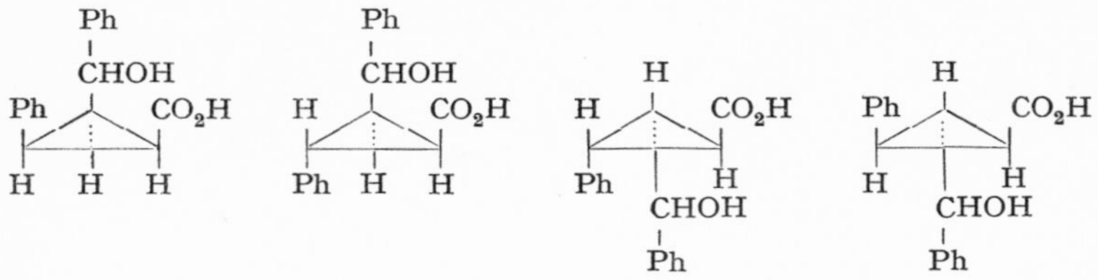

(I a, b) (II a, b) (III a, b) (IV a, b)

These hydroxy-acids contain four asymmetric carbon atoms, three in the ring and one in the side chain; eight racemic forms are therefore possible and these are represented by the above structures (each of these represents two racemates differing only in the configuration of the secondary hydroxyl group). The asymmetry of the carbon atom carrying the hydroxyl disappears when the sec. alcohol is oxidised to a ketone and each pair of the above a- and b-hydroxy-acids gives one and the same keto-acid (p. 39).

The lactone of (Ia) is the main degradation product of γ-truxillic acid; the lactones of (IIa) and (IIb) are also formed together with a trace of the lactone of (Ib). ε-Truxillic acid yields only (IIb). Under the influence of potassium hydroxide (Ia) undergoes inversion to yield (IIIa) which is incapable of forming a lactone. The last is also obtainable, together with the lactone of (IIb), by degradation of α-truxillic acid. The properties of the acids and their derivatives are given in Table 6.

TABLE 6

3-α-HYDROXYBENZYL-2-PHENYLCYCLOPROPANE-1-CARBOXYLIC ACIDS

Compound	Acid, m.p.°	Lactone, m.p.°	Methyl ester, m.p.°
I a	145–146° (dec.)	133·5–134°	124–125°
I b	171–172° (dec.)	168–169°	171–172°
II a	122° (dec.)	120–121°	73–74°
II b	153° (dec.)	115°	86–87°
III a	185–186° (dec.)	—	75–76°
III b	188–189°	—	104–105°
IV a	152–153°	—	124–126°
IV b	151–152°	—	82–83°, 125–126° (polymorphs)

The acids are named according to the c, t convention already described (p. 6). Thus (Ia) is called 3^c-α-hydroxybenzyl-2^c-phenylcyclopropane-1^c-carboxylic acid and (IIIa) is 3^t-α-hydroxybenzyl-2^t-phenylcyclopropane-1^c-carboxylic acid.

(c) *Ketocarboxylic acids*

The known keto-carboxylic acids containing the cyclopropane ring have the keto group in a side-chain. Many of these acids are degradation products of natural compounds.

1-*Methylcyclopropane-2-glyoxylic acid*, $CH_3 \cdot C_3H_4 \cdot CO \cdot CO_2H$, b.p. 100–101°/17 mm. is obtained by the permanganate oxidation of 1-methyl-2-propionylcyclopropane with permanganate (*H. Wohlgemuth*, Ann. chim., 1914, [ix], **3**, 141).

Ethyl β-keto-β-cyclopropylpropionate, $C_3H_5 \cdot CO \cdot CH_2 \cdot CO_2Et$, b.p. 115–126°/8 mm. arises from the condensation between cyclopropyl methyl ketone and diethyl oxalate (*G. V. Tchelintzev*, J. gen. Chem. U.S.S.R., 1944, **14**, 1070).

Ethyl 1-*acetylcyclopropane*-1-*carboxylate*, b.p. 195–196°, is prepared by method 3 (p. 24) from ethylene dibromide and ethyl acetoacetate, ethyl 2-methyl-4:5-dihydrofuran-3-carboxylate being formed simultaneously (*P. C. Freer* and *W. H. Perkin*, J. chem. Soc., 1887, **51**, 820). 1-*Benzoylcyclopropane*-1-*carboxylic acid*, m.p. 148°, is similarly obtained.

2:2-*Dimethyl*-3-(*γ-ketobutyl*)*cyclopropane*-1-*carboxylic acid*, m.p. 78–79°, is produced by the oxidative degradation of Δ^4-carene, or synthetically by the condensation of 6-methylhept-5-en-2-one with diazoacetic ester (*J. Owen* and *J. L. Simonsen*, J. chem. Soc., 1932, 1424).

2-*Acetyl*-1-iso*propylcyclopropane*-1-*acetic acid, α-tanacetonic acid, thujaketonic acid*, m.p. 75°, *ethyl ester* b.p. 83–84°/0·2 mm., arises from the oxidative ring fission of thujone (Vol. IIB) with potassium permanganate (*F. W. Semmler*, Ber., 1903, **36**, 4367). Thujone may be regenerated by the action of ethyl chloroacetate followed by a Dieckmann ring closure (*L. Ruzicka* and *D. R. Koolhaas*, Helv., 1932, **15**, 944).

The 3-*benzoyl*-2-*phenylcyclopropane*-1-*carboxylic acids* are prepared by chromic acid oxidation of the corresponding hydroxy-acids (for refs. see p. 38) and by decarboxylation of the corresponding 1:1-dicarboxylic acids. The condensation of benzylideneacetone (chalkone) with diazoacetic ester yields the same compounds by way of the pyrazoline derivatives. The cyclopropane ring is opened by hydrochloric acid (*E. P. Kohler*, J. Amer. chem. Soc., 1919, **41**, 1093). All four theoretically possible racemates are known.

3^c-*Benzoyl*-2^c-*phenylcyclopropane*-1^c-*carboxylic acid*, m.p. 157° (decomp.), *methyl ester* m.p. 115–116°.

3^c-*Benzoyl*-2^t-*phenylcyclopropane*-1^c-*carboxylic acid*, m.p. 174°, *methyl ester* m.p. 103°.

3^t-*Benzoyl*-2^t-*phenylcyclopropane*-1^c-*carboxylic acid*, m.p. 153–154°, *methyl ester* m.p. 66–67°.

3^t-*Benzoyl*-2^c-*phenylcyclopropane*-1^c-*carboxylic acid*, m.p. 136–137°, *methyl ester*, m.p. 66–67·5°.

(d) *Polycarboxylic acids*

Cyclopropane-1:1-dicarboxylic acid (*vinaconic acid*), m.p. 140°, is prepared by the action of ethylene dibromide on sodiomalonic ester (method 3, p. 24)

(*A. W. Dox* and *L. Yoder*, J. Amer. chem. Soc., 1921, **43**, 2097; *C. F. H. Allen*, Canad. J. Res., 1934, **9**, 159; *R. Marburg*, Ann., 1897, **294**, 89). It reacts slowly with bromine but is unaffected by nascent hydrogen, nitric acid and potassium permanganate. Hydrogen bromide converts the compound into β-bromoethylmalonic acid, $BrCH_2 \cdot CH_2 \cdot CH(CO_2H)_2$; with ethyl sodiomalonate the ethyl ester undergoes a Michael-type addition reaction to furnish butane-1:1:4:4-tetracarboxylic ester (*W. A. Bone* and *W. H. Perkin*, J. chem. Soc., 1895, **67**, 108). The mononitrile, 1-*cyanocyclopropane*-1-*carboxylic acid*, m.p. 149°, is obtained by the interaction of ethylene dibromide and sodiocyanoacetic ester (*H. C. H. Carpenter* and *W. H. Perkin*, *ibid.*, 1899, **75**, 921).

The *diethyl ester*, b.p. 72°/0·5 mm., of 2-*vinylcyclopropane*-1:1-*dicarboxylic acid*, m.p. 108°, is obtained by the action of 1:4-dibromobut-2-ene on sodiomalonic ester (*R. P. Linstead et al.*, J. chem. Soc., 1952, 3610, 3616).

2:3-*Diphenylcyclopropane*-1:1-*dicarboxylic acid*, m.p. 190°, *dimethyl ester*, m.p. 142°, is prepared by the following method.

PhCH—CH(CO₂Et)₂ / PhCH—NO₂ —(Br, KOAc/MeOH)→ 2,3-diphenyl-2-nitro-3-H-cyclopropane-1,1-dicarboxylic acid —(NaOMe)→ diphenylcyclopropene-dicarboxylic acid

The constitution is proved by the production of dibenzoylmethane on permanganate oxidation (*S. F. Darling* and *E. W. Spanagel*, J. Amer. chem. Soc., 1931, **53**, 1117).

A series of aryl-substituted keto-acids of this type has been obtained by Michael addition of sodiomalonic ester to chalkones, followed by bromination and cyclisation (*E. P. Kohler et al.*, *ibid.*, 1917, **39**, 1404, 2405; 1919, **41**, 992), e.g.

$$Ph{-}CH{=}CH{-}COPh \xrightarrow{NaCH(CO_2Me_2)} Ph{-}CH(CH(CO_2Me)_2){-}CH_2{-}COPh \xrightarrow{Br_2, -HBr} \text{Ph, COPh cyclopropane } (CO_2Me)_2$$

m.p. 92°

Cyclopropane-1:2-**dicarboxylic acid** exists in three stereoisomeric modifications a *meso-cis* form and *d*- and *l*-*trans* forms (see p. 5 for spatial diagrams). The cis-*acid* m.p. 139°, *anhydride* m.p. 59°, is obtained by the decarboxylation of cyclopropane-1:2:2-tricarboxylic and cyclopropane-1:1:2:2-tetracarboxylic acids. The dl-trans-*acid*, m.p. 175°, is produced from α-bromoglutaric ester by means of alcoholic potash. Its *methyl ester*, b.p. 210°, is prepared by the pyrolysis of dimethylpyrazoline-3:5-dicarboxylate (method 4, p. 25) (*H. von Pechmann*, Ber., 1894, **27**, 1888). On heating the *trans*-acid to 300° the *cis*-anhydride is produced (*E. Buchner*, Ann., 1895, **284**, 197). Resolution of the *dl-trans*-acid can be effected by means of quinine to give the d-*acid*, m.p. 175°, $[\alpha]_D^{27}$ $+84 \cdot 42°$ and l-*acid*, m.p. 175°, $[\alpha]_D^{27}$ $-84 \cdot 53°$ (*E. Buchner* and *R. Heide*, Ber., 1905, **38**, 3112).

The reaction of sodiomalonic ester with $\alpha\alpha'$-dibromoglutaric ester results in the ester of 1-*bromocyclopropane*-1:2-*dicarboxylic acid*, m.p. 172°. The acid is readily converted into the corresponding *hydroxy-acid*, m.p. 208–210°, and *methoxy-acid*, m.p. 121° (*C. K. Ingold*, J. chem. Soc., 1921, **119**, 305; *H. R. Ing* and *W. H. Perkin*, *ibid.*, 1925, **127**, 2387).

1-*Methylcyclopropane*-1:2-*dicarboxylic acids*, cis, m.p. 142°, trans, m.p. 168°, *anhydride*, b.p. 154–157°/20 mm., are formed by the action of alkali on the esters of α-bromo-α-methyl- or α'-bromo-α-methyl-glutaric acids (*C. K. Ingold*, *ibid.*, 1925, **127**, 387).

3-*Methylcyclopropane*-1:2-*dicarboxylic acid* exists in three optically inactive stereoisomeric forms.

(I)	(II)	(III)
CO_2H (top); Me, H (ring H); H (bottom); H, CO_2H	CO_2H (top); Me, CO_2H (ring H); H (bottom); H, H	CO_2H (top); H, CO_2H (ring H); Me (bottom); H, H
dl, m.p. 195°	meso, m.p. 108°	meso, m.p. 132°

(I) and (II) are formed by the decarboxylation of 3-methylcyclopropane-1:1:2-tricarboxylic acid on treatment with hot hydrochloric acid; (III) is obtained in similar fashion from 3-methylcyclopropane-1:1:2:2-tetracarboxylic acid (*C. K. Ingold et al.*, *ibid.*, 1923, **123**, 3342).

The remarkable compound, 3-*methylcycloprop*-2-*ene*-1:2-*dicarboxylic acid* (V), m.p. 200°, *diethyl ester*, m.p. 38°, is readily prepared from ethyl bromo*iso*-dehydracetate (IV) by the action of alcoholic potash (*idem*, *ibid.*, 1923, **123**, 327, 3342; 1924, **125**, 1929; 1925, **127**, 460; *F. Feist*, Ann., 1924, **436**, 125). The acid has been resolved with the aid of strychnine and brucine into optical enantiomorphs $[\alpha]_D$ $+116°$ and $-128°$. On distillation of the diethyl ester a truly astonishing rearrangement occurs with the production of the straight chain compound, diethyl but-1-yne-1:4-dicarboxylate* (*G. A. R. Kon* and *H. R. Nanji*, J. chem. Soc., 1932, 2557):

* For a reinterpretation of this rearrangement in terms of a new formulation for the Feist acid see *M. G. Ettlinger*, J. Amer. chem. Soc., 1952, **74**, 5805.

$$\underset{\text{(IV)}}{\text{MeC}\langle\text{C(Br)—CO—O; C(CO}_2\text{Et)=CMe}\rangle} \xrightarrow{\text{KOH}} \underset{\text{(V)}}{\text{MeC}\langle\text{C·CO}_2\text{H; CH·CO}_2\text{H}\rangle} \xrightarrow[\text{heat}]{\text{Et ester}} \text{C}\equiv\text{C·CO}_2\text{Et} \,|\, \text{CH}_2\text{·CH}_2\text{·CO}_2\text{Et}$$

1:2-*Dimethylcyclopropane*-1:2-*dicarboxylic acid*, cis, m.p. 115–117°, *anhydride*, m.p. 54–56°; trans, m.p. 230–231°, is prepared by method 4 (p. 25) from pyrocinchonic dimethyl ester and diazomethane (*K. von Auwers* and *O. Ungemach*, Ann., 1934, **511**, 152).

3:3-*Dimethylcyclopropane*-1:2-*dicarboxylic acid*, *caronic acid*, is obtained by the permanganate oxidation of carane derivatives (Vol. IIB) which must therefore contain the cyclopropane nucleus. Caronic acid and its stereoisomers are prepared synthetically by the action of alcoholic potassium hydroxide on α-bromo-ββ-dimethylglutaric ester (*W. H. Perkin* and *J. F. Thorpe*, J. chem. Soc., 1899, **75**, 48). The trans-dl-*acid*, m.p. 213°, may be resolved by nor-ψ-ephedrine into a *d*-form m.p. 212°, $[\alpha]_D$ +34·8° and *l*-form, m.p. 212°, $[\alpha]_D$ −34·5° (*J. Owen* and *J. L. Simonsen*, *ibid.*, 1933, 1223). The *trans*-acid is converted by acetic anhydride into the cis-*anhydride*, m.p. 55°, from which the cis-*acid*, m.p. 176°, *anil*, m.p. 115°, may be obtained. On heating with hydrogen bromide the caronic acids are converted into terebic acid, from which they may be regenerated by the action of thionyl chloride in benzene (*P. Barbier*, Compt. rend., 1911, **153**, 188).

$$\text{Me}_2\text{C}\langle\text{CH·CO}_2\text{H; CH·CO}_2\text{H}\rangle \underset{\text{SOCl}_2}{\overset{\text{HBr}}{\rightleftarrows}} \text{Me}_2\text{C}\langle\text{O—CO; CH(CO}_2\text{H)—CH}_2\rangle$$

Terebic acid

Ethoxycaronic acid, m.p. 138° is formed by treatment of αα′-dibromo-ββ-dimethylglutaric ester with alcoholic potassium hydroxide.

1-iso*Propylcyclopropane*-1:2-*dicarboxylic acid*, *umbellularic acid*, is produced by the oxidation of umbellulone (*F. Tutin*, J. chem. Soc., 1906, **89**, 1104; *F. W. Semmler*, Ber., 1907, **40**, 5019; 1908, **41**, 3988). The acid in all its modifications has been synthesised by method 4 (p. 25) (*J. L. Simonsen et al.*, *ibid.*, 1936, 828; *H. N. Rydon*, *ibid.*, 1936, 829; *S. K. Ranganathan*, J. Indian chem. Soc., 1936, **13**, 419); *cis dl*-form m.p. 126–127°, *d*- and *l*-forms, m.p. 119–120°, $[\alpha]_D$ +86·9° and −88·8°; *trans dl*-form, m.p. 197°, *d*- and *l*-forms, m.p. 155°, $[\alpha]_{5461}$ +232·1° and −236·2°. The action of acetyl chloride on the *trans*-acid produces the *anhydride*, b.p. 113°/4 mm., of the *cis*-form.

3:3-*Diethylcyclopropane*-1:2-*dicarboxylic acids*, cis, m.p. 170°, trans, m.p. 240°, are obtained from αα′-dibromo-ββ-diethylglutaric acid by the action of KOH at 150° (*S. S. Deshapande* and *J. F. Thorpe*, J. chem. Soc., 1922, **121**, 1437). The acid, m.p. 200°, obtained when the dibromodiethylglutaric acid is boiled with dilute alkali, is almost certainly the lactonic acid (VI) and not the cyclopropane acid (VII) as originally supposed (*J. F. Thorpe et al., ibid.*, 1922, **121**, 650; *W. N. Haworth* and *E. L. Hirst*, Annual Reports, 1928, 81).

```
              OH
Et            |                         OH
  \           |                         |
   >C--------C--CO2H                    |
Et/  |        \                Et\    C--CO2H
     |         >O                 \  / |
     |        /                    C<  |
    CH2------CO                   /  \ |
                               Et/    CH·CO2H
        (VI)                        (VII)
```

3^c-*Phenylcyclopropane*-1^t:2^t-*dicarboxylic acid*, m.p. 176°, *anhydride*, m.p. 134°, *anil*, m.p. 193° is produced by treating 1-bromo-2-phenylpropane-1:1:3:3-tetracarboxylic ester with alcoholic ammonia, by reacting phenylparaconic acid with thionyl chloride in benzene, and by addition of diazoacetic ester to cinnamic ester (*P. Barbier*, Compt. rend., 1911, **153**, 188; *E. Buchner* and *L. Perkel*, Ber., 1903, **36**, 3774; *A. Kötz*, J. pr. Chem., 1907, **75**, 490; *W. Härdi* and *J. F. Thorpe*, J. chem. Soc., 1925, **127**, 1237).

3:3-*Diphenylcyclopropane*-1:2-*dicarboxylic acid diethyl ester*, m.p. 181°, is formed from diphenyldiazomethane and diethyl fumarate (*H. Staudinger et al.*, Ber., 1916, **49**, 1938).

3:3-*Dimethylcyclopropane*-1-*acetic*-2-*carboxylic acid, homocaronic acid*, is produced as the cis-modification by gentle oxidation of Δ^3-carene (*J. L. Simonsen* and *M. G. Rau*, J. chem. Soc., 1923, **123**, 549). The cis- and trans-forms, m.ps. 136° and 191° respectively can both be obtained by the action of diazoacetic ester on 4-methylbut-2-ene-1-carboxylic ester (*J. Owen* and *J. L. Simonsen*, *ibid.*, 1933, 1225).

1-iso*Propylcyclopropane*-1-*acetic*-2-*carboxylic acid*, *α-tanacetonedicarboxylic acid*, m.p. 141·5°, is a product of oxidative degradation of sabinene (*O. Wallach*, Ann., 1908, **359**, 366; *F. W. Semmler*, Ber., 1902, **35**, 2045), sabinol (*idem*, Ber., 1900, **33**, 1459) and thujone (*idem*, Ber., 1903, **36**, 4367). When its dimethyl ester is boiled with sodium methoxide a ring enlargement occurs to a cyclopentenone derivative (see p. 17).

3:3-*Dimethylcyclopropane*-1-*propionic*-2-*carboxylic acids* are prepared by oxidation of the condensation product of methylheptenone and diazoacetic ester (*J. Owen* and *J. L. Simonsen*, J. chem. Soc., 1932, 1424). The *trans-dl*-acid, m.p. 108°, is resolvable by means of nor-ψ-ephedrine into the *d*-form, m.p. 112°, $[\alpha]_D + 37{\cdot}4°$ and the *l*-form, m.p. 112°, $[\alpha]_D - 37{\cdot}1°$. The *cis-dl*-acid has been resolved with the aid of morphine into a *d*-form, m.p. 105°, $[\alpha]_D + 39°$ and an *l*-form, m.p. 105°, $[\alpha]_D - 37{\cdot}8°$ (*idem, ibid.*, 1933, 1223). The *cis-d*-form results from the oxidation of Δ^4-carene (*J. L. Simonsen, ibid.*, 1922, **121**, 2292).

1-iso*Propylcyclopropane*-2-*propionic*-1-*carboxylic acid, homotanacetonedicarboxylic acid*, m.p. 148° has been obtained from the benzylidene compound of dihydroumbellulone by ring fission with permanganate (*F. W. Semmler*, Ber., 1907, **40**, 5017; 1908, **41**, 3988).

Cyclopropane-1:1:2-tricarboxylic acid, m.p. 187° (decomp.) may be obtained via the ethyl ester by the reaction of ethyl $\alpha\beta$-dibromopropionate or ethyl α-bromoacrylate with ethyl sodiomalonate (*M. Conrad* and *M. Guthzeit*, Ber., 1884, **17**, 1187; *A. Michael*, J. pr. chem., 1887, **35**, 132, 349). It is also furnished by the oxidative degradation of the condensation product of camphene and diazoacetic ester (*E. Buchner*, Ber., 1913, **46**, 759).

Cyclopropane-1:2:3-tricarboxylic acid, cis, m.p. 150–153°, trans, m.p. 220°, *anhydride*, m.p. 187°. The *cis*-acid is prepared by the decarboxylation of cyclopropane-1:1:2:3-tetracarboxylic acid (*W. H. Perkin*, Ber., 1834, **17**, 1652). The *trans*-acid is obtained by pyrolysis of the adduct from fumaric ester and diazoacetic ester (*E. Buchner*, Ber., 1890, **23**, 2853) or by permanganate oxidation of *pseudo*phenylacetic acid (norcaradienecarboxylic acid) (*W. Braren* and *E. Buchner*, Ber., 1901, **34**, 995). For homologues of the acid see *E. Buchner*, Ber., 1894, **27**, 868.

Cyclopropane-1:1:2:2-tetracarboxylic acid melts at 214° with decomposition into the *cis*-dicarboxylic anhydride. It is obtained via its *ethyl ester*, m.p. 43°, b.p. 187°/12 mm. by the reverse procedure of method 3 (p. 24) (*O. Dressel*, Ann., 1890, **256**, 171). An interesting method of preparation is also available from the condensation product of pyruvic acid and formaldehyde (VIII); the sequence of reactions is as follows (*V. Feofilaktov*, Chem. Ztbl., 1930, I, 1471):

```
            CH2                                               CH2
          /     \                                           /     \
CH2—CH           CH——CH2      HNO3          CO2H·C————————C·CH2OH
|    |           |    |     ———————>             |        |
O·CO·CO          CO·CO·O                         CH2      CO
                                                    \   /
        (VIII)                                        O

                                                        | HNO3
                                                        v

            CH2                                       CH2
          /     \                 KMnO4             /     \
(CO2H)2C————————C(CO2H)2        <———————    CO2H·C————————C·CO2H
                                                  |        |
                                                  CH2      CO
                                                     \   /
                                                       O
```

Cyclopropane-1:2:2:3-tetracarboxylic acid, cis, decomposes at about 95° to give the *cis*-1:2:3-tricarboxylic acid. It is prepared via the *ethyl ester*, b.p. 246° from diethyl dibromosuccinate by method 3 (p. 24). The *trans*-acid decomposes at 196–198° (*E. Buchner*, Ann., 1895, **284**, 289).

Tetranitriles of general formula (IX) have been prepared by the condensation of aldehydes and ketones with bromomalononitrile in the presence of potassium iodide (method 5; p. 25):

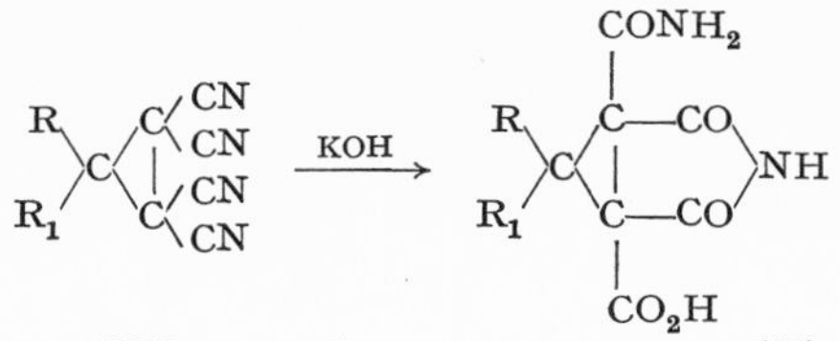

$CONH_2$

R, R_1 >C< C(CN)(CN)–C(CN)(CN) $\xrightarrow{KOH}$ R, R_1 >C< C–CO–NH–CO–C

CO_2H

(IX) (X)

On alkaline hydrolysis they give complex imidoacids of type (X).

Imidonitriles of the general formula

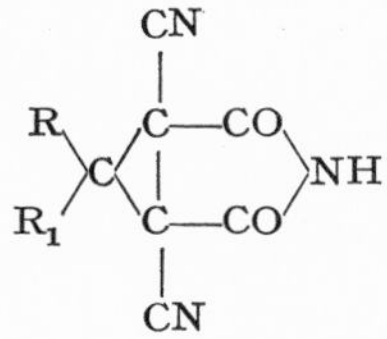

CN

R, R_1 >C< C–CO–NH–CO–C

CN

may be prepared from the corresponding dialkyldicyanodibromoglutarimides (*I. Guareschi* and *E. Grande,* Chem. Ztbl., 1899, II, 439; *E. Peano,* Chem. Ztbl., 1901, I, 582).

Triethyl 1:2:3-*tricyanocyclopropane*-1:2:3-*tricarboxylate,* m.p. 119°, results from the action of bromine or iodine on ethyl sodiocyanoacetate in ether; on hydrolysis it yields first cyclopropane-1:1:2:3-tetracarboxylic acid and then cyclopropane-1:2:3-tricarboxylic acid (*G. Errera,* Ber., 1900, **33**, 2979).

For later work on cyclopropane compounds see *F. A. Matsen et al.,* J. Amer. chem. Soc., 1950, **72**, 5256, 5260; *J. R. Lacher et al., ibid.,* 331; *S. Siegel* and *C. G. Bergstrom, ibid.,* 3815; *J. D. Roberts et al., ibid.,* 1951, **73**, 2509, 2959, 3176, 5030, 5034; *H. Rinderknecht* and *C. Niemann, ibid.,* 4259; *V. N. Ipatieff et al., ibid.,* 4343; *L. I. Smith* and *E. R. Rogier, ibid.,* 4047, 4049; *V. A. Slabey, ibid.,* 1952, **74**, 4928, 4930, 4963.

Chapter III

Cyclobutane Group

R. A. RAPHAEL

1. Occurrence, formation and properties

Compounds containing a single cyclobutane ring are rare in nature. Truxillic and truxinic acids, which are isomeric diphenylcyclobutanedicarboxylic acids, are found in coca leaf; and anemonin, a complex dilactone, occurs in the anemone and buttercup plants. The four-membered ring system forms part of the complex ring structure of some terpenoids e.g. pinene.

Preparative methods. The methods of synthesis resemble those of the cyclopropanes and may be classified similarly.

1. The Freund method (p. 23) applied to 1:4-dihalogeno-compounds results in the formation of the cyclobutane ring (*J. Cason* and *R. L. Way*, J. org. Chem., 1949, **14**, 31). An interesting extension of this method (*J. M. Derfer et al.*, J. Amer. chem. Soc., 1949, **71**, 175), consists in debrominating substituted tribromoneopentanes of type (I). The four products shown are formed, all of which may be obtained in a state of purity by fractional distillation, e.g.:

$$C_2H_5\cdot C(CH_2Br)_3 \;\text{(I)} \longrightarrow CH_3\cdot CH{=}\square + CH_2{=}CH\text{-}\square + \text{(Me)(Et)cyclopropane} + CH_3\cdot CH_2\cdot C(Et){=}CH_2$$

Pentaerythrityl tetrabromide undergoes a very similar reaction to give a mixture of methylenecyclobutane, spiropentane, 1:1-dimethylcyclopropane and 2-methylbut-1-ene (*M. J. Murray* and *E. H. Stevenson*, J. Amer. chem. Soc., 1944, **66**, 314, 812; *V. Slabey*, *ibid.*, 1946, **68**, 1335).

2. Intramolecular dehydrohalogenation may be employed as already described (p. 24):

$$\begin{array}{l} \quad CO_2Et \\ CH_2—CHBr \\ | \\ CH_2—CHBr \\ \quad CO_2Et \end{array} \xrightarrow{NaCN} \begin{array}{l} \quad CO_2Et \\ CH_2—CH \cdot CN \\ | \\ CH_2—CHBr \\ \quad CO_2Et \end{array} \longrightarrow \square \begin{array}{l} CO_2Et, CN \\ H, CO_2Et \end{array}$$

(*R. C. Fuson* and *T. Y. Kao*, *ibid.*, 1929, **51**, 1536; *H. N. Rydon*, Chem. and Ind., 1935, **54**, 315; cf. also *J. Colonge* and *D. Joly*, Ann. chim., 1943, [xi], **18**, 306).

3. Perkin's method (p. 24) may be used with 1:3-dihalides (cf. *F. H. Case*, J. Amer. chem. Soc., 1934, **56**, 715; 1933, **55**, 2927),

$$H_2C\begin{cases} CH_2Br \\ CH_2Br \end{cases} + 2\ NaCH\begin{cases} CN \\ CO_2Et \end{cases} \longrightarrow \square\begin{array}{l} CN \\ CO_2Et \end{array}$$

and the inverse procedure may also be adopted, e.g.

$$\begin{array}{l} CH_2—CNa(CO_2Et)_2 \\ | \\ CH_2—CNa(CO_2Et)_2 \end{array} \xrightarrow{Br_2} \square\begin{array}{l} (CO_2Et)_2 \\ (CO_2Et)_2 \end{array}$$

A modification of this latter method involves the use of methylene iodide and a derivative of glutaric ester:

$$H_2C\begin{cases} CH(CO_2Et)_2 \\ CH(CO_2Et)_2 \end{cases} + CH_2I_2 \longrightarrow (CO_2Et)_2\square(CO_2Et)_2$$

An extension of this procedure has been employed in the synthesis of *trans*-norpinic acid (*C. A. Kerr*, *ibid.*, 1929, **51**, 614); a glutarimide derivative (Guareschi's imide) prepared from acetone, cyanoacetic ester and ammonia is condensed with methylene iodide (scheme on next page).

Carbonyl bromide may be employed in place of methylene iodide in exactly analogous fashion.

4. A special method of forming the four-membered ring consists in the dimerisation of certain ethylenic compounds such as ketens, allenes and compounds containing an activated double bond (e.g. styrene, stilbene, cin-

namic acids, chalkones) or their interaction. The reaction is usually brought about under the influence of light of a certain wave-length. Thus ketens of the

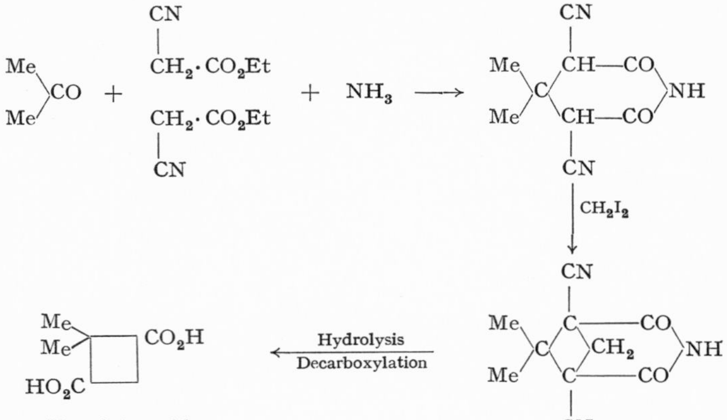

$$\begin{array}{c}Me\\ \quad\rangle CO\\ Me\end{array} + \begin{array}{c}CN\\ |\\ CH_2\cdot CO_2Et\\ \\ CH_2\cdot CO_2Et\\ |\\ CN\end{array} + NH_3 \longrightarrow \begin{array}{c}CN\\ |\\ Me\diagdown\quad CH—CO\diagdown\\ \quad C\langle\qquad\qquad \rangle NH\\ Me\diagup\quad CH—CO\diagup\\ |\\ CN\end{array}$$

$$\downarrow CH_2I_2$$

$$\underset{\text{Norpinic acid}}{\begin{array}{c}Me\\ Me\end{array}\!\!>\!\square\!\begin{array}{l}CO_2H\\ \\ HO_2C\end{array}} \xleftarrow[\text{Decarboxylation}]{\text{Hydrolysis}} \begin{array}{c}CN\\ |\\ Me\diagdown\quad C——CO\diagdown\\ \quad C\langle\ \rangle CH_2\qquad \rangle NH\\ Me\diagup\quad C——CO\diagup\\ |\\ CN\end{array}$$

general formula $R_1R_2C = C = O$ readily dimerise to yield substituted cyclobutane-1:3-diones of type:

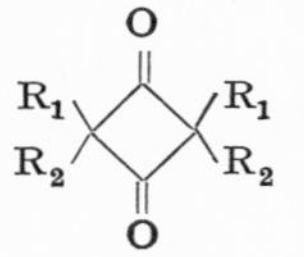

$$\begin{array}{c}O\\ \|\\ R_1\diagdown\ \diamond\ \diagup R_1\\ R_2\diagup\ \ \ \diagdown R_2\\ \|\\ O\end{array}$$

(*W. E. Hanford* and *J. C. Sauer*, Org. Reactions, **3**, 108).

It is now reasonably well established that the aldoketen ($RCH = C = O$) dimers are not of this structural type but are unsaturated β-lactones (cf. diketen, Vol. I, p. 528) derived from the basic structure

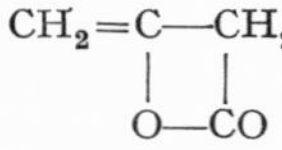

$$\begin{array}{c}CH_2{=}C—CH_2\\ \quad\ |\qquad |\\ \quad\ O—CO\end{array}$$

(*idem, ibid.*; *A. J. Blomquist* and *F. H. Baldwin*, J. Amer. chem. Soc., 1948, **70**, 29; *J. D. Roberts et al., ibid.*, 1949, **71**, 843. See, however, *R, B. Woodward* and *G. Small, ibid.*, 1950, **72**, 1297 and this chapter, p. 56).

A well-studied group are the cinnamic acid photodimers, truxillic and truxinic acids (see p. 60 ff).

A number of chalkones dimerise to yield products which are almost certainly cyclobutane derivatives (*I. M. Heilbron et al.*, J. chem. Soc., 1927, 1888; 1928, 2324).

The dimerisation of allenes is generally assumed to result in the formation of a four-membered ring but the proof is not yet based on a firm foundation (*S. Lebedev,* Chem. Ztbl., 1914, I, 1402; 1911, II, 1915; 1912, I, 1695; *K. Ziegler et al.,* Ber., 1924, **57**, 1983; 1930, **63**, 1851; *F. Strauss* and *M. Ehrenstein,* Ann., 1925, **442**, 93).

Many such dimerisations have been carried out under conditions of high temperature and pressure employing fluoro-olefines [*D. D. Coffman et al.,* J. Amer. chem. Soc., 1949, **71**, 490; *A. L. Henne* and *R. D. Ruh, ibid.,* 1947, **69**, 279; *J. Harman,* U.S.P. 2,404,374 (1946); *P. L. Barrick,* U.S.P. 2,427,116 (1947)], acrylonitrile [*E. C. Coyner* and *W. S. Hillman,* J. Amer. chem. Soc., 1949, **71**, 324; *P. L. Barrick* and *R. D. Cramer,* U.S.P. 2,441,128 (1948)] and methyl methacrylate (*idem, loc. cit.*). Certain substituted glutaconic esters dimerise in the presence of piperidine to yield polycarboxylic derivatives of cyclobutane (p. 66).

5. A few special methods of arriving at the cyclobutane nucleus have been described for individual compounds. Ring enlargement of cyclopropanes and ring diminution of cyclopentanes produce the four-membered ring (p. 11) The reaction between keten and diazomethane leads to cyclobutanone, presumably by ring enlargement of the intermediate cyclopropanone (*P. Lipp et al.,* Ber., 1931, **64**, 2823; Ann., 1932, **499**, 1; *S. Kaarsemakers* and *J. Coops,* Rec. Trav. chim., 1951, **70**, 1033). A by-product in a reaction involving the use of diazoacetic ester was found to be cyclobutane-1:2:3:4-tetracarboxylic acid, obviously derived from four molecules of the diazoester (*J. Owen* and *J. L. Simonsen,* J. chem. Soc., 1933, 1225).

Properties. The cyclobutane ring system is more resistant than the cyclopropane structure to such reagents as the halogens and the halogen acids and hydrogenation to *n*-butane derivatives requires a temperature higher than that needed for the similar fission of three-membered rings; the ring is always broken between two unequally substituted carbon atoms. The type of rupture most frequently encountered is a dissociation into two molecules of an olefinic nature (i.e. a reversal of preparative method 4); this may be brought about by heat or short wave radiation.

Apart from the obvious observation that the cyclobutane ring is made up of energetically unfavourable *a* constellations (Fig. 2, p. 9) very little work on the fine structure of the nucleus has been reported although a thermodynamic analysis on the lines associated with the name of *K. S. Pitzer* (p. 10) has recently been envisaged (*K. S. Pitzer et al.,* J. Amer. chem. Soc., 1947, **69**, 2483, 2488; *J. Cason* and *R. L. Way,* J. org. Chem., 1949, **14**, 31; for Raman spectra of cyclobutanes see *K. W. F. Kohlrausch* and *R. Skrabal,* Monatsh., 1937, **70**, 44, 377; *M. J. Murray* and *E. H. Stevenson,* J. Amer. chem. Soc., 1944, **66**, 812). Spectroscopic evidence shows the ring in cyclobutane itself to be planar (*T. P. Wilson,* J. chem. Phys., 1943, 11, 361) but it has been conclusively demonstrated by electron diffraction methods that in octafluorocyclobutane the ring is non-planar (*H. P. Lemaire* and *R. L. Livingstone,* J. Amer. chem. Soc., 1952, 74, 5732).

2. Hydrocarbons

(a) Saturated hydrocarbons

Some hydrocarbons of the cyclobutane series are listed in Table 1.

TABLE 1

SATURATED HYDROCARBONS OF THE CYCLOBUTANE SERIES

Hydrocarbon	B.p.	*d*	*n*	Reference
Cyclobutane	13·08°/741 mm.			1
Methylcyclobutane	36·3°/760 mm.	d_4^{20} 0·6933	n_D^{20} 1·3830	2
Ethylcyclobutane	70·64°/760 mm. (f.p. −142·85°)	d_4^{20} 0·7280	n_D^{20} 1·4020	3
1:2-Dimethylcyclobutane	68–70°	d_4^{17} 0·7122	n_D^{17} 1·3988	4
*iso*Propylcyclobutane	92·7°/760 mm. (f.p. −106·43°)	d_4^{20} 0·7376	n_D^{20} 1·4080	3
*iso*Butylcyclobutane	119–119·5°/743 mm.			5
1:2-Di*iso*propyl-cyclobutane	157–158·5°/760 mm.	d_4^{20} 0·7755	n_D^{20} 1·4279	6
Phenylcyclobutane	190°/755 mm.	d_4^{20} 0·9378	n_D^{20} 1·5277	7
1-Methyl-1-phenyl-cyclobutane	208·6°/760 mm.	d^{20} 0·9192	n_D^{20} 1·5132	8

[1] *G. B. Heisig,* J. Amer. chem. Soc., 1941, **63**, 1698.
[2] *N. Rosanov,* Chem. Ztbl., 1930, II, 234.
[3] *J. M. Derfer et al.,* J. Amer. chem. Soc., 1949, **71**, 175.
[4] *N. D. Zelinsky* and *M. B. Turova-Pollak,* Ber., 1932, **65**, 1171.
[5] *B. A. Kazanski* and *V. P. Golmov,* Brit. chem. Abstr., 1943, AII, 58.
[6] *S. Lebedev,* Chem. Ztbl., 1911, II, 1915.
[7] *F. H. Case,* J. Amer. chem. Soc., 1934, **56**, 715.
[8] *V. N. Ipatieff* and *H. Pines, ibid.,* 1939, **61**, 3374.

Cyclobutane is not an easily available substance. For long the only workable method of preparation was the hydrogenation of cyclobutene (*R. Willstätter* and *J. Bruce,* Ber., 1907, **40**, 3979; *G. B. Heisig,* J. Amer. chem. Soc., 1941, **63**, 1698). It was made more accessible by *J. Cason* and *R. L. Way* (J. org. Chem., 1949, **14**, 31) who prepared it by the decomposition of magnesiumcyclobutyl bromide with *n*-butanol. The same authors have shown that the Freund reaction on tetramethylene dibromide produces a 7% yield of the hydrocarbon. An interesting method of formation is the photolysis of cyclopentanone whereby cyclobutane and carbon monoxide are formed (p. 21). Cyclobutane may be catalytically hydrogenated to *n*-butane at 120° and can be dehydrogenated to butadiene at 300° (*I. Ostromysslenski*, Chem. Ztbl., 1916, II, 307). At ordinary temperatures it resists the action of the halogens and halogen acids.

(b) Unsaturated hydrocarbons

TABLE 2

UNSATURATED HYDROCARBONS DERIVED FROM CYCLOBUTANE

Hydrocarbon	B.p.	*d*	*n*	Reference
Cyclobutene	2·4°/760 mm.	d_4^0 0·733		1
1-Methylcyclobut-1-ene	37·1°/750 mm.	d_4^{20} 0·7244	n_D^{18} 1·4088	2
Methylenecyclobutane	42·22°/760 mm. (f.p. −134·68°)	d_4^{20} 0·7401	n_D^{20} 1·42087	3
Ethylidenecyclobutane	80·26°/760 mm. (f.p. −105·37°)	d_4^{20} 0·7678	n_D^{20} 1·4370	4
*iso*Propylidene-cyclobutane	107·26°/760 mm. (f.p. −58·33°)	d_4^{20} 0·7823	n_D^{20} 1·4459	4
1:2-Diethynylcyclobutane	50–53°/30 mm.	d_4^{20} 0·873	n_D^{20} 1·5081	5
1:2-Di(vinylethynyl)-cyclobutane	53–55°/1 mm.	d_4^{20} 0·9248	n_D^{20} 1·5495	6

[1] *R. Willstätter* and *J. Bruce*, Ber., 1907, **40**, 3979; *G. B. Heisig*, J. Amer. chem. Soc., 1941, **63**, 1698.
[2] *W. Shand et al.*, *ibid.*, 1944, **66**, 636.
[3] *V. A. Slabey*, *ibid.*, 1946, **68**, 1335.
[4] *J. M. Derfer et al.*, *ibid.*, 1949, **71**, 175.
[5] *H. B. Dykstra*, *ibid.*, 1934, **56**, 1625.
[6] *M. E. Cupery* and *W. H. Carothers*, *ibid.*, 1934, **56**, 1167.

Cyclobutene (Table 2) was first obtained in 1907 by the Hofmann elimination method from cyclobutyltrimethylammonium hydroxide and this procedure is still the one adopted for preparative purposes. Its reactions are those of a typical olefine; it is readily hydrogenated to cyclobutane and bromine affords the dibromide. The action of the Ziegler reagent, N-bromosuccinimide, leads to unexpected results; only about 1% of 3-bromocyclobut-1-ene is formed, the remainder of the product consisting of 1:2-dibromocyclobutane (*E. R. Buchman* and *D. R. Howton*, J. Amer. chem. Soc., 1948, **70**, 3510).

Other unsaturated hydrocarbons derived from cyclobutane are given in Table 2.

Methylenecyclobutane is one of the products obtained by the debromination of pentaerythrityl tetrabromide (see p. 46). It also reacts anomalously with N-bromosuccinimide, the products being (*E. R. Buchman* and *D. R. Howton*, *ibid.*, 1948, **70**, 2517) 1-bromo-1-bromomethylcyclobutane (56%), 2-bromo-1-methylenecyclobutane (14%) and 1-bromomethylcyclobut-1-ene (14%).

Rather unexpectedly methylenecyclobutane shows no tendency to rearrange into methylcyclobutene and the conversion must be brought about indirectly (*W. Shand et al.*, *loc. cit.*).

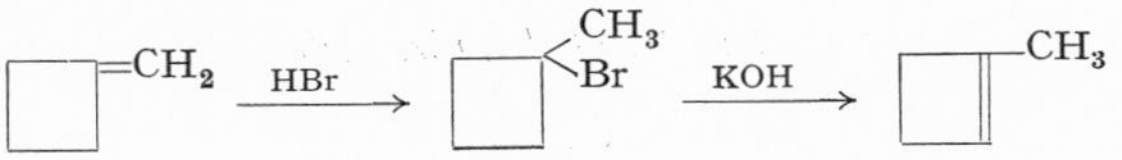

$=CH_2$ —HBr→ $<^{CH_3}_{Br}$ —KOH→ $-CH_3$

Methylenecyclobutane condenses with benzene in the presence of sulphuric acid to form a mixture of 1-methyl-1-phenylcyclobutane and *p*-bis-1-methyl-1-cyclobutylbenzene (*V. N. Ipatieff* and *H. Pines*, J. Amer. chem. Soc., 1939, **61**, 3374).

The relative ease of obtaining methylenecyclobutane renders it a useful starting material for the production of other cyclobutane derivatives (*J. D. Roberts* and *C. W. Saver*, J. Amer. chem. Soc., 1949, **71**, 3925).

Many attempts to obtain cyclobutadiene have been unsuccessful. The obvious methods when tried do not lead to the desired compound; thus 1:2-dibromocyclobutane with potassium hydroxide is decomposed to acetylene (*R. Willstätter* and *W. Schmaedel*, Ber., 1905, **38**, 1992), and the bis-trimethylammonium hydroxide (I) decomposes as shown:

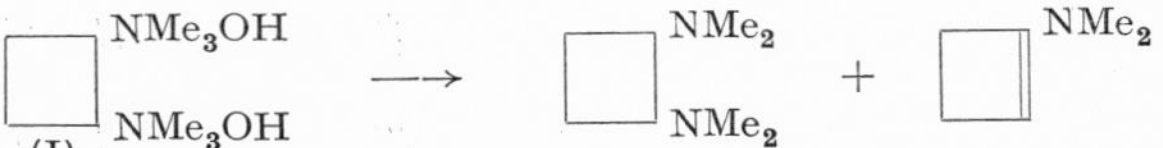

NMe_3OH, NMe_3OH (I) ⟶ NMe_2, NMe_2 + NMe_2

(*E. R. Buchman*, *M. J. Schlatter* and *A. O. Reims*, J. Amer. chem. Soc., 1942, **64**, 2701). 3-Bromocyclobut-1-ene would be a promising intermediate but, as has been shown above, attempts to obtain this have been discouraging.

1:2-Diethynylcyclobutane and 1:2-di(vinylethynyl)cyclobutane are the products of dimerisation of monovinylacetylene and divinylacetylene respectively. The structure

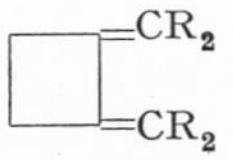

$=CR_2$, $=CR_2$

proposed for the products of dimerisation of allenes has not yet been confirmed (*S. Lebedev*, Chem. Ztbl., 1914, I, 1410).

1:2-Divinylcyclobutane, see Chapter XI, p. 400.

3. Halogen derivatives

Some halogen derivatives of saturated and unsaturated hydrocarbons of the cyclobutane series are given in Table 3.

TABLE 3

HALOGEN DERIVATIVES OF CYCLOBUTANE HYDROCARBONS

Compound	B.p.	d	n	Reference
1:1:2:2-Tetrafluoro-cyclobutane	50–50.7⁰	d_4^{25} 1·2752	n_D^{25} 1·3043	1
2:2:3:3-Tetrafluoro-1-ethylcyclobutane	91⁰	d_4^{25} 1·1506	n_D^{25} 1·3370	1
Bromocyclobutane	108·2⁰/760 mm.	d^{20} 1·434	n_D^{20} 1·4801	2
1-Bromo-1-methyl-cyclobutane	55–57⁰/100 mm.	d_4^{20} 1·3179	n_D^{20} 1·4698	3
Bromomethylcyclobutane	137–139⁰	d_{19}^{19} 1·400	n_D^{19} 1·4875	4
1:1-Dibromocyclobutane	158⁰	d_{20}^{20} 1·933	n_D^{20} 1·5362	5
1:2-Dichloro-3:4-dibromo-cyclobutane	120⁰/18 mm.		n_D^{20} 1·5757	7
1:2-Dibromocyclobutane	176·2⁰/741 mm. (m.p. 4·7–5·7⁰)			6
1-Bromo-1-bromoethyl-cyclobutane		d_4^{25} 1·801	n_D^{25} 1·532	6
1:1:2-Tribromo-cyclobutane	109⁰/19 mm.	d_4^{0} 2·374		5
1:2:3:4-Tetrabromo-cyclobutane	110⁰/1·5 mm.		n_D^{20} 1·6303	7
1:1:2:2-Tetrabromo-cyclobutane	m.p. 126⁰			5
1:1:2:2:3-Pentabromo-cyclobutane	175–178⁰/19 mm.	d_4^{0} 2·88		5
1:1:2:2:3:4-Hexabromo-cyclobutane	m.p. 186·5⁰			5
2:2:3:3-Tetra-fluoro-1-vinylcyclobutane	83–85⁰	d_4^{25} 1·1866	n_D^{25} 1·3489	1
2:2:3:3-Tetrafluoro-1-ethynylcyclobutane	82–84⁰	d_4^{25} 1·2498	n_D^{25} 1·3553	1
1:2-Dichlorocyclobut-3-ene	133⁰ (m.p. 44⁰)			7
1-Bromocyclobut-1-ene	92·5–93·5⁰	d_4^{0} 1·524		5
1:2-Dibromocyclobut-1-ene	155⁰	d_4^{0} 2·036		5
1:2-Dibromocyclobut-3-ene	173–175⁰	d_4^{20} 1·9592	n_D^{20} 1·5948	7

[1] *D. D. Coffman et al.*, J. Amer. chem. Soc., 1949, **71**, 490.
[2] *J. Cason* and *R. L. Way*, J. org. Chem., 1949, **14**, 31.
[3] *W. Shand et al.*, J. Amer. chem. Soc., 1944, **66**, 636.
[4] *N. Demjanov*, Ber., 1907, **40**, 4959.
[5] *R. Willstätter* and *J. Bruce*, Ber., 1907, **40**, 3983.
[6] *E. R. Buchman* and *D. R. Howton*, J. Amer. chem. Soc., 1948, **70**, 3510.
[7] *J. W. Reppe et al.*, Ann., 1948, **506**, 1.

Cyclobutyl bromide is formed in small yield by the action of hydrobromic acid on cyclobutanol, but the best method of preparation is by the action of bromine on the silver salt of cyclobutanecarboxylic acid (Ref. 2, Table 3).

1:2-*Dibromocyclobutane* is obtained by the action of bromine on cyclobutene; from this starting material Willstätter prepared a series of bromides of the cyclobutane group by the following reactions.

A very interesting series of halogen-substituted cyclobutanes has been obtained by *J. W. Reppe* (*loc. cit.*) from cyclo-octatetraene (p. 260)*. This substance reacts with sulphuryl chloride to form 1:2-dichlorobicyclo[4:2:0]octa-3:5-diene (p. 262) the naphthaquinone adduct of which yields 1:2-*dichlorocyclobut-3-ene* (I) on pyrolysis. The corresponding *dibromo*-compound (II) is obtained in similar fashion. The dichloride is inert to potassium acetate in acetic acid and zinc in methanol; perbenzoic acid leaves it unaffected. Some reactions of the two compounds are shown in the following diagram.

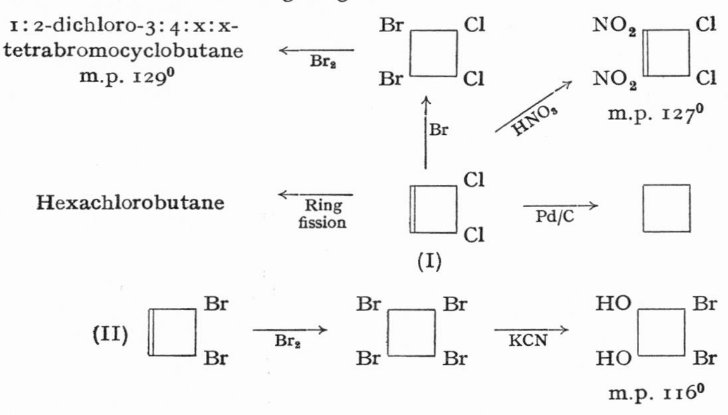

The **fluorocyclobutanes**, a very few of which are included in Table 3, have all been prepared by the addition of tetrafluoroethylene to a substituted olefine; mono-olefines, allenes, 1:3-dienes, vinylacetylene, acrylonitriles and acrylic esters have all been successfully employed. As a class these fluoro-compounds exhibit great resistance to ring cleavage. For other fluoro-compounds see Chapter XI, p. 398.

* It has now been shown that these compounds are derivatives of butadiene (*R. Criegee et al.*, Chem. Ber., 1953, **86**, 126).

4. Alcohols

TABLE 4

ALCOHOLS DERIVED FROM CYCLOBUTANE

Compound	B.p.	d	n	Reference
Cyclobutanol	123°/735 mm.	d_{19}^{19} 0·9206	n_D^{19} 1·4339	1
Cyclobutylcarbinol	142°/750 mm.	d_{20}^{20} 0·9129	n_D^{19} 1·4449	2
Cyclobutylmethyl-carbinol	144°/752 mm.	d_4^{20} 0·8997	$n_D^{18.8}$ 1·4451	3
Cyclobutyldimethyl-carbinol	147°/760 mm.	d_0^{20} 0·8952	n_D^{20} 1·4457	4
1:1-Di(hydroxymethyl)-cyclobutane	147°/20 mm.	d_4^{20} 1·0484	n_D^{20} 1·4758	5

[1] *N. J. Demjanov* and *M. Dojarenko*, Ber., 1907, **40**, 2596.
[2] *N. J. Demjanov*, Ber., 1907, **40**, 4960.
[3] *N. D. Zelinsky* and *J. Gutt*, Ber., 1908, **41**, 2432.
[4] *N. Kishner*, Chem. Ztbl., 1905, II, 761.
[5] *N. D. Zelinsky* and *M. N. Ujedinov*, Ber., 1913, **46**, 1093.

Some alcohols of the cyclobutane series are given in Table 4.

Cyclobutanol may be obtained by the action of nitrous acid on cyclobutylamine, by the electrolysis of potassium cyclobutanecarboxylate and by the hydrolysis of cyclobutyl cyclobutanecarboxylate, formed by the action of iodine on the silver salt of cyclobutanecarboxylic acid (*N. J. Demjanov et al.*, Ber., 1907, **40**, 2594, 4962; 1908, **41**, 44). The primary exocyclic alcohols are prepared by the Bouveault-Blanc reduction of the corresponding carboxylic esters, the secondary by the reduction of the corresponding ketones and the tertiary by the Grignard reaction on cyclobutyl alkyl ketones.

5. Amines

The primary amines with the amino group attached directly to the ring are made by the Hofmann, Schmidt or Curtius degradation procedures on the corresponding carboxylic acid derivatives. Cyclobutylmethylamine is prepared by reduction of the corresponding nitrile; with nitrous acid it undergoes ring enlargement (p. 12).

Cyclobutylamine, b.p. 80·5–82·5°; *NN-dimethyl* deriv., b.p. 97–98°; *quaternary bromide*, m.p. 205·6–206·5° (*J. Böeseken*, Rec. Trav. chim., 1918, **37**, 261; *R. Willstätter* and *W. Schmaedel*, Ber., 1905, **38**, 1995).

Cyclobutylmethylamine, b.p. 110°/753 mm.; *hydrochloride*, m.p.: 235·5° (*N. Demjanov* and *M. Luschnikov*, Chem. Ztbl., 1903, I, 828).

1:2-*Diaminocyclobutane*: cis-form, b.p. 147°; d_4^{20} ·09652; n_D^{20} 1·4881; *dibenzoyl* deriv., m.p. 204·5–205°; trans-form, b.p. 151°; d_4^{20} 0·9490; n_D^{20} 1·4837; *dibenzoyl* deriv., m.p. 245·5–246° (*E. R. Buchman et al.*, J. Amer. chem. Soc., 1942, **64**, 2696).

trans-*NNNN-Tetramethyl*-1:2-*diaminocyclobutane*, b.p. 83°/50 mm, d_4^{20} 0·8455; n_D^{20} 1·4472 (*idem, ibid.*, 2701).

6. Aldehydes and Ketones

Cyclobutylformaldehyde, b.p. 116–117° (*H. G. Colman* and *W. H. Perkin*, J. chem. Soc., 1887, **51**, 238), is prepared from calcium cyclobutanecarboxylate and calcium formate. On treatment with sulphuric acid at 130° it undergoes isomerisation to cyclopentanone; the action of bromine followed by barium carbonate furnishes cyclopentan-1-ol-2-one (*E. D. Venus-Danilova*, Brit. chem. Abstr., 1940, AII, 45).

Cyclobutanone, b.p. 100–102° (*semicarbazone*, m.p. 204°, 2:4-*dinitrophenylhydrazone*, m.p. 146°; *N. J. Demjanov* and *M. Dojarenko*, Ber., 1932, **55**, 2739), is formed by the Hofmann degradation of 1-bromocyclobutane -1-carboxamide or by catalytic oxidation of cyclobutanol or cyclopropylcarbinol (*M. Dojarenko*, Chem. Ztbl., 1926, II, 2291); the best method of preparation is by the action of keten on an excess of diazomethane (see p. 49). A series of polyalkylated cyclobutanones has been prepared from $\alpha\beta$-unsaturated aliphatic ketones by the following method (*J. Colonge* and *D. Joly*, Ann. Chim., 1943, [xi], **18**, 306).

$$(R_1)(R_2)C{=}CH{\cdot}CO{\cdot}CH(R_3)(R_4) \xrightarrow{HBr} (R_1)(R_2)C(Br){-}CH_2{\cdot}CO{\cdot}CH(R_3)(R_4)$$

$$\xrightarrow{-HBr} \text{cyclobutanone: } C(R_1)(R_2){-}CH_2{-}C{=}O{-}C(R_3)(R_4) \text{ (ring)}$$

2:3:3-*Triethylcyclobutan*-1-*one* has b.p. 95°/16 mm., *semicarbazone*, m.p. 179°. 2:2:3-*Triphenylcyclobutan*-1-*one*, m.p. 135–136°, is formed from diphenylketen and styrene (*H. Staudinger* and *A. Rheiner*, Helv., 1924, **7**, 8). It decomposes into the original components at about 200°.

As previously indicated (p. 48) it has been suggested that aldoketen dimers are derivatives of β-lactones rather than of cyclobutane-1:3-diones. This seems to be true for the liquid *dimer* of methylketen but not for the solid dimer m.p. 138°, *dioxime* m.p. 198–200°, *phenylhydrazone* m.p. 160°, which has been shown to possess the enolic structure 2:4-*dimethylcyclobut*-2-*en*-3-*ol*-1-*one*, a formulation in harmony with its strongly acidic nature (*R. B. Woodward* and *G. Small*, J. Amer. chem. Soc., 1950, **72**, 1297). The solid *ethylketen dimer* m.p. 76–78°, *phenylhydrazone* m.p. 132·5–133·5°, probably possesses an analogous structure (*G. Schroeter*, Ber., 1916, **49**, 2736).

The tetra-alkylcyclobutane-1:3-diones are all ketoketen dimers (cf. p. 48) formed by the action of heat on the monomer, which is readily regenerated at higher temperatures. Very little has been recorded on the chemical properties of these diketones. Tetramethylcyclobutane-1:3-dione is said to furnish the *cis*- and *trans*-diols on reduction and to give mono- and di-oximes which yield the expected products when subjected to the Beckmann rearrangement (*L. L. Miller*, "The Structure of Some Derivatives of Dimethylketen", Cornell University, 1937). The action of methylmagnesium bromide on tetramethylcyclobutane-1:3-dione takes place in the following manner with concomitant ring fission.

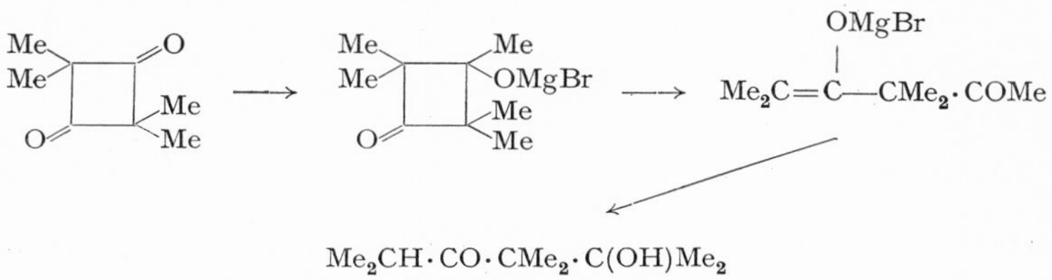

Me, Me, =O, Me, Me, O= (cyclobutane-1:3-dione) ⟶ Me, Me, Me, OMgBr, Me, Me, O= ⟶ $Me_2C{=}C(OMgBr){-}CMe_2{\cdot}COMe$

⟶ $Me_2CH{\cdot}CO{\cdot}CMe_2{\cdot}C(OH)Me_2$

Phenylmagnesium bromide and phenyllithium react analogously.

Tetramethylcyclobutane-1:3-*dione* has m.p. 116°, b.p. 159–161°; *dioxime*, m.p. 281° (*J. L. E. Erickson* and *G. C. Kitchens*, J. Amer. chem. Soc., 1946, **68**, 492). The *tetraethyl*-compound has m.p. 23–24°, b.p. 95–97°/15 mm. (*H. Staudinger* and *J. Maier*, Ann., 1914, **401**, 292) and the *tetrapropyl*-compound m.p. 61–62° (*H. Staudinger et al.*, Helv., 1923, **6**, 291).

The exocyclic monoketones are obtained by the action of zinc alkyls on cyclobutanecarboxylic chloride (cadmium alkyls would almost certainly give better results) or by the action of Grignard reagents on the carboxyamides (*W. H. Perkin et al.*, J. chem. Soc., 1887, **51**, 237; 1892, **61**, 47; *N. D. Zelinsky* and *J. Gutt*, Ber., 1908, **41**, 2432; *N. Kishner*, Chem. Ztbl., 1913, II, 2132). *Acetylcyclobutane* has b.p. 134°/748 mm.; *semicarbazone*, m.p. 148–149°; *benzoylcyclobutane*, b.p. 258°/740 mm.; *oxime*, m.p. 91–93° (*W. H. Perkin* and *W. Sinclair*, J. chem. Soc., 1892, **61**, 59).

A large number of exocyclic diketones are available by means of the photodimerisation of $\alpha\beta$-unsaturated ketones. Thus benzylideneacetophenone gives rise to "*truxillic ketone*" (I) m.p. 225–226° and "*truxinic ketone*" (II) m.p. 124° (*H. Stobbe et al.*, J. pr. Chem., 1929, **123**, 40, 54; Ber., 1926, **59**, 2254).

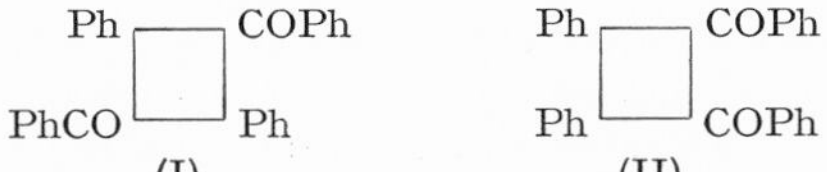

Ph, COPh, PhCO, Ph (cyclobutane) (I) Ph, COPh, Ph, COPh (cyclobutane) (II)

The styryl alkyl ketone dimers prepared by *I. M. Heilbron* and co-workers are almost certainly of the same type (see p. 48); although two keto groups are undoubtedly present the compounds form a monoxime only.

The cis- and trans-1:2-*dibenzoylcyclobutanes* are obtained by the Friedel-Crafts reaction between benzene and cyclobutane-1:2-dicarboxylic chloride. The structures have been confirmed and interrelated by the following series of reactions.

COPh COPh Br
Br_2 → Br Br + Br COPh
COPh COPh COPh
NaOH -Br -Br
COPh ← H_2 COPh
COPh COPh

cis-1:2-*Dibenzoylcyclobutane*, m.p. 121–122°, *dioxime*, m.p. 175°; trans-*form* m.p. 96–97·5°, *dioxime*, m.p. 170°. 1:2-*Dibenzoylcyclobut*-1-*ene* has m.p. 95–97° (*E. Ellingboe* and *R. C. Fuson*, J. Amer. chem. Soc., 1934, **56**, 1774). The *cis*-diketone has also been obtained by the action of molecular silver on 1:4-dibromo-1:4-dibenzoylbutane (*T. Kao*, *ibid.*, 1940, **62**, 356).

7. Carboxylic acids

(a) Cyclobutane carboxylic acids

Cyclobutanecarboxylic acid, m.p. –6°, b.p. 195° *ethyl ester* b.p. 160°, *anhydride* b.p. 160° *nitrile* b.p. 150°, *amide* m.p. 150–152°, is prepared by the decarboxylation of the 1:1-dicarboxylic acid (*W. H. Perkin et al.*, J. chem. Soc., 1892, **61**, 41; 1899, **75**, 921; *N. D. Zelinsky* and *J. Gutt*, Ber., 1907, **40**, 4744; *J. Böeseken*, Rec. Trav. chim., 1919, **37**, 261; *G. B. Heisig*, J. Amer. chem. Soc., 1941, **63**, 1698). Hydriodic acid reduction splits the ring giving *n*-valeric acid (*N. Kishner*, Chem. Ztbl., 1908, II, 1342).

1-*Phenylcyclobutane*-1-*carboxylic acid*, m.p. 106–107°, *amide* m.p. 75–76°, *anilide* m.p. 96°, is produced by hydrolysis of the *nitrile* which is obtained by the action of trimethylene bromide on phenylacetonitrile (*R. D. Kleene*, J. Amer. chem. Soc., 1941, **63**, 3538).

2:3- and 2:4-*Diphenylcyclobutane*-1-*carboxylic acids*, *distyrinic* and *distyranic acids*, m.p. 147° and 176° respectively, are obtained by boiling cinnamic acid with 50% sulphuric acid (*R. Stoermer* and *W. Becker*, Ber., 1923, **56**, 1440).

3^c-Amino-2^c:4^t-*diphenylcyclobutane*-1^t-*carboxylic acid*, m.p. 195–196° (decomp.), *methyl ester* m.p. 83·5–84°, is produced by Hofmann degradation of the corresponding amide (β-truxillamic acid); 4^c-*amino*-2^t:3^t-*diphenylcyclobutane*-

1^c-*carboxylic acid*, m.p. 161° (decomp.) is similarly obtained from β-truxinamic acid (*R. Stoermer* and *F. Schenk*, Ber., 1927, **60**, 2575, 2587).

Cyclobutane-1:1-dicarboxylic acid melts at 155° with evolution of carbon dioxide to give the monocarboxylic acid. The *diethyl ester*, b.p. 224°, and *mono-ethyl ester nitrile*, b.p. 214°, are prepared by method 3 (p. 47) (*V. P. Golmov* and *B. A. Kazonski*, Brit. chem. Abstr., 1943, AII, 92; 1940, AII, 45; *N. Kishner*, Chem. Ztbl., 1905, II, 761). With urea and its derivatives it forms spirotriketo-hexahydropyrimidines (*A. W. Dox* and *L. Yoder*, J. Amer. chem. Soc., 1931, **43**, 677).

cis-**Cyclobutane-1:2-dicarboxylic acid,** m.p. 139·5–140°, *anhydride* m.p. 76·5–77°, *dihydrazide*, m.p. 140–140.5°, is prepared by the decarboxylation of the 1:1:2:2-tetracarboxylic acid (*R. Kuhn* and *A. Wassermann*, Helv., 1928, **11**, 50, 70, 79, 600; *E. R. Buchman et al.*, J. Amer. chem. Soc., 1942, **64**, 2696). The *cis*-acid may be transformed to the *trans*-isomer, m.p. 130·5–131°, *dihydrazide*, m.p. 223–223·5°, by prolonged heating, by heating with hydrochloric acid or by sodium methoxide-catalysed alcoholysis of the dimethyl ester (*E. R. Buchman et al., loc. cit.*; *W. H. Perkin*, J. chem. Soc., 1894, **65**, 572). The corresponding *nitriles*, b.p. 108–115°/3 mm. and b.p. 140–145°/3 mm., m.p. 62° (absolute con-figuration not determined) have been obtained by the thermal dimerisation of acrylonitrile; hydrolysis of both dinitriles gives the *trans*-acid (*E. C. Coyner* and *W. S. Hillman*, J. Amer. chem. Soc., 1949, **71**, 324). Bromination of the acids gives 1:2-*dibromocyclobutane*-1:2-*carboxylic acid* which may be debrominated via the ester to give *cyclobut*-1-*ene*-1:2-*dicarboxylic acid* m.p. 178° (decomp.), which readily forms an anhydride (*W. H. Perkin*, Ber., 1893, **26**, 2243; J. chem. Soc., 1894, **65**, 572, 950; *H. Bode*, Ber., 1934, **67**, 332).

Two of the 3:4-*dimethylcyclobutane*-1:2-*dicarboxylic acids* result from the decarboxylation of the corresponding 1:1:2:2-tetracarboxylic acids; the cis-*acid* has m.p. 87–88°, *anhydride* m.p. 50–51°, the trans-*acid* m.p. 200–201·5° (*A. I. Vogel*, J. chem. Soc., 1927, 1985).

trans-**Cyclobutane-1:3-dicarboxylic acid,** m.p. 172–173°, is prepared by the intermolecular dehydrohalogenation of ethyl α-chloropropionate by means of sodium ethoxide (*W. Markovnikov* and *A. Krestovnikov*, Ann., 1881, **208**, 333; Ber., 1890, **23R**, 432; *E. Haworth* and *W. H. Perkin*, J. chem. Soc., 1898, **73**, 330). From the mother liquors of this preparation the cis-*acid*, m.p. 143–143·5°, *dihydrazide* m.p. 172–174°, may be isolated. The *cis*-acid may also be obtained from the *trans*-acid by treatment with acetic anhydride or acetyl chloride and distillation of the mixed anhydride so formed; the cis-*anhydride*, m.p. 47·5–48°, is thus obtained and may be hydrolysed to the *cis*-acid by means of hydro-chloric acid (*E. R. Buchman et al.*, J. Amer. chem. Soc., 1942, **64**, 2703 and above references). The reconversion of the *cis*-acid to the *trans*-acid is unexpectedly difficult; heating with concentrated hydrochloric acid results in carbonisation whilst heating alone furnishes the *cis*-anhydride. The configurational change has to be accomplished indirectly; treatment of the *cis*-dimethyl ester with methanolic sodium methoxide yields the *trans*-dimethyl ester from which the free *trans*-acid is obtainable by hydrolysis (*E. R. Buchman et al., loc. cit.*). The reported preparation of the *cis*-acid by the interaction of formaldehyde and malonic ester (or their equivalents) is incorrect, the product being α-methyleneglutaric acid (*E. R. Buchman et al., loc. cit.*). Doubts have been expressed concerning the correctness of the formulation of these acids as cyclobutane derivatives (*D. H. Deutsch* and *E. R. Buchman*, Experientia, 1950, **6**, 462).

2:2-*Dimethylcyclobutane*-1-*carboxylic*-3-*acetic acid* (*pinic acid*), m.p. 102°, and 2:2-*dimethylcyclobutane*-1:3-*dicarboxylic acid* (*norpinic acid*), m.p. (cis) 174°, (trans) 146°, are degradation products of α-pinene. The synthesis of *trans*-norpinic acid has already been described (p. 47).

Ethyl 1-*cyanocyclobutane*-1:2-*dicarboxylate* exists in two forms, b.p. 119–120°/2 mm. and m.p. 89·5–90°; they are made by reaction of ββ′-dibromoadipic ester with sodium cyanide (p. 47) (*E. R. Buchman et al.*, J. Amer. chem. Soc., 1942, **64**, 2696; *R. C. Fuson et al., ibid.*, 1929, **51**, 1536; 1934, **56**, 1774). Hydrolysis of the crystalline isomer yields *cyclobutane*-1:1:2-*tricarboxylic acid*, m.p. 91–92°, *hydrate* m.p. 135° (decomp.).

Cyclobutane-1:2:3-**tricarboxylic acid** is obtained in two isomeric forms, m.p. 141–143° and 168–170°, by the condensation of ethyl αβ-dibromopropionate and ethyl ethanetetracarboxylate followed by hydrolysis and decarboxylation of the oily cyclobutane-1:1:2:3:3-pentacarboxylic acid so formed (*L. J. Goldsworthy* and *W. H. Perkin*, J. chem. Soc., 1914, **106**, 2665).

Cyclobutane-1:1:2:2-*tetracarboxylic acid*, prepared by method 3 (p. 47), melts at 145–150° with decarboxylation to form the 1:2-dicarboxylic acid.

3:4-*Dimethylcyclobutane*-1:1:2:2-*tetracarboxylic acid*, m.p. 138–139°, *tetraethyl ester* b.p. 225°/16 mm., is prepared from ethylidenemalonic ester, which is reduced with moist aluminium amalgam to 2:3-dimethylbutane-1:1:4:4-tetracarboxylic ester; the latter forms a disodio-derivative which with bromine is cyclised to the above ester. By hydrolysis followed by decarboxylation, 2:3-*dimethylcyclobutane*-1:4-*dicarboxylic acid* is formed, separable into cis-, m.p. 87–88° (*anhydride*, m.p. 50–51°) and trans-, m.p. 200·5–201·5°, *forms* (*A. I. Vogel* J. chem. Soc., 1927, 1985).

Methyl 3:4-*diphenylcyclobutane*-1:1:2:2-*tetracarboxylate*, m.p. 148°, is prepared in exactly analogous fashion from dimethyl benzylidenemalonate. Complete hydrolysis is difficult but partial hydrolysis gives the *dimethyl ester*, m.p. 203–205° (*F. Bacher*, Ber., 1928, **61**, 543).

Methyl cyclobutane-1:2:2:3-*tetracarboxylate*, two isomers m.p. 78° and b.p. 195–198°/12 mm., is obtained together with bromocyclopropanedicarboxylic ester from methyl sodiomalonate and methyl αα′-dibromoglutarate (*H. R. Ing* and *W. H. Perkin*, J. chem. Soc., 1925, **127**, 2387).

(*b*) *Truxillic and truxinic acids*

The configurations of the isomeric *diphenylcyclobutanedicarboxylic acids*, the truxillic and truxinic acids, have been very fully worked out. They illustrate admirably the stereoisomerism associated with the cyclobutane ring.

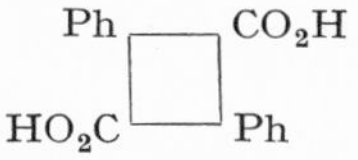

Ph ─ CO_2H / HO_2C ─ Ph

A. Truxillic acids

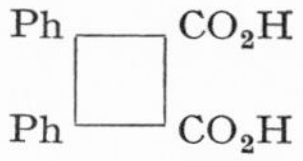

Ph ─ CO_2H / Ph ─ CO_2H

B. Truxinic acids

Acids of this structure were first reported independently by *O. Hesse* (Ann., 1892, **271**, 180) and *C. Liebermann* (Ber., 1889, **22**, 782) who isolated them from the leaves of *Erythroxylon coca*. Both identified two such acids, Hesse calling his cocaic and β-cocaic acids whilst Liebermann named his products γ- and δ-isatropic acids; γ-isatropic acid and cocaic acid were found to be identical. Liebermann further found that his two acids and two further isomers into which they could be converted were dimers of cinnamic acid possessing the basic structures A and B and he put forward the names α-, β-, γ- and δ-truxillic acids (from Truxillo, the place where is found a variety of coca particularly rich in these acids). R. Stoermer later proposed that the name "truxillic" should be reserved for the acids of structure A, the 2:4-diphenylcyclobutane-1:3-dicarboxylic acids, those possessing constitution B, the 3:4-diphenylcyclobutane-1:2-dicarboxylic acids, being termed "truxinic"; this nomenclature has met with general acceptance.

The synthetic sources of these compounds are α-truxillic and β-truxinic acids, both obtained by the photodimerisation of cinnamic acid (*C. N. Riiber*, Ber., 1902, **35**, 2908; *G. Ciamician* and *P. Silber*, Ber., 1902, **35**, 4129; *H. Stobbe et al.*, Ber., 1919, **52**, 666; 1922, **55**, 2225; 1925, **58**, 2415; 1927, **60**, 457; *R. Stoermer et al.*, Ber., 1909, **42**, 4865; 1914, **47**, 1803; 1921, **54**, 80; *A. W. K. de Jong*, Ber., 1922, **55**, 463. For review see *A. W. K. de Jong*, Chem. Weekbl., 1929, **26**, 270). A widespread assumption exists that *trans*-cinnamic acid dimerises exclusively to α-truxillic acid whilst β-truxinic acid is formed in an equally clear-cut manner from *cis*-cinnamic acid, but, as *H. J. Bernstein* and *W. C. Quimbey* (J. Amer. chem. Soc., 1943, **65**, 1845) have pointed out, this represents an oversimplification of the literature, where unanimity on the subject is lacking. The position has been considerably clarified by the American authors who found that rapidly precipitated *trans*-cinnamic acid (the metastable β-form) furnished only β-truxinic acid on irradiation, whilst slowly crystallised *trans*-cinnamic acid (the stable α-form) produces exclusively α-truxillic acid. To explain this the investigators put forward the suggestion that in the metastable β form the phenyl groups are juxtaposed in the crystal lattice whilst in the stable α form they are oppositely oriented.

Ph—CH=CH—CO_2H → Ph, CO_2H / Ph, CO_2H (cyclobutane ring)

Ph—CH=CH—CO_2H

Precipitated → *β*-Truxinic acid

Ph—CH=CH—CO_2H → Ph, CO_2H / HO_2C, Ph (cyclobutane ring)

HO_2C—CH=CH—Ph

Crystallised → *α*-Truxillic acid

The acids may also be prepared by the oxidation of the photodimers of e.g. 4-phenylbuta-1:3-diene-1:1-dicarboxylic acid (*C. N. Riiber*, Ber., 1902, **35**, 2144; *H. Stobbe* and *C. Rücker*, Ber., 1911, **44**, 870), 1-cyano-4-phenylbuta-1:3-diene (*H. Stobbe et al.*, Ber., 1912, **45**, 3396; 1925, **58**, 85) and 1-methyl-4-phenylbuta-1:3-diene-1-carboxylic acid (*M. Reimer*, J. Amer. chem. Soc., 1926, **48**, 210). Truxinic acids may be produced by method 3 (p. 47) from 2:3-diphenylbutane-1:1:4:4-tetracarboxylic ester.

All the other truxillic acids (*γ*, *ε*, *peri* and *epi*) may be obtained using *α*-truxillic acid as starting material (see below). *β*-Truxinic acid, however, only furnishes three other isomers (δ, *ε* and *neo*); the remaining two (*μ* and *ω*) have been obtained by the action of caustic soda on the compound Ph·C(CHO)=CH·CO_2Et or its cyclisation product

Ph—C=CH
| |
HOCH CO
\O/

(*M. M. Schemjakin*, Brit. chem. Abstr., 1941, AII, 169; 1940, AII, 87; 1939, AII, 422).

Truxillic acids. There are five possible theoretical configurations for the various truxillic acids; all these stereoisomers are known and are termed *α*-, *γ*-, *ε*-, *peri*- and *epi*-truxillic acids.

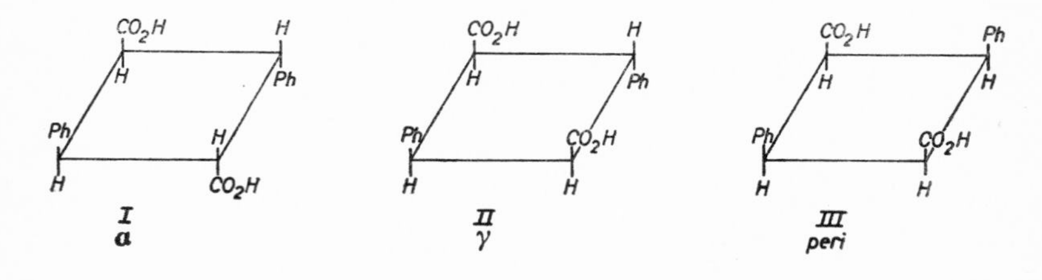

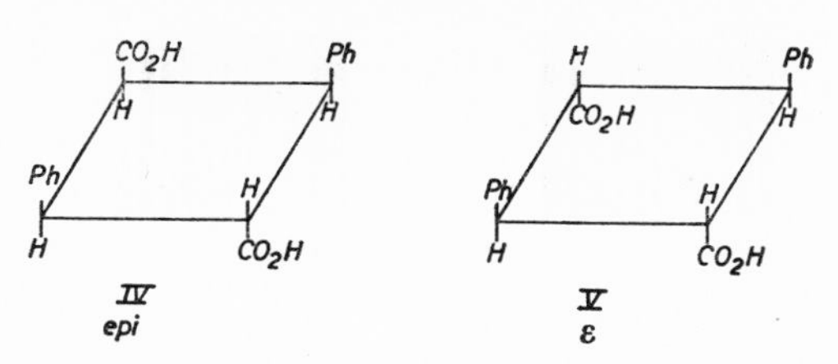

The broad outline of the assignment of configuration is as follows. All the acids possess at least one element of symmetry and are therefore *meso*, non-resolvable structures. They all form monoanilides (anilic acids) but only those derived from the α- and γ-acids can be resolved; thus the parent acids must be represented by structures (I) and (II). As only the γ-anilic acid can be dehydrated to an anil or phenylimide (containing the group CO–NPh–CO joining two diagonally situated carbon atoms) γ-truxillic acid must be represented by (II) and therefore α-truxillic acid must possess structure (I). This relationship is confirmed by the fact that α-truxillic acid (possessing *trans*-situated carboxyl groups) gives γ-truxillic anhydride with concomitant Walden inversion, whilst γ-truxillic acid yields its own anhydride. *epi*-Truxillic acid does not produce its own anhydride and no anil is obtained from its anilic acid; its carboxyl groups must therefore be *trans*-situated and its structure must thus be (IV). *peri*-Truxillic acid gives its own anhydride and an anil, whilst ε-truxillic acid yields an anil but not a simple unimolecular anhydride. From molecular models of structures (III) and (V) it can be seen that, although both are capable of forming anils, only in the case of (III) is it sterically possible to obtain a unimolecular anhydride. Thus *peri*-truxillic acid possesses constitution (III) and ε-truxillic acid is represented by (V).

The interconversions of the various acids may be delineated as follows:

α-acid $\xrightarrow{\text{heat}}$ γ-anhydride + *peri*-anhydride

γ-anhydride $\rightleftarrows$ γ-acid; *peri*-anhydride $\rightleftarrows$ *peri*-acid

peri-acid $\xrightarrow{\text{hot HCl}}$ *epi*-acid

ε-acid $\rightleftarrows$ polymeric anhydride $\leftarrow$ *epi*-acid

The configurations thus assigned receive confirmation from the nature of the products obtained when the compounds are subjected to an intramolecular Friedel-Crafts reaction. Thus α-, γ-, *peri*- and *epi*-truxillic acids produce truxonic acids of general formula A which is only possible if the participating phenyl and carboxyl groups are adjacent and *cis*-situated; as expected, therefore, ε-truxillic acid fails to yield such a product. In the case of α-truxillic and *peri*-truxillic acids, which contain two such *cis*-situated systems, the process can proceed further to give truxones (B).

Ph—□—CO / HO_2C—□—C_6H_4 (CO and C_6H_4 joined)

A. Truxonic acids

C_6H_4—□—CO / CO—□—C_6H_4 (C_6H_4 and CO joined on each side)

B. Truxones

TABLE 5

MELTING POINTS OF TRUXILLIC ACIDS AND SOME DERIVATIVES

	α	*γ*	*ε*	*peri*	*epi*
Acid	274°	228°	192°	266°	285°
Anhydride	–	191°	Polymeric	287°	–
Dimethyl ester	174°	127°	64°	104·5°	111–112°
Anilic acid	*235°	*228°		247°	
Anil	–	194°	252°		–
Amic acid	*261°	*248°	213°		
Imide			198°		
Truxonic acid	216°	152°	–	221–224°	160°
Truxone	294°	–	–	194°	–

*Resolvable

Melting points of the truxillic acids and some of their derivatives are given in Table 5 (*R. Stoermer et al.*, Ber., 1935, **68**, 2102, 2117; 1931, **64**, 2783; 1927, **60**, 2576; 1925, **58**, 2715; 1924, **57**, 16,21; 1923, **56**, 1687; 1920, **53**, 499).

Truxinic acids. Six configurations are theoretically possible for the optically inactive acids possessing the truxinic constitution and all the compounds thus predicted are known. The vicinal position of the two phenyl groups in these acids is confirmed by the formation of benzil on oxidation.

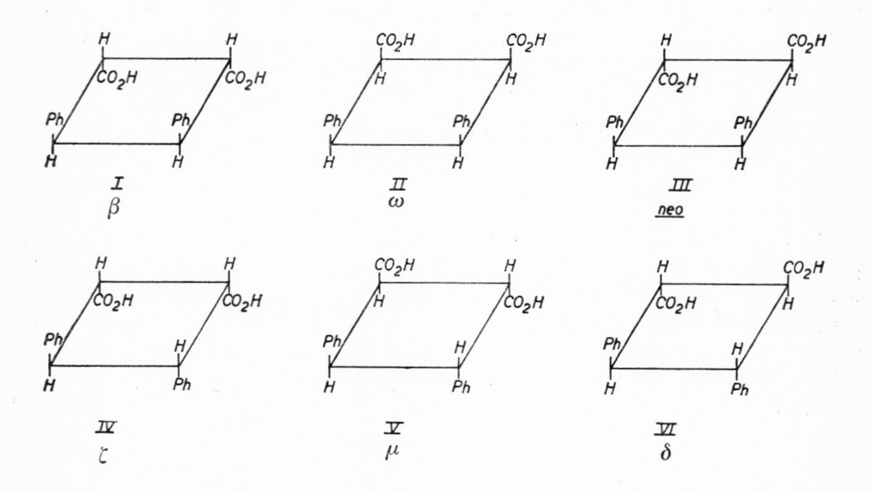

The *β*- and *ω*-acids are *meso*-compounds whilst the four other acids possess no element of symmetry and are therefore resolvable. The various configurations are established by methods closely analogous to those described in the case of the truxillic acids; the issue is complicated in this case by the fact that the *neo* and ζ acids are capable of giving rise to two series (a and b) of derivatives affecting one carboxyl group each of which is resolvable.

TABLE 6

MELTING POINTS OF TRUXINIC ACIDS AND DERIVATIVES

	β	ω	*neo*	ε	μ	δ
Acid	210°	245°	*209°	*239°	*196°	·175°
Anhydride	116°		–	*150°	–	–
Dimethyl ester	76°	133°	*127°	*116°	*199°	*77°
Monomethyl ester			a. *139° b. *234°	a. *198° b. *201°	*196°	
Anilic acid	*197°	*111° (d)		a. *214° b. *237°	*241°	*225°
Anil	180°		–		–	–
Amic acid	*194°		a. *214° b. *213°	a. *204° b. *225.5°		*189°
Imide	224°	179°	–	*168°	–	–
Semitruxinonic acid	–		224°	158°		–

*Resolvable

The melting points of the truxinic acids and derivatives are given in Table 6 (see *R. Stoermer et al.*, Ber., 1931, **64**, 2793; 1926, **59**, 642; 1925, **58**, 1164; 1922, **55**, 1872; *F. Bacher*, Ber., 1928, **61**, 543; J. pr. Chem., 1928, **120**, 301; *M. M. Schemjakin*, Brit. chim. Abstr., 1941, AII, 169; 1940, AII, 87; 1939, AII, 422).

(c) Cyclobutyl derivatives of aliphatic acids

A series of cyclobutylalkylacetic acids of general formula $C_4H_7 \cdot CH_2 \cdot CHR \cdot CO_2H$ have been made via the condensation of bromomethylcyclobutane and sodioalkylmalonic esters. The *n*-octyl substituted acid and the higher members up to the *n*-dodecyl acid possess some activity against *Mycobact. leprae* (*S. G. Ford* and *R. Adams*, J. Amer. chem. Soc., 1930, **52**, 1259).

Cyclobutane-2:4-dicarboxylic-1:3-diacetic acid occurs in five isomeric modifications corresponding with those of the truxillic acids.

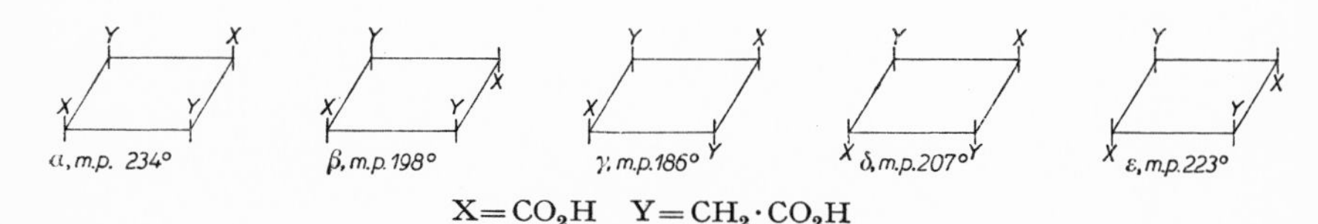

$X = CO_2H \quad Y = CH_2 \cdot CO_2H$

Four of these acids are prepared from the products of dimerisation of ethyl $\alpha\gamma$-dicarboxyglutaconate under the influence of piperidine; these consist of the two isomeric octaethyl cyclobutane-2:2:4:4-tetracarboxylate-1:3-dimalonates *cis*(α)-form m.p. 103°, *trans*(β)-form m.p. 87°.

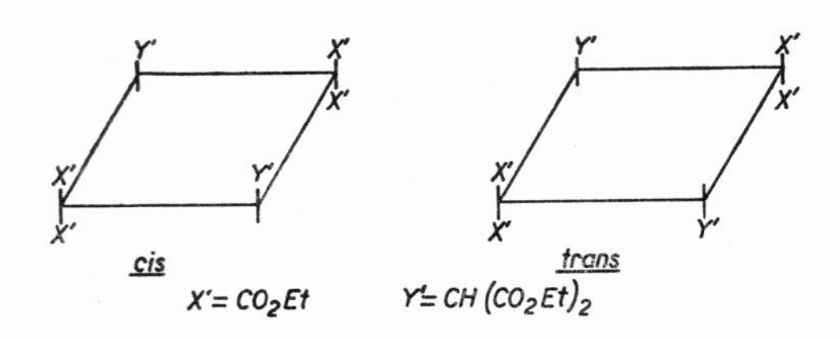

The *cis*-form on hydrolysis and decarboxylation furnishes the above γ-acid, whilst the *trans*-isomer yields the α- and β-acids; treatment of the β-acid with hydrochloric acid at 200° produces the ε-acid. The δ-acid is derived from the hydrolysis of hexaethyl cyclobutane-2:2:4:4-tetracarboxylate-1:3-diacetate prepared by dimerisation of ethyl α-carboxyglutaconate (*C. K. Ingold, E. A. Perren* and *J. F. Thorpe*, J. chem. Soc., 1922, **121**, 1765).

Oxidative degradation of caryophyllene gives rise to three related cyclobutane acids, homocaryophyllenic acid (I), caryophyllenic acid (II) and norcaryophyllenic acid (III).

(I): Me, Me on C-3; $CH_2 \cdot CH_2 \cdot CO_2H$; CO_2H

(II): Me, Me on C-3; $CH_2 \cdot CO_2H$; CO_2H

(III): Me, Me on C-3; CO_2H; CO_2H

Homocaryophyllenic acid (1-*carboxy*-3:3-*dimethylcyclobutane*-2-*propionic acid*; I) b.p. 175°/0·4 mm., $[\alpha]_D$ +105° (benzene) is a mixture of the cis and trans forms, cis-*dianilide*, m.p. 180°, trans-*dianilide*, m.p. 283° (*G. R. Ramage* and *J. L. Simonsen*, J. chem. Soc., 1936, 741; *ibid.*, 1937, 73; *L. Ruzicka* and *A. H. Wind*, Helv., 1931, **14**, 422). The correctness of the constitution (I) has been shown by synthesis (*T. L. Dawson* and *G. R. Ramage*, J. chem. Soc., 1951, 3382).

trans-*Caryophyllenic acid* (1-*carboxy*-3:3-*dimethylcyclobutane*-2-*acetic acid*; II) m.p. 81°, $[\alpha]_D$ +28·2° (benzene), *dianilide*, m.p. 282°, undergoes inversion on being heated with acetic anhydride to give cis-*caryophyllenic anhydride*, b.p. 158°/12 mm., hydrolysis of which yields cis-*caryophyllenic acid*, m.p. 78°, $[\alpha]_{5461}$ −7·4° (chloroform), *dianilide*, m.p. 190° (*G. R. Ramage* and *J. L. Simonsen*, *loc. cit.*; *ibid.*, 1935, 532; *W. Evans, G. R. Ramage* and *J. L. Simonsen*, *ibid.*, 1934, 1806). dl-trans-*Caryophyllenic acid*, m.p. 78–79° has been synthesised (*A. Campbell* and *H. N. Rydon*, Chem. and Ind., 1951, 312).

The constitution of trans-*norcaryophyllenic acid* (3:3-*dimethylcyclobutane*-1:2-*dicarboxylic acid*; III) m.p. 125–127°, $[\alpha]_D$ +118°, (chloroform), *dianilide*, m.p. 179° (*J. L. Simonsen et al.*, J. chem. Soc., 1934, 1806; *G. R. Ramage* and

J. L. Simonsen, ibid., 1935, 532; *L. Ruzicka* and *W. Zimmermann*, Helv., 1935, **18**, 219) has been confirmed by the resolution of the synthetic dl-trans-*acid*, m.p. 148°, *dianilide*, m.p. 238° (*H. N. Rydon*, J. chem. Soc., 1936, 593; *idem, ibid.*, 1937, 1340; *T. L. Dawson* and *G. R. Ramage*, *ibid.*, 1951, 3382). Heating with acetic anhydride converts the *trans*-acid into the dl-cis-*anhydride* m.p. 41°, hydrolysis of which gives dl-cis-*caryophyllenic acid* m.p. 149–150°, *dianilide* m.p. 267°; resolution yields the d- and l-*acids* m.p. 165°, $[\alpha]_{5461}^{18°}$ +4·9° and –5·9° (chloroform) respectively (*idem, ibid.*).

(d) Keto-acids

2:2-*Dimethylcyclobutan*-4-*one*-1:3-*dicarboxylic acid*, *ketonorpinic acid*, has been synthesised by the action of carbonyl bromide on Guareschi's imide (cf. pp. 47 and 48) (*P. Guha*, Curr. Sci., 1933, **2**, 52).

1:3-*Dimethylcyclobutane*-2:4-*dione*-1-*carboxylic acid*, *methyl ester* m.p. 156–157°, *ethyl ester* m.p. 133–135°, is produced by the intramolecular cyclisation of 1:3-*dimethylpropan*-2-*one*-1:3-*dicarboxylic ester* by means of sulphuric acid. The esters behave as monocarboxylic acids and dissolve in carbonate solution. A compound analogously prepared is *ethyl* 1:3-*diethylcyclobutane*-2:4-*dione*-1-*carboxylate*, m.p. 101·5–102·5°. The esters give the corresponding diketones on treatment with aqueous baryta (*G. Schroeter* and *C. Stassen*, Ber., 1907, **40**, 1604; *G. Schroeter et al.*, Ber., 1916, **49**, 2697; *H. Staudinger*, Ber., 1917, **50**, 1016).

1:3-*Diethylcyclobutane*-2:4-*dione*-1:3-*dicarboxylic ester*, b.p. about 113–116° under high vacuum, is the constitution assigned to the dimer of ethylketencarboxylic ester. On distillation at ordinary pressure it undergoes depolymerisation and the keten is regenerated. Aniline ruptures the ring to form ethylmalonanilic ester (*F. Chick* and *N. Wilsmore*, J. chem. Soc., 1910, **97**, 1978; *H. Staudinger*, Ber., 1909, **42**, 4908; *G. Schroeter et al.*, *loc. cit.*).

Alkylated cyclobutanonetricarboxylic esters of the general formula (I) are obtained by condensing sodioalkylmalonic esters with citraconic ester; the first product is presumably an acyclic tetracarboxylic ester which then undergoes an intramolecular Claisen condensation. Hydrolysis with hydrochloric acid causes decarboxylation to the cyclobutan-1-one-3-carboxylic acids (II).

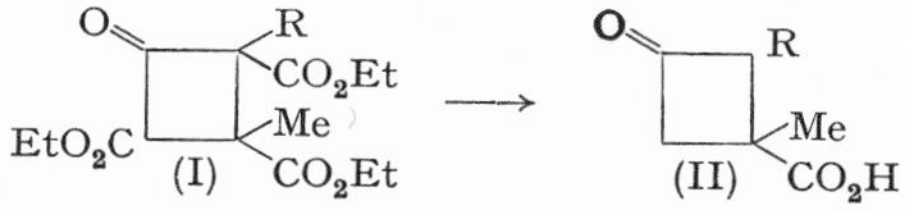

O R
CO_2Et
EtO_2C Me
(I) CO_2Et
⟶
O R
Me
(II) CO_2H

(*A. Michael*, Ber., 1900, **33**, 3751).

(e) Anemonin

Anemonin (I), m.p. 149–150°, $\lambda_{max.}$ 220 mμ ($\varepsilon_{max.}$ 14,300), is the *dilactone* of *cyclobutane*-1:2-*diol*-1:2-*diacrylic acid*. It is obtained by steam distillation of the crude oil from various species of *Anemone* and *Ranunculus* (*H. Meyer*,

Monatsh., 1896, 17, 283); it is not originally present as such but is an artefact formed during the distillation by the dimerisation of protoanemonin (anhydro-α-angelicalactone, lactone of 3-hydroxybuta-1:3-diene-1-carboxylic acid). It paralyses respiration and the beating of the heart (*Raymond-Hamet*, Chem. Ztbl., 1927, II, 121; *Y. Asakina*, Ber., 1914, 47, 914) and produces inflammation (*Y. Asakina* and *A. Fujita*, Acta Phytochim. Japan, 1922, 1, 1).

Constitution and reactions. Anemonin, $C_{10}H_8O_4$, contains two olefinic double bonds (*tetrabromide*, $C_{10}H_8O_4Br_4$, m.p. 175°) which are reducible catalytically with platinum to yield *tetrahydroanemonin* (II), m.p. 156°. Sodium amalgam and acetic acid rupture the cyclobutane ring, leaving the double bonds unattacked, to form the straight chain derivative *dihydroanemonin* (III), m.p. 172°. Reduction with sodium and alcohol gives iso*tetrahydroanemonin* (IV), m.p. 142°, a derivative of cyclohexane.

```
                                             O————————CO
                                             |        |
CH2—C—CH=CH—CO2H          NaOEt      CH2—C—CH=CH        K2CO3    CH2—CO—CH=CH—CO2I
|    \\                  <————————   |   |              ———————>  |
CH2—CO—C—CH2—CO2H                    CH2—C—CH=CH                 CH2—CO—CH2—CH2—CO
                                         |        |
                                         O————————CO

α-Anemonic acid (VIII)                Anemonin (I)              α-Anemoninic acid (VII)

                  Pt/H2                 Na/EtOH               Na-Hg/AcOH

   O————————CO               O————————CO               O————————CO
   |        |                |        |                |        |
CH2—C—CH2—CH2           CH2—CH—CH—CH2             CH2—C=CH—CH2
|   |                    |       |                 |
CH2—C—CH2—CH2           CH2—CH—CH—CH2             CH2—C=CH—CH2
    |        |              |        |                 |       |
    O————————CO             O————————CO                O———————CO

Tetrahydroanemonin (II)   isoTetrahydroanemonin (IV)   Dihydroanemonin (III)

        NaOH                                                 HCl

CH2—C(OH)—CH2—CH2—CO2Na  CH2—C—CH2—CH2—CO2H   CH2—CO—CH2—CH2—CO
|   |                    |    \\              |
CH2—C(OH)—CH2—CH2—CO2Na  CH2—CO—C—CH2—CO2H    CH2—CO—CH2—CH2—CO

        (VI)             Anhydroanemonolic acid (IX)   Anemonolic acid (V)
```

The four oxygen atoms of anemonin are present in two lactone groups; thus tetrahydroanemonin on alkaline hydrolysis gives the sodium salt VI, and acid hydrolysis of dihydroanemonin produces *anemonolic acid, octane-3:6-dione-1:8-dicarboxylic acid* (V), m.p. 158° (*dimethyl ester*, m.p. 95°). In the case of anemonin itself aqueous potassium carbonate hydrolyses the lactone groupings and also opens the cyclobutane ring to give *oct-1-ene-3:6-dione-1:8-dicarboxylic acid, α-anemoninic acid* (VII), m.p. 117° (which rearranges with HCl into the β-form, m.p. 189°).

If sodium ethoxide be used for the hydrolysis the α-anemoninic acid formed undergoes an internal aldol condensation to produce the cyclopentenone derivative *α-anemonic acid* (VIII), m.p. 120° (which rearranges with HCl into the β-form, m.p. 208°). In the same way anemonolic acid (V) self-condenses under alkaline conditions to give the cyclopentenone derivative, *anhydroanemonolic acid* (IX), m.p. 129°. Anemonic acid and anhydroanemonolic acid take up two and four atoms of hydrogen respectively on catalytic hydrogenation to form *tetrahydroanemonic acid* (*cyclopentan-1-one-2-acetic-3-propionic acid*), m.p. 135°.

```
                 CH2—CH—CH2—CH2—CO2H
(VIII) --4 H-->  |     \                    <--2 H-- (IX)
                 CH2—CO—CH—CH2—CO2H
```

As a 1:4-diketone anemonolic acid (V) on heating is converted into *furan-2:5-dipropionic acid* (XI), m.p. 154°; when heated with ammonia it gives *pyrrole-2:5-dipropionic acid*, (XII), m.p. 170°.

```
CH═C—CH2—CH2—CO2H                  CH═C—CH2—CH2—CO2H
|    >O             <—(V)—>        |    >NH
CH═C—CH2—CH2—CO2H                  CH═C—CH2—CH2—CO2H
      (XI)                               (XII)
```

When the sodium salt (VI) of tetrahydroanemonin is heated with water the intermediate compound first formed (XIII) cyclises to the tetrahydrofuran derivative, *ψ-tetrahydroanemonic acid* (XIV), m.p. 113°; this is converted by HI into *3-iodo-octan-6-one-1:8-dicarboxylic acid*, m.p. 124° which on reduction furnishes *octan-3-one-1:8-dicarboxylic acid*, m.p. 90° and sebacic acid.

```
                                                      ┌────O────┐
        ┌CH2—CO—CH2—CH2—CO2H      ┐     CH2—C—CH2—CH2—CO
(VI) --H2O--> |                         | --> |     >O
        └CH2—CH(OH)—CH2—CH2—CO2H ┘     CH2—CH—CH2—CH2—CO2H
                  (XIII)                          (XIV)
```

Oxidation of anemoninic acid (VII) yields *pentan-3-one-1:5-dicarboxylic acid*, m.p. 142° (*Y. Asahina* and *A. Fujita*, *loc. cit.*; Arch. Pharm., 1915, **253**, 590; J. pharm. Soc. Japan, 1921, no. 70, 1; *H. Meyer*, Monatsh., 1899, **20**, 634).

The synthesis of anemonin has been achieved by the dimerisation of dehydro-α-angelicalactone (protoanemonin). The best method of obtaining the latter is by treatment of β-acetylacrylic acid with acetic anhydride containing a small amount of sulphuric acid (*E. Shaw*, J. Amer. chem. Soc., 1946, **68**, 2510):

$$CH_3\cdot CO\cdot CH{=}CH\cdot CO_2H \longrightarrow \begin{array}{c} \text{OAc} \\ | \\ CH_3{-}C{-}CH{=}CH \\ |\qquad\quad | \\ O{-}{-}{-}{-}CO \end{array} \longrightarrow \begin{array}{c} CH_2{=}C{-}CH{=}CH \\ |\qquad\quad | \\ O{-}{-}{-}{-}CO \end{array}$$

Protoanemonin

Other syntheses have been evolved but they lack the advantage of the above method in convenience and yield (*Y. Asahina* and *A. Fujita, loc. cit.*; *E. Muskat et al.*, J. Amer. chem. Soc., 1930, **52**, 326; *F. B. Kipping*, J. chem. Soc., 1935, 1145). Protoanemonin possesses antibacterial activity against a wide variety of micro-organisms (*H. Baer et al.*, J. biol. Chem., 1946, **162**, 65).

Chapter IV

Cyclopentane Group

R. A. RAPHAEL

1. Occurrence, formation and properties

In agreement with the predictions of the Baeyer theory the five-membered alicyclic ring is readily formed and when obtained is highly stable. In these circumstances it is not surprising that compounds containing this system are much more numerous than those derived from cyclopropane and cyclobutane. It is all the more unexpected, therefore, to find that substances containing a single cyclopentane ring occur but sparsely in nature. This is especially true in the terpene field, no well-authenticated case being known of the occurrence of a five-membered ring system among the monocyclic terpenoids (cf. *P. G. Stevens* and *S. C. Spalding*, J. Amer. chem. Soc., 1949, 71, 1687). The odorous principle of jasmine, jasmone, is a derivative of cyclopentenone, and pyrethrolone, the alcoholic component of the pyrethrin insecticides, is a derivative of cyclopentanone. Hydnocarpic, chaulmoogric and gorlic acids, which are specific remedies against tuberculosis and leprosy, occur in the seed fats of the *Flacourtiaceae;* they are long chain fatty acids containing a cyclopentane ring. Crude petroleum is a source of some cyclopentane hydrocarbons and of the so-called naphthenic acids which consist mainly of alkylated cyclopentane fatty acids. Cyclopentadiene occurs in the low boiling fractions of coal tar.

Preparative methods

The methods of forming the five-membered ring compounds may be conveniently classified as follows.

(1) The intramolecular Wurtz reaction employing 1:5-dihalides gives poor yields of cyclopentane hydrocarbons and the method is of little practical importance.

(2) Intramolecular dehydrohalogenation of 5-halogeno-substituted ketones, nitriles or carboxylic esters under alkaline conditions yields the corresponding cyclopentane derivatives but, again, little use has been made of this as a preparative method.

(3) The condensation of 1:4-dihalides with a second component containing an active methylene group was the reaction early employed by Perkin to prepare members of the cyclopentane series (*E. Haworth* and *W. H. Perkin*, J. chem. Soc., 1894, **65**, 96), e.g.

$$\begin{array}{l} CH_2\cdot CH_2Br \\ | \\ CH_2\cdot CH_2Br \end{array} + CH_2(CO_2Et)_2 \xrightarrow{NaOEt} \square(CO_2Et)_2.$$

Ethyl acetoacetate and phenylacetonitrile may be used similarly instead of ethyl malonate (*L. J. Goldsworthy*, J. chem. Soc., 1934, 377; *F. H. Case*, J. Amer. chem. Soc., 1933, **55**, 2927; 1934, **56**, 715).

The inverse procedure (cf. p. 24) may also be employed and it is of historical interest that this was the method used for the first recorded formation of the five-membered ring (*W. H. Perkin*, Ber., 1885, **18**, 3246):

$$H_2C\begin{array}{l} \diagup CH_2\cdot CNa(CO_2Et)_2 \\ \diagdown CH_2\cdot CNa(CO_2Et)_2 \end{array} \xrightarrow{I_2} \square \begin{array}{l} (CO_2Et)_2 \\ (CO_2Et)_2. \end{array}$$

(4) The most useful practical syntheses of the five-membered ring are accomplished by the intramolecular condensation of the substituted adipic acids and their derivatives. The methods fall into three classes according to the type of starting material used.

(a) Adipic acids. When the calcium or barium salts of adipic acids are heated cyclopentanones are obtained (for details see p. 92). A useful modification of the method was described by *G. Blanc* who treated the adipic acids with acetic anhydride and slowly distilled the adipic anhydrides formed (Compt. rend., 1907, **144**, 1356). Cyclopentanone itself is obtained in fair yield (50 %) by this procedure, but the presence of alkyl substituents has a remarkable effect, the substituted cyclopentanone being produced in almost quantitative yield (*idem, ibid.*; *M. Godchot et al.*, Bull. Soc. chim. Fr., 1939, [v], **6**, 1353).

Blanc found that this method furnished cycloalkanones only when adipic and pimelic acids were employed; glutaric and succinic acids under similar conditions yield cyclic anhydrides. This generalisation, known as Blanc's rule, has been much used for the determination of the constitution of dibasic acids. Exceptions to the validity of the rule have, however, occurred (*A. Windaus* and *E. Dane*, Z. physiol. Chem., 1932, **213**, 47).

(b) Adipic esters (Dieckmann reaction). The treatment of adipic esters with alcoholic sodium ethoxide or sodium in an inert solvent results in the occurrence of an intramolecular Claisen condensation to form a cyclic β-keto-ester (*W. Dieckmann*, Ber., 1922, **55**, 2473; *inter al., M. Qudrat-I-*

Khuda and *A. Mukerji*, J. Indian chem. Soc., 1946, **23**, 435; *R. N. Chakravarti*, J. chem. Soc., 1947, 1029).

$$\begin{array}{l} CH_2\cdot CH_2\cdot CO_2Et \\ | \\ CH_2\cdot CH_2\cdot CO_2Et \end{array} \xrightarrow{NaOEt} \text{2-carbethoxycyclopentanone (I)} \longrightarrow \text{cyclopentanone}$$

Substances of type (I) are a fruitful source of cyclopentane compounds as the following series of reactions show (*G. Chiurdoglu*, C.A., 1932, **26**, 4311).

$$\text{2-}CO_2Et\text{-cyclopentanone} \xrightarrow{EtI} \text{2-}CO_2Et\text{-2-Et-cyclopentanone} \longrightarrow \text{2-Et-cyclopentanone} \xrightarrow{MeMgBr} \text{2-Et-1-Me-cyclopentan-1-ol (OH, Me)} \xrightarrow{-H_2O} \text{2-Et-1-Me-cyclopentene} \xrightarrow{H_2} \text{1-Et-2-Me-cyclopentane}$$

A useful extension of Dieckmann's method involves the intermolecular condensation of diethyl oxalate with compounds containing two β-situated activated methylene groups:

$$H_2C(CH_2\cdot CO_2Et)_2 + \begin{array}{l} CO_2Et \\ | \\ CO_2Et \end{array} \longrightarrow \text{cyclopentane-1,2-dione-3,5-dicarboxylate (}CO_2Et, =O, =O, CO_2Et\text{)}$$

(*F. M. Jaeger* and *H. B. Blumendal*, Z. anorg. Chem., 1928, **175**, 161);

$$OC(CH_2\cdot Ph)_2 + \begin{array}{l} CO_2Et \\ | \\ CO_2Et \end{array} \longrightarrow \text{3,5-diphenylcyclopentane-1,2,4-trione (Ph, O, O=, O, Ph)}$$

(*P. Ruggli* and *J. Schmidlin*, Helv., 1944, **27**, 499).

G. Komppa made use of this reaction in his classic synthesis of camphoric acid (Vol. II B).

(c) Adipic nitriles (Thorpe reaction). Adipic nitriles having an appropriately activated methylene or methine group undergo internal condensation in the presence of sodium ethoxide in the following manner:

$$\begin{array}{l} CH_2\cdot CH_2\cdot CN \\ | \\ CH_2\cdot CH_2\cdot CN \end{array} \xrightarrow{NaOEt} \text{(cyclopentane ring with CN, =NH)} \longrightarrow \text{(cyclopentanone, =O)}$$

This reaction has been modified for use in the preparation of macrocyclic ketones (p. 271).

(5) $\alpha\beta$-Unsaturated carbonyl compounds containing a cyclopentane ring may be readily obtained by an intramolecular aldol condensation on an appropriate dicarbonyl compound:

$$\begin{array}{l} CH_2\cdot CH_2\cdot COMe \\ | \qquad\qquad COMe \\ CH_2\cdot CH_2\diagup \end{array} \longrightarrow \text{(cyclopentene ring with COMe, Me)}$$

(*T. R. Marshall* and *W. H. Perkin*, J. chem. Soc., 1890, **57**, 241);

$$\begin{array}{l} CH_3\cdot CH_2\cdot CO \quad CH_2\cdot CH_3 \\ \qquad\qquad | \qquad >CO \\ \qquad CH_2\cdot CH_2 \end{array} \longrightarrow \text{(cyclopentenone ring with } CH_3\cdot CH_2\text{, } CH_3\text{, =O)}$$

(*E. E. Blaise*, Compt. rend., 1914, **158**, 708; *H. Hunsdiecker*, Ber., 1942, **75**, 455). It should be noted that in both these examples the product consists solely of a cyclopentene derivative although alternative condensations can be envisaged leading to a seven- and three-membered ring respectively.

A similar type of condensation presumably takes place in the production of cyclopentane-1:3-diones by the reaction of acyloins with ethyl acetate (*R. B. Woodward* and *E. R. Blout*, J. Amer. chem. Soc., 1943, **65**, 562).

$$\begin{array}{c} \diagup CO_2Et \\ CH_3 \quad CH_2\cdot R \\ + \;| \\ R\cdot CH_2\cdot CH—CO \\ | \\ OH \end{array} \longrightarrow \begin{array}{c} \diagup CO \diagdown \\ CH_3 \quad CH\cdot R \\ | \\ R\cdot CH_2\cdot CH—CO \\ | \\ OH \end{array} \rightleftarrows \begin{array}{c} \diagup CO \diagdown \\ CH_3 \quad CH\cdot R \\ | \\ R\cdot CH_2\cdot CO—CH \\ | \\ OH \end{array}$$

$$\downarrow$$

$$\text{(cyclopentane-1:3-dione: O, R, R}\cdot CH_2\text{, =O)} \leftrightarrows \text{(cyclopentenone: O, R, R}\cdot CH_2\text{, OH)} \longleftarrow \text{(cyclopentenone: O, R, R}\cdot CH_2\text{, OH)}$$

(6) Miscellaneous methods.

(a) The dehydration of γ-lactones leads to cyclopent-2-en-1-ones; the process has some industrial importance (*P. A. Plattner* and *A. Pfau*, Helv.,

1937, **20**, 1474; B.P. 453,518 (1936); *R. L. Frank et al.*, J. Amer. chem. Soc., 1944, 66, 4).

Cyclopentenones may also be obtained by treating aliphatic dienynes with hydrochloric acid or by cyclisation of the dienones derived from the hydrocarbons by hydration (*I. N. Nazarov et al.*, C.A., 1945, **39**, 503, 1620; 1948, **42**, 7731; 1949, **43**, 115, 1332) e.g.:

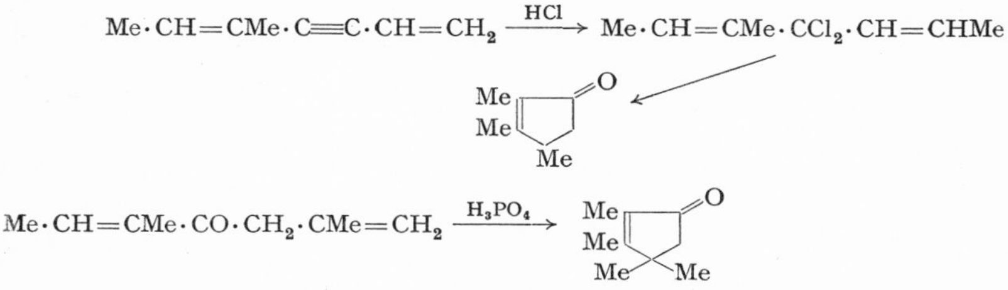

$$Me{\cdot}CH{=}CMe{\cdot}C{\equiv}C{\cdot}CH{=}CH_2 \xrightarrow{HCl} Me{\cdot}CH{=}CMe{\cdot}CCl_2{\cdot}CH{=}CHMe \rightarrow \text{(cyclopentenone: Me, Me, Me; =O)}$$

$$Me{\cdot}CH{=}CMe{\cdot}CO{\cdot}CH_2{\cdot}CMe{=}CH_2 \xrightarrow{H_3PO_4} \text{(cyclopentenone: Me, Me, Me, Me; =O)}$$

For the mechanism of this reaction see *E. A. Braude* and *J. A. Coles*, J. chem. Soc., 1952, 1430.

(b) 6-Iodohexan-2-one reacts with magnesium to give 1-methylcyclopentan-1-ol; an internal Grignard reaction is thought to occur (*N. D. Zelinsky* and *A. Moser*, Ber., 1902, **35**, 2684):

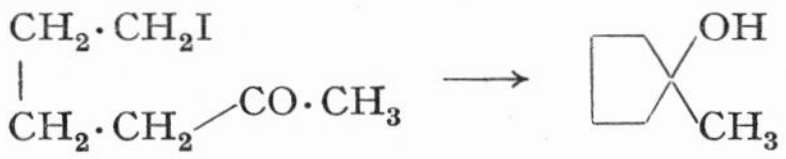

$$CH_2{\cdot}CH_2I\,|\,CH_2{\cdot}CH_2{\cdot}CO{\cdot}CH_3 \longrightarrow \text{(cyclopentane: OH, } CH_3\text{)}$$

(c) Malonic acid undergoes a Mannich type of reaction in the presence of succinaldehyde and methylamine to yield a complex cyclopentanetricarboxylic acid (*C. Mannich* and *H. Budde*, Arch. Pharm., 1932, **270**, 283).

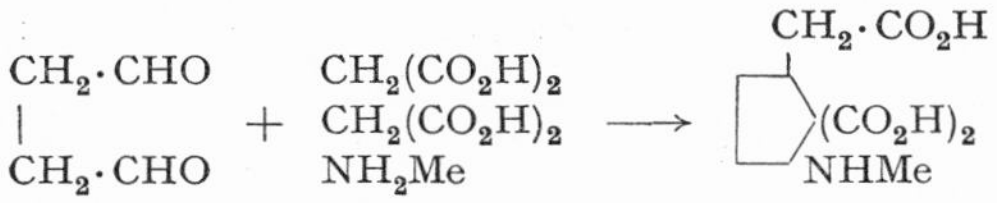

$$CH_2{\cdot}CHO\,|\,CH_2{\cdot}CHO + CH_2(CO_2H)_2,\ CH_2(CO_2H)_2,\ NH_2Me \longrightarrow \text{(cyclopentane: } CH_2{\cdot}CO_2H,\ (CO_2H)_2,\ NHMe\text{)}$$

(d) An interesting cyclisation of an aliphatic diene to an unsaturated cyclopentane has been reported (*P. G. Stevens* and *S. C. Spalding*, J. Amer. chem. Soc., 1949, **71**, 1687).

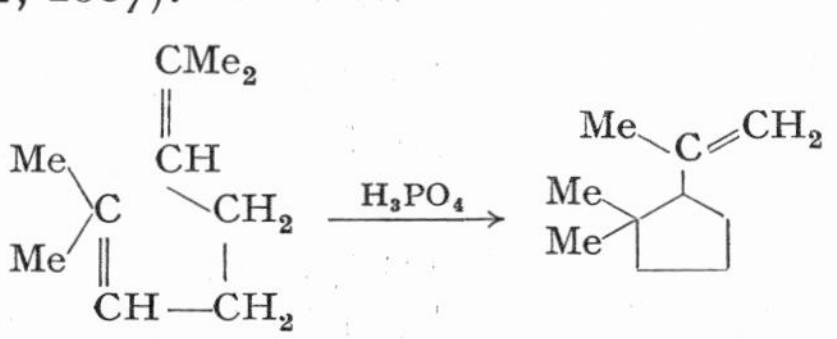

$$Me_2C{=}CH{\cdot}CH_2{\cdot}CH_2{\cdot}CH{=}CH{\cdot}CH{=}CMe_2 \text{ (as drawn: } Me_2C{=}CH{-}CH_2 \text{ and } CMe_2{=}CH{\cdot}CH_2\text{)} \xrightarrow{H_3PO_4} \text{(cyclopentane: Me, Me; } C(Me){=}CH_2\text{)}$$

(e) Cyclopentanes may be produced as a result of ring transition reactions (pp. 14 ff.).

Geometry of the cyclopentane ring

If a Stuart model of the cyclopentane ring be examined it is seen that the carbon atoms occupy the apices of a regular pentagon. This structure in fact provides a ready interpretation of the stereochemistry connected with this ring system and leads to the correct prediction of the number and resolvability of substituted cyclopentanes..

The five-membered carbocyclic ring is particularly interesting because the torsional forces about the single bonds are in opposition to the forces tending to retain tetrahedral bond angles; the latter forces favour uniplanarity of the carbon atoms whilst the torsional forces tend to pucker the ring in order to reduce the number of energetically unfavourable *c* constellations (p. 9) (*K. S. Pitzer,* Science, 1945, **101**, 672).

Measurements of the entropy of cyclopentane do in fact indicate a puckered ring structure (*J. G. Aston et al.*, J. Amer. chem. Soc., 1941, **63**, 2029; 1943, **65**, 341; *D. R. Douslin* and *H. M. Huffman, ibid.*, 1946, **68**, 173) and the whole question was examined in detail by *K. S. Pitzer* and his collaborators (*ibid.*, 1947, **69**, 2483). Their method of thermodynamic analysis indicates that the puckering is not of a definite type, the angle of maximum displacement rotating round the ring. This puckering is small enough to escape detection by electron diffraction methods; these indicate a uniplanar structure with the C–C distance 1·54 Å, the C–H distance 1·09 Å and the pentagon angles near to the expected tetrahedral value (*O. Hassel* and *H. Viervoll,* C.A., 1946, **40**, 4580).

Similar examination of cyclopentene shows that this molecule is also puckered. In this case, however, the effect is localised as the four carbon atoms subtending the double bond are necessarily coplanar; it was found that the carbon atom opposite to the double bond can move out of the plane by about 0·3 Å., the resulting puckered structure exhibiting no significant change in energy from the uniplanar configuration.

2. Hydrocarbons

(a) Saturated hydrocarbons

Cyclopentane itself is obtained by hydrogenation of the technically available cyclopentadiene; a method of formation is the reduction of cyclopentyl iodide. The substituted hydrocarbons are produced by the hydrogenation of the corresponding cyclopentenes (p. 78). The scrupulous purification and precise determination of physical constants of many cyclopentanes have been carried out at the U.S. National Bureau of Standards (*A. J. Streiff et al.*, J. Res. Nat. Bur. Stand., 1947, **38**, 53).

The five-membered ring hydrocarbons are much more stable than those of the cyclopropane or cyclobutane ring systems. Thus the catalytic hydrogenation of cyclopentanes leading to ring fission with the production of pentanes takes place only above 300° (*N. D. Zelinsky et al., loc. cit.*). High temperature pyrolysis (700°) of cyclopentane yields mostly ethylene and propylene together with a little cyclopentadiene (*F. E. Frey*, Ind. Eng. Chem., 1934, **26**, 198; *B. A. Kasansky* and *A. F. Plate*, Ber., 1934, **67**, 1023). The conversion of cyclopentane to butadiene has been achieved by passing the vapours over glowing platinum wire [*Bayer and Co.*, G.P. 262, 553 (1913)]. For the action of aluminium chloride see p. 20.

TABLE 1

SATURATED HYDROCARBONS OF THE CYCLOPENTANE SERIES

Hydrocarbon	B.p.°	M.p.°	d	n	Ref.
yclopentane	49·5	–93·3	d_4^{15} 0·7510	n_D^{15} 1·4094	1
Iethylcyclopentane	71·6		d_4^{20} 0·7480	n_D^{20} 1·4098	2
thylcyclopentane	103·7		d_4^{20} 0·7660	n_D^{20} 1·4200	2
ropylcyclopentane	130·8	–118·7	d_4^{20} 0·7761	n_D^{20} 1·4266	2
*o*Propylcyclopentane	126·4	–111·7	d_4^{20} 0·7763	n_D^{20} 1·4260	2
utylcyclopentane	156·7		d_4^{20} 0·7840	n_D^{20} 1·4319	2
rt.-Butylcyclopentane	144·9	–96	d_4^{20} 0·7894	n_D^{20} 1·4338	2
-Hexylcyclopentane	202		d_4^{20} 0·7957	n_D^{20} 1·4394	3
-Decylcyclopentane	111/0·05 mm.	–16·5	d_4^{20} 0·8290	n_D^{20} 1·4595	4
-Octadecylcyclopentane	180/0·05 mm.	30·5	d_4^{20} 0·8363	n_D^{20} 1·4665	4
is-1:2-Dimethylcyclopentane	99·23	–52·5	d_4^{20} 0·77268	n_D^{20} 1·42764	5
ans-1:2-Dimethylcyclopentane	91·78	–119	d_4^{20} 0·75137	n_D^{20} 1·41718	5
is-1-Methyl-2-ethylcyclopentane	127·7		d_4^{20} 0·7846		6
ans-1-Methyl-2-ethylcyclopentane	121·4		d_4^{20} 0·7696		6
-Methyl-3-*iso*propylcyclopentane	140–142·5		$d_4^{18.5}$ 0·7750	$n_D^{18.5}$ 1·4257	7
:2-Dimethyl-3-*iso*propylcyclopentane	159–161		d_4^{21} 0·7883	n_D^{21} 1·4319	7

[1] *F. Eisenlohr*, Chem. Ztbl., 1926, I, 75.
[2] *G. Crane, C. E. Boord* and *A. L. Henne*, J. Amer. chem. Soc., 1945, **67**, 1237.
[3] *A. F. Plate*, C.A., 1940, **34**, 994.
[4] *A. W. Schmidt* and *A. Gemassmer*, Ber., 1940, **73**, 359.
[5] *G. Chiurdoglu*, Bull. Soc. chim. Belg., 1938, **47**, 363
[6] *G. Chiurdoglu*, C.A., 1932, **26**, 4311.
[7] *B. Kasansky*, Ber., 1929, **62**, 2205.

(See also *N. D. Zelinsky et al.*, Ber., 1933, **66**, 478, 1419; 1935, **68**, 1869; *B. Kasansky*, Ber., 1936, **69**, 954, 1862; *F. Eisenlohr*, Chem. Ztbl., 1926, I, 75; *J. M. Harris*, J. Amer. Chem. Soc., 1929, **51**, 2591; *H. Suida* and *M. Gemassmer*, Ber., 1939, **72**, 1168; *H. Pines* and *V. N. Ipatieff*, J. Amer. chem. Soc., 1939, **61**, 1076, 2728; *J. I. Denisenko* and *A. D. Frolova*, Brit. chem. Abstr., 1945, AII, 291. For phenyl substituted cyclopentanes see *J. von Braun et al.*, Ber., 1912, **45**, 1267; 1927, **60**, 2557; *F. R. Japp* and *A. C. Michie*, J. chem. Soc., 1901, **79**, 1010; *G. G. Henderson* and *R. H. Corstophine*, *ibid.*, 1901, **79**, 1256; *J. Wislicenus et al.*, Ann., 1898, **302**, 223, 236; *R. D. Abell*, J. chem. Soc., 1903, **83**, 360, 367; *J. I. Denisenko*, Ber., 1936, **69**, 2183).

The 1:2-dialkylcyclopentanes exist in *cis* and *trans* modifications which may be distinguished by their differing rates of reaction with reagents such as bromine, potassium permanganate and aluminium chloride. The results of such studies have been claimed to show that the *trans* compounds are higher boiling and denser than the *cis*, contrary to the tenets of the Auwers-Skita rule (*G. Chiurdoglu*, Bull. Soc. chim. Belg., 1944, **53**, 45).

Physical properties of cyclopentane hydrocarbons are listed in Table 1.

(b) Unsaturated hydrocarbons

(i) Cyclopentenes

Cyclopentene itself is readily obtainable by the dehydration of cyclopentanol with many reagents; phosphorus pentoxide (*K. von Auwers*, Ann., 1918, **415**, 98) phosphoric acid (Org. Synth., Coll. Vol. II, 153) oxalic acid (*O. Filipov*, Chem. Ztbl., 1915, I, 1057; *N. D. Zelinsky*, Ber., 1933, **66**, 477) and potassium bisulphate (*M. Godchot*, Compt. rend., 1911, **152**, 881) have all been employed. It may also be prepared by the partial hydrogenation of cyclopentadiene (*S. David et al.*, Bull. Soc. chim. Fr., 1944, **11**, 561). It possesses all the additive properties of a typical ethylenic compound. It yields a well-defined *ozonide*, $C_5H_8O_3$, which is decomposed by water with the formation of glutaraldehyde (*F. G. Fischer et al.*, Ber., 1932, **65**, 1471). In the presence of stannic chloride or aluminium chloride acyl chlorides add to the double bond of cyclopentene giving chloroketones which readily lose hydrogen chloride to yield acylcyclopentenes (*inter al.*, *J. English et al.*, J. Amer. chem. Soc., 1948, **70**, 2859). Cyclopentene and its homologues react readily with nitrosyl chloride to form crystalline derivatives which are convertible to cyclopentenones (*I. J. Rinkes*, Rec. Trav. chim., 1938, **57**, 176). Phenyl azide readily adds to cyclopentene (*K. Alder* and *G. Stein*, Ann., 1933, **501**, 8).

At high temperatures (800°) cyclopentene undergoes disproportionation into cyclopentadiene and hydrogen (*D. W. Vanas* and *W. D. Walters*, J. Amer. chem. Soc., 1948, **70**, 4035). It is rapidly autoxidised in ultra-violet light to form the peroxide (I) which may be readily reduced to cyclopent-2-en-1-ol (*R. Criegee et. al.*, Ber., 1939, **72**, 1799).

OOH → OH

(I)

(For reaction with osmium tetroxide see R. Criegee *et al.*, Ann., 1942, **550**, 99.)

Thermochemical data for cyclopentene (heat capacity, heats of transition and fusion and entropy values) have been determined in detail (*H. M. Huffman et al.*, J. Amer. chem. Soc., 1948, **70**, 2911). For ultra-violet absorption data see *G. Scheibe*, Ber., 1926, **59**, 1333; *V, Henri* and *L. W. Pickett*, J. chem. Phys., 1939, **7**, 439; *L. W. Pickett et al.*, J. Amer. chem. Soc., 1941, **63**, 1073.

1-Alkyl-substituted cyclopentenes are readily prepared by the dehydration of the corresponding tertiary carbinols (obtained by a Grignard reaction on cyclopentanone) (refs. in Table 2 and *N. Kishner*, Chem. Ztbl., 1912, I, 1002; *H. Meerwein*, Ann., 1914, **405**, 129; *F. Eisenlohr*, Chem. Ztbl., 1926, I, 75; *B. A. Kasansky*, Ber., 1929, **62**, 2205; *F. Richter et al.*, Ber., 1931, **64**, 875). The mechanism of this reaction has been studied in some detail by *G. Chiurdoglu* employing formic acid as the dehydrating agent (Bull. Soc. chim. Belg., 1941, **50**, 8). He makes the interesting point that, whilst tertiary cyclopentanols undergo dehydration only when the temperature is above 20°, the corresponding cyclohexanols are dehydrated readily at all temperatures.

TABLE 2

HYDROCARBONS OF THE CYCLOPENTENE SERIES (ring positions 1, 2, 3, 4, 5)

Hydrocarbon	B.p.°	M.p.°	*d*	*n*	Ref.
yclopentene	44·2/751 mm.		d_4^{10} 0·7776	n_D^{10} 1·4287	1
Methylcyclopent-1-ene	75			n_D^{20} 1·4325	2
Methylcyclopent-1-ene	68/747 mm.		d_4^{20} 0·7616	n_D^{20} 1·4213	2
Ethylcyclopent-1-ene	106·5–107		$d_4^{21.4}$ 0·8000	$n_D^{21.4}$ 1·4429	3
Ethylcyclopent-1-ene	98·1		d_4^{20} 0·7830	n_D^{20} 1·4321	4
2-Dimethylcyclopent-1-ene	150·03/760 mm.	–91·3	d_4^{20} 0·79501	n_β^{20} 1·45142	5
5-Dimethylcyclopent-1-ene	95·50/760 mm.	–118·1	d_4^{20} 0·78054	n_β^{20} 1·43972	5
n-Butylcyclopent-1-ene	157·5–158		$d_4^{17.8}$ 0·8101	$n_D^{21.3}$ 1·4488	3
*iso*Butylcyclopent-1-ene	143·6		d_4^{20} 0·7936	n_D^{20} 1·4393	4
tert.-Butylcyclopent-1-ene	139·1		d_4^{20} 0·8066	n_D^{20} 1·4430	4
n-Amylcyclopent-1-ene	179/743 mm.		d_4^{20} 0·8128	n_D^{20} 1·4513	6
n-Hexylcyclopent-1-ene	204/743 mm.		d_4^{20} 0·8158	n_D^{20} 1·4540	6
n-Heptylcyclopent-1-ene	220/762 mm.		d_4^{20} 0·8176	n_D^{20} 1·4555	6
n-Octylcyclopent-1-ene	110/11 mm.	–36·5	d_4^{20} 0·8269	n_D^{20} 1·4575	7
n-Decylcyclopent-1-ene	111/0·05 mm.	–16·5	d_4^{20} 0·8290	n_D^{20} 1·4595	7
n-Decylcyclopent-1-ene	151/12 mm.				8
n-Octadecylcyclopent-1-ene	180/0·05 mm.	30·5	d_4^{20} 0·8365	n_D^{20} 1·4665	7
n-Octadecylcyclopent-1-ene	215/13 mm.				8

[1] *M. Dojarenko*, Ber., 1927, **60**, 1543.
[2] *G. A. Lutz et al.*, J. Amer. chem. Soc., 1948, **70**, 4139.
[3] *G. Chavanne* and *P. Becker*, Bull. Soc. chim. Belg., 1927, **36**, 591.
[4] *G. Crane, C. E. Boord* and *A. L. Henne*, J. Amer. chem. Soc., 1945, **67**, 1237.
[5] *G. Chiurdoglu*, Bull. Soc. chim. Belg., 1938, **47**, 363.
[6] *A. F. Plate*, Brit. chem. Abstr., 1940, AII, 9.
[7] *A. W. Schmidt* and *A. Gemassmer*, Ber., 1940, **73**, 359.
[8] *P. Cagniant, L. Jacque* and *J. Janicaud*, Bull. Soc. chim. Fr., 1943, **10**, 106.

3-Alkyl-substituted cyclopentenes are produced by the interaction of Grignard reagents with 3-chlorocyclopentene

Cl —RMgX→ R

A mixture of the above two types is obtained when cyclohexenes are isomerised to cyclopentenes by passage over heated alumina (p. 143; *H. Adkins* and *A. K. Roebuck*, J. Amer. chem. Soc., 1948, **70**, 4041), e.g.

Me Me

⟶ +

70% 30%

As these isomers are readily separable by fractional distillation the process constitutes a convenient method for their preparation in some quantity. Physical properties of some cyclopentene hydrocarbons are listed in Table 2.

Laurolene, 1:2:3-*trimethylcyclopent*-1-*ene*, b.p. 121°, n_D 1·4437 has been obtained by the slow distillation of camphanic acid or its calcium salt and by boiling the nitroso-derivative of the lactam of aminocamphonanic acid with sodium hydroxide. It is optically active but the rotations recorded by various authors vary widely from strong dextrorotation to equally strong laevorotation (for discussion see *W. A. Noyes et al.*, J. Amer. chem. Soc., 1909, **31**, 669; *ibid.*, 1910, **32**, 1061, 1068; *ibid.*, 1912, **34**, 180). The optically inactive compound, b.p. 121·6°, $n_D^{16.5}$ 1·4464 is produced by the dehydration of 1:2:3-trimethylcyclopentan-2-ol with phosphorus pentoxide (*A. W. Noyes* and *L. P. Kyriakides*, *ibid.*, 1910, **32**, 1066).

Campholene, 1:2:3:3-*tetramethylcyclopent*-1-*ene*, b.p. 134°, n_D^{20} 1·44406, *nitrosochloride* m.p. 25°, *dibromide* m.p. 97°, is formed by the pyrolytic decarboxylation of α- or better β-campholenic acid (*F. Tiemann*, Ber., 1897, **30**, 594). It has been syhthesised by the dehydration of 1:1:2:3-tetramethylcyclopentan-1-ol (*G. Blanc*, Bull. Soc. chim. Fr., 1898, [iii], **19**, 357; Compt. rend., 1907, **145**, 683).

Pulegene, 1-iso*propyl*-3-*methylcyclopent*-1-*ene*, b.p. 138°, n_D^{22} 1·4380, *nitrosochloride* m.p. 74–75°, is formed by the decarboxylation of pulegenic acid (*O. Wallach et al.*, Ann., 1903, **327**, 131, 151).

(ii) Alkylidene- and alkenyl-cyclopentanes

A number of unsaturated cyclopentanes are known containing a semicyclic double bond i.e. derivatives of **methylenecyclopentane.** This compound, b.p. 78–81°, *nitrosochloride* m.p. 81°, is prepared by the decarboxylation of cyclopentylidene-acetic acid (*O. Wallach*, Ann., 1906, **347**, 325) and is also formed in small amount by the distillation of the calcium salt of cyclopentane-1:1-diacetic acid (*G. A. R. Kon*, J. chem. Soc., 1921, **119**, 810). Oxidation with potassium permanganate yields first the glycol and then cyclopentanone (*O. Wallach*, Ann., 1906, **347**, 325). The homologues, 1-*methyl*-3-*methylenecyclopentane*, b.p. 96–97° (*W. Speranski*, Chem. Ztbl., 1902, I, 1222, 1293; *N. D. Zelinsky*, Ber., 1901, **34**,

3950; *L. Tétry*, Bull. Soc. chim. Fr., 1902, [iii], **27**, 302), *ethylidenecyclopentane*, b.p. 113–117° (*O. Wallach* and *K. Martius*, Ber., 1909, **42**, 147; Ann., 1909. **365**, 274) and iso*propylidenecyclopentane*, b.p. 136° (*O. Wallach*, Ann., 1907, **353**, 307) are obtained by similar methods. The last compound may also be prepared by the partial hydrogenation of dimethylfulvene (*B. A. Kasanski* and *G. T. Tatevosjan*, Brit. chem. Abstr., 1940, AII, 159); alcoholic sulphuric acid brings about a migration of the double bond into the ring, 1-*iso*propyl-cyclopent-1-ene being formed (*O. Wallach*, Ann., 1907, **353**, 307). 1-iso*Propyl-2-methyl-3-methylenecyclopent-1-ene, chamene*, b.p. 86–88°/50 mm. occurs in the essential oil of *Chamaecyparis obtusa* leaves (*G. Chavanne*, Bull. Soc. chim. Belg., 1928, **36**, 591; *K. Kafuku et al.*, Bull. chem. Soc. Japan, 1931, **6**, 40, 94).

Substituted cyclopentanes with unsaturated side chains are usually obtained from cyclopentyl fatty acid esters via the Grignard reaction. Crotyl bromide reacts with cyclopentylmagnesium bromide to form *but-2-enylcyclopentane* (I), b.p. 155–156°, d_4^{20} 0·8067, n_D^{20} 1·4497 and 2-*cyclopentylbut-1-ene*, (II) b.p. 146–147°, d_4^{20} 0·8019, n_D^{20} 1·4446 (*A. F. Plate et al.*, Brit. chem. Abstr., 1946, AII, 578)

$CH_2—CH=CH—CH_3$ (on cyclopentane ring) (I)

$CH_3—CH—CH=CH_2$ (on cyclopentane ring) (II)

1-*Ethynylcyclopent-1-ene* b.p. 65·5°/125 mm., n_D^{19} 1·4880 is obtained by the dehydration of 1-ethynylcyclopentan-1-ol (*I. M. Heilbron et al.*, J. chem. Soc., 1949, 1827). For cyclopentylpropyne and homologues see *B. Grédy*, Compt. rend. 1934, **199**, 153.

(iii) Cyclopentadienes

Cyclopenta-1:3-diene. This important hydrocarbon occurs in the first runnings during the distillation of crude benzene from coal tar, from which it is produced industrially (*R. Horclois*, Chim. et Industr., 1934, **31**, Special Number 4b, 357; C.A., 1935, **29**, 140). It is a colourless liquid with a characteristic odour, b.p. 41–42°, d_4^{19} 0·80475, n_D^{19} 1·4460. Its constitution has been confirmed by its synthesis by the dehydrobromination of 1:2-dibromocyclopentane (*N. D. Zelinsky et al.*, Ber., 1929, **62**, 2865; 1933, **66**, 477). The structure of cyclopentadiene is interesting in that it constitutes an ideal system for the study of the effect of hyperconjugation and many physical properties of the hydrocarbon have been interpreted on this basis (*R. S. Mulliken*, J. chem. Phys., 1939, **7**, 121, 339). Thus a comparison of the heat of hydrogenation of cyclopentadiene (50·9 kcal./mol.) with that of butadiene (57·1 kcal./mol.) indicates the stabilising role of hyperconjugation; this may be expressed by the formula

CH—CH
‖ ‖
CH CH
\C/
‖
H_2

(*R. S. Mulliken, loc. cit.*; *J. B. Conant* and *G. B. Kistiakowsky*, Chem. Reviews, 1937, **20**, 181).

As might be expected from the presence of a conjugated diene system cyclopentadiene exhibits a high chemical reactivity; thus it readily dimerises forming two isomeric dicyclopentadienes (p. 343) from which it may be regenerated by the action of heat. Heating under pressure causes the polymerisation to proceed further giving tricyclopentadiene, tetracyclopentadiene and still higher polymers. At dull red heat another type of condensation takes place to yield naphthalene as the main product (*M. Weger*, Z. angew. Chem., 1909, **22**, 344). In the presence of many inorganic halides cyclopentadiene polymerises in a different fashion to give products formulated as

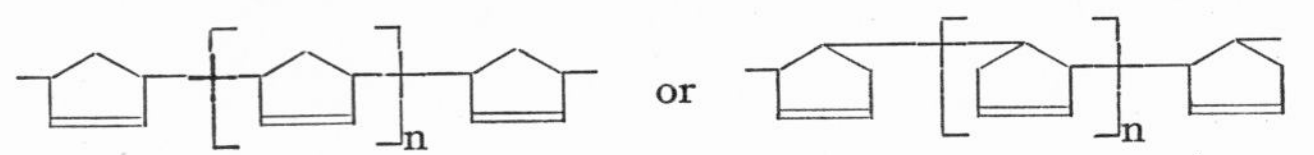

(*H. Staudinger* and *H. A. Bruson*, Ann., 1926, **447**, 97, 110).

In its character as a 1:3-diene the hydrocarbon reacts readily with dienophiles to form bridged ring (endomethylene) compounds (pp. 337, *O. Diels* and *K. Alder*, Ann., 1928, **460**, 111; 1930, **478**, 141; 1931, **486**, 202; Ber., 1929, **62**, 2350).

The hydrogen atoms of the methylene group in cyclopentadiene are characterised by a high reactivity similar to that encountered in methylene groups situated between other electron-attracting radicals e.g. $-CO-CH_2-CO-$, $-CO-CH_2-CN$ etc. Thus the hydrocarbon interacts with methylmagnesium iodide with the formation of cyclopentadienylmagnesium iodide and evolution of methane. The action of potassium furnishes the highly reactive potassium salt which readily absorbs carbon dioxide to give the potassium salt of dicyclopentadienedicarboxylic acid. Oxalic esters condense with cyclopentadiene in the presence of sodium ethoxide to form the corresponding keto-esters. For complex compounds of cyclopentadiene with certain transition metals see Vol. III.

The alkali-catalysed condensation of aldehydes and ketones with cyclopentadiene gives rise to a series of interesting coloured hydrocarbons known by the generic name of fulvenes.

The parent member, fulvene itself (I) is unknown, but employment of acetone and methyl ethyl ketone in this condensation readily yields *dimethylfulvene* (II), b.p. 46°/11 mm. and *methylethylfulvene*, b.p. 185°, as orange oils; *diphenylfulvene* forms crimson prisms m.p. 82° (*J. Thiele*, Ann., 1906, **348**, 1). Similarly fulvenes are obtainable from the ionones (*H. Willstädt*, Chem. Ztbl., 1934, II, 1620; *E. P. Kohler* and *J. Kable*, J. Amer. chem. Soc., 1934, **56**, 2756) and cyclic ketones (*A. Guillemonat*, Compt. rend., 1935, **200**, 1416).

With hydrogen halides and halogens cyclopentadiene gives a range of halogen-substituted cyclopentanes according to the following scheme (X = halogen):

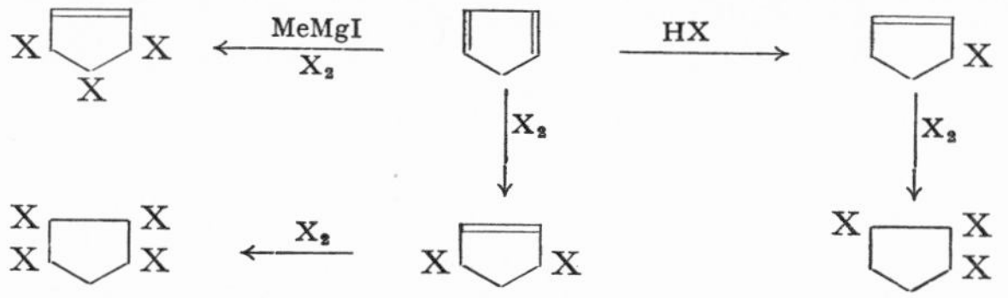

MeMgI, X_2 ; HX ; X_2 ; X_2 ; X_2

(*F. Nöldechen*, Ber., 1900, **33**, 3348; *J. Thiele*, Ann., 1901, **314**, 296). Cyclopentadiene reacts smoothly with lead tetracetate with the formation of 3:4-diacetoxycyclopent-1-ene (p. 90) (*R. Criegee*, Ann., 1930, **481**, 263). *tert.*-Butyl hydroperoxide catalysed by osmic acid leads to 1:4-addition, however, the product being *cis*-cyclopent-1-ene-3:5-diol (*N. A. Milas* and *L. S. Maloney*, J. Amer. chem. Soc., 1940, **62**, 1841); with excess of reagent, cyclopentane-1:2:3:4-tetrol is obtained.

Few alkyl-substituted homologues of cyclopentadiene have been described. 2-*Methyl*-4-*ethyl*cyclo*pentadiene* has been obtained by the decarboxylation of 2-methylcyclopentadiene-4-propionic acid (*P. Duden* and *R. Freydag*, Ber., 1903, **36**, 944). 1-*Methyl*-3-iso*propylcyclopentadiene* b.p. 50–55°/20 mm., n_D 1·4758, d^{20} 0·840 is a degradation product of carvenone (*W. Treibs*, Ber., 1938, **66**, 1483). Phenyl-substituted cyclopentadienes are a better represented class; their method of preparation may be illustrated employing 1:2:3:4-*tetraphenyl-cyclopentadiene* m.p. 178° as an example.

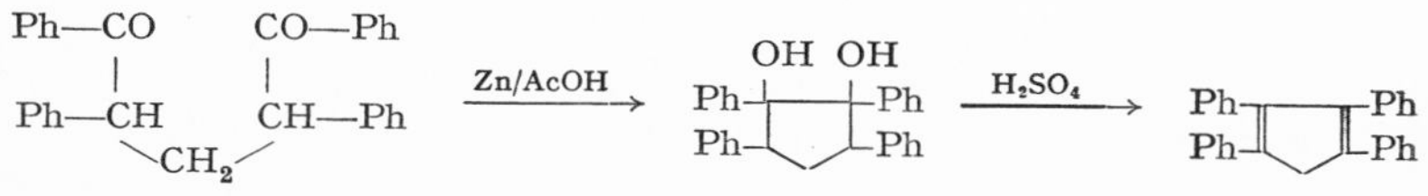

Ph—CO CO—Ph / Ph—CH CH—Ph / CH_2 —Zn/AcOH→ (OH OH, Ph, Ph, Ph, Ph) —H_2SO_4→ (Ph, Ph, Ph, Ph)

The starting material is readily obtained by condensing formaldehyde with deoxybenzoin. Similarly the 1:2:4-*triphenyl*-, m.p. 149°, 1-*methyl*-2:3:5-*triphenyl*-, m.p. 163° and 1:4-*dimethyl*-2:3:5-*triphenyl*-, m.p. 128°, -*cyclopentadienes* may be procured (*J. Wislicenus et al.*, Ann., 1898, **302**, 223, 236; *R. D. Abell*, J. chem. Soc., 1903, **83**, 360; *E. B. Auerbach*, Ber., 1903, **36**, 933; *K. Ziegler* and *B. Schnell*, Ann., 1925, **445**, 266; *W. Dilthey et al.*, J. pr. Chem., 1933, [ii], **139**, 1). 1:4-*Diphenylcyclopentadiene*, m.p. 158°, *picrate*, m.p. 145–146° (dec.) is prepared by the condensation of ethyl *β*-benzoylpropionate with acetophenone; the reaction takes the following course (*N. L. Drake* and *J. R. Adams*, J. Amer. chem. Soc., 1939, **61**, 1326):

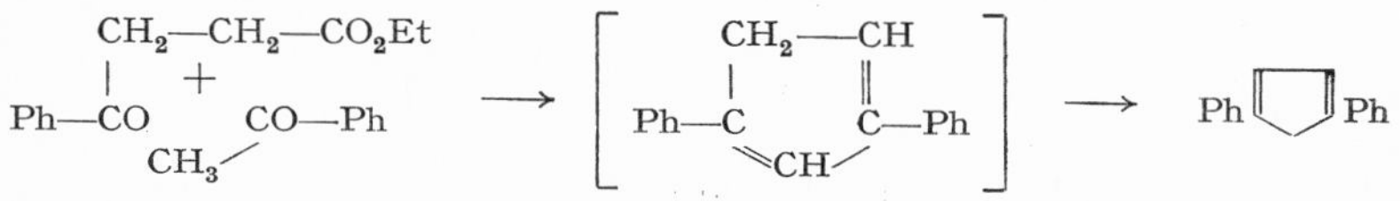

CH_2—CH_2—CO_2Et + / Ph—CO CO—Ph / CH_3 → [CH_2—CH / Ph—C C—Ph / CH] → Ph Ph

These phenylated cyclopentadienes form fulvenes in the same way as the parent hydrocarbon (*W. Dilthey* and *P. Huchtermann*, J. pr. Chem., 1940, [ii], **154**, 238).

3. Halogen derivatives

The saturated cyclopentyl halides are usually prepared from the corresponding cyclopentanols by the standard methods, e.g. *chlorocyclopentane*, b.p. 115°, is formed from hydrochloric acid and cyclopentanol (*N. D. Zelinsky*, Ber., 1908, **41**, 2627) and *bromocyclopentane*, b.p. 56°/45 mm. from cyclopentanol and hydrobromic acid-sulphuric acid (*G. R. Yohe* and *R. Adams*, J. Amer. chem. Soc., 1928, **50**, 1503). *1-Chloro-2-methylcyclopentane*, b.p. 70–72°/125 mm., n_D^{20} 1·4477, is procured by the reaction of phosphorus pentachloride on the corresponding alcohol (*G. A. Lutz et al.*, J. Amer. chem. Soc., 1948, **70**, 4135). Other methods of formation include the addition of hydrogen halides to cyclopentenes and direct halogenation of cyclopentanes (*idem, ibid.*). Halides of this type tend to dissociate into hydrogen halides and the corresponding cyclopentene.

Vicinal dihalides are readily available by the reaction of the halogens with cyclopentenes; in this way *1:2-dibromocyclopentane*, b.p. 71·5°/12 mm., n_D^{19} 1·5510, is prepared (*N. D. Zelinsky* and *R. J. Lewina*, Ber., 1933, **66**, 477). All such dihalides almost certainly possess the *trans* configuration.

Cyclopentenyl halides of the type exemplified by *3-chlorocyclopent-1-ene*, b.p. 50°/40 mm. (*C. R. Noller* and *R. Adams*, J. Amer. chem. Soc., 1926, **48**, 2444) are prepared by the low temperature addition of hydrogen halides to cyclopentadiene. The bromo-compounds may also be made by the action of N-bromosuccinimide on cyclopentenes. The halogen atom in these compounds is highly reactive; they interact with Grignard reagents to yield substituted cyclopentenes (p. 80) and with amines of all types to give aminocyclopentenes. The action of one molecule of bromine on cyclopentadiene gives rise to two stereoisomeric *3:5-dibromocyclopent-1-enes*, a liquid *cis*-isomer b.p. 53–54°/2 mm. and a solid *trans*-isomer m.p. 45°, b.p. 72–75°/2 mm.; both regenerate cyclopentadiene on treatment with zinc in acetic acid (*J. Thiele*, Ann., 1901, **314**, 300). The action of bromine on cyclopentadienylmagnesium bromide gives *3:4:5-tribromocyclopent-1-ene*, m.p. 60° (*V. Grignard*, Compt. rend., 1914, **158**, 1763).

Substituted cyclopentenes with a halogen atom in the side-chain are obtained by subjecting the corresponding carbinol to the usual metathetical reactions; thus *3-(β-bromoethyl)cyclopent-1-ene*, b.p. 71–72°/16 mm., n_D^{20} 1·4995, is prepared by the action of phosphorus tribromide on the corresponding carbinol (*J. A. Arvin* and *R. Adams*, J. Amer. chem. Soc., 1928, **50**, 1790).

A number of interesting polychlorocyclopentene derivatives have been described. *Octachlorocyclopentene*, m.p. 38°, b.p. 134°/6 mm. may be obtained by the action of phosphorus pentachloride on hexachlorocyclopentenone or xanthogallol (p. 105); the best method of preparation, however, is by the aluminium chloride-catalysed cyclisation of octachloropenta-1:3-diene (*H. J. Prins*, Rec. Trav. chim., 1932, **51**, 1065; 1946, **65**, 455; *J. A. Krynitsky* and *R. W. Bost*, J. Amer. chem. Soc., 1947, **69**, 1918).

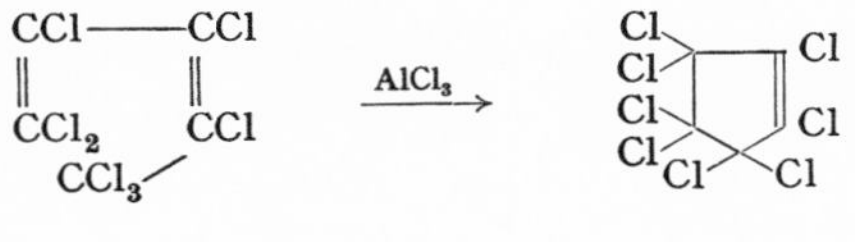

Fluorination of octachlorocyclopentene results in the formation of a series of fluorochlorocyclopentenes, the fluorine atoms replacing the chlorine atoms one by one (*A. L. Henne* and *W. J. Zimmerschied*, J. Amer. chem. Soc., 1945, **67**, 1235). Pyrolysis of octachlorocyclopentene at 470° results in dissociation to chlorine and hexachlorocyclopentadiene, b.p. 94°/5 mm., m.p. –10°. The two "methylene" chlorine atoms of this compound are reactive and may be replaced by the use of sodium ethoxide to give *tetrachlorocyclopentadienone diethyl acetal*, b.p. 114°/6 mm., m.p. –15° (*J. A. Krynitsky* and *R. W. Bost, loc. cit.*). Reaction of hexachlorocyclopentadiene with trichloroethylene under the catalytic influence of aluminium chloride results in the chlorinated compound (I), b.p. 143°/2 mm., m.p. 80°, which may be dehydrochlorinated to yield the *octachloromethylfulvene* (II), b.p. 121°/2 mm., m.p. 53° (*J. A. Krynitsky et al.*, J. Amer. chem. Soc., 1947, **69**, 1918; 1949, **71**, 816; *J. S. Newcomer* and *E. T. McBee*, *ibid.*, 1949, **71**, 946, 952).

Cl Cl Cl Cl Cl Cl $\xrightarrow[AlCl_3]{CHCl=CCl_2}$ Cl Cl Cl Cl Cl CHCl–CCl_3 (I) $\xrightarrow{KOH}$ Cl Cl Cl Cl =CCl–CCl_3 (II)

4. Nitro- and Amino-derivatives

Nitrocyclopentanes may be made by direct nitration of the hydrocarbons. Thus methylcyclopentane gives 1-*nitro*-1-*methylcyclopentane*, b.p. 92°/40 mm., n_D^{20} 1·436 and 2-*nitro*-1-*methylcyclopentane*, b.p. 99°/40 mm. (*N. Kishner*, J. pr. Chem., 1897, **56**, 369; *A. Markownikow et al.*, Ber., 1895, **28**, 1236; Ann., 1899, **307**, 352). They may also be formed by the metathetical reaction of silver nitrite with the appropriate halide (*N. Rosanov*, Chem. Ztbl., 1916, I, 925; 1924, I, 2425).

C_5H_9–CH_2I $\xrightarrow{AgNO_2}$ C_5H_9–CH_2NO_2

b.p. 110°/35 mm.

Amines are prepared by the usual methods, e.g. reaction of halides with ammonia or amines, reduction of oximes and nitriles and the Hofmann degradation of amides.

Cyclopentylamine, b.p. 106–108°, is obtained by reduction with sodium in alcohol of cyclopentanone oxime (*J. Wislicenus* and *W. Hentzschel*, Ann., 1893, **275**, 325). Hofmann degradation of cyclopentylacetamide gives *cyclopentylmethylamine*, b.p. 139–145° (*O. Wallach* and *K. Fleischer*, Ann., 1907, **353**, 305). Cyclopentenyl- and cyclopentyl-alkylamines containing a long aliphatic chain have been derived from chaulmoogric and hydnocarpic acids (*C. Nägeli* and *E. Vogt-Markus*, Helv., 1932, **15**, 60; *J. Sacks* and *R. Adams*, J. Amer. chem. Soc., 1926, **48**, 2395).

Many compounds have been obtained from 3-chlorocyclopent-1-ene by reaction with amines. Thus methylamine gives 3-*methylaminocyclopent*-1-*ene*, b.p. 100°/15 mm., aniline the *anilino*-compound b.p. 153°/25 mm. and piperidine the *piperidino*-compound b.p. 96°/23 mm. (*J. von Braun et al.*, Ber., 1927, **60**, 2551).

For aminohydroxy-compounds see *M. Mousseron et al.*, Compt. rend., 1948, **226**, 91.

Many of the primary amino-compounds undergo change in ring size when treated with nitrous acid (p. 12).

5. Alcohols

(a) Hydroxyl group in the ring

TABLE 3

SECONDARY ALCOHOLS OF THE CYCLOPENTANOL SERIES

Compound	B.p.°	Other data	Re
Cyclopentanol	129	n_D^{20} 1·4370	1
2-Methylcyclopentan-1-ol *cis*?	149	phenylurethane, m.p. 94°	2
2-Methylcyclopentan-1-ol *trans*?	150	phenylurethane, m.p. 89°	2
3-Methylcyclopentan-1-ol *cis*	70/24 mm.	phenylurethane, m.p. 78°	3
3-Methylcyclopentan-1-ol *l-cis*	62/15 mm.	$[\alpha]_{5893}^{21}$ −6·5°; phenylurethane, m.p. 82°	3
3-Methylcyclopentan-1-ol *trans*	65/23 mm.	phenylurethane, m.p. 80°	3
3-Methylcyclopentan-1-ol *l-trans*	60/15 mm.	$[\alpha]_{5893}^{28}$ −6·5°; phenylurethane, m.p. 78°	3
2-*iso*Propylcyclopentan-1-ol *cis*	94/27 mm.	phenylurethane, m.p. 63°	4
2-*iso*Propylcyclopentan-1-ol *trans*	85/20 mm.	phenylurethane, m.p. 103°	4
3-*tert*.-Butylcyclopentan-1-ol	198/744 mm.	α-naphthylurethane, m.p. 95°	5
3-*tert*.-Amylcyclopentan-1-ol	217/738 mm	α-naphthylurethane, m.p. 82°	5
2^c-3^t-Diphenylcyclopentan-1-ol	144/0·3 mm.		6
2^t-3^c-Diphenylcyclopentan-1-ol		m.p. 110–112°	6

[1] *C. R. Noller* and *R. Adams*, J. Amer. chem. Soc., 1926, **48**, 1080.
[2] *M. Godchot*, Compt. rend., 1926, **182**, 393; *W. Hückel* and *R. Kindler*, Chem. Ber., 1947, **80**, 202.
[3] *M. Godchot et al.*, Bull. Soc. chim. Fr., 1939, [v], **6**, 1353, 1358, 1366, 1370.
[4] *G. Vavon*, Bull. Soc. chim. Fr., 1928, [iv], **43**, 67.
[5] *H. Pines* and *V. N. Ipatieff*, J. Amer. chem. Soc., 1939, **61**, 2728.
[6] *H. A. Weidlich* and *M. Meyer-Delius*, Ber., 1941, **74**, 1195.

(i) Secondary cyclopentanols

Secondary cyclopentanols (Table 3) are generally prepared by reduction of the corresponding ketone. Common reducing agents for this purpose are sodium in moist ether, and catalytic hydrogenation with Raney nickel in alcohol or platinum in glacial acetic acid. Suitably substituted cyclopentanones give stereoisomeric cyclopentanols the configurations of which are generally determined by application of the Skita rule; this states that reduction in acid solution favours the formation of the *cis*-isomer while in neutral or alkaline solution the *trans*-isomer is predominantly formed (*A. Skita et al.*, Ber., 1920, **53**, 1792; 1923, **56**, 2234). Although the rule was deduced from a study of certain amino-acids of the cyclohexane series it appears capable of extension to other classes of compounds. The structures thus established usually, though not always, concur with the Auwers rule relating density and refractive index with configuration (see p. 10). 2-Substituted cyclopentanols may also be made by the action of Grignard reagents on cyclopentene oxides (*M. Godchot et al.*, Compt. rend., 1912, **154**, 1625; 1926, **182**, 393; 1927, **184**, 208).

The secondary cyclopentanols may be readily dehydrated to cyclopentenes; the rate of this reaction has been studied in detail (p. 78). Mild oxidation furnishes the ketones and more drastic methods result in ring fission with the formation of substituted glutaric acids.

Cyclopent-2-en-1-ol, b.p. 140°, $n_D^{16.5}$ 1·4778, *phenylurethane*, m.p. 128°, has been prepared from the autoxidation product of cyclopentene (*R. Criegee et al.*, Ber., 1939, **72**, 1799) and also by hydrolysis of 3-chlorocyclopent-1-ene (*S. David et al.*, Bull. Soc. chim. Fr., 1944, **11**, 561). Tetraphenylcyclopentadienol, m.p. 140°, is obtained by the reduction of the corresponding ketone (*W. Dilthey et al.*, J. pr. Chem., 1933, [ii], **139**, 1).

The action of hypochlorous acid on cyclopentene gives *2-chlorocyclopentan-1-ol*, b.p. 81°/15 mm. (*R. B. Rothstein* and *M. Rothstein*, Compt. rend., 1939, **209**, 761).

(ii) *Tertiary cyclopentanols*

Alcohols of this type (Table 4) are very numerous as they are readily obtained by the action of Grignard reagents on cyclopentanones; full details of the technique to be adopted together with precautions to be observed in purifying the products are given in reference 1 of Table 4 (cf. also *H. Meerwein*, Ann., 1914, **405**, 129; *G. Chavanne* and *P. Becker*, Bull. Soc. chim. Belg., 1927, **36**, 591; *J. M. Harris*, J. Amer. chem. Soc., 1929, **51**, 2591; *J. I. Denissenko*, Ber., 1936, **69**, 1668). The carbinols are very readily dehydrated to the corresponding cyclopentenes (p. 79); on oxidation with chromium trioxide in glacial acetic acid they are smoothly converted to δ-keto-acids (*L. F. Fieser* and *J. Szmuszkowicz*, J. Amer. chem. Soc., 1948, **70**, 3352), e.g.

$$\text{C}_5\text{H}_8(\text{R})(\text{OH}) \xrightarrow{CrO_3} \text{R·CO·CH}_2\text{·CH}_2\text{·CH}_2\text{·CO}_2\text{H}$$

1-Ethynylcyclopentan-1-ol, b.p. 78°/40 mm., m.p. 24°, is best prepared by the action of sodium acetylide in liquid ammonia on cyclopentanone. On dehydration

TABLE 4

TERTIARY ALCOHOLS OF THE CYCLOPENTANOL SERIES

Compound	B.p.	M.p.°	3:5-dinitro-benzoate m.p.°	Ref.
1-Methylcyclopentan-1-ol	110/300 mm.	36	115.5	1
1-Ethylcyclopentan-1-ol	125/300 mm.	–10	108.3	1
1:2-Dimethylcyclopentan-1-ol	151			2
1:3-Dimethylcyclopentan-1-ol	144.4			2
1-*n*-Propylcyclopentan-1-ol	143.5/300 mm.	–37.5	82	1
1:2:2-Trimethylcyclopentan-1-ol	80/49 mm.			3
1-*n*-Butylcyclopentan-1-ol	163/300 mm.		75.3	1
1-*n*-Decylcyclopentan-1-ol	133/7 mm.	–18	78	1
1-*n*-Tetradecylcyclopentan-1-ol	164/2 mm.	16.2	81.5	1

[1] *C. R. McLellan* and *W. R. Edwards*, J. Amer. chem. Soc., 1944, **66**, 409.
[2] *G. Chavanne* and *L. de Vogel*, Bull. Soc. chim. Belg., 1928, **37**, 141.
[3] *N. Kishner*, Chem. Ztbl., 1911, I, 543.

it yields ethynylcyclopentene and on boiling with formic acid it rearranges to 1-acetylcyclopent-1-ene (*I. M. Heilbron et al.*, J. chem. Soc., 1949, 1827).

1:2:3:4:5-*Pentaphenylcyclopenta-*2:4-*diene-*1-*ol*, m.p. 175–176°, is prepared by the action of phenylmagnesium bromide on tetraphenylcyclopentadienone. By treating the halides of this alcohol with silver the free radical *pentaphenylcyclopentadienyl* is obtained as brilliant crimson crystals, m.p. 260° (*K. Ziegler* and *B. Schnell*, Ann., 1925, **445**, 266; *C. F. Allen* and *J. A. van Allen*, J. Amer. chem. Soc., 1943, **65**, 1384).

2^t-*Chloro*-1^t-*methylcyclopentan*-1^c-*ol* (I), b.p. 61–64°/7 mm., m.p. 35–37°, is prepared by the addition of hypochlorous acid to 1-methylcyclopent-1-ene. The stereoisomer, 2^c-*chloro*-1^t-*methylcyclopentan*-1^c-*ol* (II), b.p. 50–57°/8 mm., is obtained by the action of methylmagnesium bromide on 2-chlorocyclopentanone. The two isomers differ in their reaction towards alkali; (I) furnishes the epoxide whilst (II) yields 2-methylcyclopentanone (*P. D. Bartlett* and *R. V. White*, J. Amer. chem. Soc., 1934, **56**, 2785; *M. Tiffeneau* and *G. Vaissière*, Compt. rend., 1939, **209**, 449; *G. Chavanne* and *L. de Vogel*, Bull. Soc. chim. Belg., 1928, **37**, 141).

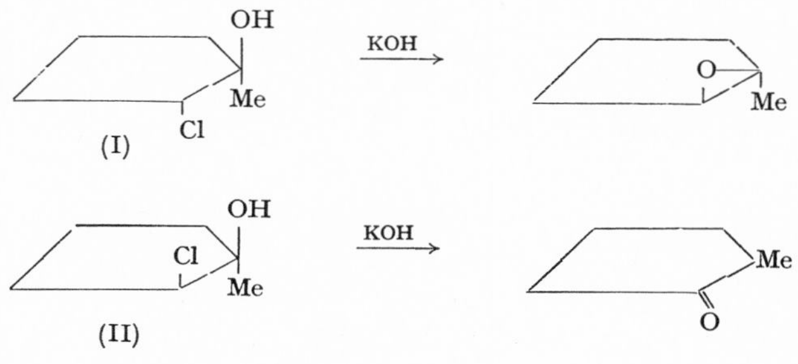

Cyclopentyl mercaptan, b.p. 131–132° is prepared from cyclopentyl bromide and potassium hydrosulphide (*J. Loevenich et al.*, Ber., 1929, **62**, 3090). A similar reaction employing potassium sulphide yields *dicyclopentyl sulphide*, b.p. 129–130°/24 mm. (*idem, ibid.*).

Cyclopentanesulphonic acid (*anilide*, m.p. 89·5–90·5°), has been obtained as a crystalline, very hygroscopic solid by treatment of cyclopentylmagnesium bromide with sulphur dioxide (*W. Borsche* and *W. Lange*, Ber., 1907, **40**, 221). The sodium salt is conveniently prepared by heating cyclopentyl chloride with sodium sulphite (*N. Turkiewicz* and *S. Pilat*, Ber., 1938, **71**, 284). The sodium salts of sulphonic acids of the type

$$\text{C}_5\text{H}_9\text{-(CH}_2)_n\text{SO}_3\text{H}$$

are surface active when n is small (*S. Pilat* and *N. Turkiewicz*, Ber., 1939, **72**, 1527).

(iii) Cyclopentanediols

The best represented class of cyclopentanediols consists of the vicinal glycols, which are readily prepared by the hydroxylation of the corresponding cyclopentenes. Peracids yield the *trans*-glycols (via the epoxide) whilst potassium permanganate or osmic acid-catalysed *tert.*-butyl hydro-

TABLE 5

CYCLOPENTANEDIOLS, GLYCOLS

Compound	B.p.°	M.p.°	Other data	Ref.
·clopentane-1:2-diol *cis*	106°/10 mm.	29–30°	bisphenylurethane m.p. 197°	1
·clopentane-1:2-diol *trans*	101°/15 mm.	54–55°	bisphenylurethane m.p. 221°	1
Methylcyclopentane-1:2-diol *cis*	95°/7 mm.	23°		2, 3
Methylcyclopentane-1:2-diol *trans*	90°/1 mm.	65°	bis-3:5-dinitrobenzoate m.p. 92°	2, 3
Methylcyclopentane-1:2-diol	97°/1 mm.		n_D^{25} 1·4760	3
3-Dimethylcyclopentane-1:2-diol	87°/1 mm.		n_D^{25} 1·4755	3
2-Dimethylcyclopentane-1:2-diol *cis*	146°/20 mm.		benzylidene compound m.p. 120–122·5°	4
2-Dimethylcyclopentane-1:2-diol *trans*		99·5–101°		4

[1] *C. van Loon*, Chem. Ztbl., 1920, I, 331; *H. G. Derx*, Rec. Trav. chim., 1922, **41**, 317.; *P. E. Verkade et al.*, Ann., 1928, **467**, 217; *L. N. Owen* and *P. N. Smith*, J. chem. Soc., 1952, 4026.
[2] *C. J. Maan*, Rec. Trav. chim., 1929, **48**, 342; *P. E. Verkade et al.*, Ann., 1928, **467**, 217.
[3] *H. Adkins* and *A. K. Roebuck*, J. Amer. chem. Soc., 1938, **70**, 4041.
[4] *P. D. Bartlett* and *A. Bawley*, J. Amer. chem. Soc., 1938, **60**, 2416.

peroxide produces the *cis*-isomers. Another method of forming the glycols is by the intramolecular pinacol reduction of 1:5-diketones, but this process is rarely used for preparative purposes. Some of these glycols are listed in Table 5.

The disecondary glycols are oxidised to glutaric acids by reaction with chromium trioxide or potassium permanganate; secondary-tertiary glycols give δ-keto-acids under these conditions whilst the tertiary diglycols yield δ-diketones (ref. 3 of Table 5).

The stereochemical configurations of the compounds may be assigned in various ways. Thus, the *cis*-diols enhance the conductivity of boric acid solutions and form *iso*propylidene compounds with acetone (ref. 2, Table 5; *J. Böeseken* and *P. H. Hermans*, Rec. Trav. chim., 1923, **42,** 1109; *H. G. Derx, ibid.*, 1922, **41,** 331; *P. H. Hermans*, Z. anorg. Chem., 1925, **142,** 88, 105). Again, the rate of fission of the glycols by means of lead tetracetate is very different for the two isomers; thus *cis*-1:2-dimethylcyclopentane-1:2-diol reacts more than a thousand times as fast as the *trans*-isomer (ref. 4, Table 5). Another difference between these two isomers is shown by their behaviour on dehydration; the *cis*-compound undergoes a pinacolone rearrangement to produce 2:2-dimethylcyclopentan-1-one whilst the *trans*-isomer yields only tarry products (ref. 4; *H. Meerwein*, Ann., 1939, **542,** 123; *M. Tiffeneau* and *G. Vaissière*, Compt. rend., 1939, **209,** 449). The configuration of *trans*-cyclopentane-1:2-diol has been confirmed by its resolution into optical enantiomorphs ($[\alpha]_D$ ±33·8°) by means of acetobromoglucose (*B. Helferich* and *R. Hiltman*, Ber., 1937, **70,** 308).

As already mentioned (p. 83) cyclopentadiene on treatment with lead tetraacetate yields the *diacetate* (b.p. 106–110°/12 mm.) of cis-*cyclopent-1-ene-3:4-diol* b.p. 110–114°/12 mm. (*R. Criegee*, Ann., 1930, **481,** 263). Previous procedures which were claimed to yield cyclopent-1-ene-3:5-diol (e.g. hydroxylation of cyclopentadiene and the action of potassium and silver acetate on 3:5-dibromocyclopent-1-ene followed by hydrolysis) have now been shown to yield mixtures containing a high proportion of cyclopent-1-ene-3:4-diol (*L. N. Owen* and *P. N. Smith*, J. chem. Soc., 1952, 4035; all earlier references are given herein). Treatment of *cis*- and *trans*-3:5-dibromocyclopent-1-ene with tetraethylammonium acetate in acetone furnishes the corresponding 3:5-*diacetoxycyclopent-1-enes*, cis-, b.p. 83°/0.5 mm., n_D^{25} 1·4575; trans-, b.p. 76°/0.5 mm., n_D^{19} 1·4635, which, by catalytic hydrogenation and hydrolysis, yield the corresponding *cyclopentane-1:3-diols*, cis-, b.p. 90°/1 mm., m.p. 30–32°, *bisphenylurethane* m.p. 173°; trans-, b.p. 80–85°/0.1 mm., m.p. 40°, *bisphenylurethane* m.p. 163° (*idem, ibid.*).

(b) Exocyclic alcohols

Cyclopentylcarbinol, b.p. 162°, *phenylurethane* m.p. 92–93°, may be prepared by the reduction of cyclopentanecarboxylic ester, by the action of formaldehyde on cyclopentylmagnesium bromide and by the action of nitrous acid on cyclopentylmethylamine (*O. Wallach*, Ann., 1907, **353**, 325; *N. D. Zelinsky*, Ber., 1908, **41**, 2629).

2-*Cyclopentylethan*-1-*ol*, b.p. 97°/24 mm., n_D^{20} 1·4577, is obtained by the action of ethylene oxide on cyclopentylmagnesium bromide or by the reduction of cyclopentylacetic ester (*W. Hückel* and *W. Gelmroth*, J. pr. Chem., 1935, [ii], **142**, 205; *G. R. Yohe* and *R. Adams*, J. Amer. chem. Soc., 1928, **50**, 1505).

Cyclopentylmethylcarbinol, b.p. 73·5–75°/31 mm., *phenylurethane* m.p. 71–71·5°, is produced from cyclopentylmagnesium bromide by the action of acetaldehyde or by the interaction of methylmagnesium bromide and cyclohexene oxide (*M. Godchot et al.*, Bull. Soc. chim. Fr., 1925, [iv], **37**, 1455; 1928, **43**, 521; *P. D. Bartlett* and *C. M. Berry*, J. Amer. chem. Soc., 1934, **56**, 2683; for higher homologues see *W. R. Edwards* and *E. E. Reid*, *ibid.*, 1930, **52**, 3235).

Cyclopentyldimethylcarbinol, b.p. 105°/80 mm., n_D^{20} 1·4060, prepared by the action of methylmagnesium bromide on cyclopentanecarboxylic ester, undergoes ring enlargement on dehydration (*S. S. Nametkin* and *D. M. Gabriedze*, J. gen. Chem. U.S.S.R., 1943, **13**, 560).

For long chain alcohols derived from chaulmoogric, hydnocarpic and gorlic acids see *N. P. Buu-Hoi*, *P. Cagniant* and *J. Janicaud*, Compt. rend., 1941, **212**, 729; *P. Burschkies*, Ber., 1940, **73**, 405.

1-(*Hydroxymethyl*)*cyclopentan*-1-*ol*, m.p. 39–41°, is the product of hydroxylation of methylenecyclopentane. When treated with sulphuric acid, it forms cyclopentanealdehyde (*O. Wallach*, Ann., 1906, **347**, 325).

2-(*Hydroxymethyl*)*cyclopentan*-1-*ol*, b.p. 137°/12 mm., is obtained by the reduction of cyclopentan-1-one-2-carboxylic ester. The corresponding dibromide on treatment with zinc, yields bicyclo-[3:1:0]-hexane (*N. D. Zelinsky* and *M. Uschakov*, Bull. Soc. chim. Fr., 1924, [iv], **35**, 484).

The glycol (I), 2-(1′-*hydroxy*-1′-*cyclopentyl*)*propan*-2-*ol*, m.p. 62°, b.p. 108°/14 mm., obtained from the action of methylmagnesium iodide on cyclopentan-1-ol-1-carboxylic ester, readily undergoes pinacolic dehydration with the formation of 2:2-dimethylcyclohexan-1-one (*O. Wallach*, Ann., 1910, **376**, 152).

(I) [cyclopentyl]–C(Me)(Me), OH OH ⟶ [cyclohexanone, O, Me, Me]

6. Aldehydes

Cyclopentanealdehyde, b.p. 136°, *semicarbazone* m.p. 123°, is most conveniently prepared by the hydrogenation of cyclopent-1-en-1-aldehyde (see below; *E. Urion*, Ann. Chim., 1934, **1**, 5). Other methods of formation include the oxidation of the corresponding alcohol (*N. D. Zelinsky*, Ber., 1908, **41**, 2629) the ring contraction of 2-iodocyclohexan-1-ol (*M. Tiffeneau*, Compt. rend., 1914, **159**, 772) or cyclohexene oxide (*P. Bedos*, Compt. rend., 1929, **188**, 962; *G. R. Clemo*, J. chem. Soc., 1933, 362) and the dehydration of 1-(hydroxymethyl)cyclopentan-1-ol (*O. Wallach*, Ann., 1906, **347**, 326).

1-*Phenylcyclopentane*-1-*aldehyde*, b.p. 134°/15 mm., is formed in small amount, together with much phenylcyclohexanone, when phenylcyclohexene oxide is distilled with acidic reagents (*J. Lévy*, Compt. rend., 1928, **187**, 45).

Cyclopent-1-ene-1-aldehyde, b.p. 48°/11 mm., n_D^{21} 1·4828, λ_{max} 237 mμ (ε 12,000), *semicarbazone*, m.p. 209°, p-*nitrophenylhydrazone*, m.p. 198°, 2:4-*dinitrophenylhydrazone*, m.p. 216°, is readily prepared by the intramolecular aldol condensation of adipaldehyde (conveniently obtained by lead tetracetate or periodate fission of cyclohexane-1:2-diol) (*J. English* and *G. W. Barber*, J. Amer. chem. Soc., 1949, **71**, 3310; *E. R. H. Jones et al.*, J. chem. Soc., 1950, 3634). It may also be made by the pyrolysis of divinyl glycol (*E. Urion*, Ann. Chim., 1934, **1**, 5) and by hydrolysis of the oxime produced by the dehydrohalogenation of methylenecyclopentane nitrosochloride (*O. Wallach*, Ann., 1906, **347**, 327). Homologues of the aldehyde have been obtained by the first procedure above (*J. English* and *G. W. Barber*, *loc. cit.*).

Cyclopent-2-enylacetaldehyde, b.p. 50°/15 mm., *semicarbazone* m.p. 116°, is procured by the dehydrogenation of the corresponding alcohol with a silver-pumice catalyst at 400°. A better method consists in passing the mixed vapours of cyclopent-2-en-1-acetic acid and formic acid over a manganous oxide-pumice catalyst at 390° (*H. Moureu et al.*, Bull. Soc. chim. Fr., 1948, **15**, 96).

7. Ketones

(a) *Ring ketones*

(i) *Saturated monoketones*

Cyclopentanone occurs naturally in the light wood-tar oils (*H. Metzner* and *D. Vorländer*, Ber., 1898, **31**, 1885). It is most conveniently prepared by the distillation of adipic acid with catalysts such as baryta (ref. 1, Table 6), barium oxide (*G. Vavon* and *A. Apchié*, Bull. Soc. chim. Fr., 1928, [iv], **43**, 667), barium oxide-iron (*A. I. Vogel*, J. chem. Soc., 1929, 721), thorium oxide (*N. D. Zelinsky*, Ber., 1929, **62**, 2180) or ferrous sulphate (*J. von Braun et al.*, Ann., 1931, **490**, 179); dry distillation of zinc adipate has also been employed (*M. Godchot*, Compt. rend., 1926, **182**, 393). Among methods of formation may be mentioned the ring enlargement of methylenecyclobutane chlorohydrin(*N. Demjanov*, Ber., 1922, **55**, 7302) the ring contraction of dibromocyclohexanone (*O. Wallach*, Chem. Ztbl., 1916, I, 365; Ann., 1918, **414**, 296; 1924, **437**, 148) and the catalytic rearrangement of 2:3-dihydropyran at 200° (*C. L. Wilson*, J. Amer. chem. Soc., 1948, **70**, 1311).

Oxidation of cyclopentanone yields glutaric acid. With hydrogen peroxide the ketone forms a *hydroperoxide*

OH
OOH

hemihydrate m.p. 75° [*N. A. Milas*, U.S.P. 2,298,405 (1932)]. When heated with acetic anhydride it yields the *acetate* of its enol form, *cyclohex*-1-*en*-1-*ol*, b.p. 158°.

TABLE 6

KETONES OF THE CYCLOPENTANONE SERIES

Compound	B.p.^{0}	Derivatives	Ref.
yclopentanone	130	semicarbazone m.p. 203; 2:4-dinitrophenylhydrazone m.p. 145^0	1
-Methylcyclopentan-1-one	139·5	semicarbazone m.p. 174^0	2
-Methylcyclopentan-1-one *dl*	144	semicarbazone m.p. 188^0 (dec.)	3
-Methylcyclopentan-1-one *d*	145	$[\alpha]^{27}_D$ +153·28^0; 2:4-dinitrophenylhydrazone m.p. 145^0	4
:2-Dimethylcyclopentan-1-one	144	semicarbazone m.p. 191^0	5
:5-Dimethylcyclopentan-1-one	147	semicarbazone m.p. 175^0	5
:4-Dimethylcyclopentan-1-one	153–155	Isomeric mixture with semi-carbazones m.p. 176^0 and 202^0	6
-*n*-Propylcyclopentan-1-one	191	semicarbazone m.p. 179^0	7
-Methyl-3-ethylcyclopentan-1-one	174	semicarbazone m.p. 170^0	7
-Methyl-4-ethylcyclopentan-1-one	180	semicarbazone m.p. 209^0	7
:2:4-Trimethylcyclopentan-1-one	158	semicarbazone m.p. 171^0; oxime m.p. 80^0	8
:3:4-Trimethylcyclopentan-1-one	175	semicarbazone m.p. 214^0 oxime m.p. 100^0	8
:4:4-Trimethyl-cyclopentan-1-one	73/37 mm.	semicarbazone m.p. 168^0	9
:2:5:5-Tetramethylcyclopentan-1-one	156	n^{20}_D 1·4288	5
-Methyl-2-*n*-amylcyclopentan-1-one	105/12 mm.	semicarbazones m.p. 166 and 192^0	10
:3-Diphenylcyclopentan-1-one *trans*	m.p. 98	2:4-dinitrophenylhydrazone m.p. 142^0	11
:4-Diphenylcyclopentan-1-one *cis*	m.p. 106	2:4-dinitrophenylhydrazone m.p. 208^0	11
:4-Diphenylcyclopentan-1-one *trans*	m.p. 177	2:4-dinitrophenylhydrazone m.p. 170^0	11
:5-Dimethyl-3:4-diphenylcyclopentan-1-one	m.p. 122		12

[1] *J. F. Thorpe* and *G. A. R. Kon*, Org. Synth., Coll. Vol. I, 192.
[2] *C. Montemartini*, Gazz., 1896, **26**, 259; *M. van Rysselberghe*, Bull. Soc. chim. Belg., 1926, **35**, 311.
[3] *C. D. Nenitzescu* and *C. N. Ionescu*, Chem. Ztbl., 1933, I, 1602; *M. Godchot*, Compt. rend., 1931, **192**, 962.
[4] *G. H. Stempel et al.*, J. Amer. chem. Soc., 1945, **67**, 344; *M. Godchot, G. Cauquil* and *R. Calas*, Bull. Soc. chim. Fr., 1939, [v], **6**, 1357; *N. D. Zelinsky*, Ber., 1902, **35**, 2489.
[5] *A. Haller* and *R. Cornubert*, Bull. Soc. chim. Fr., 1926, [iv], **39**, 1724; Compt. rend., 1914, **158**, 298, 1616; 1924, **179**, 315; 1925, **180**, 1988; 1925, **181**, 81.
[6] *F. Faltis* and *H. Wagner*, Ann., 1923, **433**, 103.
[7] *J. von Braun, W. Keller* and *K. Weissbach*, Ann., 1931, **490**, 179.
[8] *E. R. Buchman* and *H. Sargent*, J. org. Chem., 1942, **7**, 148, 154.
[9] *M. Qudrat-I-Khuda* and *A. Mukherji*, J. Indian chem. Soc., 1946, **23**, 435; *A. N. Dey* and *R. P. Linstead*, J. chem. Soc., 1935, 1063.
[10] *H. Staudinger* and *L. Ruzicka*, Helv., 1934, **7**, 258; *W. Treff* and *H. Werner*, Ber., 1933, **66**, 1521; *L. Ruzicka* and *M. Pfeiffer*, Helv., 1933, **16**, 1208.
[11] *H. Burton* and *C. W. Shoppee*, J. chem. Soc., 1939, 567.
[12] *F. R. Japp* and *W. Maitland*, J. chem. Soc., 1904, **85**, 1473.

Carbonyl compounds condense readily on the two activated methylene groups of cyclopentanone; thus benzaldehyde produces 2-mono- and 2:5-di-benzylidene derivatives (*C. Mentzel*, Ber., 1903, **36**, 1499; *O. Wallach*, Chem. Ztbl., 1908, I, 637; *R. Cornubert*, Compt. rend., 1930, **190**, 440) and aliphatic ketones react similarly (*B. Samdahl* and *B. Hansen*, J. Pharm. Chim. Paris, 1934, **19**, 573; *O. Wallach*, Ann., 1912, **394**, 362). In the presence of sodium ethoxide cyclopentanone self-condenses with the formation of *cyclopentylidenecyclopentanone*, b.p. 118^{0}/12 mm., and *dicyclopentylidenecyclopentanone*, m.p. 77^{0}, b.p. 190^{0}/12 mm. (*O. Wallach, Ber.*, 1896, **29**, 2962); under acidic conditions a different type of self-condensation occurs to yield the benzenoid hydrocarbon 1:2-3:4-5:6-tri-(trimethylene)benzene (*O. Wallach*, Ber., 1897, **30**, 1096). With formaldehyde under alkaline conditions the ketone gives the following series of *mono-*, *di-* and *tetra-hydroxymethyl-cyclopentanones* (*H. Gault* and *J. Skoda*, Bull. Soc. chim. Fr., 1946, **13**, 308, 316; *C. Mannich* and *W. Brose*, Ber. 1923, **56**, 833).

Cyclopentanone → 2-(CH_2OH)-cyclopentanone → 2,2-(CH_2OH)$_2$-cyclopentanone → 2,2,5,5-($HOCH_2$)$_2$(CH_2OH)$_2$-cyclopentanone

b.p 104^{0}/13 mm. *phenylhydrazone* m.p. 97^{0} | m.p. 27^{0} *phenylhydrazone* m.p. 117^{0} | m.p. 143^{0} *tetrabenzoate* m.p. 144^{0}

Acetaldehyde reacts in similar fashion (*J. Skoda*, Bull. Soc. chim. Fr., 1946, **13**, 327). Cyclopentanone with nitrous acid gives *bisoximinocyclopentanone*, m.p. 215^{0} (*W. Borsche*, Chem. Ztbl., 1909, II, 1549).

Homologues of cyclopentanones are prepared, like the parent ketone, by cyclisation of the corresponding substituted adipic acids (*G. Blanc*, Bull. Soc. chim. Fr., 1908, [iv], **3**, 780; *J. von Braun et al.*, Ann., 1931, **490**, 179). α-Methylated cyclopentanones may be obtained by direct methylation of the parent ketone with sodamide and methyl iodide; the four hydrogen atoms adjacent to the carbonyl group can be successively methylated but if the action of sodamide is carried still further the 2:2:5:5-tetramethylcyclopentanone undergoes fission to 2:2:5-trimethylcapramide (ref. 5, Table 6).

Alkylcyclopentanones are frequently encountered as degradation products of terpenes (*S. V. Hintikka*, Chem. Ztbl., 1914, I, 789; *S. Nametkin* and *L. Brüssoff*, Ann., 1927, **459**, 144) and naphthenic acids (*J. von Braun*, Ann., 1931, **490**, 100). The *trimethylcyclopentanone*, b.p. 174^{0}, *semicarbazone* m.p. 162^{0}, prepared by the latter author from the naphthenic acid $C_{10}H_{18}O_2$ (p. 114) was thought to be 3:3:4-trimethylcyclopentan-1-one but this has been disproved (ref. 8, Table 6). It has been reported that a ketone occurring in oil of pennyroyal is 2:4:4-*trimethylcyclopentan-1-one* although its *semicarbazone* (m.p. 158·5–159^{0}) does not agree in melting point with the derivative (m.p. 168^{0}) of the authentic substance (*Y. R. Naves*, Helv., 1944, **27**, 51).

The diphenylcyclopentanones are obtained by reduction of the anhydroacetonebenzils and related products (ref. 11, Table 6; *H. Weidlich et al.*, Ber., 1941, **74**, 1195; 1938, **71**, 1601).

Mild halogenation of cyclopentanone yields the 2-halogenated ketones. Thus chlorination yields *2-chlorocyclopentan-1-one*, b.p. 80°/10 mm. (*A. Kötz et al.*, Ann., 1913, **400**, 50; *M. Godchot* and *F. Taboury*, Compt. rend., 1913, **156**, 332; *P. D. Bartlett* and *R. V. White*, J. Amer. chem. Soc., 1934, **56**, 2785); hydrolysis furnishes *α-hydroxycyclopentanone*, b.p. 80°/12 mm. By the action of bromine a series of bromocyclopentanones may be produced as follows:

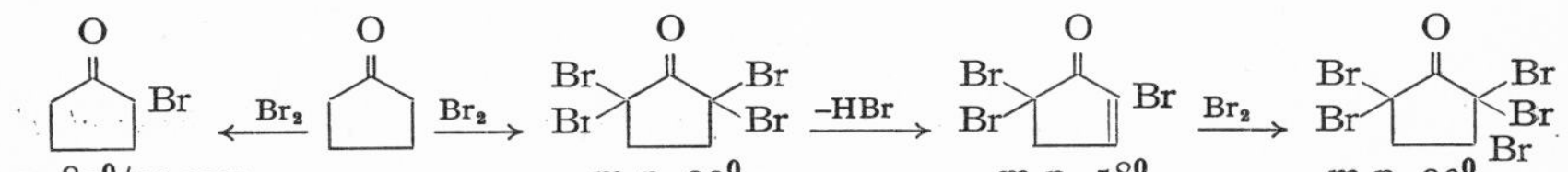

2-bromocyclopentanone, b.p. 82°/15 mm. $\xleftarrow{Br_2}$ cyclopentanone $\xrightarrow{Br_2}$ 2,2,5,5-tetrabromocyclopentanone, m.p. 99° $\xrightarrow{-HBr}$ tribromocyclopentenone, m.p. 58° $\xrightarrow{Br_2}$ pentabromocyclopentanone, m.p. 93°

(*M. Godchot et al.*, Compt. rend., 1912, **155**, 1522; Bull. Soc. chim. Fr., 1913, [iv], **13**, 542). The structures of the polybromo-compounds are not fully confirmed.

(*ii*) *Unsaturated monoketones*

The class of cyclopent-2-en-1-ones has been very well studied as some of its members, e.g. jasmone and pyrethrolone, are important natural products. The methods of preparation may be divided into five classes.

1. α-Chlorocyclopentanones may be dehydrohalogenated with dimethylaniline to furnish cyclopentenones although the yields are not good (*A. Kötz et al.*, Ann., 1913, **400**, 73; *M. Godchot* and *F. Taboury*, Compt. rend., 1913, **156**, 333; Bull. Soc. chim. Fr., 1913, [iv], **13**, 548); in this way the parent member of the series, **cyclopent-2-en-1-one** b.p. 135–137°, *semicarbazone* m.p. 214°, is obtained. Similarly dehydration of α-hydroxycyclopentanones gives members of this series e.g. *2-methylcyclopent-2-en-1-one*, b.p. 157°, *oxime* m.p. 128° (*M. Godchot*, Compt. rend., 1914, **158**, 506; *E. Looft*, Ber., 1894, **57**, 1538); this latter compound occurs naturally in light wood-tar oil (*E. Looft*, Ann., 1893, **275**, 377).

2. The intramolecular aldol condensation of γ-diketones leads to the production of cyclopentenones in yields of over 80% (*H. Hunsdiecker*, Ber., 1942, **75**, 455; *W. Borsche*, Ber., 1908, **41**, 194; *R. M. Acheson* and *R. Robinson*, J. chem. Soc., 1952, 1127), e.g.

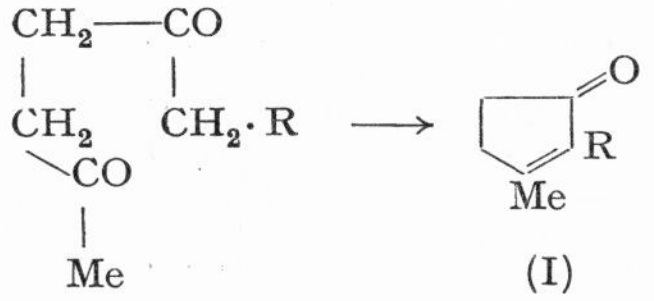

$$\mathrm{MeCO{\cdot}CH_2{\cdot}CH_2{\cdot}CO{\cdot}CH_2{\cdot}R} \longrightarrow \text{3-methyl-2-R-cyclopent-2-en-1-one (I)}$$

A range of compounds of general formula (I), where R = methyl to *n*-dodecyl, has been prepared by this method which has also been used for the synthesis of jasmone (p. 101). A modification of the method consists in the cyclisation of substituted acetoacetic esters followed by hydrolysis and decarboxylation, e.g.

R—CO CH_2—R_3 ⟶ (ring: R, R_3, R_1, =O, R_2)
R_1—CH   CO
CR_2
CO_2Et

(*H. A. Weidlich* and *G. H. Daniels*, Ber., 1939, **72**, 1590; *W. Borsche et al.*, Ber., 1906, **39**, 1813; 1908, **41**, 194).

3. The removal of the elements of water from $\gamma\delta$-unsaturated acids or γ-lactones produces cyclopentenones in 50% yields [*R. F. Frank et al.*, J. Amer. chem. Soc., 1944, **66**, 4; *P. A. Plattner* and *A. Pfau*, Helv., 1937, **20**, 1474; *L. J. Briusova* and *V. P. Osipova*, C.A., 1942, **36**, 3789; B.P. 453,518 (1936)]; *dihydrojasmone*, b.p. 91°/2 mm., *semicarbazone*, m.p. 174°, is formed thus:

Me
C_6H_{13}—C —— CH_2 $\xrightarrow{P_2O_5}$ C_5H_{11} (ring) Me
O CH_2 O=
CO

Dihydrojasmone

4. Work by Nazarov and his school has demonstrated that conjugated dienynes may be converted to cyclopentenones under acid conditions, often in high yield (see p. 75) (*I. N. Nazarov et al.*, C.A., 1946, **42**, 7731; 1949, **43**, 115, 1332; 1945, **39**, 503, 1620).

5. The nitrosochlorides of cyclopentene hydrocarbons may be dehydrochlorinated to cyclopentenone oximes whence the parent ketones may be obtained; the method is of little practical importance.

(ring) Me ⟶ (ring) Me, Cl, NO $\xrightarrow{NaOAc}$ (ring) Me, =NOH ⟶ (ring) Me, =O

(*I. J. Rinkes*, Rec. Trav. chim., 1938, **57**, 176).

3-iso**Propylcyclopent-2-en-1-one,** *tanacetophorone*, b.p. 84·5°/11 mm., *semicarbazone* m.p. 185°, occurs in heavy acetone oil and may be made from the cyclopropane derivative tanacetonedicarboxylic acid (p. 43) by distillation with soda-lime (*O. Wallach*, Ann., 1918, **414**, 200; *F. W. Semmler*, Ber., 1892, **25**, 3350; *H. Pringsheim* and *J. Bondi*, Ber., 1925, **58**, 1409).

Cyclopentenones with semicyclic double bonds are produced by condensation of aldehydes and ketones with cyclopentanones (*G. Vavon*, Bull. Soc. chim. Fr., 1928, [iv], **43**, 667; *R. Cornubert*, *ibid.*, 1930, **47**, 958). 2-iso*Propylidenecyclopentanone* has b.p. 79°/10 mm.; *oxime*, m.p. 83°.

For phenylated cyclopentenones see *H. Burton et al.*, J. chem. Soc., 1933, 720.

For the cyclopentenone derivatives jasmone, pyrethrone and cinerone see pp. 102 ff.

The interesting hexachlorocyclopentenones (I) b.p. 156°/80 mm., m.p. 28° and (II) b.p. 148°/75 mm., m.p. 92°

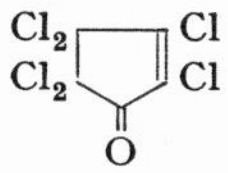

(I) 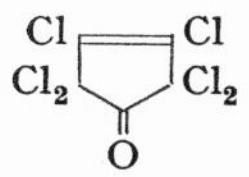 (II)

are prepared by oxidation of the corresponding hexachloro-1-hydroxycyclopentane-1-carboxylic acids; these latter are obtained by the exhaustive chlorination of benzene derivatives such as *o*-aminophenol and catechol (*T. Zincke et al.*, Ber., 1891, **24**, 926; 1892, **25**, 2697).

Benzil condenses with many ketones to yield substituted cyclopentenolones known generically as "anhydroacetonebenzils"; their formation may be illustrated by reference to the parent compound, *anhydroacetonebenzil* itself, 3:4-*diphenylcyclopent-2-en-4-ol-1-one*, m.p. 149°.

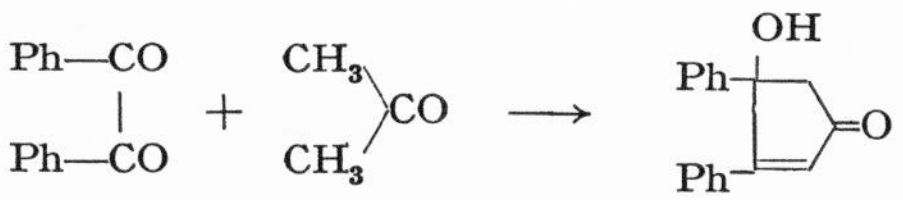

Anhydroacetone benzil

(*F. R. Japp et al.*, J. chem. Soc., 1885, **47**, 33; 1887, **51**, 425; 1897, **71**, 130; 1899, **75**, 1017; 1901, **79**, 1024; 1903, **83**, 279; 1904, **85**, 1473; 1905, **87**, 763; *F. W. Gray, ibid.*, 1909, **95**, 2131, 2138; *G. G. Henderson* and *R. H. Corstophine, ibid.*, 1901, **79**, 1256; *R. D. Abell, ibid.*, 1903, **83**, 360, 367; *D. Vorländer* and *H. von Liebig*, Ber., 1904, **37**, 1133). These compounds exhibit interesting anionotropic and prototropic rearrangements the details of which have been worked out by *H. Burton* and his collaborators (J. chem. Soc., 1933, 720; Chem. and Ind., 1932, **51**, 981; cf. also *C. F. H. Allen* and *E. W. Spanagel*, J. Amer. chem. Soc., 1932, **54**, 4338). For example the *dimethylanhydroacetonebenzil* (III) (m.p. 181°, 2:4-*dinitrophenylhydrazone* m.p. 218°) undergoes the following series of reactions:

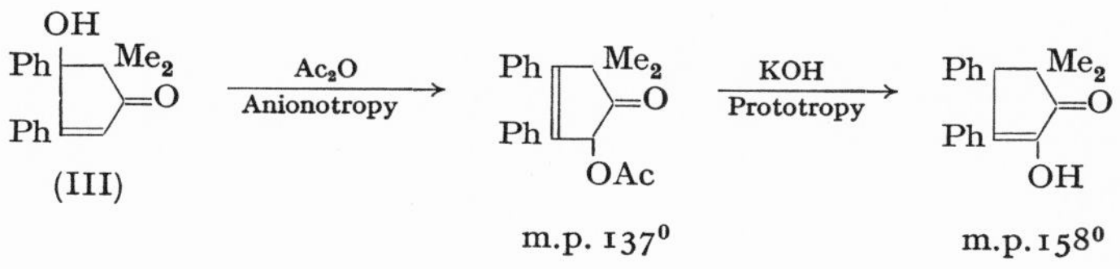

(III) —Ac_2O, Anionotropy→ m.p. 137° —KOH, Prototropy→ m.p. 158°

The final product is an α-diketone (enol form). With hydrochloric acid a similar reaction occurs with the formation of a chlorocyclopentenone:

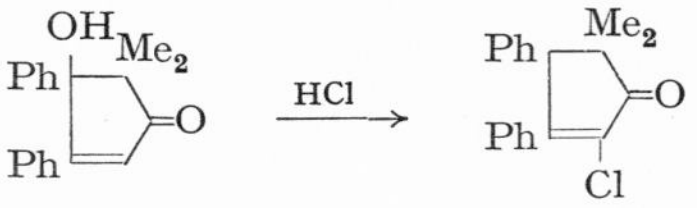

OH, Me_2, Ph, Ph, =O —HCl→ Ph, Me_2, =O, Ph, Cl

m.p. 129°

(*H. Burton* and *C. W. Shoppee,* J. chem. Soc., 1939, 1408; for further reactions see *C. F. H. Allen* and *J. W. Gates,* J. Amer. chem. Soc., 1942, **64,** 2123, 2120).

The best known representative of the *cyclopentadienones* is the *tetraphenyl* derivative (*tetracyclone*), a dark red compound, m.p. 218°; it is made by the dehydration of the *diphenylanhydroacetonebenzil,* m.p. 210°, prepared from benzil and dibenzyl ketone (*W. Dilthey et al.,* J. pr. Chem., 1930, [ii], **128,** 139; 1933, **139,** 10; 1934, **141,** 331).

Such highly arylated cyclopentadienones react readily as dienes in the Diels-Alder synthesis (*W. Dilthey et al.,* J. pr. Chem., 1937, **148,** 53; 1937, **149,** 85; Ber., 1933, **66,** 1627; 1934, **67,** 1959; *C. F. H. Allen* and *L. J. Sheps,* Canad. J. Res., 1934, **11,** 171); the adducts frequently lose carbon monoxide on heating and may also undergo dehydrogenation to yield a fully aromatic compound (*C. F. H. Allen* and *L. J. Sheps, loc. cit.*; *V. S. Abramov,* Brit. chem. Abstr., 1946, AII, 88; 1943, AII, 325; 1940, AII, 375; 1937, AII, 150), e.g.

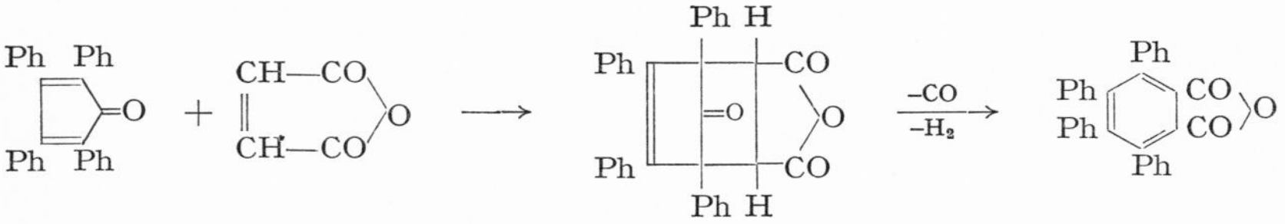

Ph Ph, =O, Ph Ph + CH—CO, CH—CO, O ⟶ Ph H, Ph, =O, CO, O, CO, Ph, Ph H —$-CO$, $-H_2$→ Ph, Ph, CO, O, Ph, CO, Ph

For an investigation of the ultra-violet absorption spectra of cyclopentenones see *H. S. French* and *L. Wiley,* J. Amer. chem. Soc., 1949, **71,** 3702.

(*iii*) *Hydroxycyclopentenones*

To this class belong the pyrethrolones and cinerolones, obtained from the closely related plant insecticides the pyrethrins and cinerins. The chemistry of these substances and of the nearly related jasmone is conveniently discussed here.

Pyrethrins, Cinerins and Jasmone

L. CROMBIE

The flower heads of pyrethrum, *Chrysanthemum cinerariifolium,* which is grown commercially in Kenya, Japan and Dalmatia, contain four highly insecticidal components. These are esters, each giving on hydrolysis an acid derived from cyclopropane and a keto-alcoholic derivative of cyclopentane. The four compounds are represented by the general formula (I):

$$\mathrm{Me(R')C{=}HC{-}C_3H_2Me_2{-}CO{\cdot}O{-}C_5H_3(Me)(R)({=}O)} \quad \text{(I)}$$

Pyrethrin I: R = $CH_2{\cdot}CH{:}CH{\cdot}CH{:}CH_2$; R′= Me.
Pyrethrin II: R = $CH_2{\cdot}CH{:}CH{\cdot}CH{:}CH_2$; R′= CO_2Me.
Cinerin I: R = $CH_2{\cdot}CH{:}CHMe$; R′= Me.
Cinerin II: R = $CH_2{\cdot}CH{:}CHMe$; R′= CO_2Me.

Pyrethrin I and cinerin I can exist in 16 stereoisomeric forms as each has two asymmetric centres and the possibility of geometrical isomerism about the cyclopropane ring and one carbon – carbon double bond. The compounds with the suffix II also show geometrical isomerism about a second double bond in the cyclopropane moiety and can exist in 32 forms.

Pyrethrins I and II were isolated in 1924 by H. Staudinger and L. Ruzicka as their impure but crystalline *semicarbazones* (*H. L. Haller* and *F. B. LaForge*, J. org. Chem., 1936, **1**, 38, give m.p. 118° and 165° resp.). The two cinerins have not themselves been isolated but their presence can be inferred from their degradation products and spectral evidence.

The structures of the hydrolysis (or alcoholysis) products of the mixed esters will first be considered. Two acids are produced, chrysanthemummonocarboxylic or chrysanthemic acid (II) and chrysanthemumdicarboxylic acid (III); these are separable by steam distillation.

$$\mathrm{Me_2C_3H(CO_2H){-}CH{=}CMe_2} \quad \text{(II)}$$

Chrysanthemic acid

$$\mathrm{Me_2C_3H(CO_2H){-}CH{=}C(Me){\cdot}CO_2H} \quad \text{(III)}$$

Chrysanthemum dicarboxylic acid

Natural (+)-trans-**chrysanthemic acid** (2-iso*butenyl*-3:3-*dimethylcyclopropane*-1-*carboxylic acid*), m.p. 17–21°, $[\alpha]_D^{16°}$ +26·1° ($CHCl_3$), *anilide* m.p. 101°, absorbs bromine equivalent to one double bond and on hydrogenation yields *dihydrochrysanthemic acid* (*anilide* m.p. 83°), saturated to bromine and permanganate. On ozonolysis (—)-*trans*-caronic acid (p. 42) and acetone are produced, leading at once to structure (II) (*H. Staudinger* and *L. Ruzicka*, Helv., 1924, **7**, 201).

Chrysanthemumdicarboxylic acid (3:3-*dimethyl-2-propenylcyclopropane*-1:2′-*dicarboxylic acid*), m.p. 164°, $[\alpha]_D^{17}$ +72·8° (methanol), *anilide* m.p. 205°, absorbs bromine but slowly. Slow distillation at atmospheric pressure eliminates CO_2

and produces an acid (IV). The structure of this is clear as ozonolysis yields (—)-*trans*-caronic acid and acetaldehyde. Formula (III), which explains the unreactivity of the double bond, was verified by ozonolysis to pyruvic acid and (—)-*trans*-caronic acid. Mild hydrolysis of pyrethrin II semicarbazone gives chrysanthemumdicarboxylic acid monomethyl ester (known as pyrethric acid) which when ozonised yields methyl pyruvate. This shows which carboxyl group is esterified with the ketol.

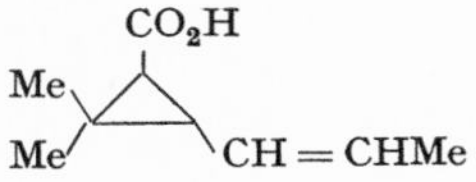

CO_2H
Me
Me — CH=CHMe

(IV)

(+)-**Pyrethrolone** [*3-methyl-2-penta-2′:4′-dienylcyclopent-2-en-4-ol-1-one*; (V), R = $CH_2CH:CH·CH:CH_2$], n_D^{25} 1·5424, $[\alpha]_D^{25}$ +11·7°, *semicarbazone* m.p. 219°, is best obtained from the pyrethrins by alcoholysis with methanolic sodium methoxide. The (±)-*pyrethrolone, semicarbazone*, m.p. 208°, which is also isolated may be an artefact. Pyrethrolone contains an $\alpha\beta$-unsaturated keto group (ultra-violet light absorption), an acetylatable hydroxyl group and three double bonds, one of which is difficult to hydrogenate. Pyrethrolone acetate undergoes hydrogenolysis to hexahydropyrethrone, first designated by Staudinger and Ruzicka as tetrahydropyrethrone. Hexahydropyrethrone gives laevulic and *n*-caproic acids on oxidation suggesting that it is either (VI) with R = $(CH_2)_4Me$ or (VII). Since the Beckmann rearrangement leads to a lactam and not an amide, structure (VI) is confirmed and the position of the keto grouping fixed.

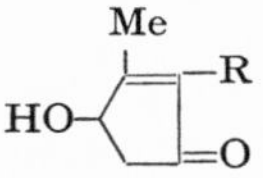

Me
—R
HO—
=O

(V)

The hydroxyl, for long placed in the position adjacent to the keto group, is now known to be in position 4. This has been confirmed by synthesis and agrees with the ready hydrogenolysis of its acetyl derivative.

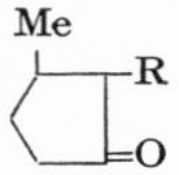

Me
—R
=O

(VI)

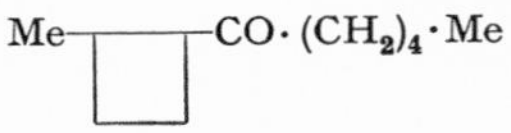

Me— —CO·$(CH_2)_4$·Me

(VII)

The Swiss authors originally considered the diene side chain of pyrethrolone (V) to be allenic, R = $CH_2·CH:C:CHMe$ but Ruzicka later altered this to R = CH:CH·CH:CH·Me. The main evidence for these opinions was the production of acetaldehyde on ozonolysis but pure specimens have been found to yield only formaldehyde; the acetaldehyde must have come from cinerolone contaminant. R is now considered to be $CH_2 \cdot CH:CH \cdot CH:CH_2$. The ultra-violet light absorption is best accounted for by the presence of two isolated chromophores, $C:CR \cdot C:O$ and $CH:CH \cdot CH:CH_2$ (*A. E. Gillam* and *T. F. West*, J. chem. Soc., 1942, 671) and recent synthetic work is in agreement.

(+)-**Cinerolone,** b.p. 124°/2 mm., n_D^{26} 1·5210, $[\alpha]_D^{25}$ +9·9°, *semicarbazone* m.p. 203°, *acetate semicarbazone* m.p. 152°, was separated from pyrethrolone by fractional distillation of the acetates and crystallisation of their semicarbazones. Some (±)-cinerolone was also isolated (*semicarbazone* m.p. 200°); again it may be an artefact (*F. B. LaForge* and *W. F. Barthel*, J. org. Chem., 1944, **9,** 242; 1945, **10,** 106, 114). It is formulated as (V), R = $CH_2 \cdot CH:CHMe$. Hydrogenation of the side chain gave (+)-*dihydrocinerolone*, 2-n-*butyl*-3-*methylcyclopent*-2-*en*-4-*ol*-1-*one*, b.p. 115–7°/1 mm., *semicarbazone* m.p. 197°. Replacement of the hydroxyl grouping by chlorine using thionyl chloride, and reductive elimination produced *dihydrocinerone*, 2-n-*butyl*-3-*methyl-cyclopent*-2-*en*-1-*one* (VIII, R = *n*-Bu), b.p. 115–7/17 mm., p-*nitrophenylhydrazone* m.p. 128–131°, 2:4-*dinitrophenylhydrazone* m.p. 156°, the structure of which was demonstrated by synthesis. Ozonolysis and Kuhn-Roth determination of the methyl groups of cinerolone demonstrate the 2′ position of the side chain unsaturation. As in pyrethrolone the hydroxyl is placed in position 4.

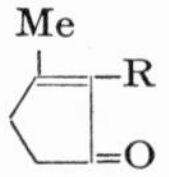

Me
—R
=O

(VIII)

Jasmone, (VIII, R = $CH_2 \cdot CH:CH \cdot Et$), 3-*methyl*-2-*pent*-2′-*enylcyclopent*-2-*en*-1-*one* b.p. 108–110°/5 mm., *semicarbazone* m.p. 200–202°, 2:4-*dinitrophenylhydrazone* m.p. 120°, is found in the oil of *Jasminium grandiflorum* and certain peppermint oils; it is closely related to cinerone and pyrethrone and has important uses in perfumery. The fundamental structure of jasmone is clear since hydrogenation (one mol. of H_2) yields *dihydrojasmone* b.p. 82°/0·7 mm. n_D^{25} 1·4764, *semicarbazone* m.p. 177°, 2:4-*dinitrophenylhydrazone* m.p. 122°, which is identical with tetrahydropyrethrone (*W. Treff* and *H. Werner*, Ber., 1933, **66,** 1521; *L. Ruzicka* and *M. Pfeiffer*, Helv., 1933, **16,** 1208). Oxidation shows that the side chain double bond is in the 2′ position; it has the *cis* configuration. Jasmone is probably identical with the dihydropyrethrone formed by reduction of pyrethrolone with aluminium amalgam (*L. Crombie* and *S. H. Harper*, J. chem. Soc., 1952, 869).

Synthesis of the rethrins and their degradation products*

(1) Cyclopropane acid fragment.

Chrysanthemic acid has been synthesised as follows (*H. Staudinger et al.*, Helv., 1924, **7**, 390; *S. H. Harper et al.*, J. chem. Soc., 1945, 283; J. Sci. Food and Agric., 1951, 94):

$$2\ CH_2{:}CMe{\cdot}CH_2Cl \xrightarrow{Mg} CH_2{:}CMe{\cdot}CH_2{\cdot}CH_2{\cdot}CMe{:}CH_2 \xrightarrow[\text{sulphonic acid}]{p\text{-Toluene-}}$$

$$Me_2C{:}CH{\cdot}CH{:}CMe_2 \xrightarrow{N_2CH_2CO_2Et} \text{(II)}$$

The synthetic acid was separated into the (±)-*cis* and (±)*trans* racemates and these resolved. Data are given in Table 7. The (+)-*trans* acid is identical with the natural acid.

TABLE 7

CHRYSANTHEMIC ACIDS

	[α]D**	M.p.	α-Phenylethylamine salt	
			m.p.	[α]D
(+)-trans	+14·2°	—	(—)*135–6°	— 3·5°
(—)-trans	—14·0°/20°	17–21°	(—)*126–8°	—14·3°
(+)-cis	+40·7°/20°	41–43°	—	—
(—)-cis	—40·8°/19°	41–43°	(+)*134–6°	+ 7·6°

* refers to the enantiomorph of α-phenylethylamine used.
** in ethanol

When treated with hot mineral acid the *cis* acid lactonises to give (IX) whilst the *trans* for steric reasons yields only the corresponding hydroxy-acid. Pyrolysis of chrysanthemic acid yields (X) with retention of optical activity (*L. Crombie, S. H. Harper* and *D. Thompson,* J. Sci. Food and Agric., 1951, 421).

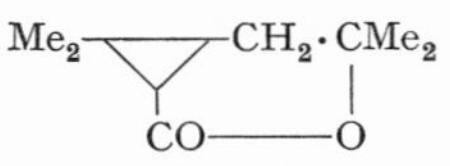

Me₂ (cyclopropane) —CH₂·CMe₂ / CO——O

(IX)

Me₂C—CH·CH:CMe₂ / CH₂ / O—CO

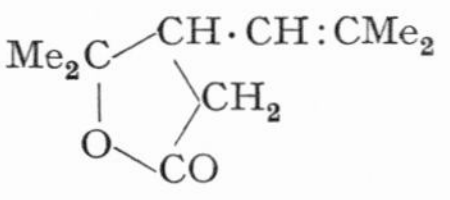

(X)

(2) Cyclopentenones.

These pyrethrin derivatives were first prepared by the Dieckmann reaction (*H. Staudinger* and *L. Ruzicka,* Helv., 1924, **7**, 245). An extension is the synthesis

* Rethrin is a generic term for the pyrethrins, cinerins and related esters. "Rethryl" is used to denote the radical formed by removal of the group R from (I). Thus cinerin I is but-2-enylrethrin I and pyrethrin II penta-2:4-dienylrethrin II. For details relating to nomenclature see *S. H. Harper,* Chem. and Ind., 1939, 636.

of a jasmone by *W. Treff* and *H. Werner* (Ber., 1935, **68,** 640); Reformatski reaction between ethyl laevulate and ethyl 2:4:5-tribromoheptanoate yields a mixture of lactone and diester which was treated with alcoholic hydrogen chloride and then cyclised using sodium.

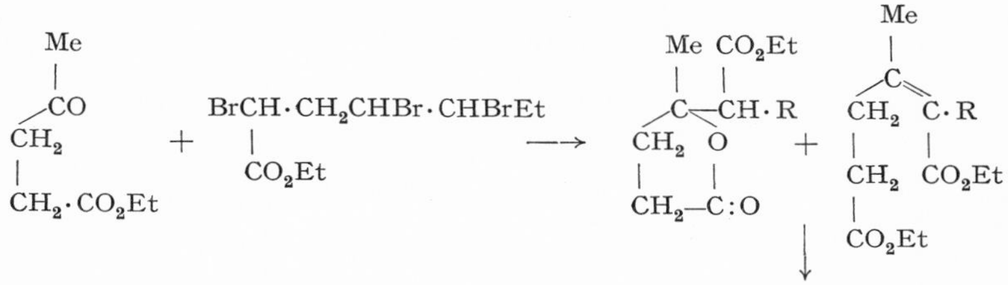

$Me\cdot CO\cdot CH_2\cdot CH_2\cdot CO_2Et$ + $BrCH(CO_2Et)\cdot CH_2CHBr\cdot CHBrEt$ ⟶ [lactone: $C(Me)$—$CH(CO_2Et)\cdot R$, CH_2—O, CH_2—$C{:}O$] + [diester: $C(Me)$=$C\cdot R$, CH_2 CO_2Et, CH_2, CO_2Et]

↓

(VIII), $R = CH_2\cdot CH{:}CHEt$

The alkali-catalysed cyclisation of 2:5-diketones has recently found considerable use and has been applied to the synthesis of jasmone (*H. Hunsdiecker,* Ber., 1942, **75,** 455, 460; *L. Crombie* and *S. H. Harper,* J. chem. Soc., 1951, 869).

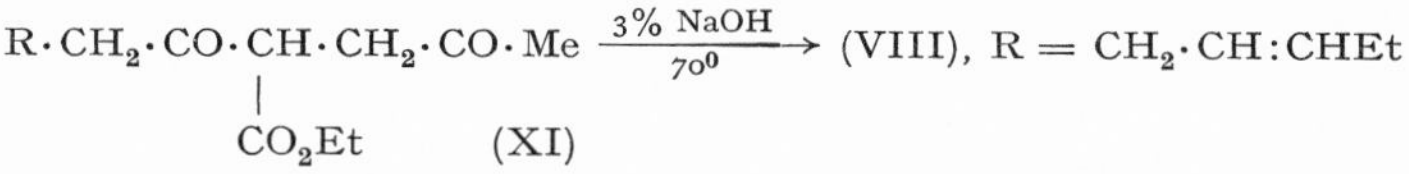

$$R\cdot CH_2\cdot CO\cdot CH(CO_2Et)\cdot CH_2\cdot CO\cdot Me \ (XI) \xrightarrow[70^0]{3\%\ NaOH} (VIII),\ R = CH_2\cdot CH{:}CHEt$$

cis and *trans*-Cinerones, *trans*-pyrethrone and a number of related ketones have been thus prepared (*L. Crombie, S. H. Harper et al.,* J. chem. Soc., 1946, 892; 1950, 1152, 3552; 1951, 2906). The naturally derived ketones have *cis*-side chains; *cis*-jasmone has a more subtle odour than *trans*. Data for some of them is summarised in Table 8.

TABLE 8

JASMONES, CINERONES AND PYRETHRONES

Compound	B.p.	n_D^{20}	Semicarbazone m.p.	2:4-Dinitrophenylhydrazone m.p.
asmone, (VIII) $R =$ *cis*-$CH_2\cdot CH{:}CHEt$	146°/27 mm.	1·4978	204–6°	117·5°
asmone, (VIII) $R =$ *trans*-$CH_2\cdot CH{:}CHEt$	142°/23 mm.	1·4974	200–2°	128·5°
inerone (VIII) $R =$ *cis*-$CH_2\cdot CH{:}CHMe$	120°/15 mm.	1·4982	214°	138°
inerone (VIII) $R =$ *trans*-$CH_2\cdot CH{:}CHMe$	119°/15 mm.	1·4983	220°	161°
yrethrone (VIII) $R =$ *trans*-$CH_2\cdot CH{:}CH\cdot CH{:}CH_2$	71°/0·08 mm.	1·5350	198–200°	—

Two main routes are used to reach compounds of type (XI):

(a) $$R\cdot CH_2\cdot CO_2H \xrightarrow{SOCl_2} R\cdot CH_2\cdot COCl \xrightarrow{MeCO\cdot CHNa\cdot CO_2Et}$$

$$R\cdot CH_2\cdot CO\cdot CH(COMe)\cdot CO_2Et \xrightarrow[MeOH]{NaOH} R\cdot CH_2\cdot CO\cdot CH_2\cdot CO_2Et\ (XII) \xrightarrow[Na]{BrCH_2\cdot CO\cdot Me} (XI)$$

(b)

$$RX \xrightarrow{Me\cdot CO\cdot CHNa\cdot CO_2Et} Me\cdot CO\cdot CHR\cdot CO_2Et \longrightarrow R\cdot CH_2\cdot CO\cdot Me$$

$$\xrightarrow[Et_2CO_3]{NaH\ or\ NaOEt} R\cdot CH_2\cdot CO\cdot CH_2\cdot CO_2Et \xrightarrow[Na]{BrCH_2\cdot CO\cdot Me} (XI)$$

Preparation of the stereochemically correct starting acid or halide presents a separate problem; configuration is normally preserved during the above steps.

(3) *Cyclopentenolones.*

Two main preparative routes have been used.

(a) A cyclopentanone of the type prepared above is converted to the 4-bromo-derivative with N-bromosuccinimide and then hydrolysed to the corresponding hydroxy compound directly by refluxing with an aqueous suspension of chalk or indirectly by proceeding *via* the acetate (*S. B. Soloway* and *F. B. LaForge*, J. Amer. chem. Soc., 1947, **69**, 979; *H. J. Dauben* and *E. Wenkert*, *ibid.*, 1947, **69**, 2075; *L. Crombie*, *M. Elliott* and *S. H. Harper*, J. chem. Soc., 1950, 971). The method is satisfactory only when the side chain is saturated.

(b) Pyruvaldehyde is condensed with the sodium salt of a substituted aceto-acetic acid (see above) at pH 8·5 and the intermediate diketone isolated on acidification. The latter is then cyclised with 2–3% sodium hydroxide (*M. Henze*, Z. physiol. Chem., 1930, **189**, 121; 1931, **200**, 101; 1931, **214**, 281; *M. S. Schechter*, *F. B. LaForge* and *N. Green*, J. Amer. chem. Soc., 1949, **71**, 1517, 3165). *L. Crombie* and *S. H. Harper* (Nature, 1949, **164**, 534; J. chem. Soc., 1950, 1152; cf. *ibid.*, 1951, 2445) have used this method to synthesise (±)-*cis*-2-but-2′-enyl-3-methylcyclopent-2-en-4-ol-1-one, (XII) b.p. 102–5°/0·05 mm., n_D^{20} 1·5120, *semicarbazone* m.p. 199°, *acetate semicarbazone* m.p. 148°, which was identical with natural racemic cinerolone. The former has been resolved using crystalline (+)-*trans*-chrysanthemic acid as the resolving agent (*F. B. LaForge* and *N. Green*, J. org. Chem., 1952, **17**, 1635). *trans*-Pyrethrolone has been prepared in a similar way (*L. Crombie*, *S. H. Harper* and *D. Thompson*, J. chem. Soc., 3951, 2906).

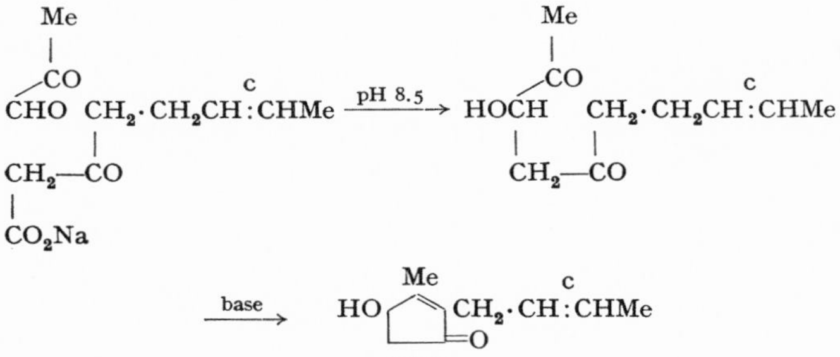
Me
CO
c
CHO CH2·CH2CH:CHMe
CH2—CO
CO2Na
pH 8.5
Me
CO
c
HOCH CH2·CH2CH:CHMe
CH2—CO
base
Me
c
HO
CH2·CH:CHMe
O

(XII)

(4) *Synthetic rethrins.*

Again two methods are available, though the first has been used only for the preparation of rethrins with saturated side chains.

(a) The (±)-4-bromocyclopentenone [see 3(a) above] is refluxed with the silver salt of chrysanthemummonocarboxylic acid in glacial acetic acid. Totally synthetic tetrahydropyrethrin I and dihydrocinerin I were thus prepared (*L. Crombie*, *M. Elliott* and *S. H. Harper*, J. chem. Soc., 1950, 971).

(b) Chrysanthemic acid chloride is esterified with a cyclopentenolone in the presence of pyridine. Using this method the total synthesis of racemic cinerin I, b.p. 132°/5 × 10^{-3}, n_D^{20} 1·5043, has been effected from racemic *cis*-cinerone (*L. Crombie* and *S. H. Harper*, *loc. cit.*). Pyrethrin I racemic only about the hydroxyl centre and with a *trans* (unnatural) side chain has also been made. A range of synthetic rethrins with more preparatively accessible side chains than those found in nature has been prepared. Allylrethrin, first synthesised by *M. S. Schechter et al.* (*loc. cit.*), which possesses considerable insecticidal potency (both paralytic action and kill) is produced commercially ("allethrin"). Unsaturation in the 2′ position of the side chain appears to be necessary for high potency and esters of the (+)-chrysanthemic acids are more effective than the (—)-. The geometrical configuration of the acid or side chain seems of only secondary importance.

Aspects of the chemistry of the pyrethrins have been reviewed by *S. H. Harper* (Annual Reports, 1948, **45**, 162; Pyrethrum Post, 1949, I, No. 3, 9; No. 4, 10). and an excellent account of the relationship between structure and insecticidal potency has been presented by *M. Elliott* (Pyrethrum Post, 1951, **2**, No. 3, 18). Ultra-violet and infra-red absorption data are available for many of the compounds described in this section.

(*iv*) 1:2-*Diketones*

Cyclopentane-1:2-dione, b.p. 97°/20 mm., m.p. 56° is obtained by the ketonic hydrolysis of the corresponding 3:5-dicarboxylic ester. It is strongly enolised forming salts of cyclopent-3-en-2-ol-1-one (*W. Dieckmann*, Ber., 1902, **35**, 3201; *G. Hesse* and *E. Bücking*, Ann., 1949, **563**, 31). The 3-*methyl*- (m.p. 106°, *phenylosazone* m.p. 136°) and 4-*methyl*- (b.p. 98°/7 mm.) homologues are similarly prepared (*G. Hesse* and *K. W. J. Böckmann*, Ann., 1949, **563**, 37). Another method of obtaining the 1:2-diones is by the halogenation of the corresponding cyclopentanone and hydrolysis of the resulting dihalide (*H. Gault* and *J. Burkhard*, Compt. rend., 1937, **205**, 1416). Oxidation by selenium dioxide of 2-methylcyclopent-2-en-1-one gives 2-*methylcyclopent*-2-*ene*-1:5-*dione* m.p. 85°, *quinoxaline* m.p. 135°, which has been employed as a dienophile in the Diels-Alder reaction. Although the last compound may be formally regarded as a lower vinylogue of the cycloheptatrienolone (tropolone) system it exhibits none of the quasi-aromatic properties associated with the latter structure (*E. Dane et al.*, Ann., 1937, **532**, 29).

On chlorination, cyclopentane-1:2-dione readily yields 3-*chlorocyclopentane*-1:2-*dione* m.p. 138° (*inter al.*, *G. Hesse* and *E. Bücking*, *loc. cit.*). Bromination of pyrogallol yields 3:4:5:5-*tetrabromocyclopent*-2-*ene*-1:2-*dione* (*xanthogallol*), orange plates m.p. 121°. The bromine atom in the 4-position is highly reactive and is replaceable by chlorine, hydroxyl, basic residues etc. (*F. J. Moore* and

R. M. Thomas, J. Amer. chem. Soc., 1917, **39**, 980; *A. Hantzsch* and *E. Strasser*, Ann., 1931, **488**, 205).

Reductic acid, m.p. 211° (dec.), *phenylosazone* m.p. 245° (dec.) is obtained from many carbohydrates by pyrolysis or treatment with dilute acids (*W. A. Sohn*, Angew. Chem., 1948, **60**, 284; for earlier references see *G. Hesse* and *E. Bücking*, Ann., 1949, **563**, 31). Its constitution was established by *T. Reichstein* and *R. Oppenauer* (Helv., 1933, **16**, 988; 1934, **17**, 390) as the stabilised enediol (I), *cyclopent-2-ene-2:3-diol-1-one*,

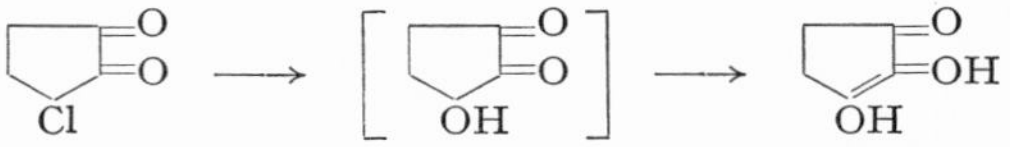

Cl (=O, =O) ⟶ [OH (=O, =O)] ⟶ OH (=O, =OH)

Reductic acid (I)

This constitution was confirmed by its later synthesis from 3-chlorocyclopentane-1:2-dione by acid hydrolysis as depicted above [*G. Hesse* and *E. Bücking*, *loc. cit.*; *A. L. M. van der Lande*, Dutch P., 57, 365; 58, 279 (1946)]. In conformation with this structure reductic acid is a strongly acidic, strongly reducing substance.

A methylreductic acid was thought to occur naturally as one of the constituents of an African arrow poison (*G. Hesse et al.*, Ann., 1936, **526**, 252; 1938, **537**, 67) but direct comparison with synthetic *methylreductic* acid, m.p. 71°, showed that the two are not identical (*G. Hesse* and *K. W. J. Böckmann*, Ann., 1949, **563**, 37).

(v) 1:3-Diketones

The parent substance of this series, **cyclopentane-1:3-dione,** m.p. 151–152°, has been isolated as a degradation product of aureomycin (*C. W. Waller et al.*, J. Amer. chem. Soc., 1952, **74**, 4978). There were earlier attempts at its synthesis; for review see *R. Richter*, Helv., 1949, **32**, 1123. Homologues of the series are known; *2-methylcyclopentane-1:3-dione*, m.p. 210·5–212·5°, is obtained in small yield by the catalytic hydrogenation of 2-methylcyclopentane-1:3:4-trione (*M. Orchin* and *L. W. Butz*, J. Amer. chem. Soc., 1943, **65**, 2296). The same compound has been obtained as a degradation product of the sapogenin sarcostin (*J. W. Cornforth* and *J. C. Earl*, J. chem. Soc., 1940, 1443). Other alkyl substituted 1:3-diones are obtained by the condensation of acyloins with ethyl acetate (*R. B. Woodward* and *E. R. Blout*, J. Amer. chem. Soc., 1943, **65**, 562; see p. 74 for details); in this way is made 4-n-*propyl-2-ethylcyclopentane-1:3-dione*, m.p. 119·4–120·5°. These 1:3-diones are strongly enolic, titrating as monobasic acids and giving a colouration with ferric chloride.

2:4-*Diphenylcyclopentane-1:3-dione*, m.p. 204–205°, is obtained by the action of sodium methoxide on either of the two diphenyllaevulic esters shown below or on the enol-lactones derived therefrom (*A. Maeder*, Helv., 1946, **29**, 120;

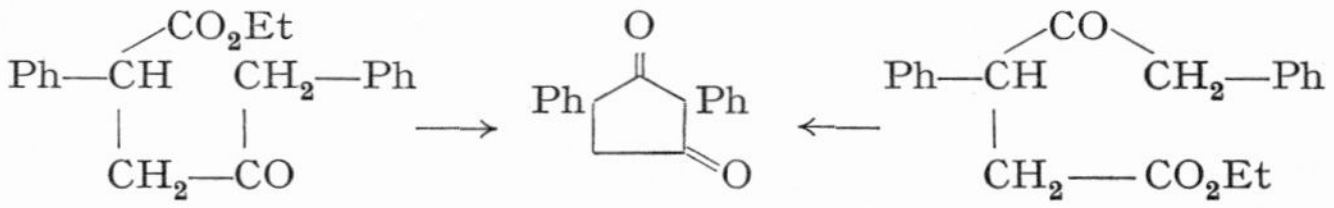

Ph—CH(CO_2Et) CH_2—Ph / CH_2—CO ⟶ (O, Ph, Ph, O ring) ⟵ Ph—CH—CO—CH_2—Ph / CH_2—CO_2Et

S. Eskola, Chem. Ztbl., 1943, II, 896; *P. Ruggli* and *J. Schmidlin*, Helv., 1946, **29**, 383, 396; 1944, **27**, 499).

2:4:5-*Triphenylcyclopent*-4-*ene*-1:3-*dione*, m.p. 167–168°, is readily prepared by the action of sodium methoxide on benzylidenediphenylmaleide (*C. F. Koelsch* and *S. Wawzonek*, J. org. Chem., 1941, **6**, 684).

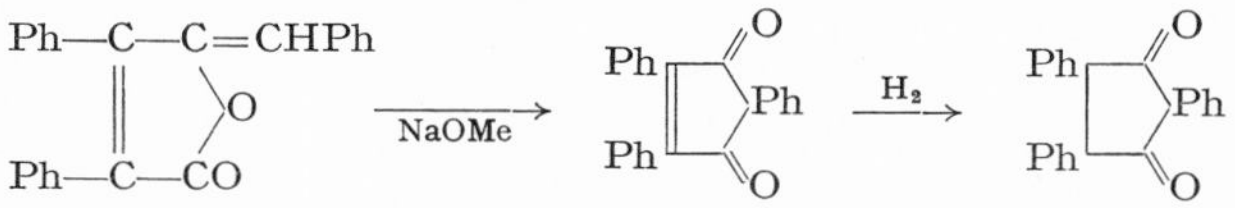

It exists solely in the diketone form shown and does not enolise. On reduction it furnishes 2:4:5-*triphenylcyclopentane*-1:3-*dione*, m.p. 203–204°, which exhibits the typical behaviour of a strongly enolised compound. Treatment of the unsaturated dione with ethyl bromoacetate gives the compound (I) which readily undergoes ring expansion to yield ethyl 3:4:6-triphenylgentisate (*C. F. Koelsch* and *S. Wawzonek*, J. Amer. chem. Soc., 1943, **65**, 755).

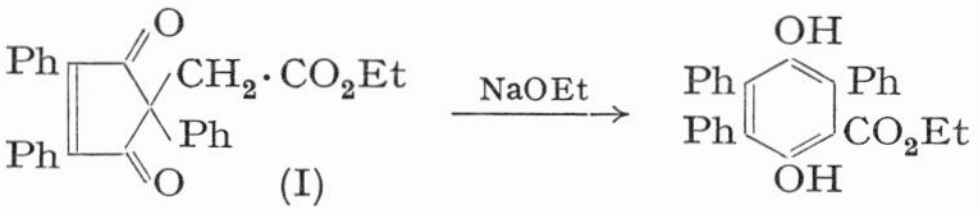

Chlorination of resorcinol yields 2:2:4:5-*tetrachlorocyclopent*-4-*ene*-1:3-*dione* m.p. 75°, b.p. 148°/27 mm. The primary product of this reaction is the perchloroacetylvinylacetic acid $CCl_3 \cdot CO \cdot CCl{:}CCl \cdot CCl_2 \cdot CO_2H$ which may be ring-closed by means of sulphuric acid to the cyclopentane derivative (*T. Zincke et al.*, Ber., 1891, **24**, 912; 1892, **25**, 2219; 1893, **26**, 513; *H. Landolt*, Ber., 1892, **25**, 842). A similar reaction has been carried out with βδ-dibromolaevulic acid, $CH_2Br \cdot CO \cdot CHBr \cdot CH_2 \cdot CO_2H$, which is converted to 2:5-*dibromocyclopent*-4-*ene*-1:3-*dione*, m.p. 99°, and the corresponding 2:2-*dibromo*-compound, m.p. 137°, on treatment with fuming sulphuric acid (*L. Wolff*, Ann., 1897, **294**, 183). 2:2:4:5-*Tetrabromocyclopent*-4-*ene*-1:3-*dione*, m.p. 143–144°, isomeric with xanthogallol (p. 105), is formed by the action of bromine on 4- or 5-nitro-2-acetamidophenol; with hypobromite solution bromoform and dibromomaleic acid are obtained (*G. Heller*, J. pr. Chem., 1931, [ii], **129**, 211).

(vi) Triketones

1:3:4-Triketones are usually made by the action of ethyl oxalate on ketones:

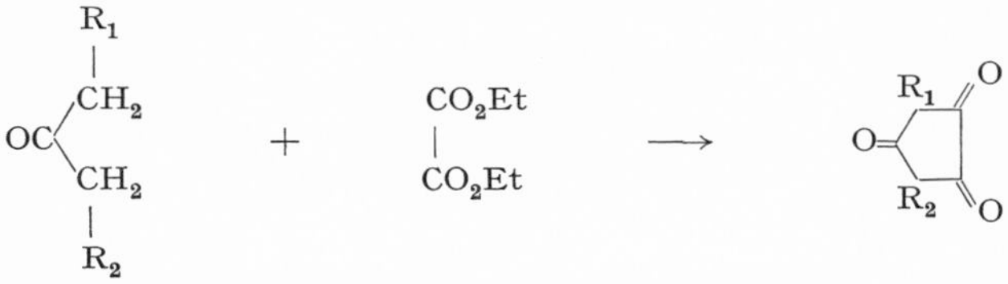

Thus methyl ethyl ketone gives 2-*methylcyclopentane*-1:3:4-*trione* m.p. 118° (*O. Diels et al.*, Ber., 1906, **39**, 1336); catalytic hydrogenation of this compound gives a mixture of *2-methylcyclopentan-2-ol-1:3-dione*, m.p. 166·8–168·2° (39%) and 2-methylcyclopentane-1:3-dione (p. 106) (15%) (*M. Orchin* and *L. W. Butz*, J. Amer. chem. Soc., 1943, **65**, 2296). Use of methyl benzyl ketone in the above synthesis gives *2-phenylcyclopentane-1:3:4-trione*, m.p. 167° (*W. Wislicenus* and *F. Melms*, Ann., 1924, **436**, 101). Dibenzyl ketone produces the mono-enolic form of *2:5-diphenylcyclopentane-1:3:4-trione* (I), m.p. 193°; this compound when heated undergoes an interesting rearrangement to *pulvinone* (*pulvinolactone*; II), m.p. 248° (*L. Claisen et al.*, Ber., 1894, **27**, 1353; Ann., 1895, **284**, 295; *P. Ruggli* and *J. Schmidlin*, Helv., 1944, **27**, 499; 1946, **29**, 383, 396).

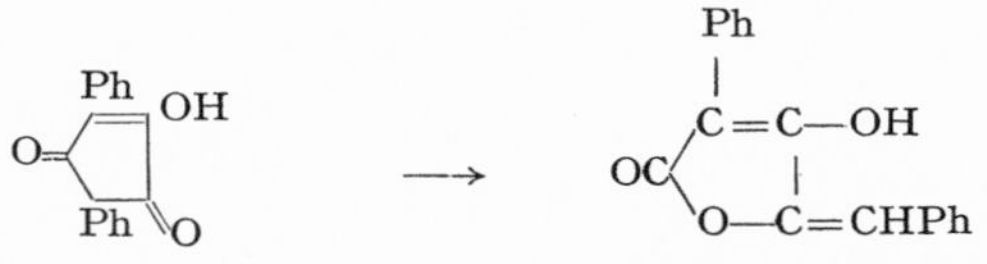

(I) → Pulvinolactone (II)

Chlorination of potassium chloranilate in water yields *2:2:5-trichlorocyclopentane-1:3:4-trione* m.p. 125°. Hydrolysis of xanthogallol (p. 105) gives the corresponding *tribromo*-compound (*xanthogallolic acid*) m.p. 137° (dec.), *enol acetate* m.p. 125–129° (*F. J. Moore* and *R. M. Thomas*, J. Amer. chem. Soc., 1917, **39**, 980; *A. Hantzsch* and *E. Strasser*, Ann., 1931, **488**, 205).

A series of interesting compounds may be obtained from triquinoyl, C_6O_6, a substance prepared by the oxidation of hexahydroxybenzene. This hexaketone undergoes a benzilic type of rearrangement to give *croconic acid, cyclopent-1-ene-1:2-diol-3:4:5-trione*, (*dimethyl ether* m.p. 114–115°); this may be oxidised to *leuconic acid, cyclopentanepentone*. The reduction product of triquinoyl, rhodizonic acid, $C_6H_2O_6$, similarly gives dihydrocroconic acid (cf. p. 16) (*R. Nietzki et al.*, Ber., 1885, **18**, 499, 1833; 1886, **19**, 293; 1887, **20**, 1617; 1890, **23**, 3136; *R. Malachowski* and *S. Prebendowski*, Ber., 1938, **71**, 2241; *O. Gelormini* and *N. E. Artz*, J. Amer. chem. Soc., 1930, **52**, 2483).

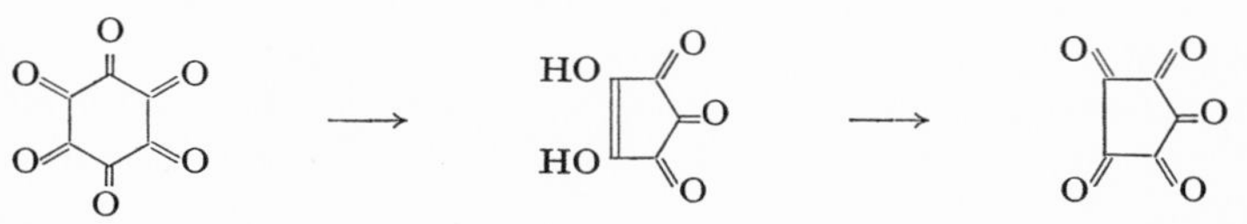

Triquinoyl → Croconic acid → Leuconic acid

Rhodizonic acid → Dihydrocroconic acid

(b) Exocyclic ketones

Acetylcyclopentane, b.p. 160°, *semicarbazone* m.p. 143°, is obtained from cyclopentane by reaction with acetyl chloride and aluminium chloride (*C. D. Nenitzescu* and *I. P. Cantuniari*, Ber., 1932, **65**, 810). 1-*Acetylmethyl*-1-*cyclopentane*, b.p. 60°/13 mm., *semicarbazone* m.p. 143°, is similarly prepared (*H. Meerwein*, Ann., 1918, **417**, 257; *S. Nametkin* and *M. Delektorsky*, Ber., 1924, **57**, 583).

2-*Acetyl*-1-*methylcyclopentane* is known in two isomeric modifications. The stable form (probably *trans*) b.p. 168°, *semicarbazone* m.p. 167°, is obtained by treating cyclohexane with acetyl chloride and aluminium chloride; the labile form (probably *cis*), *semicarbazone* m.p. 167° (depressed to 157° on admixture with the stable form) is prepared by the hydrogenation of the corresponding unsaturated ketone (*C. D. Nenitzescu et al.*, Ann., 1931, **491**, 189; Ber., 1932, **65**, 808, 1451; 1933, **66**, 969; *N. D. Zelinsky*, Ann., 1933, **508**, 115; *H. Hopff*, Ber., 1932, **65**, 482; *G. Wash et al.*, J. Amer. chem. Soc., 1941, **63**, 2975).

2-*Acetyl*-1-*phenylcyclopentane*, b.p. 165°/16 mm., is obtained by the interaction of cyclopentene, acetyl chloride, benzene and aluminium chloride (*C. D. Nenitzescu* and *I. G. Gavat*, Ann., 1935, **519**, 267). 2-*Benzoyl*-1-*methylcyclopentane*, b.p. 281°, is prepared by the Friedel-Crafts condensation of 1-methylcyclopentane-2-carboxylyl chloride and benzene (*G. Wash et al., loc. cit.*). 1:4-Dibenzoyl-1:4-dibromobutane often behaves chemically as 1-benzoyl-1:3-dibromo-2-phenylcyclopentan-2-ol (*T. Y. Kao*, J. Amer. chem. Soc., 1940, **62**, 356).

Cyclopentylacetone, b.p. 179°, *semicarbazone* m.p. 171–171·5°, is the product of the catalytic hydrogenation of cyclopentenylacetone (below).

1-*Acetylcyclopent*-1-*ene*, b.p. 69°/17 mm., n_D^{23} 1·4776, *semicarbazone* m.p. 212°, 2:4-*dinitrophenylhydrazone* m.p. 203° is readily prepared by the rearrangement of 1-ethynylcyclopentan-1-ol with formic acid. Its *oxime*, m.p. 91° is formed by the dehydrochlorination of the nitrosochloride of ethylidenecyclopentane (*W. S. Rapson* and *R. Robinson*, J. chem. Soc., 1935, 1285; *I. M. Heilbron et al., ibid.*, 1949, 1827).

1-*Acetyl*-2-*methylcyclopent*-1-*ene*, b.p. 185°/744 mm., *semicarbazone* m.p. 221°, *oxime* m.p. 85°, has been obtained from the internal aldol condensation of octane-2:7-dione and by the Friedel-Crafts acetylation of methylcyclopentane, methylcyclopentene and cyclohexane. Oxidation with permanganate yields pentan-4-one-1-carboxylic acid (*N. D. Zelinsky*, Ann., 1934, **508**, 115; *H. Hopff*, Ber., 1932, **65**, 483; *C. D. Nenitzescu et al.*, Ann., 1934, **510**, 269; Ber., 1932, **65**, 811, 1452; 1933, **66**, 969).

The reduction of mesityl oxide gives, presumably via a 1:6-diketone, 1-*acetyl*-2:4:4:5:5-*pentamethylcyclopent*-1-*ene*, b.p. 210–230° (*C. Harries*, Ann., 1897, **296**, 295; cf. also *W. Traube*, Ber., 1898, **31**, 2938; *L. Blaise*, Compt. rend., 1909, **148**, 852).

Cyclopentenylacetone, b.p. 184°, *semicarbazones* m.p. 138° and 189°, is prepared by the action of methylzinc iodide on the acid chlorides of cyclopentylideneacetic and cyclopentenylacetic acids (*G. A. R. Kon* and *R. P. Linstead*, J. chem. Soc., 1921, **119**, 810; 1925, **127**, 815; *J. von Braun* and *W. Rudolph*, Ber., 1934,

67, 278). 2-*Methylcyclopent-1-enylacetone,* b.p. 108°/27 mm. and 2-*methylcyclopentylideneacetone,* b.p. 82°/17 mm., are procured by the action of methylzinc iodide on the corresponding acid chlorides (*J. C. Bardhan,* J. chem. Soc., 1928, 2603). Similarly *cyclopent-1-enylacetophenone,* b.p. 163–165°/15 mm., is obtained by the action of phenylmagnesium bromide on the corresponding acid chloride (*M. D. Farrow* and *G. A. R. Kon, ibid.,* 1926, 2128).

Benzoylphenylcyclopentenes result from the pyrolysis of 1:4-dibenzoylbutane at 300° (*S. Skraup* and *S. Guggenheimer,* Ber., 1925, **58,** 2488).

4-*Cyclopent-1′-enylbut-3-en-2-one,*

$$\text{(cyclopentenyl)}\,CH{:}CH\cdot CO\cdot CH_3,$$

b.p. 87°/3 mm., an analogue of β-ionone, *semicarbazone* m.p. 186°, 2:4-*dinitrophenylhydrazone* m.p. 215°, may be obtained by condensing cyclopent-1-ene-1-aldehyde (p. 92) with acetone (*I. M. Heilbron et al.,* J. chem. Soc., 1949, 1827).

2-*Acetylcyclopentan-1-one,* b.p. 75°/8 mm., is obtained by the intramolecular cyclisation of hexan-5-one-1-carboxylic acid; the ring easily opens again under the influence of sodium ethoxide (*L. Blaise,* Compt. rend., 1909, **148,** 1401). Similarly 2-*acetyl-3-methylcyclopentan-1-one,* b.p. 90°/12 mm., may be derived from 3-methylhexan-5-one-1-carboxylic ester (*M. Godchot,* Compt. rend., 1923, **176,** 1151).

2-*Benzoylcyclopentan-1-one,* yellow leaflets m.p. 42°, b.p. 137°/3 mm., *semicarbazone* m.p. 223°, is prepared in analogous fashion from 5-phenylpentan-5-one-1-carboxylic ester (*H. Meerwein,* Ann., 1914, **405,** 129; *S. Grateau,* Compt. rend., 1930, **191,** 947; for examples of sterically hindered carbonyl groups in such diketones see *S. Grateau,* Compt. rend., 1933, **196,** 1619).

2:3-*Diacetyl-5-nitrocyclopenta-1:3-diene,* yellow crystals, m.p. 195° (dec.) is obtained in high yield by the condensation of nitromalonaldehyde with acetonylacetone (*W. Hale,* Ber., 1912, **45,** 1596). 1:3-Diacetylcyclopentane is an oxidation product of santene (Vol. IIB).

8. Carboxylic acids

(a) Carboxyl group attached to the ring

Cyclopentanecarboxylic acid, m.p. 4–5°, b.p. 215° may be prepared by decarboxylation of the 1:1-dicarboxylic acid, by carbonation of cyclopentylmagnesium chloride, by the action of hypobromite on acetylcyclopentane, by the hydrogenation of the cyclopentenecarboxylic acids and by the ring contraction of 2-chlorocyclohexan-1-one under the influence of alkali. 2-*Methylcyclopentane-1-carboxylic acid,* b.p. 219°, is prepared by similar means (*E. Haworth* and *W. H. Perkin,* Ber., 1893, **26,** 2246; *W. Stauss,* Ber., 1894, **27,** 1228; *E. Favorski,* Chem. Ztbl., 1915, I, 984; *H. Hopff,* Ber., 1932, **65,** 482; *C. D. Nenitzescu* and *I. P. Cantuniari,* Ber., 1932, **65,** 811).

1-**Methylcyclopentane-1-carboxylic acid,** b.p. 219°, is obtained by carbonation of the corresponding Grignard compound (*A. Tchitchibabin,* Chem. Ztbl., 1913,

I, 2028). 3-*Methylcyclopentane*-1-*carboxylic acid,* b.p. 116°/15 mm., is prepared similarly or by the ring contraction of 2-chloro-4-methylcyclohexanone (*N. D. Zelinsky,* Ber., 1902, **35,** 2690; *E. Favorski,* Chem. Ztbl., 1915, I, 984).

The three optically inactive isomers of 2:5-**dimethylcyclopentane**-1-**carboxylic acid** may be obtained by the condensation of 2:5-dibromohexane with ethyl sodiomalonate followed by hydrolysis and decarboxylation (*J. Wislicenus et al.,* Ber., 1901, **34,** 2565). The acids have been the subjects of an extensive investigation concerned with the steric hindrance of the carboxylic group (*T. L. Jacobs* and *W. H. Florsheim,* J. Amer. chem. Soc., 1950, **72,** 256, 261). The latter authors give the following constants for the purified acids: dl-2^t:5^c-*dimethylcyclopentane*-1^c-*carboxylic acid* m.p. 49–50°, *amide* m.p. 172·5–174°; meso-2^c:5^c-*dimethylcyclopentane*-1^c-*carboxylic acid,* m.p. 61–62°, *amide* m.p. 129–131°; meso-2^t:5^t-*dimethylcyclopentane*-1^c-*carboxylic acid* m.p. 73–75°, *amide* m.p. 170–172°.

1-iso*Propyl*-2-*methylcyclopentane*-1-*carboxylic acid* m.p. 53°, *anilide* m.p. 116° has been obtained by the action of methylmagnesium bromide on 1-*iso*propylcyclopentan-2-one-1-carboxylic ester, followed by obvious processes of dehydration and hydrogenation (*B. Shive et al.,* J. Amer. chem. Soc., 1941, **63,** 2979).

1-Phenylcyclopentane-1-carboxylic acid m.p. 157° and 3-*methyl*-1-*phenylcyclopentane*-1-*carboxylic acid* m.p. 124° are formed by mild oxidation of the corresponding aldehydes (*J. Lévy,* Compt. rend., 1928, **187,** 45).

Unsaturated monocarboxylic acids. A mixture of *cyclopent*-1-*ene*-1-*carboxylic acid* m.p. 124°, *anilide* m.p. 126° and *cyclopent*-2-*ene*-1-*carboxylic acid* b.p. 98°/7 mm., *anilide* m.p. 135° is obtained by the dehydration of cyclopentan-2-ol-1-carboxylic ester (*K. V. Bokril* and *K. S. Nargund,* Brit. chem. Abstr., 1940, AII, 308). The former acid is also made by the mild oxidation of the corresponding aldehyde (*E. Urion,* Compt. rend., 1930, **190,** 1512) and by the dehydration of cyclopentanone cyanohydrin via the unsaturated nitrile (*A. H. Cook* and *R. P. Linstead,* J. chem. Soc., 1934, 956).

Diethylaminoethyl esters of many cyclopentyl and cyclopentenyl acids have pronounced antispasmodic acitivity (*R. B. Moffett et al.,* J. Amer. chem. Soc., 1947, **69,** 1849).

Two modifications of **cyclopentane**-1:2-**dicarboxylic acid** are known. The *cis* form m.p. 135°, which forms an *anhydride* m.p. 72°, is obtained by treating the disodio-salt of pentane-1:1:5:5-tetracarboxylic ester with iodine followed by the usual decarboxylation procedure (*W. H. Perkin,* J. chem. Soc., 1894, **65,** 572; *A. Kötz* and *P. Spiess,* J. pr. Chem., 1901, [ii], **64,** 394; *A. Wassermann,* Helv., 1930, **13,** 207, 223). The *trans* acid, m.p. 182°, can be resolved by means of the *brucine* salt into the optical enantiomorphs m.p. 181°, $[\alpha]_D$ +87·6° and –85·9°. At 300° it undergoes rearrangement and dehydration to the cis-*anhydride* (*W. H. Perkin et al.,* J. chem. Soc., 1894, **65,** 588; 1914, **105,** 2639, 2664).

Catalytic hydrogenation of 1-methylcyclopent-2-ene-1:2-dicarboxylic acid gives a mixture of cis- and trans- 1-*methylcyclopentane*-1:2-*dicarboxylic* acids which may be transformed to the pure cis-*anhydride* b.p. 105–108°/6 mm.,; on hydrolysis the latter furnishes the pure cis-*acid* m.p. 128–129°. Boiling the *cis*-dimethyl ester with methanolic sodium methoxide results in conversion to the trans-*acid* m.p. 142–143·5° (*W. E. Bachmann* and *E. R. Struve*, J. Amer. chem. Soc., 1941, **63**, 1262; *P. C. Dutta*, J. Indian chem. Soc., 1940, **17**, 611).

cis-*Cyclopentane*-1:3-*dicarboxylic acid, norcamphoric acid*, m.p. 121° is formed by decarboxylation of the 1:1:3:3-tetracarboxylic acid; it may also be obtained by ozonolysis of bicyclo-[2:2:1]-hept-2-ene-2:3-dicarboxylic acid (*O. Diels* and *K. Alder*, Ann., 1930, **478**, 152). On being heated with hydrogen chloride the *cis*-acid undergoes partial rearrangement to the *trans*-isomer, m.p. 88° (*K. T. Pospischill*, Ber., 1898, **31**, 1950) which has been resolved (*W. H. Perkin* and *H. A. Scarborough*, J. chem. Soc., 1921, **119**, 1400). The *trans*-isomer is formed, together with *trans*-3-acetylcyclopentane-1-carboxylic acid, as an oxidation product of santene. Santenic acid, 1:2-dimethylcyclopentane-1:3-dicarboxylic acid and 1:2:2-trimethylcyclopentane-1:3-dicarboxylic acid, camphoric acid, see Vol. II B.

Cyclopentane-1:2:3-tricarboxylic acid, cis- m.p. 184°, trans- m.p. 170° is obtained from $\alpha\alpha'$-dibromoadipic ester and sodiomalonic or cyanoacetic ester (*W. H. Perkin et al., ibid.*, 1921, **119**, 1400; 1924, **125**, 1492).

Cyclopentane-1:2:4-*tricarboxylic acid* is obtained by the decarboxylation of the corresponding hexacarboxylic acid. The trans-*acid*, m.p. 129°, is obtained from the cis-*acid*, m.p. 148°, by heating with hydrochloric acid (*W. H. Perkin et al., ibid.*, 1900, **77**, 294; 1914, **105**, 2639).

Cyclopent-1-ene-1:2-dicarboxylic acid, m.p. 178°, is obtained from $\alpha\alpha'$-dibromopimelic acid by the action of sodium ethoxide and by the debromination of 1:2-dibromocyclopentane-1:2-dicarboxylic acid with alcoholic potassium iodide. The acid is converted into adipic acid by fusion with potassium hydroxide (*R. Willstätter*, Ber., 1895, **28**, 655).

Cyclopent-1-ene-1:3-dicarboxylic acid, m.p. 150·5°, is prepared from butane-1:1:4:4-tetracarboxylic ester by ring closure, reduction and dehydration (*B. L. Nandi*, J. Indian chem. Soc., 1934, **11**, 277).

(*b*) *Fatty acids*

Theo ccurrence of cyclopentane fatty acids in naphthenic acids is discussed on p. 114.

Cyclopentylacetic acid, b.p. 226–230°, *amide* m.p. 145°, has been prepared by reduction of 1-bromocyclopentyl-1-acetic acid and cyclopentenylacetic acid (*O. Wallach*, Ann., 1907, **353**, 304; *W. Hückel*, J. pr. Chem., 1935, [ii], **142**, 205).

α-*Cyclopentylpropionic acid*, b.p. 238·5–240°, *amide*, m.p. 136·5–137°, is prepared from cyclopentyl bromide and sodiomethylmalonic ester by decarboxylation of the *methylcyclopentylmalonic acid*, m.p. 150–151° (dec.) first obtained (*A. E. Tchitchibabin* and *S. I. Korjagin*, Bull. Acad. Sci. U.S.S.R., 1933, 273). For further cyclopentylpropionic acids see *R. D. Desai* and *G. S. Sahariya*, Brit. chem. Abstr., 1942, AII, 259.

Cyclopentylvaleric acid, m.p. 14–15°, b.p. 150°/9 mm., *amide* m.p. 135–136°, is prepared from cyclopentylpropyl bromide and malonic ester (*G. H. Coleman*, *J. E. Callen* and *C. A. Dornfeld*, J. Amer. chem. Soc., 1946, **68**, 1101).

a-Cyclopentylsuccinic acid m.p. 117°, p-*toluidide* m.p. 174°, is obtained by condensing cyclopentyl bromide with tricarballylic ester. It has been resolved by means of brucine to the optical enantiomorphs m.p. 135°, $[\alpha]_D^{26}$ +17·81° and −16·94° (*S. K. Ranganathan*, J. Indian chem. Soc., 1939, **16**, 107).

Cyclopent-1-enyl-and cyclopentylidene-acetic acids may be prepared by means of the Reformatsky reaction on cyclopentanones (*A. A. Goldberg* and *R. P. Linstead*, J. chem. Soc., 1928, 2343; *J. C. Bardhan*, *ibid.*, 1928, 2604); or by condensing cyclopentanones with malonic ester followcd by hydrolysis and decarboxylation of the cyclopentylidenemalonic esters thus formed (*G. A. R. Kon* and *E. A. Speight*, *ibid.*, 9126, 2727). In this way are prepared *cyclopentylideneacetic acid*, m.p. 64°, b.p. 130°/13 mm. which undergoes rearrangement under alkaline conditions to yield *cyclopent-1-ene-1-acetic acid*, m.p. 52°, and the 2-*methyl*-homologues, m.p. 108–109° and b.p. 150°/28 mm. respectively. These acids lose carbon dioxide on dry distillation to furnish methylenecyclopentanes (*O. Wallach*, Ann., 1909, **365**, 273; see also p. 80).

Cyclopent-2-ene-1-acetic acid, b.p. 95°/3 mm., is prepared from 3-chlorocyclopent-1-ene and sodiomalonic ester (*C. R. Noller* and *R. Adams*, J. Amer. chem. Soc., 1926, **48**, 2444; *G. A. R. Kon* and *R. P. Linstead*, J. chem. Soc., 1932, 2454). The higher cyclopentene fatty acids, hydnocarpic and chaulmoogric acids, are given a special discussion (p. 117 ff).

Cyclopentylidenesuccinic acid, m.p. 205–207° (dec.), *anhydride* m.p. 53–54°, and *cyclopent-1-enylsuccinic acid*, m.p. 157–159°, are formed by the condensation between cyclopentanone and succinic ester. They may be separated by chloroform (*H. Stobbe*, J. pr. Chem., 1914, [ii], **89**, 329).

Cyclopentane-1-acetic-1-carboxylic acid, m.p. 160°, *anhydride* m.p. 32°, is prepared from cyclopentylidenecyanoacetic ester by means of potassium cyanide followed by acid hydrolysis (*A. I. Vogel*, J. chem. Soc., 1928, 2010).

Cyclopent-2-ene-1-acetic-2-carboxylic acid, m.p. 156°, is obtained by the exhaustive methylation of 3-*methylaminocyclopentane-1-acetic-2:2-dicarboxylic acid* (itself prepared by the condensation of succindialdehyde, malonic acid and methylamine) (*C. Mannich* and *H. Budde*, Arch. Pharm., 1932, **270**, 286). Reduction gives the two *cyclopentane-1-acetic-2-carboxylic acids*, cis, m.p. 89°, trans, m.p. 66° (*A. H. Cook* and *R. P. Linstead*, J. chem. Soc., 1934, 956).

Cyclopentane-1:1-diacetic acid, m.p. 176–177°, *anhydride* m.p. 68°, is obtained by decarboxylation of the corresponding dimalonic acid (*G. A. R. Kon* and *J. F. Thorpe*, *ibid.*, 1919, **115**, 686). Similarly prepared are the 2-*methyl*-derivative m.p. 90–91°, *anhydride* m.p. 48° (*J. C. Bardhan*, *ibid.*, 1928, 2591) and the 3-*methyl*-homologue, m.p. 134–135° (*A. I. Vogel*, *ibid.*, 1931, 907).

A number of *cyclopentylidenemalonic esters* have been prepared by the condensation of cyclopentanones with malonic ester in the presence of acetic anhydride or zinc chloride (*G. A. R. Kon* and *E. A. Speight*, *ibid.*, 1926, 2727); the corresponding cyanoacetic esters are analogously obtained (*A. I. Vogel*, *ibid.*, 1928, 2010). Treatment with alkali causes the semicyclic double bond of these compounds to move into the ring.

Cyclopent-2-ene-1-malonic esters are procured by the action of 3-chlorocyclopent-1-enes on sodiomalonic ester (*C. R. Noller* and *R. Adams*, J. Amer. chem. Soc., 1926, **48**, 2444; *G. A. R. Kon* and *R. P. Linstead*, J. chem. Soc., 1932, 2454; B.P., 348,140, 349,455).

The substance obtained by the action of sodium ethoxide on laevulic ester is probably 4-*methylcyclopenta*-1:3-*diene*-1-*carboxylic*-2-*propionic acid*, m.p. 218° with decarboxylation to form first 4-*methylcyclopenta*-1:3-*diene*-2-*propionic acid*, m.p. 65° and then 4-*methyl*-2-*ethylcyclopenta*-1:3-*diene* (*P. Duden* and *R. Freydag*, Ber., 1903, **36**, 944).

Naphthenic acids

Although the main constituents of petroleum are of the hydrocarbon type they are accompanied by relatively small amounts of acidic substances; these are probably artefacts produced during the refining process in which atmospheric oxygen is involved. The components of this mixture of acids (which varies in composition according to the source of the petroleum) may be divided into three types.

(a) Acyclic acids (e.g. formic, oxalic, stearic, dimethylmaleic etc. For a full list see *K. Hancock* and *H. L. Lochte*, J. Amer. chem. Soc., 1939, **61**, 2448).

(b) Phenols (e.g. phenol, cresols, xylenols; *idem, ibid.*).

(c) Monocyclic acids or naphthenic acids.

This last class, the naphthenic acids, are by far the most important from a commercial point of view; the trade name "naphthenic acid" signifies the complex mixture of monocyclic acids obtained from petroleum. The alkali metal naphthenates find considerable use as emulsifying agents; other derivatives such as the sodium salt, the aluminium salt, the stannous salt and cellulose ester are incorporated in many greases and lubricants to obtain a desired texture. Copper and zinc naphthenates are effective insecticides and fungicides and are used to protect wood against dry rot and mildew. Heavy metal naphthenates find very wide application as driers. (For a full account of the technical preparation of the naphthenic acids and their derivatives and of the uses thereof see *E. R. Littmann* and *J. R. M. Klotz*, Chem. Reviews, 1942, **30**, 97.)

As a result of intensive investigations into the nature of the naphthenic acids from various sources it is fairly well established that they are in the main a mixture of substituted cyclopentane carboxylic and fatty acids. The isolation of cyclohexane acids has been reported (*H. G. Shultze*, *B. Shive* and *H. L. Lochte*, Ind. Eng. Chem. Anal. Ed., 1940, **12**, 262) but they were obtained from a cracked petroleum and the possibility remains that they are artefacts of the cracking process; however, *trans*-2:2:6-trimethylcyclohexane-1-carboxylic acid has been isolated from both Californian and Iranian straight run petroleum (*B. Shive et al.*, J. Amer. chem. Soc., 1942, **64**, 385; *T. Kennedy*, Nature, 1939, **144**, 832).

The isolation of pure individuals from this complex mixture of homologues is a tedious and difficult task as, owing to the very small boiling-point differences, fractional distillation is useless. The following indirect methods must therefore be employed.

(a) The amines derived from the acids by Schmidt or Hofmann degradation exhibit much greater differences in boiling point and lend themselves well to fractionation (*J. von Braun*, Ann., 1931, **490**, 105). An improved method of separation is based on the differential acid hydrolysis of the benzoyl derivatives (*J. von Braun* and *E. Anton*, Ber., 1933, **66**, 1373).

(b) Differential esterification (*K. Hancock* and *H. L. Lochte*, J. Amer. chem. Soc., 1939, **61**, 2448) or amide formation (*C. D. Nenitzescu et al.*, Ber., 1938, **71**, 2056) may also be used.

(c) *J. von Braun* succeeded in obtaining individual acids by the complex procedure indicated below (Ann., 1931, **490**, 114).

$$\underset{\text{(mixture)}}{R{\cdot}CO_2H} \xrightarrow[\text{HBr}]{\text{Reduction}} R{\cdot}CH_2Br \xrightarrow[\text{ester}]{\text{Sodiomalonic}} R{\cdot}CH_2{\cdot}CH(CO_2Et)_2$$

$$\xrightarrow{\text{Urea}} R{\cdot}CH_2{\cdot}CH\left\langle\begin{matrix}CO{\cdot}NH\\CO{\cdot}NH\end{matrix}\right\rangle CO \xrightarrow[\text{Degradation}]{\text{Fractionation}} \underset{\text{(pure compounds)}}{R{\cdot}CO_2H}$$

The fundamental points in the elucidation of the structure of the acids are to determine the nature of the carboxyl group (primary, secondary or tertiary) and its position (on the ring or in the side-chain). To accomplish this the following methods have been developed.

(a) *J. von Braun*'s imidochloride method has been frequently used to determine the nature of the carboxyl group (Ann., 1927, **453**, 113); it is based on the different behaviour of the substituted amides towards phosphorus pentachloride:

$$-CH_2{\cdot}CONHEt \longrightarrow -CCl_2{\cdot}CONHEt$$

$$>CH{\cdot}CONHEt \longrightarrow >CCl{\cdot}CONHEt$$

$$\rightarrow\!\!C{\cdot}CONHEt \longrightarrow \text{unchanged}$$

In the case of primary acids two chlorine atoms are introduced into the molecule, secondary acids yield a monochloro-compound whilst tertiary acids are unaffected.

(b) Another diagnostic method consists in pyrolysing the phenyl esters of the acids (*S. Skraup* and *O. Binder*, Ber., 1929, **62**, 1127). Primary esters are decarboxylated to give a hydrocarbon,

$$-CH_2{\cdot}CO_2Ph \longrightarrow -CH_2{\cdot}Ph + CO_2$$

whilst secondary esters yield *o*-hydroxyphenyl ketones

$$\rangle CH\cdot CO_2Ph \longrightarrow \rangle CH\cdot CO\text{-}C_6H_4\text{-}OH$$

and tertiary esters disproportionate into phenyl formate and an olefine.

$$\rangle C\cdot CO_2Ph \longrightarrow \rangle C{=} + H\cdot CO_2Ph$$

(c) Many methods are available for stepwise degradation of the side chain. One such procedure is based on the following series of reactions:

$$R\cdot CH_2\cdot CO_2H \longrightarrow R\cdot CH_2\cdot CH_2OH \longrightarrow R\cdot CH_2\cdot CH_2NH_2$$

$$\xrightarrow[\text{elimination}]{\text{Hofmann}} R\cdot CH{=}CH_2 \xrightarrow{O_3} R\cdot CO_2H$$

It is seen that the product possesses one carbon atom less than the starting material.

To eliminate two carbon atoms at a time the following variant may be adopted:

$$R\cdot CH_2\cdot CH_2\cdot CO_2H \longrightarrow R\cdot CH_2\cdot CH_2\cdot CONH_2 \longrightarrow R\cdot CH_2\cdot CH_2NH_2,$$

then proceeding as above (*J. von Braun et al.*, Ann., 1931, **490**, 109; 1929, **472**, 121).

Acids in which the carboxyl group is attached directly to the ring are converted by the first procedure of (c) into cyclic ketones; homologous acids do not give ketones until the above operations have been repeated the requisite number of times.

(d) The degradation method associated with the names of Barbier and Wieland is well known from its employment in the sterol field (*P. Barbier* and *L. Locquin*, Compt. rend., 1913, **156**, 1443; *H. Wieland et al.*, Z. physiol. Chem., 1926, **161**, 80):

$$R\cdot CH_2\cdot CO_2Et \xrightarrow{PhMgBr} R\cdot CH_2\cdot C(OH)Ph_2 \xrightarrow{CrO_3} R\cdot CO_2H$$

$$R\cdot CH_2\cdot C(OH)Ph_2 \searrow R\cdot CH{=}CPh_2 \nearrow R\cdot CO_2H$$

A new, but rather lengthy method used by *T. F. Gallagher* and *V. P. Hollander* eliminates two carbon atoms at a time (J. biol. Chem., 1946, **162**, 549).

$$R\cdot CH_2\cdot CH_2\cdot CO_2H \xrightarrow{\text{via acid chloride}} R\cdot CH_2\cdot CH_2\cdot CO\cdot CHN_2$$

$$R\cdot CH_2\cdot CH_2\cdot CO\cdot CHN_2 \xrightarrow{HCl} R\cdot CH_2\cdot CH_2\cdot CO\cdot CH_2Cl$$

$$R\cdot CH_2\cdot CH_2\cdot CO_2H \xrightarrow{LiMe} R\cdot CH_2\cdot CH_2\cdot CO\cdot CH_3 \xleftarrow{Zn} R\cdot CH_2\cdot CH_2\cdot CO\cdot CH_2Cl$$

$$R\cdot CH_2\cdot CH_2\cdot CO\cdot CH_3 \xrightarrow[-HBr]{Br_2} R\cdot CH{=}CH\cdot CO\cdot CH_3 \xrightarrow{CrO_3} R\cdot CO_2H$$

The sequence could no doubt be shortened by employing lithium methyl as shown.

A most elegant procedure devised by *K. Miescher* and his co-workers (Helv., 1944, **27**, 1815) eliminates three carbon atoms at a time.

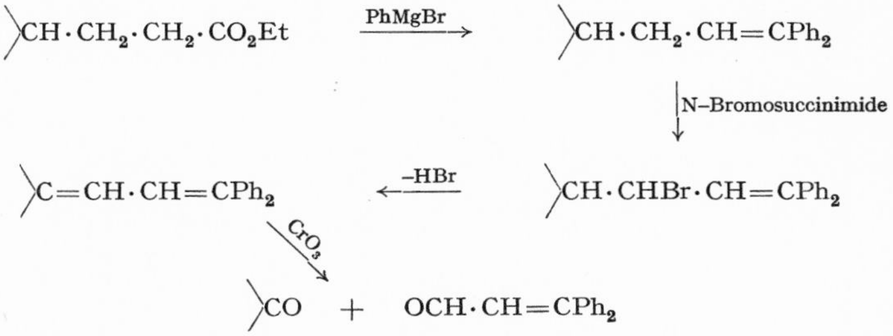

$$\rangle CH\cdot CH_2\cdot CH_2\cdot CO_2Et \xrightarrow{PhMgBr} \rangle CH\cdot CH_2\cdot CH{=}CPh_2$$

$$\downarrow \text{N-Bromosuccinimide}$$

$$\rangle C{=}CH\cdot CH{=}CPh_2 \xleftarrow{-HBr} \rangle CH\cdot CHBr\cdot CH{=}CPh_2$$

$$\xrightarrow{CrO_3} \rangle CO + OCH\cdot CH{=}CPh_2$$

The pure naphthenic acids isolated from petroleum and definitely identified are as follows: cyclopentanecarboxylic, cyclopentylacetic, 3-methylcyclopentylacetic (*C. D. Nenitzescu et al.*, Ber., 1938, **71**, 2056), *dl*-1:2:2-trimethylcyclopentane-1-carboxylic (*K. Hancock* and *H. L. Lochte*, J. Amer. chem. Soc., 1939, **61**, 2448), 4-methylcyclohexanecarboxylic (*H. G. Schutze et al.*, Ind. Eng. Chem. Anal. Ed., 1940, **12**, 262) and *trans*-2:2:6-trimethylcyclohexane-1-carboxylic acids (*B. Shive et al.*, J. Amer. chem. Soc., 1942, **64**, 385). The acid $C_{10}H_{18}O_2$, b.p. 145^0/14 mm., amide m.p. 124^0 isolated by *J. von Braun* from Rumanian petroleum was once given the structure 3:3:4-trimethylcyclopentylacetic acid (Ann., 1931, **490**, 100, 179; Ber., 1933, **66**, 1500) but later work has shown this formulation to be in error (*E. R. Buchmann* and *H. Sargent*, J. org. Chem., 1942, **7**, 148).

(For further information on the naphthenic acids see *N. Chercheffsky*, "Les acides de naphthes et leur application", Paris, 1910; *M. Naphtali*, "Naphtensäuren und Naphtensulfosäuren", Stuttgart 1934, *M. Naphtali*, "Chemie, Technologie und Analyse der Naphtensäuren", Stuttgart, 1927; *J. von Braun*, Angew. Chem., 1928, **41**, 29; 1931, **44**, 661; 1932, **45**, 231).

Hydnocarpic, chaulmoogric, gorlic and related acids

L. CROMBIE

The seed oils of members of the *Flacourtiaceae*, e.g. chaulmoogra oil from *Hydnocarpus alcalae*, contain the glycerides of an unusual group of cyclopentene acids of general formula (I).

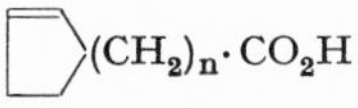

$$\text{(cyclopentenyl)}\rangle(CH_2)_n\cdot CO_2H$$

(I)

The two acids present in predominant amount are chaulmoogric [(I), n = 12] and hydnocarpic [(I), n = 10]. Minor amounts of their lower homologues are also found. These are alepric [(I), n = 8], aleprylic [(I), n = 6], aleprestic [(I), n = 4] and aleprolic [(I), n = 0]. Furthermore a diene acid, gorlic acid (II) may occur in substantial quantity. Certain physical properties of these acids are summarised in Table 9 (*H. I. Cole* and *H. T. Cardoso*, J. Amer. chem. Soc., 1939, **61**, 2351.)

$$\text{C}_5\text{H}_7\text{·}(CH_2)_6\cdot CH{:}CH\cdot(CH_2)_4\cdot CO_2H$$

(II)

Chaulmoogra oil has long been used in the East as a native remedy for tuberculosis and leprosy. R. Adams has prepared a large number of analogues of the cyclopentene acids and these have been examined for *in vitro* anti-bacterial activity against *B. lepreae*. (For a summary see *A. W. Ralston*, "Fatty Acids and their Derivatives", p. 213; Wiley, 1948).

TABLE 9

CHAULMOOGRIC AND RELATED CYCLOPENTENE FATTY ACIDS

	Acid			Ethyl ester	
	m.p.	$[\alpha]_D^{25}$*	b.p./10mm	$[\alpha]_D^{25}$*	n_D^{20}
Chaulmoogric acid	68·5°	60·3	222°	55·4°	1·4592
Hydnocarpic acid	60·5°	69·3°	200°	61·9°	1·4578
Alepric acid	48·0°	77·1°	174°	66·5°	1·4562
Aleprylic acid	32·0°	90·8°	148°	79·1°	1·4550
Aleprestic acid	–	100·5°	122°	86·5°	1·4538
Aleprolic acid	–	120·5°	70°	101·8°	1·4514
Gorlic acid	6·0°	60·7°	232°	55·6°	1·4667

* Solvent $CHCl_3$

The isolation of hydnocarpic and chaulmoogric acids and the determination of their structures is largely due to Power and co-workers (*F. B. Power* and *F. H. Gornall*, J. chem. Soc., 1904, **85**, 838, 851; *F. B. Power* and *M. Barrowcliff*, *ibid.*, 1905, **87**, 884; 1907, **91**, 557) though *R. L. Shriner* and *R. Adams* (J. Amer. chem. Soc., 1925, **47**, 2727) have extended and corrected this work.

Chaulmoogric acid, $C_{18}H_{32}O_2$, absorbs two atoms of bromine only, and on hydrogenation gives a *dihydro*-compound, m.p. 73° (*ethyl ester*, b.p. 216–8°/0·12 mm.). It must therefore contain one ring and a double bond. On oxidation with alkaline permanganate *pentadecane-1:3:15-tricarboxylic acid* $CO_2H\cdot(CH_2)_2\cdot CH(CO_2H)\cdot(CH_2)_{12}\cdot CO_2H$ (*trimethyl ester* m.p. 37–8°) was isolated; further oxidation with permanganate gave pentadecan-3-one-1:15-dicarboxylic acid which could be degraded to malonic acid and dodecane-1:12-dicarboxylic acid. The side chain thus contains 13 carbon atoms and this suggests (I), (n = 12). Ozonolysis and oxidation of the ozonide gave pentadecane-3-one-1:15-dicarboxylic acid and final confirmation of the presence of a five-membered ring came from the synthesis of dihydrochaulmoogric acid (*C. R. Noller* and *R. Adams*, J. Amer. Chem. Soc., 1926, **48**, 1080):

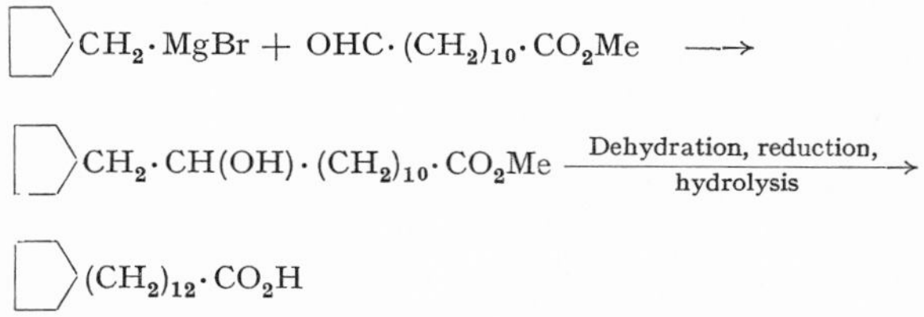

$$\text{C}_5\text{H}_9\cdot CH_2\cdot MgBr + OHC\cdot(CH_2)_{10}\cdot CO_2Me \longrightarrow$$

$$\text{C}_5\text{H}_9\cdot CH_2\cdot CH(OH)\cdot(CH_2)_{10}\cdot CO_2Me \xrightarrow[\text{hydrolysis}]{\text{Dehydration, reduction,}}$$

$$\text{C}_5\text{H}_9\cdot(CH_2)_{12}\cdot CO_2H$$

Chaulmoogric acid is therefore 12-*cyclopent-2'-enyldodecane*-1-*carboxylic acid*.

Racemic chaulmoogric acid has been synthesised by *G. A. Perkin* and *A. O. Cruz* (*ibid.*, 1927, **49**, 1070):

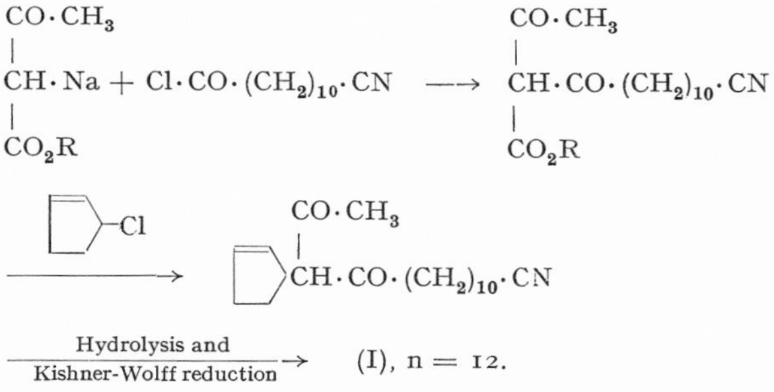

$$R'O_2C\cdot CH(Na)\cdot CO\cdot CH_3 + Cl\cdot CO\cdot(CH_2)_{10}\cdot CN \longrightarrow R'O_2C\cdot CH(CO\cdot CH_3)\cdot CO\cdot(CH_2)_{10}\cdot CN$$

(in the printed scheme: CO·CH₃ / CH·Na / CO₂R + Cl·CO·(CH₂)₁₀·CN ⟶ CO·CH₃ / CH·CO·(CH₂)₁₀·CN / CO₂R)

$$\xrightarrow{\text{cyclopentenyl chloride (ring)-Cl}} \text{(cyclopentenyl)}CH(CO\cdot CH_3)\cdot CO\cdot(CH_2)_{10}\cdot CN$$

$$\xrightarrow[\text{Kishner-Wolff reduction}]{\text{Hydrolysis and}} \text{(I), n = 12.}$$

Though the general behaviour of the synthetic acid was similar to that of the natural acid a direct comparison was not possible as it was not resolved. Racemic natural chaulmoogric acid has since been prepared by heating the active amide with P_2O_5 and hydrolysing the resultant racemic nitrile.

The structure of **hydnocarpic acid** as bisnorchaulmoogric acid follows directly from that of chaulmoogric acid. When ethyl hydnocarpate is reduced by the Bouveault-Blanc process, an alcohol is obtained which can be converted via its bromide and reaction with diethyl malonate to chaulmoogric acid, identical with the natural material (*W. M. Stanley* and *R. Adams*, *ibid.*, 1929, **51**, 1515). It is therefore [(I), n = 10], 10-*cyclopent-2'-enyldecane*-1-*carboxylic acid*.

Indications that chaulmoogra and related oils contain a diethenoid liquid acid were given by *A. L. Dean* and *R. Wrenshall* (*ibid.*, 1920, **42**, 2626, cf. U.S. Pub.

Health Service Bull., 1924, No. 141, 24). *E. Andre* and *D. Jouatte* (Bull. Soc. chim. Fr., 1928, [iv], **43**, 347) obtained a similar acid from Gorli seed oil and named it **gorlic acid,** whilst *H. Paget* (J. chem. Soc., 1937, 955) obtained what was apparently the same acid from sapucainha oil (derived from *Carpotroche brasiliensis* Endl.). On hydrogenation gorlic acid absorbs two mols of hydrogen and dihydrochaulmoogric acid is produced. Gorlic acid must be (II) since oxidation with chromic acid produces nonane-1:3:9-tricarboxylic acid and adipic acid.

Analysis for component acids of a number of oils of this type have been reported. Thus the following data are given for *Hydnocarpus wightiana* oil: hydnocarpic acid 48·7, chaulmoogric acid 27, gorlic acid 12·2, oleic acid 6·5, palmitic acid 1·8, other lower homologues of chaulmoogric acid 3·4 %.

For further information on these acids and their analogues see *R. Adams et al.*, J. Amer. chem. Soc., 1926, **48**, 1080; 1927, **49**, 2934, 2940; 1928, **50**, 1475, 1503; 1932, **54**, 1548; *N. G. Buu-Hoi et al.*, Compt. rend., 1946, **222**, 224; 1941, **212**, 1105; Bull. Soc. chim. Fr., 1942, [v], **9**, 99, 107, 355; Ann. Chim., 1944, **19**, 446; Ber., 1942, **75**, 1181; *K. S. Nargund et al.*, Brit. chem. Abstr., 1942, AII, 282; 1941, AII, 251; *M. M. Katznelsov* and *M. S. Kondakova, ibid.*, 1938, AII, 97; *B. Baltzly, W. S. Ide* and *J. S. Buck*, J. Amer. chem. Soc., 1942, **64**, 2514.

(c) Hydroxy-acids

Cyclopentan-1-ol-1-carboxylic acid, m.p. 103°, is obtained by the hydrolysis of cyclopentanone cyanohydrin. Similarly prepared are the 2-*methyl*-, m.p. 59° and the 3-*methyl*-homologue, m.p. 87° (*C. Gärtner*, Ann., 1893, **275**, 333; *B. Tchoubar* and *C. Collin*, Bull. Soc. chim. Fr., 1947, **14**, 680).

2:3:4:4:5:5-*Hexachlorocyclopentan-1-ol-1-carboxylic acid,* m.p. 111°, is obtained by chlorinating cyclohexane-1:2-dione and treating the product with alkali. On boiling with water it gives perchloroindene (*T. Zincke et al.*, Ber., 1890, **23**, 824; Ann., 1893, **272**, 243).

Reduction of diphenacylacetic acid (I) with sodium amalgam gives 3^t:4^t-*diphenylcyclopentane*-3^c:4^c-*diol*-1^c-*carboxylic acid,* m.p. 163°, *methyl ester* m.p. 126° and 3^c:4^c-*diphenylcyclopentane*-3^t:4^t-*diol*-1^c-*carboxylic acid,* m.p. 210°, *methyl ester* m.p. 134–135°.

Ph—CO—CH_2
　　　　　　>CH·CO_2H
Ph—CO—CH_2
(I)

⟶

OH
Ph
　　>CO_2H
Ph
OH

The similarly substituted malonic ester affords a single 3:4-*diphenylcyclopentane*-3:4-*diol*-1:1-*dicarboxylic acid,* m.p. 210–215° (dec.), *dimethyl ester* m.p. 209°, presumably the meso-form (*E. Larsson*, Brit. chem. Abstr., 1947, AII, 400).

2:2:4-*Trichlorocyclopent-3-ene-1:3-diol-1-carboxylic acid,* m.p. 176–177°, is one of the products of the alkaline chlorination of phenol (*A. Hantzsch*, Ber., 1889, **22** 2827; *C. Hoffmann*, Ber., 1889, **22**, 1264).

Ethyl cyclopentan-1-ol-1-acetate, b.p. 107°/11 mm., is obtained by the action of zinc and ethyl bromoacetate on cyclopentanone. Higher homologues are similarly prepared (*O. Wallach et al.*, Ann., 1902, **323**, 159; 1906, **347**, 325; 1909, **365**, 272; 1901, **314**, 160; *W. H. Perkin*, Ber., 1909, **42**, 147).

Cyclopentene oxide condenses with malonic ester to give, after hydrolysis and decarboxylation, trans-*cyclopentan-1-ol-2-acetic acid*, m.p. 53·4°; on being heated it forms the cis-*lactone* (*W. E. Grigsby et al.*, J. Amer. chem. Soc., 1942, **64**, 2606; *R. B. Rothstein* and *M. Rothstein*, Compt. rend., 1939, **209**, 761).

(*d*) *Keto-acids*

Ethyl cyclopentan-1-one-2-carboxylate, b.p. 117°/26 mm., is prepared by the cyclisation of ethyl adipate (p. 73). It displays the typical reactions of a β-keto-ester; although containing only 4% of enol it is strongly acidic and the salts are not decomposed by carbon dioxide, thus showing that acidity and enol content are not related. Homologues are prepared in the usual fashion. Ketonic hydrolysis gives cyclopentanone and acid hydrolysis regenerates adipic acid (*W. Dieckmann*, Ber., 1922, **55**, 2473; Ann., 1901, **317**, 27; *L. Bouveault* and *R. Locquin*, Compt. rend., 1908, **146**, 138; *A. Haller* and *R. Cornubert*, Bull. Soc. chim. Fr., 1926, [iv], **39**, 1621; *R. N. Chakravarti*, J. chem. Soc., 1947, 1028; *S. N. Naumov* and *L. P. Danilewski*, Brit. chem. Abstr., 1940, A II, 46). The corresponding 1-*imino-2-nitrile*, m.p. 147°, is obtained by the Thorpe cyclisation of adiponitrile (p. 74). Acid treatment converts it first into 2-*cyanocyclopentan-1-one*, b.p. 229° and finally into cyclopentanone (*S. R. Best* and *J. F. Thorpe*, J. chem. Soc., 1909, **95**, 685).

Ethyl cyclopentan-1-one-2:3-dicarboxylate, b.p. 166°/18 mm., is obtained by the cyclisation of ethyl butane-1:2:4-tricarboxylate. On hydrolysis and decarboxylation it yields *cyclopentan-1-one-3-carboxylic acid*, m.p. 65° (*W. N. Haworth* and *W. H. Perkin*, *ibid.*, 1908, **93**, 579; cf. also *H. Stobbe*, Ann., 1901, **315**, 219).

Cyclopentan-1-one-3:4-dicarboxylic acid, m.p. 189°, is prepared by condensing aconitic ester with malonic ester (*K. von Auwers*, Ber., 1893, **26**, 373).

Many *cyclopentane-1:2-dione-3:5-dicarboxylic esters* have been made by the condensation of oxalic ester with substituted glutaric esters (p. 73) (*W. Dieckmann*, Ber., 1902, **35**, 3206; *J. F. Thorpe et al.*, J. chem. Soc., 1922, **121**, 1496; *G. Komppa*, Ann., 1909, **368**, 126; *E. Rimini*, Gazz., 1896, **26**, 374; *W. Wislicenus et al.*, Ann., 1897, **297**, 98; J. pr. Chem., 1917, [ii], **95**, 269; 1917, **96**, 174).

Ethyl cyclopentane-1:3-dione-2:4-carboxylate, m.p. 61°, is prepared by reacting ethyl acetonedicarboxylate with chloroacetyl chloride; it exhibits no ketonic properties (*P. Ruggli* and *K. Doebel*, Helv., 1946, **29**, 600).

Methyl 3-iso*propylcyclopent-2-en-1-one-5-carboxylate*, b.p. 142°/14 mm., is formed when the cyclopropane ring of tanacetonedicarboxylic acid is disrupted by methanolic sodium methoxide (*N. J. Toivonen*, Chem. Ztbl., 1928, II, 38).

For cyclopentanonepolycarboxylic acids see *N. J. Toivonen*, Chem. Ztbl., 1923, I, 1357; *F. Mahla* and *F. Tiemann*, Ber., 1900, **33**, 1929.

The ester of *cyclopentan-1-one-3-acetic acid, semicarbazone*, m.p. 199° (dec.), is obtained by ring closure of the condensation product of dihydromuconic ester and malonic ester (*E. H. Farmer*, J. chem. Soc., 1923, **123**, 3324).

1-*Acetylcyclopentane*-1-*acetic acid*, m.p. 83–84°, is obtained from ethyl cyclopentane-1-acetate-1-carboxylic chloride and methylzinc iodide (*J. C. Bardhan*, J. chem. Soc., 1928, 2591, 2604).

The *ethyl ester*, m.p. 115°, of *cyclopentan*-1-*one*-2:5-*bis-glyoxylic acid*, m.p. 210° (dec.) is prepared by the condensation of cyclopentanone with ethyl oxalate (*S. Ruhemann*, J. chem. Soc., 1912, **101**, 1729).

Ethyl cyclopentan-1-*thione*-2-*carboxylate*, b.p. 110°/5·5 mm. (free *acid* m.p. 122°) is obtained by treating ethyl cyclopentanone-2-carboxylate with hydrogen chloride and hydrogen sulphide (*K. Chandra et al.*, J. Indian chem. Soc., 1942, **19**, 139).

Auxins. The natural occurrence of hydroxy- and keto-carboxylic acids of the cyclopentene series is found in the auxins, the only group of plant hormones yet investigated in detail by chemical methods.

New plant cells are formed by division at the growing tips and this process is controlled by the auxins which are produced at these points. Thus if an oat seedling is decapitated its growth ceases; if the tip be replaced the growth begins afresh but not if a piece of tinfoil is placed between the two pieces of the plant. Pieces cut from the base of the seedling produce no growth. If the tip be attached to the side of the seedling the shoot grows in a curve since one side obtains more growth hormone than the other. Light and gravity both influence the distribution of the hormone, the concentration being greater on the shady side and also on the side towards the earth; this fact explains the phenomena of phototropism and geotropism in plants. The growth hormone may be obtained from decapitated growing tips by diffusion into agar gel. The impregnated agar when placed laterally on a decapitated oat-seedling causes a bending of the seedling proportional to the quantity of hormone present. A unit of auxin is taken as that amount which causes the decapitated seedling to bend through 10° (for reviews see *P. Boysen-Jensen*, Ann. Rev. Biochem., 1938, **7**, 513; *F. W. Went*, *ibid.*, 1939, **8**, 521; *J. van Overbeek*, *ibid.*, 1944, **13**, 631).

The chemical investigation of the auxins is due to *F. Kögl* and his collaborators (Z. physiol. Chem., 1933, **214**, 241; 1933, **216**, 31; 1933, **220**, 137, 162; 1934, **225**, 215; 1934, **227**, 51; 1935, **235**, 181; 1936, **244**, 266; Naturwiss., 1942, **30**, 392; 1933, **21**, 17). Male urine, maize-germ oil, malt and yeast were employed as sources for the isolation of the hormones. It was soon realised that the auxins are acids and, by taking advantage of this fact, four growth-promoting substances were isolated in the pure state. These were auxin-*a*, $C_{18}H_{32}O_5$, m.p. 196°, auxin-*b*, $C_{18}H_{30}O_4$, m.p. 183° and auxin-lactone, $C_{18}H_{30}O_4$ m.p. 173° which were found to be cyclopentane derivatives; and heteroauxin which was discovered to be identical with β-indolylacetic acid.

Auxin-*a* is a monocyclic trihydroxymonocarboxylic acid with one double bond and auxin-*b* is a monocyclic hydroxyketomonocarboxylic acid also with one double bond; auxin-lactone is probably the δ-lactone of auxin-*a*. The side-chain of dihydroauxin-*b* may be eliminated by means of chromium trioxide to furnish the 2:4-bis-*sec*.-butylcyclopentanone (I); this corresponds in structure to a dicarboxylic acid, ***auxin-glutaric acid***, *2:8-dimethylnonane-4:6-dicarboxylic acid* (II), m.p. 129°, which is obtained by permanganate oxidation of the auxins. The constitution of (II) has been confirmed by synthesis.

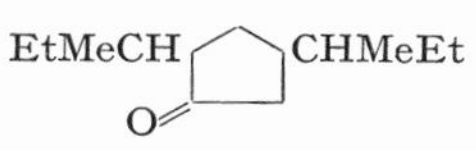

EtMeCH CHMeEt
O

(I)

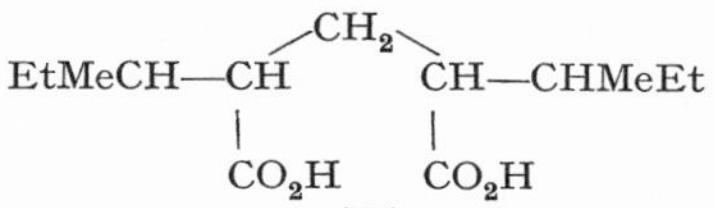

CH_2
EtMeCH—CH CH—CHMeEt
CO_2H CO_2H
(II)

On this and other evidence the structures of auxin-*a* and auxin-*b* are formulated as shown.

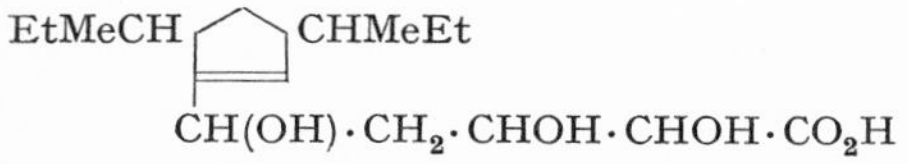

EtMeCH CHMeEt
CH(OH)·CH_2·CHOH·CHOH·CO_2H
Auxin-*a*

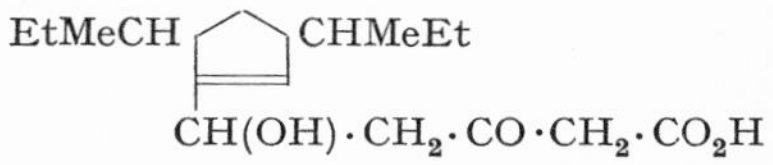

EtMeCH CHMeEt
CH(OH)·CH_2·CO·CH_2·CO_2H
Auxin-*b*

A synthetic analogue of auxin-*b*, possessing the structure shown without the two *sec*.-butyl groups, has been obtained by *E. R. H. Jones* and his collaborators (J. chem. Soc., 1950, 754, 3628, 3634) and by *F. Kögl* and coworkers (Rec. Trav. chim., 1950, **69**, 729, 1576).

Chapter V

Cyclohexane Group

R. A. RAPHAEL

1. Occurrence, formation and properties

The derivatives of cyclohexane constitute a very large and important section of carbocyclic chemistry; they far exceed in number the derivatives of any other alicyclic system. The reason for this is not far to seek; in addition to the usual methods of ring formation there exist in the case of the six-membered rings two highly convenient and widely applicable procedures—the reduction of benzenoid compounds (whence derives the term "hydro-aromatic" for this system) and the Diels-Alder synthesis, which cannot be employed for monocyclic systems of other sizes. In nature also the preponderance of cyclohexane derivatives over those of other alicyclic systems is overwhelming.

(a) Methods of formation

The two important processes mentioned above will be described first.

(i) The reduction of benzenoid compounds

The ease of reduction of derivatives of benzene to derivatives of cyclohexane varies enormously according to the nature of the substituents attached to the benzene nucleus. One of the earliest transformations of this type is due to *G. Merling* (Ann., 1894, **278**, 20) who found that resorcinol is smoothly reduced by sodium amalgam to give an excellent yield of cyclohexane-1:3-dione.

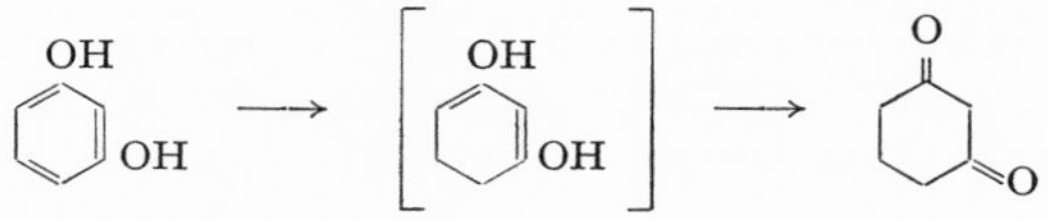

In general, however, the reduction of aromatic compounds does not proceed with such facility and the first method of general applicability was discovered by *P. Sabatier* and *J. B. Senderens*. This consists in passing the vapour of the aromatic compound admixed with excess of hydrogen over heated, finely-divided nickel; by this means aromatic hydrocarbons, phenols and amines may be readily hydrogenated to the corresponding cyclohexane derivatives (Ann. Chim., 1905, **4**, 319; 1907, **10**, 527; Compt. rend., 1901, **132**, 210, 566, 1254). Modifications of this procedure have led to the familiar present day technique of catalytic hydrogenation; thus reduction of the nucleus in benzenoid compounds may be conveniently carried out in glacial acetic acid at atmospheric pressure using a platinum or platinic oxide catalyst (*inter al.*, *R. Willstätter* and *D. Hatt*, Ber., 1912, **45**, 1471; *A. Skita* and *W. A. Meyer*, Ber., 1912, **45**, 3589; *R. Adams* and *J. R. Marshall*, J. Amer. chem. Soc., 1928, **50**, 1970). The reduction may be completed in a matter of minutes at room temperature if the hydrogen pressure be raised to 200 atmospheres (*R. H. Baker* and *R. D. Schuetz*, *ibid.*, 1947, **69**, 1250). If Raney nickel* be used as catalyst the reduction proceeds at moderate pressures but relatively high temperatures are necessary (100–300°); nickel on kieselguhr has also been employed (*inter al.*, *L. Palfray*, Bull. Soc. chim. Fr., 1940, [v], **7**, 407; *H. E. Ungnade* and *A. D. McLaren*, J. Amer. chem. Soc., 1944, **66**, 118; *H. Adkins et al.*, *ibid.*, 1931, **53**, 1425; 1932, **54**, 1669; *R. Schröter*, "Newer Methods of Preparative Organic Chemistry", Interscience Publishers, 1948, p. 93).

The effect of substituents on the rate of hydrogenation of the benzene ring has been the subject of much investigation but the results are very dependent on experimental conditions and no universal conclusions are possible (see *K. N. Campbell* and *B. U. Campbell*, Chem. Reviews, 1942, **31**, 160). Studies employing nickel-alumina as catalyst have led to the formulation of the expression $2^{-n}V$ for the velocity of hydrogenation of substituted benzenes, where V is the value for benzene itself and n is the number of substituents (*A. V. Lozovoi et al.*, J. gen. Chem. U.S.S.R., 1939, **9**, 895; 1940, **10**, 1, 1843, 1855). Further investigations along these lines employing platinum in glacial acetic acid have determined the scope and limitations of the Lozovoi formula (*H. A. Smith et al.*, J. Amer. chem. Soc., 1945, **67**, 272, 276, 279; 1949, **71**, 81).

The correlation between the ease of hydrogenation of the benzene nucleus and the crystal structure of platinum, palladium and nickel catalyst has been investigated (*A. A. Balandin*, Z. phys. Chem., 1929, **B2**, 289; *H. S. Taylor*, J. Amer. chem. Soc., 1938, **60**, 627; *J. H. Long et al.*, *ibid.*, 1934, **56**, 1101; *P. H. Emmett* and *N. Skau*, *ibid.*, 1943, **65**, 1029) and the reduction has been studied kinetically (*R. H. Baker* and *R. D. Schuetz*, *ibid.*, 1947, **69**, 1250; *H. A. Smith* and *H. T. Meriwether*, *ibid.*, 1949, **71**, 413).

* A highly active form of the metal prepared by the action of alkali on nickel-aluminium alloy.

The catalytic hydrogenation of benzene and its homologues cannot be regulated so as to obtain the intermediate dihydro- and tetrahydro-derivatives as these are hydrogenated so much more rapidly than the starting materials. From phenols, however, either cyclohexanols or cyclohexanones may be obtained by suitable variation in conditions.

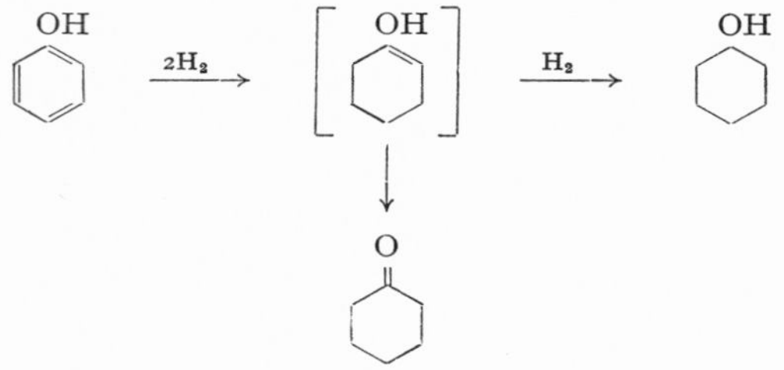

OH $\xrightarrow{2H_2}$ [OH] $\xrightarrow{H_2}$ OH

↓

O

In order to accomplish the partial hydrogenation of the single benzene nucleus a different technique is employed; this entails carrying out the reduction by means of sodium in liquid ammonia in the presence of a proton source, usually ethyl alcohol [*C. B. Wooster*, U.S.P., 2,182,242 (1938); *A. J. Birch*, J. chem. Soc., 1944, 430; 1945, 809; 1946, 593; 1947, 102, 1270, 1642; Nature, 1946, **158**, 60, 585; *J. P. Wibaut* and *F. A. Haak*, Rec. Trav. chim., 1948, **67**, 85]. The product of this reaction is invariably a dihydrobenzene and the mode of addition of hydrogen is highly specific, only 1:4-dihydro-compounds being produced.

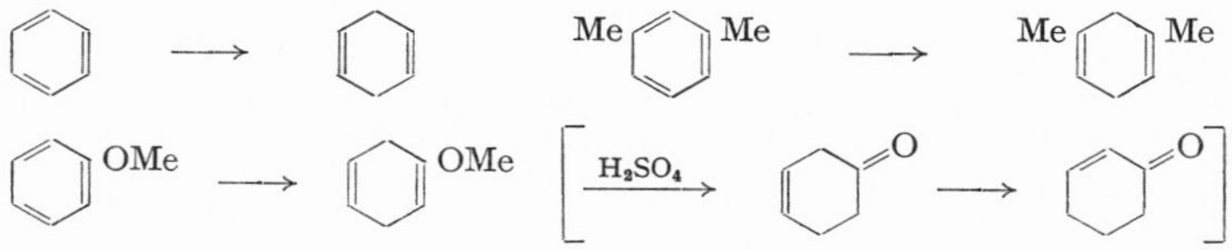

→ Me Me → Me Me

OMe → OMe [$\xrightarrow{H_2SO_4}$ O → O]

The orientation of the 1:4-addition in substituted benzenes is dependent on the positions of the substituents; for a full discussion of this point the original memoirs should be consulted.

The technique of catalytic hydrogenation is readily adaptable to large scale work and the technical application of the method has been widespread (cf. *C. Ellis*, "Hydrogenation of Organic Substances", van Nostrand & Co., New York; *S. Berkmann, J. C. Morrell* and *G. Egloff*, "Catalysis", Reinhold Publishing Corporation, New York; U.S.P. 1,247,629; 1,643,619; G.P. 444,665; 473,960).

The hydrogenation of a benzene derivative with two or more substituents always leads to a mixture of the possible stereoisomeric correspondingly substituted cyclohexanes but the proportions of the isomers produced depend very largely on the reaction conditions. Most of the investigations on this topic have been carried out on disubstituted benzenes. A review of the mass of literature indicates that it is now reasonably well established that hydrogenation with platinum in glacial acetic acid takes place mainly by *cis*-addition leading to a product consisting predominantly of the *cis* isomer of the disubstituted cyclohexane (*inter al., R. H. Baker* and *R. D. Schuetz,* J. Amer. chem. Soc., 1947, **69**, 1250; *A. Skita,* Ber., 1920, **53**, 1792; 1922, **55**, 144; 1923, **56**, 1014; Ann., 1923, **431**, 1; *K. von Auwers,* Ann., 1920, **420**, 84). A detailed discussion of this phenomenon together with a theoretical explanation has been provided in a noteworthy series of memoirs by *R. P. Linstead* and his collaborators (J. Amer. chem. Soc., 1942, **64**, 1985, et seq.). Skita made the further observation that reduction in neutral and basic media yielded a product consisting in the main of the *trans* isomer. Production of *trans* compounds also seems to predominate when the hydrogenation is carried out at elevated temperatures (*E. I. Margolis,* Ber., 1936, **69**, 1710; *N. D. Zelinsky* and *E. I. Margolis,* Ber., 1932, **65**, 1613; *A. Skita, loc. cit.*). The configuration of the products has generally been assigned on the basis of their physical properties and von Auwers' empirical rule (see p. 10) but in many cases absolute methods depending on resolvability have been employed.

The reverse of the above process, i.e. the dehydrogenation of cyclohexane derivatives to benzenoid compounds, is an important diagnostic procedure in the determination of the carbon skeleton of many naturally occurring compounds. The transformation may be brought about by treatment at elevated temperatures with one of the metallic hydrogenation catalysts, platinum, palladium or nickel. Chemical reagents such as sulphur, selenium, chloranil or N-bromosuccinimide may also be employed. (For reviews see *R. P. Linstead,* Annual Reports, 1936, **33**, 294; *P. A. Plattner,* "Newer Methods of Preparative Organic Chemistry", Interscience Publishers, 1948, p. 21.)

(ii) The Diels-Alder diene synthesis

This synthetic method (Vol. I, p. 268), one of the most flexible and versatile organic procedures known, entails in essentials the condensation of a 1:3-diene (the diene component) with an olefinic or acetylenic compound (the dienophile) in which the centre of unsaturation is subtended by one or more electron attracting groups (carbonyl, carboxyl and derivatives, nitro, cyano, acetoxyl, sulphonyl etc.). These two classes of compound interact smoothly under mild conditions in the absence of a catalyst, sometimes with evolution of heat, to furnish cyclohexane derivatives; the reaction may be represented diagrammatically thus:

The following examples give some idea of the wide applicability of the reaction for the synthesis of the six-membered carbon ring:

$$\begin{array}{l} CH{=}CH_2 \\ | \\ CH{=}CH_2 \end{array} + \begin{array}{l} CH{-}CO \\ \| \qquad\quad \rangle O \\ CH{-}CO \end{array} \longrightarrow \begin{array}{l} -CO \\ \qquad \rangle O \\ -CO \end{array}$$

$$\begin{array}{l} Ph\cdot C{=}CH_2 \\ | \\ Ph\cdot C{=}CH_2 \end{array} + \begin{array}{l} CH{-}CH_3 \\ \| \\ CH{-}CHO \end{array} \longrightarrow \begin{array}{l} Ph \qquad CH_3 \\ Ph \qquad CHO \end{array}$$

$$\begin{array}{l} EtO\cdot C{=}CH_2 \\ | \\ CH{=}CH_2 \end{array} + \begin{array}{l} C{-}CH_3 \\ ||| \\ C{-}COCH_3 \end{array} \longrightarrow \begin{array}{l} EtO \qquad CH_3 \\ \qquad\quad COCH_3 \end{array}$$

$$\begin{array}{l} CH{=}CH \\ | \quad O \\ CH{=}CH \end{array} + \begin{array}{l} C{-}CO_2Et \\ ||| \\ C{-}CO_2Et \end{array} \longrightarrow \begin{array}{l} (O) \quad CO_2Et \\ \qquad\quad CO_2Et \end{array}$$

1:3-Enynes and 1:3-diynes may also be used as the "diene" component but the reaction then needs more drastic conditions. For a full exposition of the ramifications and scope of the reaction the many excellent reviews available may be consulted (*M. C. Kloetzel* and *H. L. Holmes*, Org. Reactions, 4, 1; *K. Alder*, F.I.A.T. Review of German Science, 1948, p. 125; "Newer Methods of Preparative Organic Chemistry", Interscience Publishers, New York, 1948, p. 381; *J. A. Norton*, Chem. Reviews, 1942, 31, 319; *C. F. H. Allen*, *ibid.*, 1945, 37, 209).

The Diels-Alder reaction is reversible and frequently the initial components may be regenerated by pyrolysis of the adduct. The equilibrium position varies widely, however, and this is reflected by the large variation in the thermostability of these products.

An interesting aspect of the diene synthesis is its stereochemical specificity; a *cis* dienophile will not give rise to a *trans* adduct and *vice versa.* Thus the product of reaction between butadiene and maleic acid is solely *cis*-cyclohex-4-ene-1:2-dicarboxylic acid, whilst with fumaric acid butadiene yields the corresponding *trans* acid only.

$$\text{CH}_2\!=\!\text{CH–CH}\!=\!\text{CH}_2 + \text{HO}_2\text{C–CH}\!=\!\text{CH–CO}_2\text{H} \longrightarrow$$

For a summary and references concerning the direction of addition of an unsymmetrical diene to an unsymmetrical dienophile and the configuration of the adduct see *A. J. Birch*, Annual Reports, 1950, 47, 177.

The above type of reaction, in which the unsaturated centre of the dienophile is activated by the vicinal substituents, takes place most readily in polar solvents and almost certainly involves an ionic mechanism. A second type is distinguishable, however, in which the diene type of synthesis occurs between hydrocarbons; as the rate of this reaction is independent of environment, being much the same in the gas phase as in solution, a radical mechanism is postulated (for details of these mechanisms see *M. J. S. Dewar*, "Modern Theory of Organic Chemistry", Oxford University Press, 1949, p. 150; *F. Bergmann et al.*, J. Amer. chem. Soc., 1943, **65**, 1405; J. org. Chem., 1943, **8**, 179; *B. J. F. Hudson* and *R. Robinson*, J. chem. Soc., 1941, 715; *R. B. Woodward et al.*, J. Amer. chem. Soc., 1942, **64**, 3058; 1944, **66**, 645; *A. Wasserman et al.*, J. chem. Soc., 1935, 828; 1939, 362; 1942, 612). Examples of this second type are

$$\text{CH}_2\!=\!\text{CH–CH}\!=\!\text{CH}_2 + \text{CH}_2\!=\!\text{CH}_2 \longrightarrow \text{cyclohexene}$$

$$\text{CH}_2\!=\!\text{CH–C(Me)}\!=\!\text{CH}_2 + \text{CH}_2\!=\!\text{CH–C(Me)}\!=\!\text{CH}_2 \longrightarrow$$

Isoprene Dipentene

The ease with which the diene synthesis occurs suggests that the biogenesis of many naturally occurring cyclohexane derivatives may involve a very similar process, e.g. terpenes from isoprene.

(iii) Other synthetic methods

The other methods of obtaining the cyclohexane ring closely resemble those already described for the formation of five-membered ring systems

(p. 71 ff). Thus the Wurtz reaction applied to 1:6-dihalides yields the six-membered ring hydrocarbons but the method has no preparative importance. Intramolecular dehydrohalogenation of 6-halogenoketones, nitriles or carboxylic esters and intermolecular condensation of 1:5-dihalides with a compound containing an active methylene group have been fairly widely employed to obtain the cyclohexane system. The cyclisation of substituted pimelic acids and their derivatives by the Blanc, Dieckmann and Thorpe procedures to furnish cyclohexanones has been much used.

Many acyclic unsaturated compounds smoothly cyclise to cyclohexane derivatives under acid conditions; most compounds undergoing this transformation belong to the terpene class, e.g. methylgeraniolene forms cyclomethylgeraniolene whilst dipentene is produced from geraniol (Vol. II B) (*F. Tiemann et al.*, Ber., 1893, **26**, 2727; 1900, **33**, 3711; *D. C. Hibbitt* and *R. P. Linstead*, J. chem. Soc., 1936, 470. For reviews see *R. P. Linstead*, Annual Reports, 1936, **33**, 315).

The internal aldol condensation of 1:7 or 1:5-diketones followed by loss of water leads to unsaturated ketones of the cyclohexane series.

$$CH_2(CH_2 \cdot CH_2 \cdot COMe)(CH_2 \cdot CH_2 \cdot COMe) \xrightarrow{-H_2O} \text{(cyclohexene with COMe, Me)}$$

$$2\,CH_3 \cdot CO \cdot CH_2 \cdot CO_2Et + OCH \cdot R \longrightarrow (CH_3 \cdot CO \cdot CH \cdot CO_2Et)_2CH \cdot R \longrightarrow \text{(Me, R, 2 } CO_2Et\text{-substituted cyclohexenone)}$$

The latter series of reactions is sometimes known as the Knoevenagel synthesis. In an allied synthesis the Claisen type of condensation is employed to produce cyclohexane-1:3-diones.

$$Me_2C{=}CH \cdot CO \cdot CH_3 + CH_2(CO_2Et)_2 \longrightarrow Me_2C(CH(CO_2Et)_2) \cdot CH_2 \cdot CO \cdot CH_3 \xrightarrow{NaOEt} \text{(5,5-dimethylcyclohexane-1,3-dione)}$$

Dimethyldihydroresorcinol

(b) Configuration of the cyclohexane ring

The question of the fine structure of the cyclohexane nucleus has been under investigation for a considerable time and the subject has been studied from many angles employing both chemical and physical methods. From the nature of the problem the latter are far more informative and by their use an accurate picture of the configuration of the six-membered carbocyclic ring is now available.

The Baeyer concepts (p. 2) required that the six carbon atoms be united in a uniplanar structure (symmetry D_{6h}*); the improbability of this assumption was demonstrated by *H. Sachse* (Vol. I., p. 115), who pointed out that two strainless multiplanar forms of cyclohexane could be visualised without distortion of the normal tetrahedral valency angle.

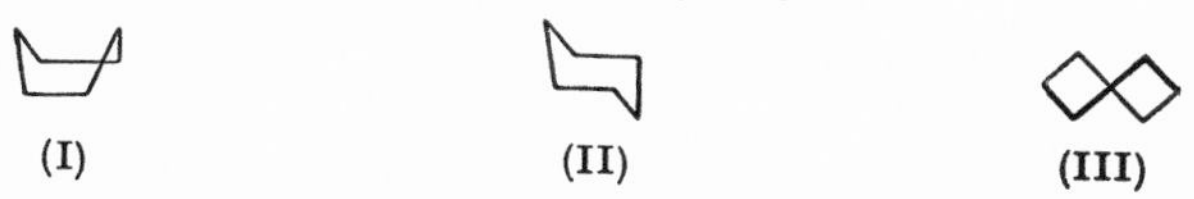

From their shapes the two configurations are designated as the "boat" form (I) ("C" form, "bed" form, "tub" form, "cradle" form; in German "wannenform"; symmetry C_{2v}*) and the "chair" form (II) ("Z" form; in German "sesselform"; symmetry D_{3d}*). It may be seen from models that the chair form is a rigid structure whilst the boat form possesses a considerable degree of flexibility; indeed, as W. H. Mills has pointed out, the configuration (I) for the latter represents an extreme structure of a number of mobile modifications and it is often helpful to visualise this form in the mean phase (III) (*W. H. Mills*, Dict. appl. Chem., 1935, **2**, 433).

The results of many investigations by physical methods have conclusively demonstrated the soundness of the above concepts of multiplanarity (X-ray analysis: *O. Hassel* and *H. Kringstad*, C.A., 1931, **25**, 1500. Electron diffraction: *L. Pauling* and *L. O. Brockway*, J. Amer. chem. Soc., 1937, **59**, 1223; *R. Wierl*, Ann. Physik, 1931, **8**, 521; *H. Mark*, Z. angew. Chem., 1931, **44**, 531. Infra-red absorption spectra: *R. S. Rasmussen*, J. chem. Phys., 1943, **11**, 249. See also references below).

The above conception would seem to imply the existence of two discrete modifications of cyclohexane whereas in fact only one form is found to occur. Calculation, however, shows that the height of the energy barrier between the two forms is very low and that the energy derivable from thermal collision would be more than enough to cause frequent traversal of the barrier with consequent very facile interconversion of the two forms (cf. *C. W. Shoppee*, J. chem. Soc., 1946, 1138; *D. H. R. Barton*, *ibid.*, 1948, 340; *P. Hazebroek* and *L. T. Oosterhoff*, Faraday Soc. Discussions, 1951, No. 10, 87). The constitution of the chair form involves six energetically favourable *b* constellations (see p. 9) whilst in the boat form this arrangement occurs only four times, the remaining two constellations being of the energetically unfavourable *a* variety. In view of this it is not surprising to find that the chair form is the more stable configuration, the energy

* For explanation of symmetry symbols see H. Eyring, J. Walter and G. E. Kimball, "Quantum Chemistry", 1944, Wiley and Sons, p. 376.

difference being approximately 5·6 kcals./mol. Indeed, many physical methods show conclusively that at room temperature cyclohexane exists mainly in the chair form (*V. Schomaker* and *D. P. Stevenson*, J. chem. Phys., 1940, **8**, 637; *K. W. F. Kohlrausch* and *H. Wittek*, Z. physik. Chem., 1941, **B48**, 177; *O. Hassel et al.*, C.A., 1944, **38**, 2532; 1941, **35**, 4653). The presence of a small proportion of the boat form must, however, be envisaged in order to account for the thermal properties of cyclohexane (*C. W. Beckett, K. S. Pitzer* and *R. Spitzer*, J. Amer. chem. Soc., 1947, **69**, 2488) and this proportion increases rapidly with rise in temperature.

As in the case of cyclohexane itself the substituted derivatives exist mainly in the chair form (*R. G. Dickenson* and *C. Bilicke*, J. Amer. chem. Soc., 1928, **50**, 764; *E. Holmöy* and *O. Hassel*, Z. physik. Chem., 1932, **B16**, 234; *C. W. Beckett et al., loc. cit.*; *G. W. van Vloten et al.*, Nature, 1948, **162**, 771). This does not apply, of course, to 1:4-bridged ring derivatives where the exigencies of the molecular structure constrain the ring into the boat form, e.g.

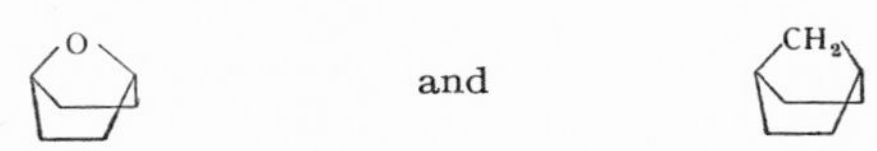

The fact that the number of isomeric substituted cyclohexanes actually found agrees with the number predictable from a uniplanar cyclohexane ring is due to the above-mentioned circumstance of the facile interconversion of the boat and chair forms; the uniplanar structure may be regarded as the mean configuration of the oscillatory boat and chair phases. Although there have been many reports of the isolation of cyclohexane derivatives in boat and chair forms investigation has usually shown them to be misconstructions (Claims: *R. D. Desai et al.*, Nature, 1938, **142**, 798; Brit. chem. Abstr., 1942, AII, 284; *M. Qudrat-I-Khuda et al.*, J. Indian chem. Soc., 1931, **8**, 277; 1938, **15**, 462, 489; Nature, 1933, **132**, 210; 1935, **136**, 301; *A. I. Vogel*, Chem. and Ind., 1938, **541**, 772; *A. I. Vogel et al.*, J. chem. Soc., 1939, 1862; *H. A. Ungnade* and *A. Ludutsky*, J. org. Chem., 1945, **10**, 520. Rebuttals: *W. A. Wightman*, J. chem. Soc., 1926, 2541; *J. P. Wibaut et al.*, Chem. and Ind., 1938, 753; *C. C. Price*, J. Amer. chem. Soc., 1939, **61**,

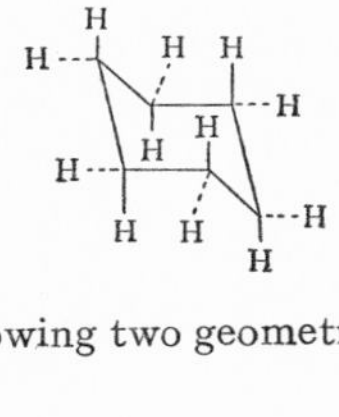

(A) Cyclohexane, showing two geometrical types of hydrogen

1847; *R. Malachowski et al.*, Ber., 1938, **71**, 759; *R. D. Desai et al.*, Chem. and Ind., 1938, 1059; J. chem. Soc., 1939, 84; Nature, 1935, **135**, 434; **136**, 608, 953; *S. Goldschmidt* and *G. Gräfinger*, Ber., 1935, **68**, 279; *R. F. Miller* and *R. Adams*, J. Amer. chem. Soc., 1936, **58**, 787).

It may be seen from the accompanying diagram (A) that the hydrogen atoms in the chair form of the cyclohexane molecule may be divided into two geometrical types. There are three hydrogen atoms markedly above and three markedly below the ring (shown with solid valency bonds) while the remaining six hydrogen atoms lie in an "equatorial belt" round the ring (shown with broken valency bonds); a Stuart model shows this very clearly. The six hydrogen atoms above and below the ring are termed "polar"* (abbreviated as *p* or ε) the others being designated as "equatorial" (abbreviated as *e* or $\varkappa$); a numerical notation has also been proposed (*O. Hassel et al., loc. cit.*; Acta Chem. Scand., 1947, **1**, 158, 683, 929; Research, 1950, **3**, 504; *C. W. Beckett et al., loc. cit.*; *D. H. R. Barton*, Experientia, 1950, **6**, 316; *D. H. R. Barton* and *W. J. Rosenfelder*, J. chem. Soc., 1951, 1048; *J. J. A. Blekkingh*, Rec. Trav. chim., 1949, **68**, 345; *A. J. Birch*, Annual Reports, 1951, **48**, 192). A similar distinction may be applied to the boat conformation of cyclohexane when this becomes a stereochemically unambiguous entity (i.e. locked by a 1:4-bridge or by incorporation in a tricyclic system) (*C. W. Shoppee*, Chem. and Ind., 1952, 87).

The statistically preferred conformation of a mono-substituted cyclohexane is that in which the substituent occupies one of the equatorial positions, which are less sterically hindered and thermodynamically more stable than the polar positions. A similar situation obtains in the case of *trans*-1:2-, *cis*-1:3- and *trans*-1:4-disubstituted cyclohexanes, the equatorial-equatorial (*ee*) conformation being energetically more favourable than the polar-polar (*pp*) (the two conformations do not, of course, constitute discrete isomeric modifications since the energy barrier between them is low). The corresponding *cis*-1:2-, *trans*-1:3- and *cis*-1:4-derivatives all possess an equatorial-polar (*ep*) conformation. It may be seen that this concept provides a satisfying explanation of long known relationships between geometrical isomers, e.g. the greater stability of a trans-1:2-disubstituted cyclohexane (*ee*) as compared with the corresponding cis-isomer (*ep*). The argument may similarly be extended to polysubstituted cyclohexanes.

This type of conformational analysis has also been of great use in providing a rationale for the steric course of reactions involving substituents in a cyclohexane ring (e.g. dehydration and oxidation of cyclohexanols, reduction of cyclohexanones, hydrogenation of cyclohexenes). Its extension to polycyclic systems such as steroids and triterpenes has proved especially fruitful (*D. H. R. Barton, loc. cit.; W. S. Johnson*, Experientia, 1951, **8**, 315). This modern treatment of cyclohexane chemistry underlines the point that for interpretative

* In view of possible confusion with the electrical connotation of the word "polar" it has been suggested that it be replaced by "vertical" (*v*) (*D. H. R. Barton* and *W. Klyne*, personal communication).

purposes the six-membered ring should always be envisaged as a multiplanar structure; if a planar configuration be assumed misconstructions very easily occur.

The fine structure of cyclohexene has not been studied to such an extent as that of cyclohexane but it has been shown to exist in forms related to the boat and chair configurations, the energy difference being about 2.7 kcal./mol. (*C. W. Beckett, N. K. Freeman* and *K. S. Pitzer*, J. Amer. chem. Soc., 1948, **70**, 4227). Although cyclohexene and the cyclohexadienes are genetically related to the uniplanar benzene, their structures are undoubtedly multiplanar and their double bonds exhibit all the familiar ethylenic properties. This fundamental difference between benzene and its hydrogenation products is very well illustrated by the values of their heats of hydrogenation; the magnitude of this property on reduction of the first double bond is shown below.

	kcal./mol.	
Cyclohexene	—28.59	Heat evolved
Cyclohexa-1:3-diene	—26.76	Heat evolved
Benzene	+ 5.57	Heat absorbed

(*G. B. Kistiakowsky et al., ibid.*, 1935, **57**, 65, 876; 1936, **58**, 137, 146; 1937, **59**, 831. For a comparison of the rates of hydrogenation see *H. A. Smith* and *H. T. Meriwether, ibid.*, 1949, **71**, 413).

(c) Differentiation between cyclohexane and cyclopentane compounds

In view of the great similarity in stability and chemical properties between corresponding derivatives of the cyclohexane and cyclopentane series a discriminating factor would be very desirable. The Diels-Alder adducts between the cyclopentadienes and maleic anhydride readily dissociate into the initial components on heating whereas the adducts from cyclohexa-1:3-dienes are thermostable (*K. Alder* and *H. F. Rickert*, Ann., 1936, **524**, 180). A more useful diagnostic is the series of reactions described for distinguishing between five and six-membered ring ketones (*W. S. Johnson* and *W. E. Shelberg*, J. Amer. chem. Soc., 1945, **67**, 1745). The ketone is condensed with ethyl formate, the resulting hydroxymethylene compound treated with hydroxylamine and the behaviour of the final products towards alkali examined. In the case of cyclohexanones the following reactions ensue.

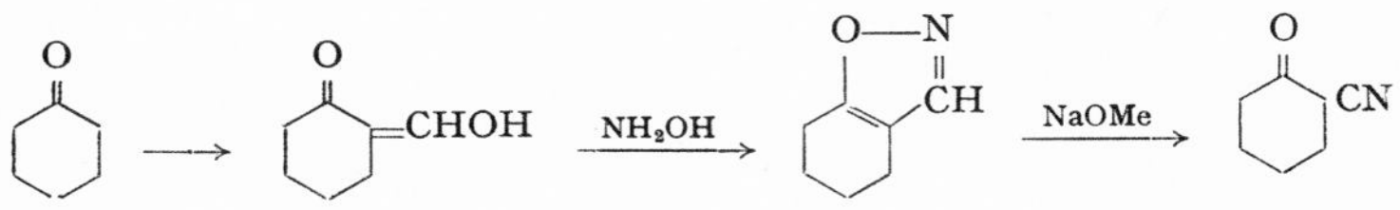

O → O =CHOH $\xrightarrow{NH_2OH}$ O—N ‖ CH $\xrightarrow{NaOMe}$ O CN

An isoxazole is formed which undergoes ring fission with alkali to produce an α-ketonitrile. With cyclopentanones the final reactions assume a different course.

$$C_5H_8O \longrightarrow C_5H_6O{=}CHOH \xrightarrow{NH_2OH} C_5H_6O{=}CH{-}N(OH){-}CH{=}C_5H_6O$$

(I)

Two molecules of the hydroxymethylene compound react with one molecule of hydroxylamine to give orange compounds of type (I) which dissolve in alkali forming purple solutions.

2. Hydrocarbons

(a) Saturated hydrocarbons

Cyclohexanes (hexahydrobenzenes or cyclanes)

Cyclohexane hydrocarbons occur naturally in petroleum derived from various sources. They are found, together with cyclopentane hydrocarbons, in the so-called naphtha obtained from Caucasian petroleum and are, accordingly, sometimes termed naphthenes (*F. K. Beilstein* and *A. Kurbatov*, Ber., 1880, **13**, 1818). Cyclohexanes have also been isolated from New Zealand and Borneo petroleum, from low-temperature coal-tar, from lignite and shale tars, from rosin oil and from acetone oil, the high-boiling fraction from the distillation of crude acetone (*T. H. Easterfield* and *N. McClelland*, Chem. and Ind., 1923, **42**, 936; *S. Iimuri*, Chem. Ztbl., 1928, II, 189; *H. Pringsheim*, Angew. Chem., 1927, **40**, 1387; *F. B. Ahrens*, *ibid.*, 1908, **21**, 1411; for review see A. N. Sachanen "The Chemical Constituents of Petroleum", 1945, Reinhold Co.).

In the laboratory the cyclohexanes may be obtained from their halogen substitution products by reduction or by interaction with alkyl halides in the presence of aluminium chloride. The most convenient and widely used method of preparation, however, is the catalytic hydrogenation of benzene hydrocarbons or of cyclohexenes; the process is discussed on p. 124 *et seq.* Hydriodic acid will reduce alkylbenzenes at elevated temperatures but considerable isomerisation to alkylcyclopentanes occurs (*V. B. Markovnikov*, Ber., 1897, **30**, 1214; *O. Aschan*, Ann., 1902, **324**, 6).

Properties of cyclohexanes. The cyclohexanes behave chemically like the paraffin hydrocarbons. They may be distinguished from the isomeric olefines by their higher specific gravity and their inability to react with bromine. In the homologous series of alkylcyclohexanes the melting-points, boiling-points and refractive indices are a regular function of the number of carbon atoms and the odd-even alternation observed in aliphatic compounds is absent. Dehydrogenation to benzene derivatives occurs when the cyclohexanes are treated at elevated temperatures with noble metals, sulphur or selenium (see p. 127); with a vanadium sesquioxide-alumina catalyst at 500° cyclohexenes are also produced (*A. F. Plate* and *G. A. Tarasova,* J. gen. Chem. U.S.S.R., 1945, **15**, 120). As already described, cyclohexanes undergo isomerisation to alkylcyclopentanes by treatment with aluminium chloride (p. 20); in the case of some higher homologues side-chains may be eliminated as paraffin hydrocarbons (*H. Hopff,* Ber., 1932, **65**, 482; *N. D. Zelinsky, ibid.*, 1249; *A. Skita,* Angew. Chem., 1932, **45**, 286; *M. B. Turowa-Pollak,* Ber., 1935, **68**, 1781). Chlorine and bromine under vigorous conditions convert cyclohexanes to the monohalogen derivatives; in the presence of aluminium bromide bromine gives rise to bromobenzenes. Heating the cyclohexanes with dilute nitric acid effects nitro-substitution, tertiary hydrogen atoms being replaced with especial ease (*S. S. Nametkin,* Chem. Ztbl., 1910, II, 1376; *V. B. Markovnikov,* Ann., 1898, **301**, 154; 1898, **302**, 1).

Properties of some cyclohexanes are given in Table I.

Cyclohexane *(hexahydrobenzene, hexamethylene, "naphthene")* is obtained by the reduction of benzene [*I.G. Farbenind.*, B.P., 322,445 (1930); see p. 125], of cyclohexene and cyclohexadiene (*N. D. Zelinsky,* Ber., 1924, **57**, 1066) and of cyclohexanol (*A. Kling,* Bull. Soc. chim. Fr., 1929, [iv], **41**, 1341). It is also formed in small amount by the action of sodium on 1:6-dibromohexane and by boiling *n*-hexane with aluminium chloride. Pure cyclohexane may be obtained from its mixtures with benzene by fractional distillation in the presence of a third component, e.g. ethylene chlorohydrin; the distillate consists of pure cyclohexane, the benzene remaining behind with the ethylene chlorohydrin [*J. Y. Johnson,* B.P., 324,350, 324,357 (1928)]. Traces of benzene may be removed from cyclohexane by chromatographic methods.

Cyclohexane is decomposed by heat at 700–800° to give a small yield of butadiene (*P. K. Frolich,* Ind. Eng. Chem., 1930, **22**, 240). At 500°/100 at. in the presence of alumina, or at 380° in the presence of molybdenum sulphide, it is transformed into methylcyclopentane and various benzenoid hydrocarbons (*V. N. Ipatiev,* Ber. 1911, **44**, 2987; *S. Ando,* J. chem. Soc. Japan, 1933, **36**, 396; *idem,* J. Soc. chem. Ind. Japan, 1940, **43**, 355). Its aluminium chloride-catalysed isomerisation to methylcyclopentane is discussed on p. 20.

Cyclohexane is oxidised by air in the presence of an appropriate catalyst (e.g., vanadium pentoxide) at elevated temperatures, maleic acid being the main product (*N. A. Milas* and *W. L. Walsh,* J. Amer. chem. Soc., 1939, **61**, 633). Pervanadic acid has also been employed (for review see *W. Treibs,* Angew. Chemie, 1939, **52**, 698). Oxidation with pure nitric acid at 90–120°/15 at. takes a different course to yield adipic acid [*E. K. Ellinghoe,* U.S.P., 2,228,261 (1941); see also *O. Aschan,* Ann. 1902, 324, 3]. Biological oxidation of cyclohexane may be achieved using *Pseudomonas aeruginosa,* the products being valeric acid,

TABLE 1

HYDROCARBONS OF THE CYCLOHEXANE SERIES

Compound	M.p.°	B.p.°/mm	d_4^{20}	n_{20}^{D}	Ref. (p. 138)
yclohexane	6·54	80·3	0·7753	1·4268	1, 2, 3
lethylcyclohexane	–126·3	100	0·7748	1·4263	2, 3, 4, 5
:1-Dimethylcyclohexane		119·3	0·7810	1·4294	1, 6
s-1 : 2-Dimethylcyclohexane		126·5	0·7822	1·4360	1, 21
ans-1 : 2-Dimethylcyclohexane		124·5	0·7798	1·4270	1, 21
s-1 : 3-Dimethylcyclohexane		119	0·7735	1·4235	1, 7, 21
ans-1 : 3-Dimethylcyclohexane		124	0·7750	1·4284	1, 5, 2, 7, 21
s-1 : 4-Dimethylcyclohexane		120·5	0·7671	1·4297	1, 21
ans-1 : 4-Dimethylcyclohexane		119	0·7638	1·4209	1, 21
thylcyclohexane	–128·9	129·5	0·7840	1·4325	1
s-1 : 2 : 3-Trimethylcyclohexane		144	0·7930	1·4368	1
ans-1 : 2 : 3-Trimethylcyclohexane		142	0·7914	1·4358	1
s-1 : 2 : 4-Trimethylcyclohexane		141·5	0·7850	1·4334	1
ans-1 : 2 : 4-Trimethylcyclohexane		138·5	0·7813	1·4312	1
s-1 : 3 : 5-Trimethylcyclohexane		140	0·7773	1·4301	1
ans-1 : 3 : 5-Trimethylcyclohexane		138	0·7720	1·4271	1
s-1-Ethyl-3-methylcyclohexane		147·5	0·7830	1·4311	7
ans-1-Ethyl-3-methylcyclohexane		148·5	0·7860	1·4295	7
·Propylcyclohexane	–94·5	155	0·7898	1·4359	4, 5, 8
*o*Propylcyclohexane	–90·6	154·7	0·7902	1·4364	4
:2 : 3 : 4-Tetramethylcyclohexane		84/5	0·8219	1·4531	19
s-1 : 2 : 4 : 5-Tetramethylcyclohexane		171	0·8122	1·4465	1
ans-1 : 2 : 4 : 5-Tetramethylcyclohexane		169	0·8100	1·4453	1
s-1 : 3 : 4 : 5-Tetramethylcyclohexane		168	0·8166	1·4485	1
ans-1 : 3 : 4 : 5-Tetramethylcyclohexane		162	0·8140	1·4466	1
s-1-Methyl-3-*n*-propylcyclohexane		168·5	0·7910	1·4360	7
ans-1-Methyl-3-*n*-propylcyclohexane		169·5	0·7920	1·4326	7
·Ethyl-3 : 5-dimethylcyclohexane		168	0·7929		2, 9
·Methyl-2-*iso*propylcyclohexane		171	0·8135	1·447	20
·Methyl-3-*iso*propylcyclohexane		167	0·7963	1·440	20
·Methyl-4-*iso*propylcyclohexane		167	0·7929	1·4375	5
·Butylcyclohexane	–78·6	177	0·8001	1·4420	4, 8, 10
*o*Butylcyclohexane		169	0·7950	1·4420	1
c.-Butylcyclohexane		177·2	0·8156	1·4487	4
rt.-Butylcyclohexane		167	0·8205	1·4538	11
: 3-Diethylcyclohexane		169	0·8118	1·4449	11
Butyl-2-ethylcyclohexane		205		1·4479	12
·Amylcyclohexane		199	0·8020	1·4440	8
·Hexylcyclohexane		221	0·8060	1·4460	8
·Heptylcyclohexane	41	109/12	0·8124	1·4520	10
·Octylcyclohexane		117/11			13
·Dodecylcyclohexane	12	131/0·8	0·8250	1·4580	10
'rans"-Hexaethylcyclohexane	104·7				14
Dodecyl-2-methylcyclohexane		178/10	0·8236	1·4570	15
Dodecyl-3-methylcyclohexane	–14	177/5	0·8247	1·4590	15
·Tetradecylcyclohexane	25	155/0·8	0·8258	1·4581	10
·Hexadecylcyclohexane	32·5	163/1·5	0·8260	1·4611	10, 15
henylcyclohexane	7	107/13	0·9375	1·5249	16
Naphthylcyclohexane		152/3·5		1·5856	17
s-1 : 4-Dibenzhydrylcyclohexane	248				18
ans-1 : 4-Dibenzhydrylcyclohexane	224				18

[1] *F. Eisenlohr*, Chem. Ztbl., 1926, I, 75.
[2] *V. B. Markovnikov*, Ber., 1896, **28**, 1234.
[3] *T. H. Easterfield*, Chem. & Ind., 1923, **42**, 936.
[4] *J. Timmermans*, Bull. Soc. chim. Belg., 1927, **36**, 502.
[5] *V. B. Markovnikov*, Ann., 1898, **302**, 2.
[6] *A. L. Liberman* and *B. A. Kazanski*, Bull. Acad. Sci. U.R.S.S., 1946, 77.
[7] *M. Mousseron*, Bull. Soc. chim. Fr., 1946, **13**, 218.
[8] *M. Bourguel*, Bull. Soc. chim. Fr., 1927, [iv], **41**, 1475.
[9] *V. B. Markovnikov*, Chem. Ztbl.. 1899, I, 176.
[10] *A. W. Schmidt* and *A. Grosser*, Ber., 1940, **73**, 930.
[11] *R. Stratford*, Chem. Ztbl., 1929, II, 1285.
[12] *M. S. Kharasch* and *E. Sternfeld*, J. Amer. chem. Soc., 1939, **61**, 2318.
[13] *A. V. Lozovoi et al.*, J. gen. Chem. U.S.S.R., 1939, **9**, 540.
[14] *H. Locha* and *H. Steinbrink*, Brennstoff Chem., 1938, **19**, 277, 704.
[15] *A. D. Petrov* and *M. A. Tscheltzova*, C. A., 1943, **37**, 1993.
[16] *O. Neunhoffer*, J. pr. Chem., 1932, [ii], **133**, 95.
[17] *M. Orchin* and *L. Reggel*, J. Amer. chem. Soc., 1947, **69**, 505.
[18] *G. Wittig* and *H. Pook*, Ber., 1937, **70**, 2485.
[19] *D. T. Mitchell* and *C. S. Marvel*, J. Amer. chem. Soc., 1933, **55**, 4276.
[20] *P. Sabatier*, Ann. Chim., 1902, **4**, 274.
[21] *G. A. Haggis* and *L. N. Owen*, J. chem. Soc., 1953, 408.

formic acid and formaldehyde; cyclohexanol is similarly oxidised but cyclohexanone is unaffected (*B. Imelik*, Compt. rend., 1948, **226**, 2082). Fuming sulphuric acid reacts with cyclohexane to give benzenesulphonic acid and other products (*B. Menschutkin*, Chem. Ztbl., 1930, II, 1541; *R. Sperling*, J. chem. Soc., 1949, 1932).

The action of chlorine and bromine in light gives the cyclohexyl halide [*E. C. Britten* and *R. P. Perkins*, U.S.P., 2,287,665 (1942)]. The kinetics of this substitution has been studied in detail by *M. S. Kharasch et al.* (J. org. Chem., 1941, **6**, 818). They find that the reaction proceeds best in the presence of both air and light, slowly in the absence of one of these factors, and not at all when both are excluded. Under these conditions cyclohexane gives a monobromo-derivative only but methylcyclohexane gives some of the dibromo-compound. At 150° bromine gives 1:2:4:5-tetrabromocyclohexane. Condensation of cyclohexane with phosgene or oxalyl chloride yields hexahydrobenzoyl chloride (p. 222) (*M. S. Kharasch* and *H. C. Brown*, J. Amer. chem. Soc., 1940, **62**, 454). Cyclohexyl derivatives of the heavy metals, e.g. tin and lead, are formed when the halides of these metals react with cyclohexylmagnesium halides.

Methylcyclohexane is prepared by the hydrogenation of toluene or of a mixture of benzene and methane; it is also formed by the action of hydrogen iodide on cycloheptanol (*V. B. Markovnikov*, Compt. rend., 1892, **114**, 1068) and methylcyclohexanol (*N. D. Zelinsky*, Ber., 1896, **29**, 731). The action of bromine and aluminium tribromide produces pentabromotoluene.

1:1-**Dimethylcyclohexane** (gem.-*dimethylcyclohexane*) is best prepared by the catalytic hydrogenation of dimedone (p. 203) in the presence of platinum; 3:3-dimethylcyclohexanol is obtained as a by-product (Ref. 6, Table 1). The presence of the *gem*.-dimethyl group renders this compound very resistant to aromatisation.

The 1:2-, 1:3- and 1:4-dimethylcyclohexanes are prepared by the catalytic hydrogenation of the corresponding xylenes; the relative amounts of *cis*- and *trans*-isomers formed depend on the reaction conditions (*R. H. Baker* and *R. D. Schultz*, J. Amer. chem. Soc., 1937, **69**, 1250; *N. D. Zelinsky* and *E. I. Margolis*, Ber., 1932, **65**, 1613). The 1:3-isomer is also formed by the hydriodic acid reduction of camphoric acid and methylcyclohexane-3-carboxylic acid (*W. Lossen*, Ann., 1884, **225**, 10; *O. Aschan*, Ber., 1891, **24**, 2718; *O. Wallach*, *ibid.*, 1892, **25**, 920; *L. Balbiano*, Gazz., 1905, **35**, 144). The assignment of *cis* and *trans* configurations to the geometrical isomers of the dimethylcyclohexanes has heretofore been made on the basis of the Auwers-Skita generalisation that the *cis*-form possesses the higher boiling point, density and refractive index (*A. Skita* and *A. Schneck*, Ber., 1922, **55**, 144; *K. von Auwers et al.*, Ann., 1920, **420**, 89; Ber., 1924, **57**, 437). Later work, however has shown that these attributes should be allotted to the isomer of higher energy content. This criterion is fulfilled in the cases of the *cis*-1:2- and *cis*-1:4-isomers, but in the case of the 1:3-dimethylcyclohexanes it is the *trans*-isomer which answers to this specification (for discussion, see p. 10). The older assignments for the two 1:3-dimethylcyclohexanes must therefore be reversed (*K. S. Pitzer* and *C. W. Beckett*, J. Amer. chem. Soc., 1947, **69**, 977; *F. D. Rossini* and *K. S. Pitzer*, Science, 1947, **105**, 647; Ref. 21, Table 1).

Ethylcyclohexane is obtained by the complete hydrogenation of ethylbenzene or acetophenone; the latter reaction also furnishes hexahydroacetophenone and cyclohexylmethylcarbinol as by-products (*M. Faillebin*, Ann. Chim., 1925, **4**, 156, 410; *S. van Woerden*, Rec. Trav. chim., 1926, **45**, 124; *R. Adams* and *J. R. Marshall*, J. Amer. chem. Soc., 1928, **50**, 1970).

n-**Propylcyclohexane** is formed by the action of zinc on cyclohexyl chloride and *n*-propyl iodide (*N. Kurssanov*, Ber., 1901, **34**, 2035).

1-**Butyl**-2-**ethylcyclohexane** is formed by the hydrogenation of the dimer of hexatriene (p. 147) or, more conventionally, of the corresponding cyclohexene (Ref. 12, Table 1).

Hexaethylcyclohexane is produced as a mixture of stereoisomers when hexaethylbenzene is hydrogenated at 240°. From this may be isolated a solid isomer, m.p. 104.7–105°, which is equivocally termed the "*trans*"-form (Ref. 14, Table 1).

For other alkylcyclohexanes see *F. K. Signiano* and *P. L. Cramer*, J. Amer. chem. Soc., 1933, **55**, 3326; *R. Adams* and *J. R. Marshall*, *loc. cit.* For cyclohexanes with long hydrocarbon side-chains see *F. C. Whitmore et al.*, J. Amer. chem. Soc., 1947, **69**, 235; *A. D. Petrov* and *M. A. Tscheltzova*, C.A., 1943, **37**, 1993.

Phenylcyclohexane is produced by a Friedel-Crafts reaction between cyclohexyl chloride, benzene and aluminium chloride (Ref. 16, Table 1).

(b) Unsaturated hydrocarbons

(i) Cyclohexenes

These unsaturated hydrocarbons occur naturally to a limited extent; the low-temperature tar from East Indian coal, and rosin spirit both contain simple cyclohexene homologues (*B. Rassow* and *R. C. Bhattacharyya*, Chem. Ztbl., 1926, II, 2648).

Cyclohexenes are formed by the elimination of hydrogen halide from cyclohexyl halides by the action of alkali metal hydroxides, carbonates, acetates or phenates, or by interaction with tertiary amines (e.g. quinoline). They are also produced by the dry distillation of the hydrochlorides or phosphates of cyclohexylamines. An interesting method of formation is the Diels-Alder addition of olefines to dienes (*L. M. Joshel* and *L. W. Butz*, J. Amer. chem. Soc., 1941, **63**, 3350; see p. 129). The most widely used method of preparation involves the dehydration of cyclohexanols; agents which have been employed for this purpose include potassium bisulphate, phosphorus pentoxide, phosphoric acid, sulphuric acid, *p*-toluenesulphonic acid, anhydrous oxalic acid, formic acid, phthalic anhydride, zinc chloride, aluminium chloride and contact catalysts (*C. C. Price*, J. Amer. chem. Soc., 1939, **61**, 1847; *H. Barbier*, Helv., 1940, **23**, 519; *G. Chiurdoglu*, Bull. Soc. chim. Belg., 1938, **47**, 241; *A. Lacourt*, *ibid.*, 1927, **36**, 346; *H. Inoue*, Bull. chem. Soc. Japan, 1926, **1**, 219; *N. D. Zelinsky*, Ber., 1901, **34**, 3249). The dehydration of the tertiary cyclohexanols, readily prepared by the action of Grignard reagents on cyclohexanones, may frequently be accomplished by mere heating. A very mild method of preparing cyclohexenes from cyclohexanols which minimises the danger of isomerisation of the product is that introduced by *L. Tschugaev* (Ber., 1899, **32**, 3332). In this process the sodium or potassium derivative of the alcohol is treated with carbon disulphide to form the xanthate which is then methylated to give the methyl xanthate (I). Distillation of this latter ester gives the cyclohexene with elimination of methyl mercaptan and carbonyl sulphide.

$$C_6H_{11}\text{-OCSSMe} \longrightarrow C_6H_{10} + COS + MeSH$$

(I)

This reaction is of further interest since it takes place by *cis*-elimination, in contrast with the ionic type of dehydration where *trans*-elimination is the rule (*D. H. R. Barton*, J. chem. Soc., 1949, 2174; *D. J. Cram*, J. Amer. chem. Soc., 1949, **71**, 3883).

3-Alkylcyclohex-1-enes may be readily prepared in a pure state by the action of alkylmagnesium halides on 3-chlorocyclohex-1-ene (*A. Berlande*, Compt. rend., 1941, **213**, 437).

Properties of cyclohexenes. Cyclohexenes undergo addition to the double bond in the same way as acyclic olefines. The additions of nitrosyl chloride, nitrogen trioxide and nitrogen tetroxide to give respectively nitrosochlorides, nitrosites and nitrosates are of particular value, especially in the terpene field, the products being usually well-defined, crystalline compounds.

The cyclohexenes undergo very ready autoxidation to give the corresponding cyclohex-2-enyl hydroperoxides (see p. 174). In the presence of metallic phthalocyanines the corresponding cyclohex-1-en-3-ones are formed (*C. Paquot,* Bull. Soc. chim. Fr., 1941, [v], **8**, 695). Peracids react with the hydrocarbons to form epoxides (p. 169); similar products have been obtained using benzoyl peroxide (*S. S. Nametkin,* Ber., 1923, **56**, 1803) but later work on the interaction of this reagent with cyclohexene resulted in a complicated mixture containing cyclohexyl and cyclohex-2-enyl benzoates, cyclohex-2-enylcyclohex-2-ene and 3-phenylcyclohex-1-ene (*E. H. Farmer* and *S. E. Michael,* J. chem. Soc., 1942, 513).

In the presence of catalysts such as palladium (*R. P. Linstead et al.*, Nature, 1952, **169**, 100; *N. D. Zelinsky,* Ber., 1924, **57**, 1066), vanadium sesquioxide-alumina (*A. F. Plate* and *G. A. Tarasova,* Brit. chem. Abstr., 1947, A II, 14) or nickel (*B. B. Corson* and *V. N. Ipatiev,* J. Amer. chem. Soc., 1939, **61**, 1056) cyclohexenes disproportionate into a mixture of the corresponding cyclohexanes and benzenoid hydrocarbons. The ease of this hydrogen exchange has been made the basis of an elegant method of hydrogenation not involving gaseous hydrogen (*R. P. Linstead et al., loc. cit.*). Complete dehydrogenation to benzenes may readily be accomplished at relatively low temperatures by reaction with chloranil or other quinones with high oxidation potentials (*R. T. Arnold et al.*, J. Amer. chem. Soc., 1940, **62**, 983).

Acid chlorides react with cyclohexenes under the influence of aluminium chloride to form 1-acylcyclohexenes (*K. Dimroth* and *O. Lüderitz,* Ber., 1948, **81**, 242; *C. D. Nenitzescu* and *V. Przemetzky, ibid.*, 1941, **74**, 676; *L. Ruzicka et al.*, Helv., 1931, **14**, 1151). This reagents also brings about the condensation of cyclohexenes with phenols to give cyclohexylphenols (*E. Levas,* Bull. Soc. chim. Fr., 1948, [v], **15**, 469; *M. Nortz, ibid.*, 1947, [v], **14**, 893). Similar condensations take place in the presence of acetic acid-sulphuric acid mixtures (*W. Schrauth,* Ber., 1924, **57**, 854).

The thermal decomposition of cyclohexenes has been shown to differ fundamentally from the cracking of paraffins. Instead of the formation of radicals, ring fission occurs into two unsaturated molecules, an ethylene and a butadiene; the process is thus the reverse of one of the methods of formation described above. Cyclohexene itself breaks down at 800°/10 mm. to give nearly quantitative yields of ethylene and butadiene and similar results are obtained with 1-methyl-, 1-phenyl- and 1-vinyl-cyclohex-1-enes; 1-ethylcyclohex-1-ene is exceptional in giving much methane and hydrogen but no butadiene (*F. O. Rice et al.*, J. Amer. chem. Soc., 1944, **66**, 765; 1938, **60**, 955).

TABLE 2

HYDROCARBONS OF THE CYCLOHEXENE SERIES

Compound	B.p.°/mm	$n_D^{20°}$	Ref.
Cyclohexene	83 (m.p. –103·7)	1·4450	See text
Methylenecyclohexane	102·5	1·4491	1
1-Methylcyclohex-1-ene	110·6	1·4496	2, 3
3-Methylcyclohex-1-ene	103·5	1·4408	4
4-Methylcyclohex-1-ene	102·1	1·4419	4
1:2-Dimethylcyclohex-1-ene	135·5	1·4587	5, 6
1:4-Dimethylcyclohex-1-ene	128·7 (m.p. –59·4)	1·4437	6, 7, 8, 9
1:5-Dimethylcyclohex-1-ene	129	1·4466	7, 10
3:5-Dimethylcyclohex-1-ene	126	1·4508	9, 11
4:4-Dimethylcyclohex-1-ene	120	1·4456	12
Ethylidenecyclohexane	136	1·4639	9
1-Ethylcyclohex-1-ene	134	1·4577	13, 14
3-Ethylcyclohex-1-ene	131·5	1·4490	15
1-Vinylcyclohex-1-ene	143	1·4950	16
1:3:5-Trimethylcyclohex-1-ene	139	1·4491	9
1-Ethyl-3-methylcyclohex-1-ene	148	1·4532	7
2-Ethyl-4-methylcyclohex-1-ene	150	1·4527	7
3-Methyl-2-vinylcyclohex-1-ene	157	1·4978	17
1-Methyl-3-vinylcyclohex-1-ene	146	1·4513	7
1-*n*-Propylcyclohex-1-ene	156	1·4577	7, 14
3-*n*-Propylcyclohex-1-ene	153	1·4515	18
1-*iso*Propylcyclohex-1-ene	155	1·4615	7, 14
3-*iso*Propylcyclohex-1-ene	150	1·4510	18
1-Ethylidene-3-methylcyclohexane	152	1·4590	7
Allylcyclohexane	149	1·4536	19
n-Propylidenecyclohexane	158	1·4631	14, 20
*iso*Propylidenecyclohexane	161	1·4723	14, 20
1-*n*-Butylcyclohex-1-ene	180	1·4600	7
3-*n*-Butylcyclohex-1-ene	178	1·4530	18
1-*tert.*-Butylcyclohex-1-ene	170	1·4533	21
4-*tert.*-Butylcyclohex-1-ene	169	1·4600	21
1:2:4:5-Tetramethylcyclohex-1-ene	169	1·4605	22
1-Phenylcyclohex-1-ene	136/25 (m.p. 11)		23
3-Phenylcyclohex-1-ene	235	1·5440	15, 18
1-Benzylcyclohex-1-ene	125/11·5	1·5410	24, 25
3-Benzylcyclohex-1-ene	150/35	1·5360	18

[1] *R. T. Arnold* and *J. F. Dowdall*, J. Amer. chem. Soc., 1948, **70**, 2590.
[2] *C. C. Price, ibid.*, 1939, **61**, 1847.
[3] *O. Wallach*, Ann., 1908, **359**, 287.
[4] *H. Adkins* and *A. K. Roebuck*, J. Amer. chem. Soc., 1948, **70**, 4041.
[5] *H. Meerwein*, Ann., 1914, **405**, 147.
[6] *G. Chiurdoglu*, Bull. Soc. chim. Belg., 1938, **47**, 241.
[7] *M. Mousseron et al.*, Bull. Soc. chim. Fr., 1946, **13**, 222.
[8] *N. D. Zelinsky* and *A. Gorsky*, Ber., 1908, **41**, 2632.
[9] *K. von Auwers et al.*, Ann., 1915, **410**, 257.

[10] *O. Wallach*, Ann., 1913, **395**, 80.
[11] *M. Mousseron* and *F. Winternitz*, Bull. Soc. chim. Fr., 1945, [v], **12**, 71.
[12] *D. C. Hibbitt* and *R. P. Linstead*, J. chem. Soc., 1936, 470.
[13] *F. O. Rice* and *M. T. Murphy*, J. Amer. chem. Soc., 1944, **66**, 765.
[14] *O. Wallach*, Ann., 1908, **360**, 26.
[15] *A. Berlande*, Compt. rend., 1941, **213**, 437, 484.
[16] *P. A. Robins* and *J. Walker*, J. chem. Soc., 1952, 642.
[17] *P. A. Robins* and *J. Walker*, *ibid.*, 1952, 1610.
[18] *A. Berlande*, Bull. Soc. chim. Fr., 1942, [v], **9**, 642, 644.
[19] *B. de Resseguier*, *ibid.*, 1910, [iv], **7**, 431.
[20] *W. A. Mosher*, J. Amer. chem. Soc., 1940, **62**, 552.
[21] *L. Schmerling*, *ibid.*, 1947, **69**, 1121.
[22] *A. Skita* and *A. Schneck*, Ber., 1922, **55**, 152.
[23] *C. R. Noller* and *G. K. Kaneko*, J. Amer. chem. Soc., 1935, **57**, 2442.
[24] *K. von Auwers*, Ber., 1935, **68**, 2174.
[25] *D. N. Kurssanov*, Chem. Ztbl., 1931, I, 3112.

Some examples of hydrocarbons of the cyclohexene series are given in Table 2.

Cyclohexene is formed by the dehydrohalogenation of cyclohexyl halides with quinoline or alcoholic potassium hydroxide (*V. B. Markovnikov*, Ann., 1898, **302**, 27), by the action of sodium on 1:2-dibromocyclohexane (*N. D. Prjanishnikov*, Ber., 1934, **67**, 64) and by the addition of ethylene to butadiene at 200°/400 at. (p. 129). It is prepared by the dehydration of cyclohexanol which may be accomplished by heating with sulphuric acid (Org. Synth., Coll. Vol. I, 1941, 183), phosphoric acid (Org. Synth., Coll. Vol. II, 1943, 152), oxalic acid (*N. D. Zelinsky*, Ber., 1901, **34**, 3252), potassium bisulphate (*L. Brunel*, Bull. Soc. chim. Fr., 1905, [iii], **33**, 270) or thionyl chloride (*P. Carré*, *ibid.*, 1936, [v], **3**, 144).

High temperature cracking of cyclohexene leads to ethylene and butadiene as described above; in the presence of palladium or nickel disproportionation to benzene and cyclohexane occurs. With alumina at 480° isomerisation to 1- and 3-methylcyclopentenes takes place (*H. Adkins* and *A. K. Roebuck*, J. Amer. chem. Soc., 1948, 70, 5041). Treatment of cyclohexene with hydrogen fluoride gives dicyclohexyl, cyclohexylcyclohex-1-ene and higher polymers (*S. M. McElvain* and *J. W. Langston*, J. Amer. chem. Soc., 1944, **66**, 1759). Polymerisation also takes place at 350° under very high pressure, the highest polymer detected being a pentamer (*N. D. Zelinsky* and *L. F. Vereschtschagin*, Brit. chem. Abstr., 1945, B II, 358).

Cyclohexene undergoes the general oxidation reactions already described. Ozone gives a stable *ozonide*, m.p. 75°, which is decomposed by water with the formation of adipaldehyde and adipic acid (*C. Harries*, Ber., 1909, **42**, 694; *F. G. Fischer*, *ibid.*, 1932, **65**, 1471). Air oxidation at 410° in the presence of vanadium pentoxide gives rise to maleic acid (*N. A. Milas* and *W. L. Walsh*, J. Amer. chem. Soc., 1939, **61**, 633); gaseous oxygen in the presence of colloidal osmium yields cyclohex-2-en-1-ol (*A. Kötz* and *K. Richter*, J. pr. Chem., 1925, **111**, 373). The action of chromium trioxide yields cyclohex-2-en-1-one (*F. C.

Whitmore and *C. W. Pedlow*, J. Amer. chem. Soc., 1941, **63**, 758); this product is also obtained with *tert.*-butyl chromate (*R. V. Oppenauer* and *H. Oberrauch*, C.A., 1950, **44**, 3871). Selenium dioxide in acetic anhydride solution gives mainly 1-acetoxycyclohex-2-ene together with a little 1:4-diacetoxycylohex-2-ene (*J. A. Arbusov et al.*, Bull. Acad. Sci. U.S.S.R., 1945, 163). A similar type of allyl substitution takes place with N-bromosuccinimide to yield 1-bromocyclohex-2-ene and 1:4-dibromocyclohex-2-ene (*K. Ziegler et al.*, Ann., 1942, **551**, 80).

Nitrosyl chloride adds to cyclohexene to give the *nitrosochloride*, m.p. 152°. With methanolic mercuric chloride cyclohexene furnishes two stereoisomeric 1-*chloromercuri-2-methoxycyclohexanes*, α-form m.p. 63·5, β-form m.p. 114°; mercuric acetate reacts similarly (*J. Romeyn* and *G. F. Wright*, J. Amer. chem. Soc., 1947, **69**, 697). The reaction between cyclohexene and *tert.*-butyl chloride in the presence of aluminium chloride yields chiefly 1-chloro-3-*tert.*-butylcyclohex-1-ene, 1-chloro-1-*tert.*-butylcyclohexane and 1-*tert.*-butylcyclohex-1-ene (*L. Schmerling, ibid.*, 1947, **69**, 1121). The same catalyst and acyl chlorides yield acylcyclohexenes as described above. Cyclohexene condenses with formaldehyde in the presence of acetic acid and sulphuric acid to give a mixture of products including 2-hydroxymethylcyclohexan-1-ol diacetate and 1-hydroxymethylcyclohex-1-ene acetate (*S. Olsen* and *H. Padberg*, Brit. chem. Abstr., 1947, A II, 494). In the absence of acetic acid this reaction gives the methylene ether of 2-hydroxymethylcyclohexan-1-ol; with hydrochloric acid and zinc chloride the product is 1-hydroxymethyl-2-chlorocyclohexane (*C. D. Nenitzescu* and *V. Przemetzky*, Ber., 1941, **74**, 676).

1-**Methylcyclohex**-1-**ene** is the most stable of the three possible isomers as would be expected from its greatest degree of hyperconjugation; it may be identified as its solid *nitrol-piperidide*, $C_7H_{12}(NO)NC_5H_{10}$, m.p. 153°. It is obtained by the dehydration of 1- or 2-methylcyclohexan-1-ols (*C. C. Price*, J. Amer. chem. Soc., 1939, **61**, 1847). Oxidation with ethanolic selenium dioxide gives 2-methylcyclohex-2-en-1-one (*L. W. Butz et al.*, J. Org. Chem., 1947, **12**, 122) and with lead tetra-acetate it yields a mixture of 1-methylcyclohex-1-en-3-ol and -6-ol acetates (*M. Mousseron et al.*, Compt. rend., 1947, **224**, 1230). More vigorous oxidation of the hydrocarbon gives 6-ketoheptanoic acid thereby confirming its structure (*O. Wallach*, Ann., 1908, **359**, 287).

3-**Methylcyclohex**-1-**ene** is obtained, admixed with the 4-methyl isomer from which it is separated by fractional distillation, by the dehydration of 3-methylcyclohexan-1-ol; the optically active alcohol gives the optically active hydrocarbon, $[\alpha]_{579}$ 80·44°. The structure of the hydrocarbon is proved by oxidation to α-methyladipic acid. As mentioned above 4-**methylcyclohex**-1-**ene** is one of the products of dehydration of 3-methylcyclohexanol; it may be obtained in a purer form by the dehydration of 4-methylcyclohexanol (*R. Dupont*, Bull. Soc. chim. Belg., 1936, **45**, 57). Attempts to achieve an asymmetric synthesis by employing optically active dehydrating agents such as camphor-10-sulphonic acid led only to inactive products.

1:2-**Dimethylcyclohex**-1-**ene** is formed by dehydration of 2:2-dimethylcyclohexanol, a methyl group migrating in a Wagner-Meerwein type of transformation. It forms a crystalline *dibromide*, m.p. 154° (*H. Meerwein*, Ann., 1914, **405**, 147). 3:5-**Dimethylcyclohex**-1-**ene** is obtained (mainly as the *cis* isomer) by the action of methylmagnesium iodide on 3-chloro-5-methylcyclohex-1-ene (*M. Mousseron* and *F. Winternitz*, Bull. Soc. chim. Fr., 1945, [v], **12**, 71). 1:5:5-**Trimethylcyclohex**-1-**ene** (*α-cyclogeraniolene*) and 1:3:3-**trimethylcyclohex**-1-**ene** (*β-cyclogeraniolene*) are produced from the terpene geraniolene by the action of sulphuric acid (*C. Harries*, Ber., 1904, **37**, 848); the *α*-isomer is also obtained by the zinc chloride dehydration of 3:5:5-trimethylcyclohexanol (*O. Wallach*, Ann., 1902, **324**, 97, 112).

(ii) Compounds with unsaturated side chains

1-**Vinylcyclohex**-1-**ene**, *benzoquinone adduct*, m.p. 87–88°, *maleic anhydride adduct*, m.p. 52–53°, is prepared by potassium bisulphate dehydration of 1-vinylcyclohexanol (Ref. 16, Table 2; *J. W. Cook* and *C. A. Lawrence*, J. chem. Soc., 1938, 58). Similar dehydration of either geometrical isomer of 2-methyl-1-vinylcyclohexan-1-ol yields a mixture of the isomeric 1-*methyl*-2-*vinyl*- and 3-*methyl*-2-*vinyl-cyclohex*-1-*enes*; only the latter forms a *benzoquinone adduct*, m.p. 125–126° (Ref. 17).

Unsaturated derivatives of cyclohexane are known in which the double bond is neither completely contained in the ring (e.g., as in cyclohexene) nor completely outside the nucleus (e.g., as in vinylcyclohexane). These are the alkylidenecyclohexanes where one of the carbon atoms involved in the double bond is part of the ring, the other being outside the ring; such a double bond may conveniently be termed "semicyclic". These compounds are of special importance in the terpene field. They are generally prepared by the decarboxylation of cyclohexylideneacetic acids, the dehydration of cyclohexylcarbinols and the dehydrohalogenation of cyclohexylcarbinyl halides. The alkylidenecyclohexanes are thermodynamically less stable than the isomeric 1-alkylcyclohex-1-enes and may be readily transformed into these latter compounds by acid catalysts. Thus conversion of methylenecyclohexane into 1-methylcyclohex-1-ene is attended by an energy release of 21 kcal./mol. (*W. A. Roth*, Z. Elektrochem., 1911, **17**, 793). On the other hand, a cyclic double bond will in general only become semicyclic when a conjugated system is thereby set up (see *W. Hückel*, "Der gegenwärtige Stand der Spannungstheorie", Berlin, 1927). The alkylidenecyclohexanes may readily be distinguished from their cyclohexene isomers by their higher specific gravities, higher boiling points and abnormal molecular refractivities (*O. Wallach*, Ann., 1908, **360**, 36; *K. von Auwers*, *ibid.*, 1915, **410**, 287).

The parent member of the series, **methylenecyclohexane**, may be obtained by the decarboxylation of cyclohexylideneacetic acid (*O. Wallach*, Ann., 1908, **359**, 291) and by the action of alcoholic potassium hydroxide on cyclohexylmethyl iodide (*A. Favorsky* and *I. Borgmann*, Ber., 1907, **40**, 4863). It is best prepared by the pyrolytic elimination of acetic acid from cyclohexylmethyl acetate (*R. T. Arnold* and *J. F. Dowdall*, J. Amer. chem. Soc., 1948, **70**, 2590). On being treated with alcoholic sulphuric acid it undergoes rearrangement to 1-methylcyclohex-1-ene. Potassium permanganate oxidation furnishes cyclohexanone and 1-hydroxymethylcyclohexan-1-ol. Oxidation with selenium dioxide in acetic acid solution gives 2-methylenecyclohexyl acetate (*M. Mousseron et al.*, Compt. rend., 1947, **224**, 1230). Methylenecyclohexane undergoes various addition reactions with concomitant shift of the double bond into the ring. Thus formaldehyde gives 2-cyclohex-1-enylethanol (I), sulphur trioxide yields cyclohex-1-enylmethanesulphonic acid (II) and maleic anhydride, after subsequent hydrolysis, furnishes cyclohex-1-enylmethylsuccinic acid (III) (*R. T. Arnold* and *J. F. Dowdall, loc. cit.*; *K. Alder et al.*, Ann., 1949, **565**, 73, 99).

$CH_2·CH_2OH$ (I) $CH_2·SO_3H$ (II) $CH_2·CH(CO_2H)·CH_2·CO_2H$ (III)

M. Mousseron et al. (Bull. Soc. chim. Fr., 1946, [v], **13**, 222) have prepared optically active semicyclic compounds by reacting active 3-methylcyclohexanone with zinc and the appropriate α-bromo-ester followed by dehydration, hydrolysis and decarboxylation.

Ethylidenecyclohexane may be obtained by the above general methods and also by the Kishner-Wolff reduction of 1-acetylcyclohex-1-ene (*G. Lardelli* and *O. Jeger*, Helv., 1949, **32**, 1817). This latter interesting method, involving an unexpected double bond shift, provides a useful preparative procedure for hitherto inaccessible semicyclic unsaturated cyclohexanes.

1-Methylene-2-allylidenecyclohexane (VI), b.p. 62–63/7 mm., n_D^{20} 1·5225 is the simplest compound containing the characteristic conjugated triene system of the vitamins D. It is obtained by the reaction between allylmagnesium bromide and 2-dimethylaminomethylcyclohexanone (IV), dehydration of the resulting carbinol (V) and removal of the tertiary amino group by exhaustive methylation (*N. A. Milas* and *W. L. Alderson*, J. Amer. chem. Soc., 1939, **61**, 2534).

CH_2NMe_2, =O (IV) ⟶ CH_2NMe_2, OH, $CH_2·CH{=}CH_2$ (V) ⟶ $=CH_2$, $=CH·CH{=}CH_2$ (VI)

3-*Cyclohexylidene-2-methylprop-1-ene*, b.p. 103–103·5°/62 mm., is prepared by the action of methylmagnesium bromide on methyl cyclohexylideneacetate (*D. N. Kursanov* and *A. S. Kursanova*, J. gen. Chem. U.S.S.R., 1943, **13**, 184).

Unsaturated derivatives of cyclohexane with a completely exocyclic double bond may be obtained by dehydration of the corresponding carbinol or by partial catalytic hydrogenation of the corresponding acetylenic compound (*M. Bourguel*, Bull. Soc. chim. Fr., 1927 [iv], **41**, 1475). Allylcyclohexanes may also be prepared by the action of allyl bromide on the relevant cyclohexylmagnesium halide (Ref. 19). An interesting highly unsaturated compound of this type is the dimer of hexatriene, b.p. 50–55°/3 mm., n_D^{20} 1·5137, *maleic anhydride adduct* m.p. 178°, which possesses the constitution 3-*allyl*-4-*butadienylcyclohex*-1-*ene* (VII) (*M. S. Kharasch* and *E. Sternfeld*, J. Amer. chem. Soc., 1939, **61**, 2318).

$CH{=}CH_2$

$CH{=}CH{-}CH{=}CH_2$

(VII)

(iii) Cyclohexadienes (dihydrobenzenes)

Compounds of this class fall into two series, the conjugated cyclohexa-1:3-dienes and the unconjugated cyclohexa-1:4-dienes. Some of the naturally occurring terpenes, e.g. α-phellandrene, α- and γ-terpinenes, which may be regarded as dihydro-*p*-cymenes, belong to this class.

The cyclohexadienes may be obtained:

(1) by the dehydration of cyclohexanediols or cyclohexenols by the methods already detailed for the preparation of cyclohexenes;

(2) by the dehydrohalogenation of dihalogenocyclohexanes by quinoline (*C. Harries*, Ber., 1909, **42**, 693) or by alcoholic sodium ethoxide (*A. Berlande*, Compt. rend., 1941, **213**, 437; *M. Mousseron* and *F. Winternitz*, Bull. Soc. chim. Fr., 1945, [v], **12**, 70);

(3) by the dry distillation in carbon dioxide of diaminocyclohexane phosphates (*C. Harries* and *W. Antoni*, Ann., 1903, **328**, 88; *A. W. Crossley*, J. chem. Soc., 1909, **95**, 930).

These methods give fairly pure 1:3-dienes when applied to the relevant 1:2-disubstituted cyclohexanes, but a mixture of the 1:3- and 1:4-dienes is obtained when 1:3- and 1:4-disubstituted cyclohexanes are employed. By far the best method of obtaining pure cyclohexa-1:4-dienes is by the reduction of aromatic hydrocarbons by sodium and alcohol using liquid ammonia as solvent (*A. J. Birch*, J. chem. Soc., 1944, 430; *J. P. Wibaut* and *F. A. Haak*, Rec. Trav. chim., 1948, **67**, 85).

The cyclohexadienes are highly reactive compounds and are readily dehydrogenated to aromatic hydrocarbons (aromatised) by many oxidising agents. They give characteristic red or purple colours in the presence of sulphuric acid in alcohol or in acetic anhydride. The two types of diene may be readily distinguished by the characteristic maximal absorption in the ultra-violet displayed by the 1:3-dienes and also by the ready reaction of the latter with dienophiles to give bridged-ring compounds (p. 337).

Some members of the series are shown in Table 3.

Cyclohexa-1:3-diene ($\Delta^{1:3}$-*dihydrobenzene*) may be prepared by the dehydrohalogenation of 1:2- or 1:3-dihalogenocyclohexanes with triethanolamine,

TABLE 3

HYDROCARBONS OF THE CYCLOHEXADIENE SERIES

Compound	B.p.°/mm.	n_D(°)	Ref.
Cyclohexa-1:3-diene	80·5 m.p. –95	1·4712 (18)	1, 2
Cyclohexa-1:4-diene	88·9 m.p. –49·2	1·4725 (20)	1, 3
1-Methylcyclohexa-1:3-diene	110	1·4763 (20)	4
1-Methylcyclohexa-2:4-diene	106	1·4613 (18)	2, 5, 6
1-Methylcyclohexa-2:6-diene	108	1·4662 (18)	2, 5, 6
1:2-Dimethylcyclohexa-2:6-diene	135·5	1·4895 (20)	1, 7, 8, 9
1:3-Dimethylcyclohexa-1:3-diene	135	1·4856 (20)	8
1:3-Dimethylcyclohexa-3:5-diene	129	1·4747 (16)	1, 10
1:3-Dimethylcyclohexa-2:4-diene	129	1·4675 (20)	11
1:4-Dimethylcyclohexa-2:6-diene	127	1·4637 (18)	2, 6
1:4-Dimethylcyclohexa-1:3-diene	138	1·4797 (20)	6, 12
1:4-Dimethylcyclohexa-2:4-diene	128·5	1·4457 (20)	11
1-Ethylcyclohexa-1:3-diene	137		13
1-Ethylcyclohexa-2:6-diene	133	1·4650 (18)	2,6
1:1:4-Trimethylcyclohexa-3:5-diene	135		14
1:3-Diethylcyclohexa-1:3-diene	68/9		15
1:1:3:5-Tetramethylcyclohexa-2:4-diene	155		16
1-*n*-Propylcyclohexa-2:6-diene	157	1·4743 (18)	2, 6
1-*iso*Propylcyclohexa-2:6-diene	151	1·4704 (18)	2, 6
1-*iso*Propylcyclohexa-2:4-diene	31/4	1·4842 (15)	17
1-*n*-Butylcyclohexa-2:6-diene	180	1·4737 (18)	2, 6
1-Phenylcyclohexa-1:3-diene	m.p. 66		13

[1] *C. Harries* and *W. Antoni*, Ann., 1903, **328**, 88, 115.
[2] *M. Mousseron* and *F. Winternitz*, Bull. Soc. chim. Fr., 1946, [v], **13**, 232.
[3] *J. P. Wibaut* and *F. A. Haak*, Rec. Trav. chim., 1948, **67**, 85.
[4] *C. Harries*, Ber., 1908, **41**, 1698.
[5] *N. D. Zelinsky* and *A. Gorsky*, Ber., 1908, **41**, 2484.
[6] *M. Mousseron* and *F. Winternitz*, Bull. Soc. chim. Fr., 1945, [v], **12**, 67, 70.
[7] *J. Piccard*, Ber., 1892, **25**, 2453.
[8] *W. N. Haworth*, J. chem. Soc., 1913, **103**, 1242.
[9] *P. C. Guha* and *G. D. Nazra*, Brit. chem. Abstr., 1940, AII, 87.
[10] *K. Auwers* and *G. Peters*, Ber., 1910, **43**, 3111.
[11] *N. D. Zelinsky* and *A. Gorsky*, Ber., 1908, **41**, 2630.
[12] *K. Auwers et al.*, Ber., 1908, **41**, 1816; 1909, **42**, 2404.
[13] *A. Berlande*, Compt. rend., 1941, **213**, 437.
[14] *V. P. Hirsjärvi*, C.A., 1939, **33**, 6255.
[15] *E. E. Blaise* and *M. Maire*, Bull. Soc. chim. Fr., 1908, [iv], **3**, 420.
[16] *J. Schmitt*, Ann., 1941, **547**, 256.
[17] *D. T. C. Gillespie et al.*, J. chem. Soc., 1938, 1820.

quinoline, triethylamine or alcoholic sodium ethoxide. The first two reagents give rise to benzene, cyclohexene and cyclohexa-1:4-diene as by-products but the last two reagents yield a much purer compound (Ref. 2, Table 3; *F. Hofmann* and *P. Damm*, Chem. Ztbl., 1926, I, 2342). The elimination of acetic acid from cyclohex-2-enyl acetate by potassium bisulphate gives the diene in high yield (*J. A. Arbusov et al.*, Bull. Acad. Sci. U.R.S.S., 1945, 163). The diene is also formed by the distillation of 1:3-diaminocyclohexane diphosphate (Ref. 1) and cyclohex-1-enyltrimethylammonium bromide (*M. Tiffeneau* and *B. Tchoubar*, Compt. rend., 1941, **212**, 581).

Cyclohexa-1:3-diene readily dimerises to a bridged ring compound, dicyclohexadiene (p. 348). It reacts with bromine to form firstly 1:4-*dibromocyclohex-2-ene*, m.p. 109° and then *tetrabromocyclohexane*, m.p. 87–88°. Perbenzoic acid gives 1:2-epoxycyclohex-3-ene (*M. Tiffeneau* and *B. Tchoubar*, *loc. cit.*; cf. Table 8). The hydrocarbon has had notable application in many diene syntheses whereby bridged ring compounds are formed (p. 337).

Cyclohexa-1:4-diene ($\Delta^{1:4}$-*dihydrobenzene*) is most readily obtained in pure form by the sodium-alcohol reduction of benzene at −50° in liquid ammonia solution (Ref. 3, Table 3). It is also obtained by the dehydration of cyclohexane-1:3- and 1:4-diols with sulphuric acid (*J. B. Senderens*, Compt. rend., 1923, **177**, 1183; *M. Tiffeneau* and *B. Tchoubar*, *loc. cit.*) and by the thermal decomposition of 1:4-diaminocyclohexane phosphate.

The 1:4-diene is stable if kept in the dark under nitrogen, but otherwise shows a ready tendency to polymerise. With bromine it yields firstly 4:5-*dibromocyclohex-1-ene*, m.p. 35°, and then two stereoisomeric 1:2:4:5-*tetrabromocyclohexanes*, m.p. 188° and 218° (see p. 154). The products of oxidation of the hydrocarbon depend upon the reagent; chromium trioxide yields benzoquinone, potassium permanganate forms firstly cyclohexane-1:2:4:5-tetrol and then malonic acid and perbenzoic acid gives firstly 1:2-epoxycyclohex-4-ene (*M. Tiffeneau* and *B. Tchoubar*, *loc. cit.*) and then 1:2:4:5-*diepoxycyclohexane*, m.p. 110° (*N. D. Zelinsky*, Ber., 1931, **64**, 1399; *P. Bedos*, Compt. rend., 1934, **196**, 625).

Cyclohexa-1:2-diene, which would be a cyclic allene, appears to be incapable of stable existence (see *C. W. A. Lely*, Chem. Weekbl., 1925, **22**, 501; *N. A. Domnin*, J. gen. Chem. U.S.S.R., 1945, **15**, 461).

1-**Methylcyclohexa**-1:3-**diene** ($\Delta^{1:3}$-*dihydrotoluene*) is obtained in an impure state by the thermal decomposition of 3-amino-1-methylcyclohexane phosphate. Permanganate oxidation gives 3-methylcyclohexan-1-one-2:3-diol and thence succinic and oxalic acid (Ref. 4, Table 3).

1-**Methylcyclohexa**-2:4-**diene** has been prepared in an optically active (*d*-) form by the action of bases on *d*-3:4-dibromo-1-methylcyclohexane (Ref. 6). The same authors prepared several dienes of this type, the constitutions of which were established by the addition of hydrogen chloride to give 1-alkyl-3-chlorocyclohex-1-enes; these latter compounds were simultaneously hydrolysed and oxidised to the corresponding ketones, identified by their semicarbazones.

1:2-**Dimethylcyclohexa**-2:6-**diene** (*dihydro-o-xylene; cantharene*) is obtained by the distillation with soda-lime of cantharic acid, a rearrangement product of cantharidin. It is also produced by the dehydration of 1:2-dimethylcyclohex-2-en-1-ol (Ref. 8, Table 3).

1:3-**Dimethylcyclohexa**-3:5-**diene** has been obtained from 1:3-dimethyl-3:5-

diaminocyclohexane and by the reductive dehalogenation of 5-chloro-1:3-dimethylcyclohexa-3:5-diene (Refs. 1, 10; Table 3).

1:4-**Dimethylcyclohexa**-1:3-**diene** is obtained by a curious reaction in which 2:5-dimethyl-2-dichloromethylcyclohex-5-en-1-one is boiled with alcoholic potassium hydroxide. The reaction course is postulated as follows.

Confirmation of the structure is afforded by the formation of acetonylacetone by oxidation of the compound with potassium permanganate.

The laevorotatory form of 1-iso**propylcyclohexa**-2:4-**diene,** $[\alpha]_D$ $-29{\cdot}16^0$ is obtained by the potassium bisulphate dehydration of *l*-4-*iso*propylcyclohex-2-en-1-ol (*l*-cryptol) (Ref. 17, Table 3).

1:2-**Dimethyl**-3-β-**phenylethylcyclohexa**-1:3-**diene** is of interest since, by treatment with stannic chloride, it is cyclised to 1:2-dimethylhexahydrophenanthrene (*A. Bergmann* and *A. Weizmann,* J. org. Chem., 1939, **4,** 266).

Semibenzenes. This name is applied to cyclohexa-1:4-dienes with an additional semicyclic double bond of the general formula (I).

They are obtained as shown by the dehydration of the corresponding tertiary carbinols by cold dilute sulphuric acid. They are unstable compounds, polymerising with great ease; on being heated with acids they rearrange to benzenoid compounds (*K. Auwers* and *K. Ziegler,* Ann., 1921, **425,** 217).

(iv) Cyclohexylacetylenes

Cyclohexane derivatives with a triple bond in the ring are not known and would not be expected to be capable of existence from steric considerations. In an attempt to prepare a compound of this type, 3:4-dibromo-1-methylcyclohex-3-ene was treated with sodium in ether but only resins resulted (*N. A. Domnin,* J. gen. Chem. U.S.S.R., 1939, **9,** 1983). Cyclohexylacetylenes with a triple bond in the side-chain can, however, be readily obtained by methods analogous to those used in the aliphatic series.

Cyclohexylacetylene, b.p. 132^0, n_D^{20} $1{\cdot}4597$, is obtained by the dehydrohalogenation of 1-chloro-1-cyclohexylethylene or of 1:1-dichloro-1-cyclohexylethane. 3-**Cyclohexylprop**-1-**yne,** b.p. $63^0/24$ mm., is prepared by the action of sodamide on 2-bromo-3-cyclohexylprop-1-ene (Org. Synth., Coll. Vol. I, 191); homologues are obtained in like fashion (*M. Mousseron*, Compt. rend., 1943, **217**, 155; Bull. Soc. chim. Fr., 1946 [v], **13**, 239; *M. Bourguel*, Ann. Chim., 1925, **3**, 385).

1-Ethynylcyclohex-1-enes, prepared by the dehydration of the corresponding 1-ethynylcyclohexan-1-ols by means of aluminium phosphate or phosphorus oxychloride-pyridine, are important starting materials for the synthesis of vitamin A and its analogues. In this way are prepared **1-ethynylcyclohex-1-ene** itself, b.p. 56°/40 mm., n_D^{17} 1·4978 and the 2-*methyl*-, b.p. 70°/35 mm. n_D^{15} 1·4937, 6:6-*dimethyl*-, b.p. 88°/60 mm., n_D^{15} 1·4873 and 2:6:6-*trimethyl*-derivative, b.p. 69°/18 mm., n_D^{14} 1·4925 (*I. M. Heilbron, E. R. H. Jones et al.*, J. chem. Soc., 1949, 287, 742, 2023, 3120, 3123; 1950, 633; *E. R. H, Jones et al.*, *ibid.*, 1951, 2652; *B. A. Hems et al.*, *ibid.*, 1952, 1094; *N. A. Milas et al.*, J. Amer. chem. Soc., 1948, **70**, 1829; *H. Sobotka* and *J. D. Chanley*, *ibid.*, 1949, **71**, 4136).

3. Halogen derivatives of the hydrocarbons

(a) Saturated halogen compounds

These compounds may be obtained by the direct halogenation of the hydrocarbons [*E. C. Britton* and *R. P. Perkins*, U.S.P., 2,287, 665 (1942)] and by the addition of halogens and hydrogen halides to cyclohexenes and cyclohexadienes. The preparation of the monohalogenocyclohexanes is usually accomplished by the action of hydrogen halides or phosphorus halides on the corresponding cyclohexanol; in the case of *trans*-monoalkyl-cyclohexanols it is claimed that hydrogen halides give chiefly the *cis*-halide whilst phosphorus pentahalides yield predominantly the *trans*-isomer (*M. Mousseron et al.*, Bull. Soc. chim. Fr., 1946, [v], **13**, 244). Fission of cyclohexyl ethers with concentrated halogen acids in the presence of red phosphorus also gives halogenocyclohexanes (*A. Lacourt*, Bull. Soc. chim. Belg., 1927, **36**, 346). Polyhalogenoderivatives are obtained by the addition of halogens to benzenes and halogenobenzenes.

Properties of halogeno compounds. The action of nucleophilic reagents (e.g., alkalis, silver oxide, ammonia, amines, silver oxide, potassium cyanide, potassium hydrogen sulphide) gives rise only to a small extent to the expected metathesis of the halogen atom with the functional group of the reagent, the main result being the elimination of hydrogen halide with the production of a cyclohexene or cyclohexadiene (*W. F. Faragher* and *F. H. Garner*, J. Amer. chem. Soc., 1921, **43**, 1715; *B. W. Tronov* and *L. W. Ladigina*, Ber., 1930, **63**, 3060; *F. E. King*, J. chem. Soc., 1935, 982). This strong tendency to eliminate hydrogen halide renders these compounds useful for the preparation of cyclohexenes and cyclohexadienes (q.v.). On the other hand the halogenocyclohexanes readily form Grignard reagents which react quite

TABLE 4

HALOGEN DERIVATIVES OF CYCLOHEXANE HYDROCARBONS

Compound	B.p.°/mm.	n_D(°)	Ref.
Fluorocyclohexane	100·2 (m.p. 13°)	1·4147 (20)	1, 2
Chlorocyclohexane	143	1·4626 (20)	3
Bromocyclohexane	72/32	1·4956 (15)	3
Iodocyclohexane	69/10		19
1:1-Dichlorocyclohexane	62/20 (f.p. −47°)	1·4803 (20)	14
cis-1:2-Dichlorocyclohexane	91/20 (f.p. −1·5°)	1·4967 (20)	14
trans-1:2-Dichlorocyclohexane	71/20 (f.p. −6·3°)	1·4902 (20)	14, 4
cis-1:4-Dichlorocyclohexane	96/25 (m.p. 18°)	1·4942 (20)	20
trans-1:4-Dichlorocyclohexane	m.p. 102°		21
trans-1-Chloro-2-bromocyclohexane	85/16	1·5180 (25)	5
trans-1:2-Dibromocyclohexane	100/13 (f.p. −4·5°)	1·5506 (25)	6, 7, 8
cis-1:3-Dibromocyclohexane	116/16 (f.p. 1°)		9, 10, 11
trans-1:3-Dibromocyclohexane	m.p. 112°		9, 10, 11
cis-1:4-Dibromocyclohexane	111/13	1·5531 (20)	12
trans-1:4-Dibromocyclohexane	m.p. 112°		12
1:2:4:5-Tetrabromocyclohexane (a)	m.p. 118°		13
(b)	m.p. 218°		
Dodecafluorocyclohexane	50		15
1-Chloro-1-methylcyclohexane	38/10	1·4565 (25)	4
2-Chloro-1-methylcyclohexane (a)	42/10	1·4569 (28)	4
(b)	39/10	1·4586 (28)	
cis-3-Chloro-1-methyl-cyclohexane	40/10	1·4562 (23)	4
trans-3-Chloro-1-methylcyclohexane	39/10	1·4583 (23)	4
cis-4-Chloro-1-methylcyclohexane	41/10	1·4560 (23)	4
trans-4-Chloro-1-methylcyclohexane	40/10	1·4570 (23)	4
cis-3-Bromo-1-methylcyclohexane	59/10	1·4867 (25)	4
trans-3-Bromo-1-methylcyclohexane	58/10	1·4918 (25)	4
3-Iodo-1-methylcyclohexane	72/10	1·5335 (25)	4
2:2-Dichloro-1-methylcyclohexane	64/8		16
1:2:2-Trichloro-1-methylcyclohexane	102/8·5		16
2:3-Dibromo-1-methylcyclohexane	130/35		17
cis-3:4-Dibromo-1-methylcyclohexane	105/15	1·5303 (25)	4, 6
trans-3:4-Dibromo-1-methylcyclohexane	108/15	1·5410 (25)	4, 6
1-Chloro-1-*tert*.-butylcyclohexane	58/2 (f.p. −9°)	1·4778 (20)	18

[1] *S. M. McElvain* and *J. W. Langston*, J. Amer. chem. Soc., 1944, **66**, 1759.
[2] *A. V. Grosse* and *C. B. Linn*, J. org. Chem., 1938, **3**, 26.
[3] *E. C. Britton* and *R. P. Perkins*, U.S.P., 2, 287, 665 (1942).
E. E. Reid et al., Org. Synth., 1935, **15**, 26.
[4] *M. Mousseron et al.*, Bull. Soc. chim. Fr., 1946, **13**, 244.
[5] *M. Mousseron et al.*, ibid., 1947, **14**, 244.

[6] *M. Mousseron* and *F. Winternitz*, ibid., 1945, **12**, 67.
[7] *H. Greengard*, Org. Synth., 1932, **12**, 26.
[8] *S. Winstein*, J. Amer. chem. Soc., 1942, **64**, 2792.
[9] *L. Palfray*, Compt. rend., 1930, **190**, 189.
[10] *A. Skita*, Monatsh., 1929, **53/54**, 753.
[11] *H. Lindemann* and *H. Baumann*, Ann., 1929, **477**, 78.
[12] *R. C. Olberg et al.*, J. Amer. chem. Soc., 1944, **66**, 1096.
[13] *J. P. Wibaut* and *F. A. Haak*, Rec. Trav. chim., 1948, **67**, 85.
[14] *B. Carroll et al.*, J. Amer. chem. Soc., 1951, **73**, 5382.
[15] *N. Fukuhara* and *L. A. Bigelow*, ibid., 1941, **63**, 2792.
[16] *N. A. Domnin*, J. gen. Chem. U.S.S.R., 1940, **10**, 1939.
[17] *A. Berlande*, Compt. rend., 1941, **213**, 484.
[18] *L. Schmerling*, J. Amer. chem. Soc., 1947, **69**, 1121.
[19] *N. D. Zelinsky*, Ber., 1901, **34**, 2801.
[20] *T. W. Lunney et al.*, J. Amer. chem. Soc., 1952, **74**, 3428.
[21] *B. Rothstein*, Ann. chim., 1930, **14**, 461.

normally (see *H. Gilman* and *E. A. Zoellner*, J. Amer. chem. Soc., 1931, **53**, 1945).

It has been noted that the rate of reaction of monohalogenocyclohexanes with displacement reagents of the above type is far lower than that obtaining in the cases of similarly constituted cyclopentyl, cycloheptyl or alkyl halides; a theoretical explanation for this phenomenon has been proposed (*H. C. Brown et al.*, J. Amer. chem. Soc., 1951, **73**, 212; 1952, **74**, 1894; *J. B. Conant* and *R. E. Hussey*, *ibid.*, 1925, **47**, 476).

Some halogenated derivatives of cyclohexane are indicated in Table 4. The polychlorocyclohexanes are described on p. 154.

Fluorocyclohexane *(cyclohexyl fluoride)* is obtained by the direct fluorination of cyclohexane at -80^0 (*W. Bockemuller*, Ann., 1933, **506**, 20) and by the addition of hydrogen fluoride to cyclohexene at a similar temperature (Ref. 1, Table 4). Exhaustive fluorination of benzene gives dodecafluorocyclohexane as the major product; other perfluorocyclohexanes are similarly obtained (for review see *L. A. Bigelow*, Chem. Reviews, 1947, **40**, 51).

Chloro- and **bromo-cyclohexane** are generally prepared from cyclohexanol by the usual metathetical reagents. They are also obtained by the direct halogenation of cyclohexane in the presence of light (*P. Sabatier*, Compt. rend., 1903, **137**, 240; Ref. 3) and the kinetics of the process has been studied (*M. S. Kharasch et al.*, J. org. Chem., 1941, **6**, 818). The condensation of halogenocyclohexanes with ethylene in the presence of aluminium or ferric chloride has been investigated by *L. Schmerling* (J. Amer. chem. Soc., 1949, **71**, 698). Under these conditions chlorocyclohexane gives firstly β-chloroethylcyclohexane (I) and then 1-β-*chloroethyl-1-ethylcyclohexane* (II), b.p. $78^0/3$ mm.; the same product (II) is obtained from 1-chloro-1-ethylcyclohexane and ethylene.

Cl-cyclohexane $\xrightarrow{CH_2:CH_2}$ $CH_2\cdot CH_2Cl$-cyclohexane (I) $\xrightarrow{CH_2:CH_2}$ Et, $CH_2\cdot CH_2Cl$-cyclohexane (II) $\xleftarrow{CH_2:CH_2}$ Et, Cl-cyclohexane

1:1-**Dichlorocyclohexane** is prepared by the action of phosphorus pentachloride on cyclohexanone at low temperature. Addition of chlorine to cyclohexene gives *trans*-1:2-dichlorocyclohexane; the *cis*-isomer is produced by the action of thionyl chloride-pyridine on *trans*-2-chlorocyclohexan-1-ol, Walden inversion taking place. All methods of preparation give the same *trans*-1:2-**dibromocyclohexane**; the *cis*-isomer seems to be incapable of existence (Ref. 8). The stereochemical course of replacement reactions of this dibromide has been studied in detail (*S. Winstein* and *R. E. Buckles*, J. Amer. chem. Soc., 1942, **64**, 2780); thus reaction with silver acetate in dry acetic acid gave almost entirely the *trans*-glycol diacetate but in the presence of a small amount of water almost complete conversion to the *cis*-ester occurs.

The two isomers of 1:2:4:5-**tetrabromocyclohexane** are obtained by the addition of bromine to cyclohexa-1:4-diene; both isomers regenerate the diene by treatment with zinc and acetic acid.

Polychlorocyclohexanes

1:2:3:4:5:6-**Hexachlorocyclohexanes** *(benzene hexachlorides)* have become of great interest and importance since the discovery in 1943 of the potency of the γ-isomer ("Gammexane"*) as an insecticide. The observation that different preparations of crude benzene hexachloride, prepared from benzene and chlorine, differed in insecticidal activity led to the discovery that the γ-isomer was the active principle. *T. van der Linden* (Ber., 1912, **45**, 236) first established the existence of four isomers (α, β, γ, δ) and a fifth (ε) has been subsequently added. The most reliable figures for the melting-points of the isomers are: α, 153–154°; β, 298–300°; γ, 112·2–113·8°; δ, 136–137°; ε, 216–217°. The isomers are separated by taking advantage of their considerably different solubilities in methanol, followed by fractional crystallisation from this and other solvents (for the history and a general discussion of the isomers see *R. E. Slade*, Chem. and Ind., 1945, 314). In a typical manufacturing process chlorine and benzene are allowed to interact in the light of a mercury arc and the resulting mixture of α- and γ-isomers is separated by treatment with methanol [*L. J. Burrage* and *J. C. Smart*, B.P., 573,693 (1943)].

Eight possible configurations may be constructed for the benzene hexachlorides on the basis of the more stable "chair" form of cyclohexane. The detailed assignment of structure to the five known isomers has been carried out by means of electron diffraction, X-ray diffraction and X-ray analysis methods (*O. Bastiensen, O. Ellefsen* and *O. Hassel*, Research, 1949, **2**, 248; *idem*, Acta chem. Scand., 1949, **3**, 918; *J. M. Bijvoet*, Rec. Trav. chim., 1948, **67**, 777; *G. W. van Vloten et al.*, Nature, 1948, **162**, 771; *R. C. Dickinson* and *C. Bilicke*, J. Amer. chem. Soc., 1928, **50**, 764; *S. B. Hendricks* and *C. Bilicke*, *ibid.*, 1926, **48**, 3007). These investigations indicate the configurations to be as follows (for terminology see p. 133): α, *ppeeee*; β, *eeeeee*; γ, *pppeee*; δ, *peeeee*; ε, *peepee*. Thus the γ-isomer is not structurally analogous to *meso*inositol (configuration *peeeee*) as has been previously suggested. Dipole moment data have also been

* Now known as "lindane" after the discover (Van der Linden, 1912).

called upon as structural criteria for these compounds but their interpretation is equivocal (*M. Rolla et al.*, Gazz. chim., 1949, **79**, 491; *E. Hetland*, Acta chem. Scand., 1948, **2**, 678; *C. Melander*, Svensk Kem. Tidsk., 1946, **58**, 231). The α-isomer is the only one of the above structure to possess no element of symmetry; this has been confirmed by its resolution (*S. J. Cristol*, J. Amer. chem. Soc., 1949, **71**, 1894).

The β-isomer is the most stable, the least soluble in organic solvents and the least volatile. All five isomers are largely dehydrochlorinated by the action of alcoholic potassium hydroxide to a mixture of trichlorobenzenes from which the 1:2:4-isomer can be isolated (*F. A. Gunther* and *R. C. Blinn*, J. Amer. chem. Soc., 1947, **69**, 1215); the kinetics of the process has been studied (*S. J. Cristol et al.*, *ibid.*, 1951, **73**, 674).

A sixth hexachlorocyclohexane *isomer*, m.p. 145°, has been prepared by passing chlorine into cooled, irradiated cyclohexane and chlorocyclohexane (*O. Bastiensen* and *O. Hassel*, Acta chem. Scand., 1947, **1**, 683). Its exact configuration is as yet undetermined but it may contain a CCl_2 group.

Several more highly chlorinated cyclohexanes have been obtained. The α- and **β-heptachlorocyclohexanes,** m.p. 146° and 260°, both yield 1:2:3:5-tetrachlorobenzene by treatment with potassium hydroxide (*R. Otto*, Ann., 1867, **141**, 101). The action of liquid chlorine on α-hexachlorocyclohexane gives **nonachlorocyclohexane,** m.p. 96°, also formed by similar means from β-hexachlorocyclohexane. This latter reaction also furnishes **octachlorocyclohexane** (p-*dichlorobenzene hexachloride*) which can be further chlorinated to **undecachlorocyclohexane,** m.p. ca. 85° (*T. van der Linden*, Rec. Trav. chim., 1938, **57**, 217).

α- and **β-Hexabromocyclohexanes,** m.p. 212° and 253°, are obtained by the action of bromine on heated, irradiated benzene; the α-isomer is isomorphous with the α-chloro compound. The two isomers readily undergo dehydrobromination to give 1:2:4-tribromobenzene (*J. Meunier*, Compt. rend., 1885, **101**, 328; *F. E. Matthews*, J. chem. Soc., 1898, **73**, 243).

(b) Unsaturated halogen compounds

1-Halogenocyclohex-1-enes are prepared by the action of phosphorus pentahalides on cyclohexanones. The 3-halogenocyclohex-1-enes are obtained by the addition of the halogen hydracids to cyclohexa-1:3-dienes; the 3-bromo-compounds may also be conveniently prepared from cyclohexenes by the action of N-bromosuccinimide. As would be expected the halogen atom in the 1-halogeno-compounds is very firmly bound while that of the 3-halogeno-compounds is highly reactive.

Some representatives of the halogenated cyclohexenes are shown in Table 5.

1-**Chlorocyclohex**-1-**ene** is prepared by the action of phosphorus pentachloride on cyclohexanone (Refs. 1, 2, 3). It reacts with hydrogen bromide to form

TABLE 5

HALOGEN DERIVATIVES OF CYCLOHEXENE HYDROCARBONS

Compound	B.p.°/mm.	n_D(°)	Ref.
1-Chlorocyclohex-1-ene	95/160	1·4798 (20)	1, 2, 3
3-Chlorocyclohex-1-ene	62/35	1·4860 (20)	4
3-Bromocyclohex-1-ene	27·5/0·04	1·5292 (20)	4, 5
3-Iodocyclohex-1-ene	95/15		4
2:3-Dichlorocyclohex-1-ene	84/15	1·5098 (25)	2, 3
2:3-Dibromocyclohex-1-ene	111/7		6
4:5-Dibromocyclohex-1-ene	119/20 (m.p. 35·2°)		5
2-Chloro-1-methylcyclohex-1-ene	57/16	1·4725 (20)	2, 7
3-Chloro-1-methylcyclohex-1-ene	65/18	1·4779 (18)	8, 9
2-Chloro-4-methylcyclohex-1-ene	55/20	1·4727 (20)	2
6-Chloro-4-methylcyclohex-1-ene	70/15	1·4838 (12·5)	9, 10
2:3-Dichloro-3-methylcyclohex-1-ene	82/8		7
3-Chloro-1:4-dimethylcyclohex-1-ene	71/18	1·4805 (18)	8
3-Chloro-1-ethylcyclohex-1-ene	75/18	1·4791 (18)	8
2-Chloro-4-(1′-chlorovinyl)cyclohex-1-ene	105/20	1·5156 (24)	11
3-Chloro-1-*n*-propylcyclohex-1-ene	87/18	1·4889 (18)	8
3-Chloro-1-*iso*propylcyclohex-1-ene	85/18	1·4886 (18)	8
3-Chloro-1-*n*-butylcyclohex-1-ene	96/18	1·4952 (18)	8
2:4-Dichlorocyclohexa-1:3-diene	89/29		12

[1] *E. A. Braude* and *J. A. Coles*, J. chem. Soc., 1950, 2014.
[2] *M. Mousseron et al.*, Bull. Soc. chim. Fr., 1947, [v], **14**, 81.
[3] *N. A. Domnin*, J. gen. Chem. U.S.S.R., 1945, **15**, 461.
[4] *A. Berlande*, Bull. Soc. chim. Fr., 1942, [v], **9**, 641, 644.
[5] *J. P. Wibaut* and *F. A. Haak*, Rec. Trav. chim., 1948, **67**, 85.
[6] *W. G. Christiansen*, U.S.P., 2,117,299 (1938); 2,146,720 (1939).
[7] *N. A. Domnin*, J. gen. Chem. U.S.S.R., 1940, **10**, 1939.
[8] *M. Mousseron* and *F. Winternitz*, Bull. Soc. chim. Fr., 1945, [v], **12**, 71.
[9] *Idem, ibid.*, 1946, **13**, 232.
[10] *Idem, ibid.*, 1945, **12**, 67.
[11] *J. G. T. Brown, J. D. Rose* and *J. L. Simonsen*, J. chem. Soc., 1944, 101.
[12] *A. W. Crossley*, J. chem. Soc., 1903, **83**, 494.

1-chloro-2-bromocyclohexane and with hypochlorous acid to give a mixture of 2-chlorocyclohexanone and 2:3-dichlorocyclohex-1-ene. It may be oxidised with chromium trioxide to furnish 1-chlorocyclohex-1-en-3-one; with selenium dioxide in acetic acid solution oxidation to 2-chloro-3-acetoxycyclohex-1-ene occurs (*M. Mousseron et al.*, Compt. rend., 1947, **224**, 1230). More drastic oxidation leads to adipic acid. The compound shows little tendency to form a Grignard reagent with magnesium but reacts readily with lithium to furnish lithium cyclohexenyl which undergoes the expected reaction with carbonyl compounds (Ref. 1; see also *E. A. Braude et al.*, J. chem. Soc., 1952, 1414, 1419). Homologous 1-chlorocyclohex-1-enes are similarly prepared and undergo similar reactions.

3-**Chlorocyclohex**-1-**ene** is prepared by the addition of hydrogen chloride to cyclohexa-1:3-diene. Its reactive chlorine atom undergoes very ready metathesis; thus hydrolysis with sodium bicarbonate solution gives cyclohex-2-enol and dicyclohex-2-enyl ether, potassium iodide produces the unstable 3-iodocyclohex-1-ene, sodium alkoxides furnish 3-alkoxycyclohex-1-enes and sodium acetate produces 3-acetoxycyclohex-1-ene. Reaction with alkylmagnesium halides gives rise to 3-alkylcyclohex-1-enes, dicyclohex-2-enyl being obtained as a by-product (Ref. 4). Treatment with chromium trioxide and sulphuric acid causes simultaneous hydrolysis and oxidation with the production of cyclohex-2-enone (p. 209). For homologues see Refs. 8, 9 (Table 5).

3-**Bromocyclohex**-1-**ene** may be obtained by the addition of hydrogen bromide to cyclohexa-1:3-diene but is more conveniently prepared by the action of N-bromosuccinimide on cyclohexene. With quinoline it yields cyclohexa-1:3-diene.

2:4-**Dichlorocyclohexa**-1:3-**diene** is the product of the reaction between phosphorus pentachloride and cyclohexane-1:3-dione.

2:3-**Dibromocyclohex**-1-**ene** is formed by the action of alkali on 1:2:3-tribromocyclohexane. 4:5-*Dibromocyclohex*-1-*ene* is produced by the action of one mol. of bromine on cyclohexa-1:4-diene at low temperature; it undergoes photolytic dehydrobromination to benzene.

One of the products of the dimerisation of chloroprene has been shown to be 2-*chloro*-4-(1′-*chlorovinyl*)*cyclohex*-1-*ene* (I) by ozonolysis to butane-1:2:4-tricarboxylic acid and reductive dehalogenation to ethylcyclohexane (Ref. 11).

Et ← H_2 — $CCl{=}CH_2$ Cl (I) — O_3 → CO_2H, CH, CH_2, CH_2, CH_2, CO_2H, CO_2H

4. Alcohols

(a) Saturated ring alcohols; cyclohexanols

Members of this series which occur naturally include the saturated monocyclic terpene alcohols (e.g. menthol), which are discussed under terpenoids (Vol. IIB), the quercitols (pentahydroxycyclohexanes) and the inositols (hexahydroxycyclohexanes).

(i) Monohydric cyclohexanols

Preparation. The commonest method employed for the secondary cyclohexanols is the catalytic hydrogenation of cyclohexanones, cyclohexenols and phenols in the presence of platinum or Raney nickel. The ease of complete hydrogenation of phenols has been shown to depend markedly on the substituents present (*A. C. Whitaker,* J. Amer. chem. Soc., 1947, **69,** 2414). Secondary cyclohexanols may also be obtained by the action of oxygen on cyclohexylmagnesium halides, by the action of nitrous acid on cyclohexylamines and by the hydration of cyclohexenes. Tertiary cyclohexanols are prepared by the action of Grignard reagents on cyclohexanones, and also by an interesting process involving the reaction of pentamethylene-1:5-dimagnesium dibromide with esters (*C. D. Nenitzescu* and *I. Necsoiu,* J. Amer. chem. Soc., 1950, **72,** 3483)

$$H_2C\begin{cases}CH_2—CH_2MgBr\\CH_2—CH_2MgBr\end{cases} + R\cdot CO_2Et \longrightarrow \text{(cyclohexane ring with OH and R)}$$

The stereochemistry of substituted cyclohexanols has been very extensively studied. Separation of geometrical isomers may be achieved by fractional crystallisation of solid derivatives e.g. 3:5-dinitrobenzoates or hydrogen phthalates (*inter al., J. Kenyon et al.,* J. chem. Soc., 1926, 2052) and by azeotropic methods (*A. Lacourt,* Bull. Soc. chim. Belg., 1927, **36,** 346).

Properties of cyclohexanols. The *cis*-isomers of alkylcyclohexanols have a greater specific viscosity than the corresponding *trans*-forms but differences in other physical properties are less marked (*K. Auwers* and *F. Dersch,* J. pr. Chem., 1930, [ii], 124, 209). *cis*-2-Alkylcyclohexan-1-ols have been found to undergo dehydration more readily than the *trans*-isomers when an ionic *trans*-elimination mechanism is involved, the products in the former case being 1-alkylcyclohex-1-enes and in the latter 3-alkylcyclohex-1-enes. These results are reversed when the dehydration is carried out by a pyrolytic process involving *cis*-elimination (*D. H. R. Barton,* J. chem. Soc., 1949, 2174; *G. Vavon* and *M. Barbier,* Bull. Soc. chim. Fr., 1931, [iv], **49,** 567). The geometrical isomers of tertiary cyclohexanols may be distinguished by their markedly different rates of hydrogenolysis to the corresponding cyclohexane hydrocarbons. Thus hydrogenation with platinum in acetic acid of a mixture of the isomeric 1:4-dimethylcyclohexan-1-ols results in the reduction only of the 1^c:4^t-dimethylcyclohexan-1^t-ol; the isomer remaining unreduced, 1^c:4^c-dimethylcyclohexan-1^t-ol, may thus be readily isolated in a state of purity (*G. Chiurdoglu,* Bull. Soc. chim. Belg., 1941, **50,** 31).

Cyclohexanols resemble acyclic alcohols in many respects. Thus the action of halogen acids or phosphorus pentahalides yields the corresponding halogenocyclohexanes and esters are formed in the usual fashion with organic acids, the secondary cyclohexanols reacting more readily than the tertiary.

A characteristic reaction of the cyclohexanols is the ease with which they may be dehydrated to cyclohexenes, the tertiary alcohols undergoing this process with especial facility. A discussion of the reagents employed has already been provided in the section on cyclohexenes (p. 140) and some stereochemical aspects of the process are mentioned above. A study of the correlation between structure and ease of dehydration by means of formic acid has been carried out (*G. Chiurdoglu*, Bull. Soc. chim. Belg., 1941, **50**, 8).

Oxidation of secondary cyclohexanols with chromium trioxide generally proceeds smoothly to give high yields of the corresponding cyclohexanone; more drastic oxidation, e.g. with nitric acid, results in fission of the ring with the formation of the corresponding adipic acid. Dehydrogenation with copper-manganese chromite at 600° produces phenols [*E. P. Bartlett* and *E. Field*, U.S.P. 2,291,585 (1942)]. Chromium trioxide oxidation of tertiary cyclohexanols gives rise to aliphatic ε-keto-acids and the method is of considerable preparative value (*L. F. Fieser* and *J. Szmuszkovicz*, J. Amer. chem. Soc., 1948, **70**, 3352).

$$\text{1-R-cyclohexan-1-ol (R, OH)} \xrightarrow{CrO_3} R{-}CO{-}CH_2{-}CH_2{-}CH_2{-}CH_2{-}CO_2H$$

Some members of the cyclohexanol series are shown in Table 6.

Cyclohexanol may be prepared by the reduction of cyclohexanone (*K. von Auwers*, Chem. Ztbl., 1927, II, 1564) and by the hydrogenation of phenol in the presence of nickel (G.P. 383,540; 408,811; 444,685) or platinic oxide (*R. H. Baker* and *R. D. Schultz*, J. Amer. chem. Soc., 1947, **69**, 1250). It is also formed by the hydrogenation of cyclohex-2-en-1-ol (*R. Criegee*, Ann., 1930, **481**, 285), by the action of nitrous acid on cyclohexylamine (*V. B. Markovnikov*, Ann., 1898, **302**, 20) and by the action of oxygen on cyclohexylmagnesium halides (*P. Sabatier*, Ann. chim., 1907, [8], **10**, 527; *H. Wuyts*, Bull. Soc., chim. Belg., 1927, **36**, 222).

Its reactions in general resemble those of the aliphatic alcohols. It forms a *phenylurethane*, m.p. 81.5°, and a 3:5-*dinitrobenzoate*, m.p. 112°, and other esters are obtained in the usual way. These esters may also be prepared by the catalytic reduction of the corresponding phenyl esters with Raney nickel (*W. R. McClellan* and *R. Connor*, J. Amer. chem. Soc., 1941, **63**, 484). Cyclohexyl ethers, e.g. *cyclohexyl methyl ether (hexahydroanisole)*, b.p. 131°, are obtained by the action of the relevant halogen compound on sodium cyclohexoxide (prepared by the action of sodium or sodamide on cyclohexanol) or by the controlled catalytic hydrogenation of phenyl ethers; in this latter process fission of the resulting cyclohexyl ether frequently occurs (*E. Waser et al.*, Helv., 1929, **12**, 418). The preparation of the ethers by the interaction of halogenocyclohexanes with sodium

TABLE 6

CYCLOHEXANOLS

Compound	M.p.°	B.p.°/mm.	n_D(°)	Ref.
Cyclohexanol	23·5	161·5	1·4650 (22)	See te
1-Methylcyclohexan-1-ol		70/25	1·4546 (20)	1, 2
cis-2-Methylcyclohexan-1-ol	–9·3	165	1·4649 (20)	3, 4
trans-2-Methylcyclohexan-1-ol	–21	167	1·4616 (20)	3, 4
trans-3-Methylcyclohexan-1-ol		175·5	1·4583 (20)	4, 5
cis-3-Methylcyclohexan-1-ol		175	1·4573 (20)	4, 5
cis-4-Methylcyclohexan-1-ol		52/2	1·4614 (20)	4
trans-4-Methylcyclohexan-1-ol		54/3	1·4561 (20)	4
3:3-Dimethylcyclohexan-1-ol	12	73/8	1·4606 (15)	6
cis-1:2-Dimethylcyclohexan-1-ol	23·2	82·8/25	1·4649* (20)	7
trans-1:2-Dimethylcyclohexan-1-ol	13·2	74/25	1·4614* (20)	7
cis-1:3-Dimethylcyclohexan-1-ol	27·5	84/25	1·4599* (20)	7
trans-1:3-Dimethylcyclohexan-1-ol	14·5	77·5/25	1·4531* (20)	7
cis-1:4-Dimethylcyclohexan-1-ol	24	83·7/25	1·4588* (20)	7
trans-1:4-Dimethylcyclohexan-1-ol	72·5	76/25		7
2^c:6^c-Dimethylcyclohexan-1^t-ol	47	75/16		9
2^c:6^c-Dimethylcyclohexan-1^c-ol	40	80/22		9, 10
2^c:6^t-Dimethylcyclohexan-1^c-ol		76/16	1·4660 (19)	9
3^c:5^t-Dimethylcyclohexan-1^c-ol		84/17	1·4572 (20)	8, 11
3^c:5^c-Dimethylcyclohexan-1^c-ol	39	80/17	1·4513 (20)	8, 11
3^c:5^c-Dimethylcyclohexan-1^t-ol	16	84/17	1·4550 (20)	8, 11
1-Ethylcyclohexan-1-ol	33	166	1·4638 (21)	2, 12
2:2:5-Trimethylcyclohexan-1-ol		89/18	1·4569 (20)	13
3:3:5-Trimethylcyclohexan-1-ol	59	95/15		14
1-*iso*Propylcyclohexan-1-ol		80/18	1·4579 (20)	2
cis-2-*n*-Propylcyclohexan-1-ol		84/10	1·4688 (11)	15
trans-2-*n*-Propylcyclohexan-1-ol		90/14	1·4668 (11)	15
cis-4-*n*-Propylcyclohexan-1-ol		104/20	1·4624 (25)	16
trans-4-*n*-Propylcyclohexan-1-ol		210	1·4605 (25)	16
3-*iso*Propylcyclohexan-1-ol		114/28		17
4-*iso*Propylcyclohexan-1-ol		84/5	1·4667 (20)	18
1:3:3:5-Tetramethylcyclohexan-1-ol	82	185		19
3-Methyl-1-*n*-propylcyclohexan-1-ol		96/18	1·4566 (24)	21
2-*tert.*-Butylcyclohexan-1-ol	52			20
2-Methyl-6-*tert.*-butylcyclohexan-1-ol		107/20	1·4673 (20)	22
3-Methyl-6-*tert.*-butylcyclohexan-1-ol		108/20	1·4561 (20)	22
2-*m*-Tolylcyclohexan-1-ol		114/1	1·5396 (25)	23
2-*p*-Tolylcyclohexan-1-ol	73	113/1		23
cis-2:6-Dibenzylcyclohexan-1-ol	123			24
trans-2:6-Dibenzylcyclohexan-1-ol	70			24

* Denotes n_{He}

[1] *V. Grignard*, Compt. rend., 1907, **144**, 1358.
[2] *W. A. Mosher*, J. Amer. chem. Soc., 1940, **62**, 552.
[3] *W. Hückel* and *K. Hagenguth*, Ber., 1931, **64**, 2892.
[4] *L. M. Jackman et al.*, J. chem. Soc., 1949, 1717.
A. Skita and *W. Faust*, Ber., 1931, **64**, 2878.
[5] *A. K. MacBeth* and *J. A. Mills*, J. chem. Soc., 1945, 709.
H. L. Goering and *C. Serres*, J. Amer. chem. Soc., 1952, **74**, 5908.
D. S. Noyce and *D. B. Denney*, ibid., 5912.

[6] *A. L. Liberman* and *B. A. Kazanski*, Bull. Acad. Sci. U.S.S.R., 1946, 77.
[7] *G. Chiurdoglu*, Bull. Soc. chim. Belg., 1938, **47**, 241.
[8] *J. von Braun* and *E. Anton*, Ber., 1927, **60**, 2438.
[9] *P. A. Plattner et al.*, Helv., 1947, **30**, 100.
[10] *R. Cornubert et al.*, Compt. rend., 1947, **225**, 878.
[11] *A. Skita* and *W. Faust*, Ber., 1939, **72**, 1127.
[12] *P. Sabatier* and *A. Mailhe*, Ann. chim., 1907, [8], 10, 544.
[13] *V. P. Hirsjärvi*, C.A., 1939, **33**, 6255.
[14] *A. A. Dodge* and *E. Kremers*, J. Amer. pharm. Assn., 1952, **31**, 527.
[15] *G. Vavon* and *P. Anziani*, Bull. Soc. chim. Fr., 1927, [iv], **41**, 1638.
[16] *H. E. Ungnade* and *A. Ludutsky*, J. org. Chem., 1945, **10**, 520.
[17] *A. W. Crossley* and *W. R. Pratt*, J. chem. Soc., 1915, **107**, 171.
[18] *D. T. C. Gillespie et al.*, J. chem. Soc., 1938, 1820.
[19] *H. Barbier*, Helv., 1940, **23**, 519.
[20] *L. Schmerling*, J. Amer. chem. Soc., 1947, **69**, 1121.
[21] *N. D. Zelinsky*, Ber., 1901, **34**, 2881.
[22] *A. C. Whitaker*, J. Amer. chem. Soc., 1947, **69**, 2414.
[23] *B. C. McKusick*, J. Amer. chem. Soc., 1948, **70**, 1976.
[24] *R. Cornubert et al.*, Compt. rend., 1946, **223**, 358.

alkoxides is unsatisfactory, the main product being cyclohexene (p. 143). *Dicyclohexyl ether*, b.p. 116°/15 mm., is obtained by the catalytic reduction of diphenyl ether (*V. N. Ipatiev*, Ber., 1908, **41**, 1001) or by the dehydration of cyclohexanol with *p*-toluenesulphonic acid at 170° (*A. Lacourt*, Bull. Soc. chim. Belg., 1937, **36**, 346).

Cyclohexanol may be converted to cyclohexene by a wide variety of dehydrating agents (see p. 140). Oxidation with chromium trioxide yields cyclohexanone; more drastic oxidising agents such as nitric acid or potassium permanganate leads to ring fission with the formation of adipic acid (*C. Mannich* and *V. H. Hancu*, Ber., 1908, **41**, 575; *L. Bouveault*, Bull. Soc. chim. Fr., 1908, [iv], **3**, 432; *J. von Braun* and *G. Lemke*, Ber., 1922, **55**, 3526). The action of chlorine leads to 2:3:5:6-tetrachlorocyclohexanone (p. 199).

A mixture of the geometric isomers of 2-**methylcyclohexanol** may be obtained by the catalytic hydrogenation of *o*-cresol (*R. H. Baker* and *R. D. Schuetz*, J. Amer. chem. Soc., 1947, **69**, 1250; Refs. 3, 4) or 2-methylcyclohexanone (*P. Anziani* and *R. Cornubert*, Bull. Soc. chim. Fr., 1945, [v], **13**, 359; Compt. rend., 1946, **223**, 358; 1947, **225**, 878). The French authors have investigated in detail the proportion of isomers produced by a wide variety of reducing agents. The isomers may be separated by means of their *hydrogen phthalates*, *cis*-form, m.p. 104°, *trans*-form, m.p. 124°. The dehydration of the alcohol has been studied by *C. C. Price* (J. Amer. chem. Soc., 1939, **61**, 1847).

cis-3-**Methylcyclohexanol,** *a-naphthylurethane*, m.p. 128-129°, is the main product of the catalytic hydrogenation of *m*-cresol, whilst the trans-*isomer*, *a-naphthylurethane*, m.p. 177–118°, is formed predominantly by the catalytic hydrogenation of 3-methylcyclohexanone (Ref. 5)*. The two isomers may readily be separated by a mechanical flotation process applied to the piperazine salts of the hydrogen phthalates. Both isomers have been resolved via the quinine salts

* The former stereochemical assignment of these two alcohols has been reversed.

of the hydrogen phthalates (*A. K. MacBeth* and *J. A. Mills*, J. chem. Soc., 1947, 205; for optically active ethers see *M. Mousseron et al.*, Bull. Soc. chim. Fr., 1947, [v], **14**, 459).

Similarly, trans-4-**methylcyclohexanol,** 3:5-*dinitrobenzoate*, m.p. 142°, is prepared from *p*-cresol and the cis-*isomer*, 3:5-*dinitrobenzoate*, m.p. 107° is obtained from 4-methylcyclohexanone (Ref. 4, Table 6).

The configurations of the 1:2-, 1:3- and 1:4-**dimethylcyclohexan**-1-**ols** have been deduced from their Raman spectra (*C.* and *A. Guillemonat*, Bull. Soc. chim. Fr., 1938, [v], **5**, 1328). The dehydration of these cyclohexanols with formic acid has been studied in detail (*G. Chiurdoglu*, Bull. Soc. chim. Belg., 1938, **47**, 241).

3:3-**Dimethylcyclohexanol** may be prepared by the catalytic hydrogenation of dimedone (Ref. 6, Table 6; see p. 203).

trans-2-n-**Propylcyclohexanol,** *phenylurethane*, m.p. 69°, is best obtained by the sodium-ethanol reduction of 2-*n*-propylcyclohexanone, whilst the cis-*isomer*, *phenylurethane*, m.p. 97°, is isolated via its hydrogen phthalate from the product of catalytic hydrogenation of *o*-allylphenol (Ref. 15, Table 6).

Catalytic hydrogenation of 4-*n*-propylcyclohexanone furnishes a mixture of cis- and trans-4-n-**propylcyclohexanols** which are separated by the fractional crystallisation of their α-naphthylurethanes. The *trans*-isomer is also obtained by the catalytic hydrogenation of *p*-hydroxypropiophenone (Ref. 16, Table 6).

4-iso**Propylcyclohexanol** *(dihydrocryptol)*, *phenylurethane*, m.p. 88°, is obtained by the electrolytic reduction of cryptone (p. 210). The geometrical *isomer*, *phenylurethane*, m.p. 114°, is produced by the catalytic hydrogenation of 4-*iso*-propylcyclohex-2-en-1-ol (Ref. 18, Table 6).

(ii) Dihydric and polyhydric alcohols

Preparation. These compounds may be obtained by the catalytic hydrogenation of polyhydric phenols and by the reduction of polyketocyclohexanes. Other methods include the hydroxylation of cyclohexenes with peracids, osmium tetroxide-catalysed hydrogen peroxide or potassium permanganate, the hydrolysis of halohydrins and the addition of the elements of water to epoxycyclohexanes.

Some examples of cyclohexanediols and cyclohexanetriols are shown in Table 7. The tetrols, pentols and hexols form convenient sub-groups and are discussed on pp. 166 ff.

cis-**Cyclohexane**-1:2-**diol,** *dibenzoate*, m.p. 63·5°, *dimethanesulphonate*, m.p. 85·5°, is best prepared by the hydroxylation of cyclohexene with potassium permanganate or osmium-tetroxide-catalysed sodium chlorate (*inter al.*, Ref. 3; *W. Rigby*, J. chem. Soc., 1950, 1907; *M. Mugdan* and *D. P. Young*, *ibid.*, 1949, 2899). The *trans*-diol, *dibenzoate*, m.p. 94·5°, *dimethanesulphonate*, m.p. 135°, is most conveniently obtained by the action of performic acid on cyclohexene

TABLE 7

CYCLOHEXANEDIOLS AND CYCLOHEXANETRIOLS

Compound	M.p.°	Ref.
cis-Cyclohexane-1 : 2-diol	98 (b.p. 225°)	1,2,3,4, 5,6,7,8
trans-Cyclohexane-1 : 2-diol	104 (b.p. 236°)	
cis-1-Methylcyclohexane-1 : 2-diol	68·5	9,10
trans-1-Methylcyclohexane-1 : 2-diol	84·5 (b.p. 108°/2 mm.)	4,10,11
cis-3-Methylcyclohexane-1 : 2-diol	81	4,12
trans-3-Methylcyclohexane-1 : 2-diol	90	12
4-Methylcyclohexane-1 : 2-diol	81 (b.p. 104°/1 mm.)	4
1 : 2-Dimethylcyclohexane-1 : 2-diol	50 (b.p. 103°/10 mm.)	13
cis-1 : 4-Dimethylcyclohexane-1 : 2-diol	89	2,14
trans-1 : 4-Dimethylcyclohexane-1 : 2-diol	77	2,14
cis-4-Methyl-1-ethylcyclohexane-1 : 2-diol	82	2,14
trans-4-Methyl-1-ethylcyclohexane-1 : 2-diol	76	2,14
cis-Cyclohexane-1 : 3-diol	85·5	15,16,17
trans-Cyclohexane-1 : 3-diol	116	15,16,17
2 : 5 : 5-Trimethylcyclohexane-1 : 3-diol	117	18
2 : 2 : 5 : 5-Tetramethylcyclohexane-1 : 3-diol	206	18
cis-Cyclohexane-1 : 4-diol	112·4	16,19,20,21
trans-Cyclohexane-1 : 4-diol	143	16,19,20,21
cis-1 : 4-Dibenzylcyclohexane-1 : 4-diol	196	22
trans-1 : 4-Dibenzylcyclohexane-1 : 4-diol	253	22
α-Cyclohexane-1 : 2 : 3-triol	108	7,23,27
β-Cyclohexane-1 : 2 : 3-triol	125	7,23,27
γ-Cyclohexane-1 : 2 : 3-triol	148	7,23,27
α-Cyclohexane-1 : 3 : 5-triol	184	7
β-Cyclohexane-1 : 3 : 5-triol	145	7
Cyclohexane-1 : 2 : 4-triol	122	24
1-Methylcyclohexane-1 : 2 : 3-triol	95 (b.p. 154°/1 mm.)	25
1 : 2-Dimethylcyclohexane-1 : 2 : 3-triol	109	25
2 : 2 : 4 : 4 : 6 : 6-Hexamethylcyclohexane-1 : 3 : 5-triol	251	26

[1] *V. B. Markovnikov*, Ann., 1898, **302**, 21.
[2] *S. S. Nametkin et al.*, Chem. Ztbl., 1925, I, 222.
[3] *M. F. Clarke* and *L. N. Owen*, J. chem. Soc., 1949, 315.
[4] *H. Adkins* and *A. K. Roebuck*, J. Amer. chem. Soc., 1948, **70**, 4041.
[5] *S. Winstein* and *R. E. Buckles*, *ibid.*, 1942, **64**, 2780, 2787.
[6] *S. Winstein*, *ibid.*, 1942, **64**, 2794.
[7] *H. Lindemann* and *A. Lange*, Ann., 1930, **483**, 31.
L. Brunel, Compt. rend., 1910, **150**, 986.
[8] *R. Criegee*, Ber., 1936, **69**, 2753.
[9] *P. E. Verkade et al.*, Ann., 1928, **467**, 217.
[10] *M. Tiffeneau*, Compt. rend., 1936, **202**, 1931.
[11] *R. Dupont*, Bull. Soc. chim. Belg., 1936, **45**, 57, 113.

[12] *M. Mousseron et al.*, Compt. rend., 1946, **223**, 909.
[13] *H. Meerwein*, Ann., 1939, **542**, 123.
[14] *O. Wallach*, Ann., 1913, **396**, 267.
[15] *M. F. Clarke* and *L. N. Owen*, J. chem. Soc., 1950, 2013.
[16] *J. Coops et al.*, Rec. Trav. chim., 1938, **57**, 303.
[17] *W. Rigby*, J. chem. Soc., 1949, 1586, 1588.
[18] *N. J. Toivonen* and *V. P. Hirsjärvi*, C.A., 1939, **33**, 6255.
[19] *L. N. Owen* and *P. A. Robins*, J. chem. Soc., 1949, 320.
[20] *T. D. Perrins* and *W. C. White*, J. Amer. chem. Soc., 1947, **69**, 1542
[21] *R. C. Olberg et al.*, *ibid.*, 1944, **66**, 1096.
[22] *G. Wittig* and *H. Pook*, Ber., 1937, **70**, 2485.
[23] *T. Posternak* and *F. Ravenna*, Helv., 1947, **30**, 441.
[24] *N. D. Zelinsky* and *A. N. Titowa*, Ber., 1931, **64**, 1403.
[25] *E. H. Farmer* and *A. Sundralingam*, J. chem. Soc., 1942, 121.
[26] *E. B. Ayres* and *C. R. Hauser*, J. Amer. chem. Soc., 1942, **64**, 2461.
[27] *J. A. McRae et al.*, J. org. Chem., 1952, **17**, 1621.

(Ref. 4; *E. R. H. Jones et al.*, *ibid.*, 1950, 3639). The *cis*-diol forms an iso-*propylidene* derivative, b.p. 182°, with acetone but the *trans*-isomer does not undergo this reaction. In a series of classical papers by S. Winstein and his collaborators the replacement reactions of these two diols have been studied from the point of view of retention or inversion of configuration (J. Amer. chem. Soc., 1942, **64**, 2780, 2787, 2791, 2972, 2796; 1943, **65**, 613, 2196; cf. Ref. 3). Fission of the glycols with lead tetra-acetate or sodium bismuthate gives adipaldehyde (*W. Rigby*, *loc. cit.*; *E. R. H. Jones et al.*, *loc. cit.*). The diethers of the diols are obtained by means of alkylation employing alkyl iodide and silver oxide (*M. Mousseron et al.*, Bull. Soc. chim. Fr., 1947, [v], **14**, 459). Monoethers are produced by the addition of the relevant alcohol to epoxycyclohexane, the reaction being catalysed by the corresponding sodium alkoxide or sulphuric acid (*S. Winstein* and *R. E. Buckles*, J. Amer. chem. Soc., 1943, **65**, 716; *S. C. McKusick*, *ibid.*, 1948, **70**, 1976).

cis-1-**Methylcyclohexane**-1:2-**diol** is obtained by the permanganate hydroxylation of 1-methylcylohex-1-ene; the trans-*isomer* is prepared by the action of performic acid on the same hydrocarbon (Ref. 4). The behaviour of the two isomers on dehydration has been studied (Ref. 10).

trans-3-**Methylcyclohexane**-1:2-**diol,** prepared by the action of dilute hydrochloric acid on 3-methyl-1:2-epoxycyclohexane, apparently exists in a liquid *form*, b.p. 99°/1 mm., and a solid *form*, m.p. 96°, both forms yielding 3:5-*dinitrobenzoates*, m.p. 186° (Ref. 4). The *cis*-diol is produced by the action of potassium permanganate on 1-methylcyclohex-2-ene.

cis-1:2-**Dimethylcyclohexane**-1:2-**diol,** obtained by the permanganate hydroxylation of 1:2-dimethylcyclohex-1-ene, undergoes a pinacol rearrangement on being treated with dilute sulphuric acid to give 1-acetyl-1-methylcyclopentane (*H. Meerwein*, Ann., 1919, **417**, 264).

Cyclohexane-1:3-**diol** *(resorcitol)* is prepared by the Raney nickel-catalysed hydrogenation of resorcinol at 130°/120 atm. The cis- and trans-*isomers* may by separated by fractional crystallisation from acetone (Ref. 17) and purification may be achieved through derivatives such as the *ditrityl ethers* (Ref. 16), the *benzoate*-3:5-*dinitrobenzoates* (cis-, m.p. 169°; trans-, m.p. 124°) (*K. Dimroth* and *K. Resin*, Ber., 1942, **75**, 322) or the *dibenzoates* (cis-, m.p. 67·5°; trans-, m.p. 124°) (Ref. 15). The assignment of the *trans*-configuration to the higher-melting glycol is confirmed by its resolution via the brucine salt of the bis (hydrogen phthalate) (Ref. 17).

Cyclohexane-1:4-diol *(quinitol)* is prepared by the catalytic hydrogenation of hydroquinone; it may also be formed by the sodium amalgam reduction of cyclohexane-1:4-dione. It is freely soluble in water and possesses an initially sweet taste with a very bitter after-taste. Chromic acid oxidises it to benzoquinone (*A. von Baeyer*, Ber., 1892, **25**, 1038). Reaction of the diol with strong sulphuric acid gives a product which is probably phenylcyclohexane (*R. Willstätter*, Ber., 1901, **34**, 506). The separation of the diol into the geometrical isomers has been extensively studied. The cis-*diacetate*, m.p. 41°, may be separated from the trans-*diacetate*, m.p. 103°, by fractional crystallisation from light petroleum (Refs. 20, 21). Alternatively the mixed diacetates may be partially hydrolysed to the monoacetates which may be separated by solvent extraction into the liquid cis-*monoacetate*, and the trans-*monoacetate*, m.p. 73° (*J. B. Aldersley et al.*, J. chem. Soc., 1940, 10). The most convenient mono-acyl derivative of the diol to prepare is the *monobenzoate*, cis-, b.p. $100°/10^{-5}$ mm., trans-, m.p. 87° (Ref. 19; *E. R. H. Jones* and *F. Sondheimer*, *ibid.*, 1949, 615). Other derivatives employed for purification include the *dibenzoates*, cis-, m.p. 110°, trans-, m.p. 150°, the *ditrityl ethers*, cis-, m.p. 234°. trans-, m.p. 252°, and the *acetate*-3:5-*dinitrobenzoates*, cis-, m.p. 122°, trans-, m.p. 146° (Ref. 16; *K. Dimroth*, Ber., 1939, **72**, 2043). The *monomethyl ether*, b.p. 99°/11 mm., is prepared by the catalytic hydrogenation of *p*-methoxyphenol (*P. Ruggli et al.*, Helv., 1941, **24**, 339).

The three cyclohexanediols react differently and with varying readiness with dilute sulphuric acid. The 1:2-diol forms mainly condensed hydrocarbons and a small amount of cyclohexa-1:3-diene, the 1:3-diol furnishes the 1:3-diene with a little of the 1:4-isomer whilst the 1:4-diol gives mainly the 1:4-diene (*J. B. Senderens*, Compt. rend., 1923, **177**, 1183). Dehydrogenation of the three diols with Raney nickel at 250° has been shown to produce cyclohexan-1-ol-2-one from the 1:2-diol, cyclohexanone from the 1:3-diol and cyclohexane-1:4-dione from the 1:4-diol (*L. Palfray et al.*, Compt. rend., 1939, **208**, 1654).

Cyclohexane-1:2:3-triol *(pyrogallitol)* exists in the three following optically inactive stereoisomeric modifications of which only the β-isomer possesses no element of symmetry and is therefore resolvable.

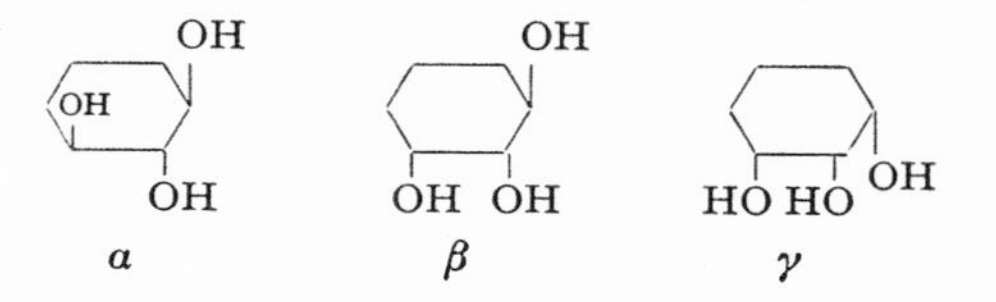

The α- and β-triols are obtained by the potassium permanganate hydroxylation of 3-ethoxycyclohex-1-ene followed by hydrolysis of the resulting ether with hydrobromic acid. The γ-isomer is isolated from the mixture obtained by catalytic hydrogenation of pyrogallol (Refs. 7, 23, 27). The configurations of the triols are deduced from their rates of reaction with lead tetra-acetate and the products of their bacterial oxidation. The micro-organisms used attacked only polyhydroxy-cyclohexanes with at least one pair of vicinal *cis*-hydroxyl groups; since the α-isomer alone remains unoxidised it must possess the configuration shown. The optically active enantiomorphs of the β-triol, *tribenzoates*, m.p. 143°, $[\alpha]_D^{20}$ ± 19°, are obtained indirectly by microbiological methods.

Cyclohexane-1:3:5-triol *(phloroglucitol)* occurs in α- and β-forms, both being obtained by the catalytic hydrogenation of phloroglucinol (Ref. 7, Table 7).

2:2:4:4:6:6-**Hexamethylcyclohexane-1:3:5-triol** is prepared by the copper chromite-catalysed hydrogenation of the triketone. By treatment with sulphuric acid at 0° it undergoes rearrangement to give hexamethylbenzene (Ref. 26, Table 7).

Cyclohexanetetrols

A **cyclohexane-1:2:3:4-tetrol** (I), m.p. 229° is obtained from its *dimethylene ether*, m.p. 215°, which is prepared by the action of silver powder on 1:6-diiodo-1:6-dideoxymannitol dimethylene ether (*F. Micheel*, Ann., 1932, **496**, 77).

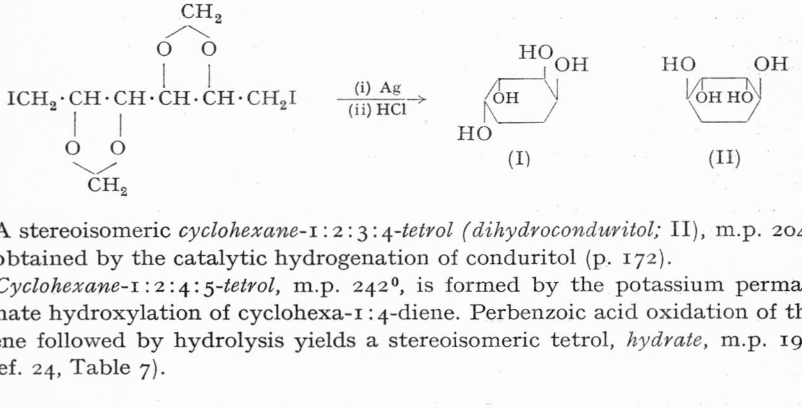

(I) (II)

A stereoisomeric *cyclohexane*-1:2:3:4-*tetrol (dihydroconduritol;* II), m.p. 204°, is obtained by the catalytic hydrogenation of conduritol (p. 172).

Cyclohexane-1:2:4:5-*tetrol*, m.p. 242°, is formed by the potassium permanganate hydroxylation of cyclohexa-1:4-diene. Perbenzoic acid oxidation of this diene followed by hydrolysis yields a stereoisomeric tetrol, *hydrate*, m.p. 195° (Ref. 24, Table 7).

Cyclohexanepentols (quercitols, deoxyinositols)

Theory predicts the possibility of sixteen compounds of this structure, i.e. four meso compounds and six enantiomorphous pairs. Four of these isomers are known possessing the following configurations.

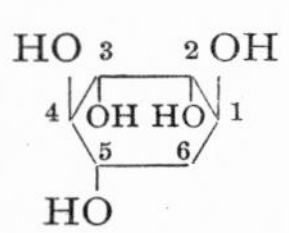

*proto*Quercitol

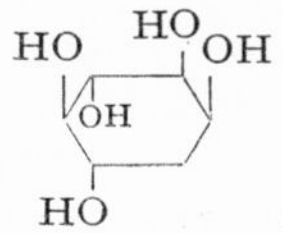

*vibo*Quercitol

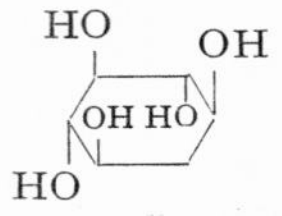

*scyllo*Quercitol

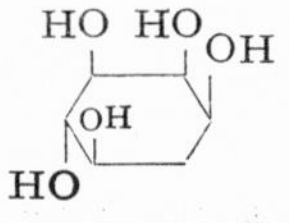

*dl-epi*Quercitol

The compounds may be named as cyclohexanepentols prefixed with a fraction, the numerator of which shows the hydroxyl groups above the plane of the ring and the denominator those below the plane. This *proto*quercitol may be termed 1,4/2,3,5-cyclohexanepentol. For a detailed discussion of the nomenclature and enumeration of such systems see *S. J. Angyal* and *C. G. Macdonald*, J. chem. Soc., 1952, 686.

proto**Quercitol** *(quercitol, acorn sugar)*, m.p. 235°, $[\alpha]_D^{20}$ +25·6°, was first obtained from acorns (the name is derived from *Quercus*, oak) but has since been isolated from a variety of plants (*H. Braconnot*, Ann. chim., 1849, **27**, 392; *M. Dessaignes*, Compt. rend., 1851, **33**, 308; *H. Müller*, J. chem. Soc., 1907, **91**, 1766). Its configuration has been deduced by oxidative degradation to metasaccharinic acid (*T. Posternak*, Helv., 1932, **15**, 948).

vibo*Quercitol* (*viburnitol*, laevorotatory quercitol), m.p. 181°, $[\alpha]_D^{19}$ −49·5°, *penta-acetate*, m.p. 126°, is isolated from the leaves of *Gymnema sylvestre* (*F. B. Power* and *F. Tutin*, J. chem. Soc., 1904, **85**, 624) and *Viburnum tinus* (*H. Hérissey* and *G. Poirot*, J. pharm. Chim., 1937, **26**, 385; *T. Posternak* and *W. H. Schopfer*, Helv., 1950, **33**, 343). The configuration has been elucidated by *T. Posternak* (Helv., 1950, **33**, 350).

scyllo*Quercitol*, m.p. 233–235°, *penta-acetate*, m.p. 190°, is produced by catalytic hydrogenation of *scyllo*inosose (p. 201) with platinic oxide in acid solution (*T. Posternak*, Helv., 1941, **24**, 1056).

dl-epi-*Quercitol*, m.p. 206–208°, *penta-acetates*, m.p. 124·5° and 143° (dimorphs) is obtained by the catalytic hydrogenation of *dl-epi*inosose (p. 201) or its oxime in acid solution (*E. L. May* and *E. Mosettig*, J. org. Chem., 1949, **14**, 1137).

Cyclohexanehexols (inositols)

Of the nine stereoisomeric theoretically predictable cyclohexanehexols (seven *meso*-forms and one enantiomorphous pair) the following seven are known:

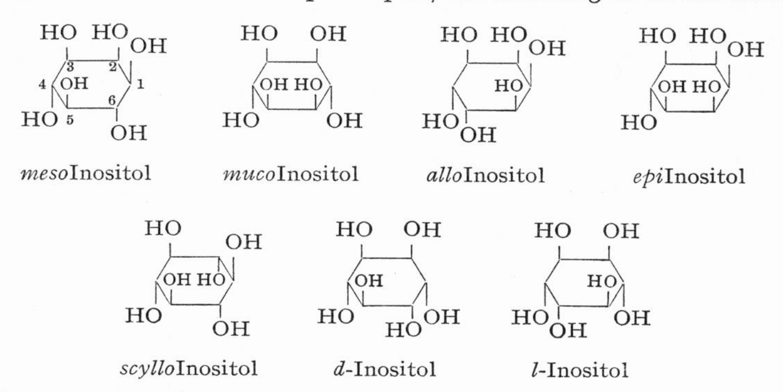

*meso*Inositol *muco*Inositol *allo*Inositol *epi*Inositol

*scyllo*Inositol *d*-Inositol *l*-Inositol

The most widely distributed naturally-occurring cyclohexanehexol is meso-**inositol**, m.p. 225°, *hexa-acetate*, m.p. 217°. It was first isolated from Liebig's meat extract (*J. Scherer*, Ann., 1850, **73**, 322) but has since been found in a large variety of plant and animal sources (see Beilstein, **6**, 1194; Suppl. I, **6**, 588; Suppl. II, **6**, 1158). It also occurs as the calcium and magnesium salts of its *hexaphosphoric acid ester, phytin*, $C_6H_6(OPO_3H_2)_6$, the organic phosphorus reserve material of green plants. Two monomethyl ethers are known, *bornesitol*, isolated from rubber (*A. Girard*, Compt. rend., 1871, **73**, 426) and *sequoitol*, obtained from the redwood *Sequoia sempervirens* (*E. C. Sherrard* and *E. F. Kurth*, J. Amer. chem. Soc., 1929, **51**, 3139); a dimethyl ether, *dambonitol*, occurs in Sumatran latex (*A. W. K. de Jong*, Rec. Trav. chim., 1908, 27, 257). The photosynthesis of *meso*inositol has been discussed by *P. R. Kögl* (Biochem. Z., 1919, **93**, 313; 1919, **97**, 21). The discovery that an essential growth factor for certain yeasts, Bios I, is identical with *meso*inositol has provided considerable impetus to research in this field (*E. V. Eastcott*, J. phys. Chem., 1928, **32**, 1094). The structure of *meso*inositol as a cyclohexanetetrol was first recognised by *L. Maquenne* (Compt. rend., 1887, **104**, 225, 297) and has been confirmed by its synthesis from hexahydroxybenzene by catalytic hydrogenation (*H. Wieland* and *R. S. Wishart*, Ber., 1914, **47**, 2082; *R. C. Anderson* and *E. S. Wallis*, J. Amer. chem. Soc., 1948, **70**, 2931; *R. Kuhn et al.*, Ann., 1949, **565**, 1). The determination of its configuration has been accomplished by *T. Posternak* (Helv., 1929, **12**, 1165; 1935, **18**, 1283; 1942, **25**, 746) and *G. Dangschat* (Naturwiss., 1942, **30**, 146), the key reaction being the isolation of DL-idosaccharic acid by oxidative degradation.

d-*Inositol*, m.p. 247° $[\alpha]_D$ +68°, is obtained by the hydriodic acid hydrolysis of its *monomethyl ether, pinitol*, m.p. 188°, which occurs in the redwood and Douglas pine and in two varieties of loco weed (*D. C. Pease et al.*, J. org. Chem., 1940, **5**, 198 where earlier refs. are given). l-*Inositol*, m.p. 247°, $[\alpha]_D^{28}$ −64·1° also occurs as a *monomethyl ether*, **quebrachitol**, m.p. 192–3° (see p. 410), isolated originally from the quebracho tree (*C. Tanret*, Compt. rend., 1889, **109**, 908) but more conveniently obtained from rubber latex; its configuration has been determined by *T. Posternak* (Helv., 1936, **19**, 1007). The racemic dl-*inositol*, m.p. 253°, occurs in mistletoe berries and in a certain species of liana.

scyllo*Inositol (scyllitol)*, m.p. 348·5°, *hexa-acetate*, m.p. 290°, occurs in the organs of various plagiostomes (e.g. sharks, rays, dogfish) and also in the leaves of various varieties of *Cocos* whence it may be separated by means of its sparingly soluble lead complex (*H. Müller*, J. chem. Soc., 1907, **91**, 1767; 1912, **101**, 2383; *J. Müller*, Ber., 1907, **40**, 1821). Its configuration has been established by *T. Posternak* (Helv., 1942, **25**, 746; 1941, **24**, 1045).

allo*Inositol*, m.p. 270–275°, and muco*inositol*, m.p. 285–290° (dec.) are obtained by the hydroxylation of conduritol (p. 172) (*G. Dangschat* and *H. O. L. Fischer*, Naturwiss., 1939, **27**, 756).

epi*Inositol*, m.p. 285° (dec.), *hexa-acetate*, m.p. 188°, is produced by reduction of *epi*inosose (p. 201) (*T. Posternak*, Helv., 1936, **19**, 1333).

A C-*methylinositol, mytilitol*, m.p. 266–268°, *hexa-acetate*, m.p. 181°, occurs in the mussel *Mytilis edulis* (*B. C. P. Jansen*, Z. physiol. Chem., 1913, **85**, 231; *D. Ackermann*, Ber., 1921, **54**, 1938). Its constitution has been established as methyl*scyllo*inositol (*T. Posternak*, Helv., 1944, **27**, 457).

It must be realised that the delineation of the polyhydroxycyclohexanes as above is purely a useful convention. Later work is concerning itself with the interpretation of the reactions of these compounds in terms of the chair configuration of the cyclohexane ring and the modern concepts of equatorial and polar substituents (p. 133) (*S. J. Angyal* and *C. G. MacDonald*, J. chem. Soc., 1952, 686; *C. L. Angyal* and *S. J. Angyal*, *ibid.*, 1952, 695).

For a detailed review of the polyhydroxycyclohexanes aee *H. G. Fletcher* (Adv. Carb. Chem., **3**, 45) and *J. K. N. Jones* (Annual Reports, 1946, **43**, 167).

(iii) Epoxycyclohexanes

Three types of such compound are theoretically possible, i.e. 1:2-epoxy-, 1:3-epoxy- and 1:4-epoxy-cyclohexanes.

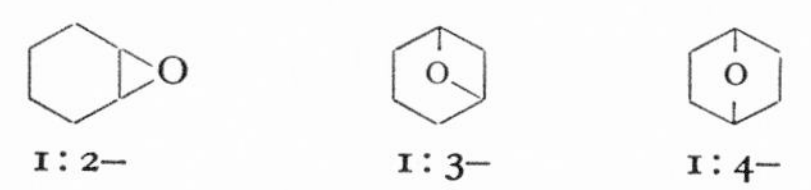

Attempts to prepare 1:3-epoxycyclohexanes have so far failed (cf. *M. F. Clarke* and *L. N. Owen*, J. chem. Soc., 1950, 2103); in the 1:4-series only the parent compound, 1:4-epoxycyclohexane, an unsaturated derivative, 1:4-epoxycyclohex-2-ene, and a naturally occurring terpenoid, 1:4-cineole, are known.

On the other hand the 1:2-epoxycyclohexanes constitute a large and well-studied class. They may be obtained from cyclohexenes by treatment with peracids (*D. Swern*, Chem. Reviews, 1949, **45**, 16) but are best prepared by the dehydrohalogenation of a cyclohexane 1:2-halohydrin.

Some epoxycyclohexanes are described in Table 8.

TABLE 8

EPOXYCYCLOHEXANES

Compound	B.p.°/mm.	n_D(°)	Ref. (p. 170)
1:2-Epoxycylohexane	132	1·4519 (20)	1
1:4-Epoxycyclohexane	120	1·4477 (20)	2
1-Methyl-1:2-epoxycylohexane	138	1·4430 (20)	5
4-Methyl-1:2-epoxycyclohexane	147	1·4473 (20)	6
1:4-Dimethyl-1:2-epoxycyclohexane	153	1·4406 (20)	7
1:3-Dimethyl-1:2-epoxycylohexane	152·5	1·4399 (25)	9
2:4-Dimethyl-1:2-epoxycyclohexane	152	1·439 (25)	9
1-Chloro-1:2-epoxycylohexane	62/20	1·4724 (20)	8
3-Chloro-1:2-epoxycyclohexane	72/15	1·4830 (20)	8
3-Chloro-1-methyl-1:2-epoxycyclohexane	69/10	1·4637 (25)	8
1:2:4:5-Diepoxycyclohexane	m.p. 110		4
1:2-Epoxycyclohex-4-ene	43/14		3
1:4-Epoxycyclohex-2-ene	119	1·4629 (20)	10

[1] *A. E. Osterberg*, Org. Synth., Coll. Vol. I, 185.
[2] *R. C. Olberg et al.*, J. Amer. chem. Soc., 1944, **66**, 1096.
[3] *M. Tiffeneau* and *B. Tchoubar*, Compt. rend., 1941, **212**, 581.
[4] *N. D. Zelinsky* and *A. N. Titowa*, Ber., 1931, **64**, 1399.
[5] *S. Nametkin* and *A. Jarzeff*, Ber., 1913, **56**, 1083.
[6] *S. S. Nametkin* and *L. Brüssoff*, Ber., 1923, **56**, 1807.
[7] *S. S. Nametkin et al.*, Chem. Ztbl., 1925, I, 222.
[8] *M. Mousseron et al.*, Compt. rend., 1946, **223**, 1014.
[9] *M. Mousseron et al.*, Bull. Soc. chim. Fr., 1946, [v], **13**, 629.
[10] *W. Nudenberg* and *L. W. Butz*, J. Amer. chem. Soc., 1944, **66**, 307.

The reactions of the 1:2-**epoxycyclohexanes** closely resemble those of the acyclic epoxides (Vol. IA; p. 668) and may be conveniently described with reference to the parent compound. The characteristic reaction is fission of the type

O + RH ⟶ —OH —R

the product (when R is not hydrogen) being the *trans*-2-substituted cyclohexan-1-ol. Among the addenda employed may be listed water, halogen acids, sulphonic acids, ammonia, primary and secondary amines, mercaptans, alcoholic sodium alkoxides and hydrogen; this last addition may be carried out by zinc-acetic acid or lithium aluminium hydride, the product being cyclohexanol. Reaction with sodiomalonic ester furnishes, after hydrolysis, the lactone of *trans*-cyclohexan-1-ol-2-malonic acid (*M. S. Newman* and *C. A. VanderWerf*, J. Amer. chem. Soc., 1945, **67**, 233).

The action of Grignard reagents on 1:2-epoxycyclohexane is complex; thus methylmagnesium iodide gives 1-cyclopentylethanol, other Grignard reagents behaving similarly (*M. Godchot* and *P. Bedos*, Bull. Soc. chim. Fr., 1928, [iv], **43**, 521). The formation of this product may be explained by an initial rearrangement of the epoxide to cyclopentylformaldehyde followed by interaction of the aldehyde with the Grignard reagent. This mechanism derives support from the fact that cyclopentylformaldehyde itself may be obtained from 1:2-epoxycyclohexane by heating with magnesium bromide etherate (*M. Tiffeneau* and *B. Tchoubar*, Compt. rend., 1937, **205**, 144; 1938, **207**, 918; **208**, 355; *P. Bedos, ibid.*, 1949, **228**, 1141). Dimethylmagnesium, however, reacts normally with 1:2-epoxycyclohexane to yield the expected *trans*-2-methylcyclohexan-1-ol (*P. D. Bartlett* and *C. M. Berry*, J. Amer. chem. Soc., 1934, **56**, 2683) and lithium aryls behave similarly to furnish *trans*-2-arylcyclohexan-1-ols (*B. C. McKusick, ibid.*, 1948, **70**, 1976). Such Grignard reactions with aliphatic epoxides have been reviewed by *N. G. Gaylord* and *E. I. Becker* (Chem. Reviews, 1951, **49**, 413).

1:4-**Epoxycyclohexane** is prepared by the dehydration of *trans*-cyclohexane-1:4-diol over alumina at 275° (Ref. 2); with hydrogen bromide it yields *trans*-1:4-dibromocyclohexane. 1:4-Epoxycyclohex-2-ene is obtained by a high temperature Diels-Alder condensation between ethylene and furan (Ref. 10); with phenyl azide it forms an *adduct*, m.p. 166–167°.

(b) Unsaturated ring alcohols

(i) Cyclohexenols

Monohydric alcohols of the cyclohexene series may be obtained by the direct osmium or osmium dioxide-catalysed air oxidation of cyclohexenes or by the alkaline hydrolysis of the cyclohexene hydroperoxides (*S. Medvedev* and *A. Alexejeva*, Chem. Ztbl., 1927, II, 1012; for other refs. see under cyclohex-2-en-1-ol, below). Reduction of the carbonyl group of cyclohexenones furnishes alcohols of this type (*E. Knoevenagel*, Ann., 1896, **289**, 131). They are also produced by the dehydration of cyclohexanediols or their derivatives and by the dehydrohalogenation of halogenocyclohexanols (*L. N. Owen et al.*, J. chem. Soc., 1949, 320; 1950, 2103; *S. Sabetay et al.*, Bull. Soc. chim. Fr., 1928, [iv], **43**, 906; 1930, [iv], **47**, 463). Another method of formation involves the hydrolysis of halogenocyclohexenes or the action of oxygen on cyclohexenyl magnesium halides (*A. Berlande, ibid.*, 1942, **9**, 644; *F. Hofmann* and *P. Damm*, Chem. Ztbl., 1926, I, 2343).

Several terpenoid alcohols belong to this class.

Cyclohex-1-en-1-ol, the enolic tautomer of cyclohexanone, is unknown but most of its derivatives are stable entities. Thus the *methyl ether*, b.p. 36°/12 mm., is obtained by the loss of one molecule of methyl alcohol from cyclohexanone dimethyl ketal (*H. Wieland* and *P. Garbsch*, Ber., 1926, **59**, 2490). The *acetate*, b.p. 96°/50 mm., n_D^{20} 1·4573, has been obtained by heating cyclohexanone with sodium acetate and acetic anhydride (*C. Mannich*, Ber., 1908, **41**, 564) but is best prepared by the action of *iso*propenyl acetate on the ketone (*H. J. Hagemeyer* and *D. C. Hull*, Ind. Eng. Chem., 1949, **41**, 2920); on being treated with alkali it reverts to cyclohexanone (*B. Tchoubar* and *C. Collin*, Bull. Soc. chim. Fr., 1947, **14**, 680).

Cyclohex-2-en-1-ol, b.p. 163°, *phenylurethane*, m.p. 108°, is prepared by the oxygenation of cyclohexene in the presence of colloidal osmium (*A. Kötz* and *K. Richter*, J. pr. Chem., 1925, [ii], **111**, 383) or by the alkaline hydrolysis of cyclohexene hydroperoxide (*H. Hock* and *K. Gänicke*, Ber., 1938, **71**, 1430; *E. H. Farmer* and *A. Sundralingam*, J. chem. Soc., 1942, 121). The acetate is produced by the action of lead tetra-acetate on cyclohexene (*R. Criegee*, Ann., 1930, **481**, 265). The derived ethers, e.g. the *methyl ether*, b.p. 139°, are most conveniently obtained by the action of the relevant sodium alkoxide on 3-chlorocyclohex-1-ene (*A. Berlande*, Bull. Soc. chim. Fr., 1942, [v], **9**, 64).

Cyclohex-3-en-1-ol, b.p. 166°, n_D^{17} 1·4820, *phenylurethane*, m.p. 81°, is produced by removal of the elements of the relevant acid from 4-iodocyclohexan-1-ol and cyclohexane-1:4-diol monomethanesulphonate and by the partial dehydration of cyclohexane-1:3- and -1:4-diol (*S. Sabetay et al., loc. cit.*; *H. Lindemann* and *H. Baumann*, Ann., 1930, **477**, 78; *L. N. Owen* and *P. A. Robins*, J. chem. Soc., 1949, 423).

1-Methylcyclohex-2-en-1-ol, b.p. 65°/20 mm., n_D^{20} 1·4732, is formed by the action of methylmagnesium iodide on cyclohex-2-en-1-one (*F. C. Whitmore* and *G. W. Pedlow*, J. Amer. chem. Soc., 1941, **63**, 758).

4-iso**Propylcyclohex**-2-**en**-1-**ol** *(cryptol)*, b.p. 82°/2 mm., *phenylurethane*, m.p. 105°, is obtained by the Ponndorf reduction of cryptone (p. 210) (*D. T. C. Gillespie et al.*, J. chem. Soc., 1938, 1820).

By treatment with silver oxide followed by potassium hydroxide 1:4-dibromocyclohex-2-ene furnishes 1:2-*epoxycyclohex*-3-*ene*, b.p. 45°/22 mm. which on hydration gives a mixture of trans-**cyclohex**-3-**ene**-1:2-**diol,** m.p. 77° and trans-**cyclohex**-2-**ene**-1:4-**diol,** m.p. 86° (*P. Bedos*, Compt. rend., 1936, **202,** 671). A 1:2-*diethoxycyclohex*-2-*ene*, b.p. 161°, is obtained by treating 2:3-dibromo-1-ethoxycyclohexane with alcoholic sodium ethoxide (*M. Mousseron et al.*, Bull. Soc. chim. Fr., 1947, [v], **14**, 459). A 1:4-*diacetoxycyclohex*-2-*ene*, b.p. 115°/9 mm., is produced by oxidation of cyclohexene with selenium dioxide in acetic acid (*J. A. Arbusov et al.*, Bull. Acad. Sci. U.S.S.R., 1945, 163).

Cyclohex-5-**ene**-1:2:3:4-**tetrol** (*conduritol;* I), m.p. 143°, is a constituent of the bark of the condurango tree (*K. Kubler*, Arch. Pharm., 1908, **246,** 620; *W. Kern et al.*, *ibid.*, 1940, **278,** 145; *G. Dangschat* and *H. O. L. Fischer*, Naturwiss., 1939, **27**, 756). For the products of its hydrogenation and hydroxylation see pp. 166 and 168.

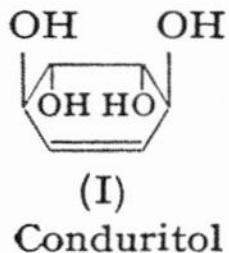

(I)
Conduritol

Very few representatives of cyclohexenols with semicyclic double bonds are known. 2-*Methylenecyclohexan*-1-*ol* is known as its *acetate*, b.p. 83°/15 mm., obtained by the oxidation of methylenecyclohexane with selenium dioxide in acetic acid (*M. Mousseron et al.*, Compt. rend., 1947, **224**, 1230). 2-*Methylene*-1-*methylcyclohexan*-1-*ol*, b.p. 58°/10 mm., is produced by the action of methylmagnesium iodide on methylenecyclohexanone (*C. Mannich*, Ber., 1941, **74**, 554).

(ii) Cyclohexadienols (dihydrophenols)

Ethers of cyclohexa-1:4-dien-1-ols may be obtained by the reduction of aromatic ethers with sodium and alcohol in liquid ammonia solution (see p. 126). Thus anisole gives the *methyl ether* of *cyclohexa*-1:4-*dien*-1-*ol*, (2:5-*dihydroanisole*), b.p. 150°, which, by treatment with potassamide in liquid ammonia, isomerises to the conjugated *methyl ether* of *cyclohexa*-1:3-*dien*-1-*ol* (2:3-*dihydroanisole*), b.p. 145° (*A. J. Birch*, J. chem. Soc., 1946, 593; 1947, 102). Both dihydroanisoles are readily hydrolysed by acid to cyclohex-2-en-1-one (p. 209).

A different type of cyclohexadienol possesses the general formula (III) and may be obtained by sodium and moist ether reduction of the corresponding dichloroderivatives (II); these latter compounds are produced by the action of Grignard reagents on the corresponding ketones (p. 212). Alcohols such as (III) are unstable and tend to polymerise; they are dehydrated to semibenzenes (p.

150) by the action of ice-cold dilute sulphuric acid. Typical members of the series are 1:4:4-**trimethylcyclohexa**-2:5-**dien**-1-**ol** (III; R = H), m.p. 44°, and the 1-*ethyl*-homologue (III; $R = CH_3$), m.p. 47° (*K. Auwers* and *K. Ziegler*, Ann., 1921, **425**, 222).

$CHCl_2$, OH, CH_3, CH_2R (II) ⟶ CH_3, OH, CH_3, CH_2R (III

(*c*) *Acetylenic alcohols*

Alcohols of this type, as exemplified by the parent compound 1-**ethynylcyclohexan**-1-**ol**, m.p. 30°, b.p. 78°/18 mm., are of importance in the synthesis of vitamin A and analogously constituted substances. They may be prepared from cyclohexanones by the action of alkali metal acetylides in solvents such as liquid ammonia, ether, amyl or *tert*.-butyl alcohol and methylal. Among the many homologues may be mentioned the 2-*methyl*-, isomer A, m.p. 58°, isomer B, b.p. 77°/14 mm. (*I. M. Heilbron et al.*, J. chem. Soc., 1949, 2023; *P. A. Robins* and *J. Walker*, *ibid*., 1952, 1610; *N. A. Milas et al.*, J. Amer. chem. Soc., 1948, **70**, 1829), the 2:2-*dimethyl*-, b.p. 89°/20 mm., 3:5-*dinitrobenzoate*, m.p. 115° (*I. M. Heilbron et al., loc. cit.*; *J. D. Chanley*, J. Amer. chem. Soc., 1948, **70**, 244), and the 2:2:6-*trimethyl*-, b.p. 93°/13 mm., 3:5-*dinitrobenzoate*, m.p. 141° (*N. A. Milas et al., loc. cit.*; *H. Sobotka* and *J. D. Chanley*, J. Amer. chem. Soc., 1949, **71**, 4136; *B. A. Hems et al.*, J. chem. Soc., 1952, 1094). The alcohols may be partially hydrogenated to the corresponding 1-vinylcyclohexan-1-ols. Dehydration to 1-ethynylcyclohex-1-enes may be carried out in various ways (p. 151). On being heated with formic acid the alcohols undergo isomerisation to give mainly the corresponding 1-acetylcyclohex-1-ene (p. 216) together with a little of the isomeric cyclohexylideneacetaldehyde:

OH, C≡CH ⟶ $-COCH_3$ + =CH·CHO

(*inter al.*, *J. D. Chanley*, J. Amer. chem. Soc., 1948, **70**, 224).

Cyclohexanone undergoes a Reformatsky type of reaction with propargyl bromide in the presence of zinc to yield mainly 3-(1′-*hydroxycyclohexyl*)*prop*-1-*yne* (I), m.p. 56·5°, together with a little 1:3-*di*(1′-*hydroxycyclohexyl*)*prop*-1-*yne* (II), m.p. 113° (*K. Zeile* and *H. Meyer*, Ber., 1942, **75**, 356). This type of reaction has been extended to substituted propargyl halides (*E. R. H. Jones et al.*, J. chem. Soc., 1949, 2696; 1950, 3646).

OH, $CH_2 \cdot C \equiv CH$ (I) OH HO, $CH_2 \cdot C \equiv C$ (II) OH, $C \equiv C \cdot CH_2OH$ (III)

The Grignard reagent from propargyl alcohol reacts with cyclohexanone to give 1-(1'-*hydroxycyclohexyl*)*prop*-1-*yn*-3-*ol* (III), m.p. 51° (*K. Zeile* and *H. Meyer, loc. cit.*).

For an exhaustive review of the preparation and properties of these acetylenic alcohols see *A. W. Johnson*, "Acetylenic Compounds", Vol. I, E. Arnold & Co., 1946.

(d) Peroxides of the cyclohexane series

Cyclohexanes, cyclohexenes and cyclohexadienes all react with gaseous oxygen under various conditions to give peroxides (for review see *R. Criegee*, Fortschr. chem. Forschg., 1950, **1**, 509).

(i) Cyclohexane peroxides

Cyclohexane itself slowly reacts at its boiling point with oxygen under pressure to give **cyclohexyl hydroperoxide** (*R. Criegee, loc. cit.*); this compound is postulated as an intermediate in the bacterial oxidation of cyclohexane by *Pseudomonas aeruginosa* to adipic, valeric and formic acids (*B. Imelik*, Compt. rend., 1948,

OOH

226, 2082). Methylcyclohexane undergoes this reaction more easily, especially in the presence of ultra-violet light or a peroxide; the tertiary hydrogen is attacked yielding **1-hydroperoxy-1-methylcyclohexane,** b.p. 53°/0·1 mm., n_D^{20} 1·4642 (*K. I. Ivanov* and *V. K. Savinova*, C.A., 1948, **42**, 6757). The constitution is confirmed by zinc-acetic acid reduction to 1-methylcyclohexan-1-ol.

(ii) Cyclohexene peroxides

These form a very well-studied class. Cyclohexenes react readily with gaseous oxygen even at room temperature and the process may be catalysed by ultra-violet light, peroxides, phthalocyanines and finely divided metals (e.g. osmium). Under these conditions the oxygen invariably reacts at the allyl position to give 3-hydroperoxycyclohex-1-enes of type (I). The reported isolation of a true peroxide (II) from this reaction is probably a misapprehension (*H. Hock* and *O. Schrader*, Naturwiss., 1936, **24**, 159).

R $\xrightarrow{O_2}$ OOH R (I) O O (II)

Thus an irradiated mixture of cyclohexene and oxygen furnishes in high yield **3-hydroperoxycyclohex-1-ene,** b.p. 48°/0·2 mm., together with a little cyclohexenol and epoxycyclohexane (*E. H. Farmer* and *A. Sundralingam*, J. chem.

Soc., 1942, 121; *R. Criegee et al.*, Ber., 1939, **72**, 1799; *H. Hock* and *K. Gänicke* *ibid.*, 1938, **71**, 1430). Similarly 1-methylcyclohex-1-ene yields mainly 1-*methyl*-6-*hydroperoxycyclohex*-1-*ene* (I; R = Me), b.p. 67°/0·2 mm. For other homologues see above references and *E. H. Farmer* and *D. A. Sutton*, J. chem. Soc., 1946, 10; *H. Hock* and *S. Lang*, Ber., 1942, **75**, 1051; *K. Suzuki*, Chem. Ztbl., 1937, I, 2612.

The properties of these compounds may be conveniently described with reference to the parent member. As an unsaturated compound it absorbs one mol. of bromine. Catalytic hydrogenation furnishes cyclohexanol but milder reducing agents, e.g. sulphites, aluminium amalgam, give cyclohex-2-en-1-ol. With strong alkali a disproportionation takes place yielding cyclohexenol and, α-hydroxyadipic acid. In the presence of dilute sulphuric acid a remarkable hydrolytic rearrangement occurs to give a mixture of stereoisomeric cyclohexane-1:2:3-triols.

OH OH OH ←(Acid)— OOH —(Alkali)→ OH + CH_2(—CH(OH)—CO_2H)—CH_2—CH_2—CO_2H

(iii) *Cyclohexa*-1:3-*diene peroxides*

Oxygen undergoes 1:4-addition to cyclohexa-1:3-dienes in the presence of light and chlorophyll to yield true peroxides of the transannular type.

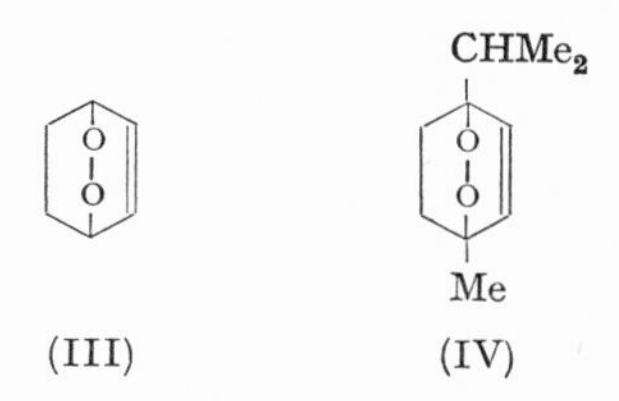

(III) (IV)

Thus cyclohexa-1:3-diene furnishes the parent compound **norascaridole** (III), m.p. 84°. The name of this compound is derived from its well-known naturally occurring homologue, ascaridole (IV) (Vol. IIB), b.p. 97°/8 mm., n_D^{20} 1·4769, which has been synthesised from α-terpinene (*G. O. Schenk* and *K. Ziegler*, Naturwiss., 1944, **32**, 157). For a review of transannular peroxides see *W. Bergmann* and *M. J. McLean*, Chem. Reviews, 1941, **28**, 367.

(e) *Halogenated cyclohexanols*

These compounds may be obtained by treatment of diols with hydrogen halides under controlled conditions, by addition of hydrogen halides to epoxides and cyclohexenols, by reaction of the monomethanesulphonates of diols with lithium halides and by the reduction of halogenated ketones.

The most widely studied members of the series are the 2-halogenocyclohexan-1-ols; the *trans*-compounds are obtained by the addition of hypohalous acids to cyclohexenes or by the fission of 1:2-epoxycyclohexanes with hydrogen halides whilst the *cis*-isomers are produced by the action of Grignard reagents on 2-halogenocyclohexan-1-ones. Dehydrohalogenation of the *cis*-compounds with Grignard reagents yields cyclohexanones whilst subjection of the *trans*-isomers to this reaction results in ring-contraction to furnish cyclopentyl ketones (*M. Tiffeneau et al.*, Compt. rend., 1943, **216**, 856). Milder dehydrohalogenation of the *trans*-isomers, e.g. with aqueous alkali, produces 1:2-epoxycyclohexanes (p. 169).

Some halogenocyclohexanols are shown in Table 9.

TABLE 9

HALOGENATED CYCLOHEXANOLS

Compound	M.p.°	Ref.
cis-2-Chlorocyclohexan-1-ol	87/17 (m.p. 31·5°)	1,2,5
trans-2-Chlorocyclohexan-1-ol	85/17	1,2,4
trans-4-Chlorocyclohexan-1-ol	99/10 (m.p. 83°)	16,17
trans-2-Bromocyclohexan-1-ol	86/10 (m.p. 27·5°)	3,6,7,8
trans-2-Iodocyclohexan-1-ol	m.p. 42°	7,9
cis-2-Chloro-1-methylcyclohexan-1-ol	84/13	10
cis-2-Chloro-4-methylcyclohexan-1-ol	98/15	12
2-Chloro-5-methylcyclohexan-1-ol	104/16	11
2-Bromo-1-methylcyclohexan-1-ol	101/16	7
2-Chloro-1:5-dimethylcyclohexan-1-ol	90/14	10
2-Chloro-1:4-dimethylcyclohexan-1-ol	94/17	10
2-Bromo-1:4-dimethylcyclohexan-1-ol	111/17	13
cis-2-Chloro-1-ethylcyclohexan-1-ol	100/18	10
cis-2-Chloro-1-*n*-butylcyclohexan-1-ol	99/18	10
cis-2-Chloro-1-phenylcyclohexan-1-ol	165/16	14
2-Chlorocyclohexane-1:3-diol	(a) m.p. 90° (b) m.p. 135°	15

[1] *M. Godchot*, Compt. rend., 1923, **176**, 448.
[2] *P. D. Bartlett*, J. Amer. chem. Soc., 1935, **57**, 224.
[3] *F. Swarts*, Bull. Soc. chim. Belg., 1937, **46**, 13.
[4] *M. S. Newman* and *C. A. VanderWerf*, J. Amer. chem. Soc., 1945, **67**, 233.
[5] *M. Mousseron et al.*, Compt. rend., 1946, **222**, 1503.
[6] *S. Winstein*, J. Amer. chem. Soc., 1939, **61**, 1610.
[7] *M. Tiffeneau* and *B. Tchoubar*, Compt. rend., 1938, **207**, 918.
[8] *S. Winstein* and *R. E. Buckles*, J. Amer. chem. Soc., 1942, **64**, 2780, 2787.
[9] *S. Winstein et al.*, *ibid.*, 1948, **70**, 820.
[10] *M. Tiffeneau et al.*, Compt. rend., 1943, **216**, 856.
[11] *M. Mousseron et al.*, Bull. Soc. chim., Fr., 1946, [v], **13**, 610.
[12] *Idem*, *ibid.*, 1947, **14**, 598.

[13] *B. Tchoubar*, Compt. rend., 1939, **208**, 355.
[14] *M. Tiffeneau et al.*, ibid., 1943, **217**, 588.
[15] *A. Kötz* and *K. Richter*, J. pr. Chem., 1925, [ii], **111**, 373.
[16] *L. N. Owen* and *P. A. Robins*, J. chem. Soc., 1949, 320.
[17] *E. A. Fehnel et al.*, J. Amer. chem. Soc., 1951, **73**, 4978.

cis-2-**Chlorocyclohexan-1-ol,** *a-naphthylurethane* m.p. 84°, is obtained by the reduction of 2-chlorocyclohexanone with *tert.*-butylmagnesium chloride and also by the action of nitrous acid on 2-chlorocyclohexylamine; the latter process has been used to procure the optically active compounds from the corresponding optically active amines (Ref. 5, Table 9). Heating it with sodium hydroxide solution results in the formation of cyclohexanone. The trans-*isomer, a-naphthylurethane* m.p. 165°, is prepared by the addition of hypochlorous acid to cyclohexene (Org. Synth., Coll. Vol. I, p. 158); it may also be obtained by the action of hydrogen chloride on 1:2-epoxycyclohexane.

The configuration of the diacetate obtained by the reaction between silver acetate and *trans*-2-halogenocyclohexan-1-ol acetates is highly dependent on the solvent employed. In dry glacial acetic acid only the *trans*-diacetate is formed but, in the presence of water, nearly complete inversion occurs with the production of the *cis*-diacetate (Ref. 9). *cis*-2-Chlorocyclohexan-1-ol acetate is almost completely resistant to these reaction conditions (*S. Winstein et al.*, *ibid.*, 1948, **70**, 816).

A mixture of *cis*- and *trans*-4-chlorocyclohexan-1-ols is obtained by the action of hydrogen chloride on cyclohexane-1:4-diol (Ref. 16); the pure *trans*-isomer is produced by the fission of 1:4-epoxycyclohexane with hydrogen chloride (Ref. 17).

(f) Exocyclic cyclohexane alcohols

Hydroaromatic alcohols having an exocyclic hydroxyl group may be prepared by the reaction of cyclohexylmagnesium and cyclohexylalkylmagnesium halides with ethylene oxide, aldehydes and ketones. They are also obtained by the reduction of cyclohexanecarboxylic esters and exocyclic cyclohexyl ketones and by the action of Grignard reagents on these two types of compound. Catalytic hydrogenation of aromatic alcohols and esters also yields exocyclic alcohols.

Some members of this series are contained in Table 10; other, more complex, examples are described in the following text.

Cyclohexylcarbinol *(hexahydrobenzyl alcohol)* is prepared by the action of formaldehyde on cyclohexylmagnesium bromide or chloride (*A. Favorsky* and *I. Borgmann*, Ber., 1907, **40**, 4863; *H. Gilman*, Org. Synth., 1921, **1**, 182), and also by the catalytic hydrogenation of benzyl methyl ether, using first Raney nickel catalyst at 2500 lbs./sq. in. followed by copper chromite catalyst at 4000 lbs./sq. in. (*R. T. Arnold* and *J. F. Dowdall*, J. Amer. chem. Soc., 1948, **70**,

2590). Other methods of formation include the sodium/alcohol reduction of ethyl cyclohexanecarboxylate (*L. Bouveault*, Compt. rend., 1903, **137**, 60) and the reaction of cyclohexene with carbon monoxide at elevated pressures and temperatures (*G. Natta et al.*, J. Amer. chem. Soc., 1952, **74**, 4496). Its chemical behaviour is that of a typical aliphatic alcohol. Pyrolysis of its *acetate*, b.p. 196°, gives methylenecyclohexane (pp. 145–146).

TABLE 10

EXOCYCLIC CYCLOHEXANE ALCOHOLS

Compound	B.p.°/mm.	Ref.
Cyclohexylcarbinol	181	See text
2-Methylcyclohexylcarbinol	117/22	1
3-Methylcyclohexylcarbinol	117/23	1
cis-4-Methylcyclohexylcarbinol	75/2·5	2
trans-4-Methylcyclohexylcarbinol	74/3	2
cis-4-*iso*Propylcyclohexylcarbinol	101/2	2
Cyclohexyldimethylcarbinol	96/20	3
2-Cyclohexylethyl alcohol	99/15	4, 5
3-Cyclohexyl-*n*-propyl alcohol	105/12	5
1-Cyclohexyl*iso*propyl alcohol	97/27	6
1-Hydroxymethylcyclohexan-1-ol	(m.p. 77°)	8
2-Hydroxymethylcyclohexan-1-ol	137/9	9, 10, 11
cis-3-Hydroxymethylcyclohexan-1-ol	117/0·2	12
cis-4-Hydroxymethylcyclohexan-1-ol	147/3	13
trans-4-Hydroxymethylcyclohexan-1-ol	(m.p. 103°)	13
3(4′-Hydroxycyclohexyl)-*n*-propyl alcohol	127/1	14
1:1-Di(hydroxymethyl)cyclohexane	143/10 (m.p. 95°)	15
1:1-Di(hydroxymethyl)cyclohex-3-ene	(m.p. 92·5°)	16

[1] *A. Skita*, Ann., 1923, **431**, 1.
[2] *R. G. Cooke* and *A. K. MacBeth*, J. chem. Soc., 1939, 1245.
[3] *C. Hell* and *O. Schaal*, Ber., 1907, **40**, 4165.
[4] *N. D. Zelinsky*, Ber., 1908, **41**, 2628.
[5] *G. S. Hiers* and *T. Adams*, J. Amer. chem. Soc., 1926, **48**, 2388.
[6] *W. A. Mosher*, *ibid.*, 1940, **62**, 552.
[7] *C. D. Nenitzescu* and *V. Przemetzky*, Ber., 1941, **74**, 676.
[8] *M. Mousseron et al.*, Compt. rend., 1947, **224**, 1230.
[9] *H. Rupe* and *O. Klemm*, Helv., 1938, **21**, 1538.
[10] *S. Olsen*, Z. Naturforsch., 1946, **1**, 671.
[11] *M. Mousseron et al.*, Compt. rend., 1948, **226**, 1909.
[12] *M. F. Clarke* and *L. N. Owen*, J. chem. Soc., 1950, 2108.
[13] *L. N. Owen* and *P. A. Robins*, J. chem. Soc., 1949, 326.
[14] *E. Bowden* and *H. Adkins*, J. Amer. chem. Soc., 1940, **62**, 2422.
[15] *A. Franke* and *F. Sigmund*, Monatsh., 1925, **46**, 61.
[16] *H. E. French* and *D. M. Gallagher*, J. Amer. chem. Soc., 1942, **64**, 1497.

cis-4-**Methylcyclohexylcarbinol,** *hydrogen phthalate*, m.p. 127°, and the **trans-***isomer, hydrogen phthalate*, m.p. 148°, are obtained by the catalytic hydrogenation of the corresponding carboxylic esters. The geometrical isomers of 4-iso-

propylcyclohexylcarbinol, hydrogen phthalates of both m.p. 108° (depressed on admixture) are similarly prepared (Ref. 2; Table 10).

2-**Cyclohexylethyl alcohol** is formed by the action of formaldehyde on cyclohexylmethylmagnesium iodide (Ref. 4) and in small quantities by the Bouveault-Blanc reduction of ethyl phenylacetate (*G. Darzens*, Compt. rend., 1929, 189, 852; *S. Sabetay*, Bull. Soc. chim. Fr., 1929, [iv], **45**, 482).

3-**Cyclohexyl-n-propyl alcohol** is obtained by the complete hydrogenation of cinnamaldehyde (*A. Skita*, Ber., 1915, **48**, 1692). Other alcohols of the general formula $C_6H_{11}\cdot(CH_2)_n\cdot CH_2OH$ are procured by the normal homologation methods (Ref. 5).

1-**Hydroxymethylcyclohexan**-1-**ol** is obtained by the potassium permanganate hydroxylation of methylenecyclohexane, or by hydrolysis of the corresponding diacetate formed by the action of lead tetra-acetate on the same hydrocarbon. It is also formed by hydrolysis of the corresponding epoxide which is obtained as a by-product in the reaction of diazomethane with cyclohexanone. Acids convert the diol to cyclohexanealdehyde (Ref. 8; *O. Wallach*, Ann., 1906, **347**, 331).

2-**Hydroxymethylcyclohexan**-1-**ol** (*hexahydrosaligenin, hexahydrosalicyl alcohol) bisphenylurethane*, double m.p., 152·5° and 161°, is obtained by the catalytic hydrogenation of 2-hydroxymethyl- and 2-hydroxymethylene-cyclohexanone, by the reduction of methyl cyclohexan-1-ol-2-carboxylate, by the action of nitrous acid on 2-aminomethylcyclohexan-1-ol and by the action of formaldehyde and sulphuric acid (Prins reaction) on cyclohexene (Refs. 7, 9, 10, 11). Dehydration of the diol with sulphuric acid gives a small yield of the corresponding epoxide (I). The diol condenses with aldehydes in the presence of hydrochloric acid to give cyclic acetals of the general formula (II).

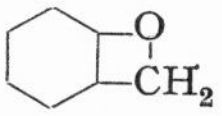

(I)

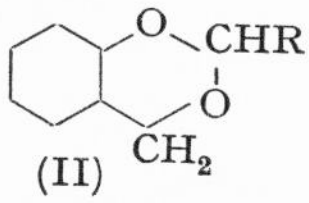

(II)

1:1-**Di(hydroxymethyl)cyclohexane** is the product of the crossed Cannizzaro reaction between cyclohexanealdehyde and formaldehyde (Ref. 15); corresponding unsaturated diols are similarly obtained from cyclohexenealdehydes (Ref. 16). For 1:2-(cis-, m.p. 43°, trans-, m.p. 57°), 1:3-(cis-, m.p. 55°, trans-, b.p. 114°/0·1 mm.) and 1:4-(cis-, m.p. 43°, trans-, m.p. 67°) *di(hydroxymethyl)cyclohexanes* see *G. A. Haggis* and *L. N. Owen*, J. chem. Soc., 1953, 389 *et seq*.

1:2-**Bis(diphenylhydroxymethyl)cyclohexane** (III) is obtained as the two geometrical isomers, cis-, m.p. 206°, trans-, m.p. 185·5°, by the action of ethereal phenyllithium on *cis*- and *trans*-cyclohexane-1:2-dicarboxylic esters. Methanolic hydrogen chloride or boiling acetic acid convert the diols to the corresponding *anhydrides* (IV), cis-, m.p. 199°, trans-, m.p. 221·5°. The isomeric diol *dimethyl ethers*, cis-, m.p. 172°, trans-, m.p. 175°, react with potassium-sodium alloy to give red organometallic compounds of structure (V); these latter substances are decomposed by alcohol to give *cis*- and *trans*-dibenzhydrylcyclohexanes and by tetramethylethylene dibromide to give the acyclic 1:1:8:8-tetraphenylocta-1:7-diene (VI) (*G. Wittig* and *G. Waltnitzki*, Ber., 1934, **67**, 667).

(III) $C_6H_{10}[C(OH)Ph_2]_2$ ⟶ (IV) $C_6H_{10}(CPh_2)_2O$ (V) $C_6H_{10}(CPh_2K)_2$ ⟶ (VI) $CH_2(CH_2CH{=}CPh_2)$ / $CH_2(CH_2CH{=}CPh_2)$ ($Ph_2C{=}CH\cdot CH_2\cdot CH_2\cdot CH_2\cdot CH_2\cdot CH{=}CPh_2$)

2-Chloro-1-hydroxymethylcyclohexane, b.p. 107°/15 mm., is obtained by the condensation of formaldehyde with cyclohexene in the presence of hydrochloric acid (Ref. 7); the corresponding *bromo*-compound, b.p. 120°/15 mm. is similarly prepared.

1-Hydroxymethylcyclohex-1-ene, b.p. 93°/23 mm., is formed by the dehydrohalogenation of the above two halogeno-alcohols. On being heated to 300° with copper it isomerises to cyclohexanealdehyde (Ref. 7, Table 10).

1-Hydroxymethylcyclohex-3-ene, b.p. 82°/12 mm., p-*nitrobenzoate,* m.p. 62° is obtained by the Ponndorf reduction of the corresponding aldehyde (*H. Fiesselmann,* Ber., 1942, **75,** 881).

2-(**Cyclohex-1′-enyl**)**ethyl alcohol,** b.p. 68°/1·8 mm., is produced by the action of formaldehyde on methylenecyclohexane (*R. T. Arnold* and *J. F. Dowdall,* J. Amer. chem. Soc., 1948, **70,** 2590).

1-Hydroxymethyl-4-iso**propenylcyclohex-1-ene** *(dihydrocuminalcohol; perillalcohol),* b.p. 121°/11 mm., occurs naturally in spearmint and gingergrass oils. It may be synthesised by the zinc-acetic acid reduction of perillaldehyde (Vol. II B) or by the action of dilute sulphuric acid on β-phellandrene glycol. 4-iso-*Propenyl-1-hydroxymethylcyclohexane (dihydroperillalcohol),* b.p. 113°/13 mm., which has a rose-like odour, is obtained by the reduction of methyl perillate or by the action of nitrous acid on the corresponding amine (*F. W. Semmler* and *B. Zaar,* Ber., 1911, **44,** 460; *W. W. Williams,* Chem. Ztbl., 1930, I, 2087).

The polyene exocyclic cyclohexane alcohol, vitamin A, is dealt with on pp. 365ff.

5. Sulphur-containing cyclohexane compounds

(a) Mercaptans and sulphides

Cyclohexyl mercaptan *(cyclohexanethiol),* b.p. 158–160°, is a colourless, highly refractive liquid with the typical smell of its class. It may be obtained by treating cyclohexyl halides with potassium hydrogen sulphide, by the interaction of ammonia and ethyl cyclohexyl xanthate, $C_6H_{11}S\cdot CSOEt$, b.p. 152°/16 mm., by the reduction of cyclohexanesulphonyl chloride with tin and hydrochloric acid and by the action of sulphur on cyclohexylmagnesium chloride (*A. Mailhe* and *M. Murat,* Bull. Soc. chim. Fr., 1910, [iv], **7,** 288). An interesting method of formation involves the photochemical chlorination of a mixture of cyclohexane and carbon disulphide in the presence of a trace of pyridine; this reaction yields cyclohexyl dithiotrichlorocarbonate, $C_6H_{11}S\cdot CCl_2\cdot SCl$, which is decomposed by potassium hydroxide to give cyclohexyl mercaptan (*M. S. Kharasch* and *K. Eberly,* J. Amer. chem. Soc., 1941, **63,** 625). Treatment of the sodium salt of the mercaptan with methyl iodide gives *cyclohexyl methyl sulphide*, b.p. 180°; reaction of the sodium salt with iodine furnishes *dicyclohexyl disulphide*, $(C_6H_{11}S\cdot)_2$, b.p. 288° (*W. Borsche* and *W. Lange*, Ber., 1906, **39**, 392; 1907, **40**, 2220).

For substituted mercaptans and sulphides see *M. Mousseron*, Compt. rend., 1942, **215**, 357; Bull. Soc. chim. Fr., 1948, [v], **15**, 84.

1:2-**Thioepoxycyclohexane** (*cyclohexene sulphide*), b.p. 68°/16 mm., n_D^{20} 1·5309, is best prepared by the action of potassium thiocyanate on 1:2-epoxycyclohexane (*E. van Tamelen*, J. Amer. chem. Soc., 1951, **73**, 3444; *C. C. J. Culvenor et al.*, J. chem. Soc., 1949, 282, 278; 1946, 1050; *H. R. Snyder et al.*, J. Amer. chem. Soc., 1947, **69**, 2672). It polymerises much more readily than the corresponding epoxide. It undergoes ring-fission with hydrogen chloride to give *trans*-2-chlorocyclohexyl mercaptan.

(*b*) *Sulphinic and sulphonic acids*

Cyclohexanesulphinic acid, *monohydrate*, m.p. 33–35°, is obtained by the action of sulphur dioxide on cyclohexylmagnesium halides (*H. Gilman* and *H. H. Parker*, J. Amer. chem. Soc., 1924, **46**, 2822; *J. von Braun* and *K. Weissbach*, Ber., 1930, **63**, 2042).

Oxidation of this sulphinic acid with permanganate yields **cyclohexanesulphonic acid,** $C_6H_{11}\cdot SO_3H$, b.p. 180°/0·1 mm., *monohydrate*, m.p. 90–92° (*W. Borsche* and *W. Lange*, Ber., 1905, **38**, 2776; 1907, **40**, 2221). The acid *chloride*, b.p. 124°/16 mm., may be prepared by the action of chlorine on S-cyclohexyl*iso*thiouronium bromide (*J. M. Sprague* and *T. B. Johnson*, J. Amer. chem. Soc., 1937, **59**, 1837) or by the light-catalysed interaction of cyclohexane and sulphuryl chloride [*M. S. Kharasch*, U.S.P. 2,383,319 (1945)].

A study of the action of sulphonating agents on cyclohexene has been carried out by *R. Sperling* (J. chem. Soc., 1949, 1925, 1932, 1938, 1939).

SO_3H / SO_3H (VI) ← NH_4HSO_3 — cyclohexene — SO_3 → SO_3H (I) + SO_2–O–O–SO_2 (II)

(VI) ↑ HNO_3 — SCN / SCN (VII)

cyclohexene ↓ Ac_2O, H_2SO_4 → SO_3H (V) + SO_3H / OH (IV)

(II) ↓ H_2O → SO_3H / OH (III)

The action of sulphur trioxide on cyclohexene produces a mixture of **cyclohex-2-ene-1-sulphonic acid,** *phenylhydrazine salt*, m.p. 143°, and anhydro-2-sulphocyclohexyl hydrogen sulphate (II); hydrolysis of this latter gives cis-**cyclohexan-2-ol-1-sulphonic acid** (III), *phenylhydrazine salt*, m.p. 158–159°. trans-**Cyclohexan-2-ol-1-sulphonic acid** (IV), *phenylhydrazine salt*, m.p. 140–141°, is obtained by treating cyclohexene with acetic anhydride-sulphuric acid; *cyclohex-1-ene-1-sulphonic acid* (V), *phenylhydrazine salt,* m.p. 141–143°, is also produced in this reaction. The configuration of (IV) as the *trans*-isomer is shown by its formation from 1:2-epoxycyclohexane with sodium bisulphite. Cyclohexene reacts with ammonium bisulphite in the presence of oxygen to furnish trans-**cyclohexane-1:2-disulphonic acid** (VI), *phenylhydrazine salt,* m.p. 264–265°; this compound is also produced by the nitric acid oxidation of 1:2-*dithiocyanato-cyclohexane* (VII), m.p. 57·5°. (The author gives the opposite configurations to the above compounds but the above assignments are more probable.)

Cyclohexylmethanesulphonic acid, $C_6H_{11}\cdot CH_2SO_3H$, S-*benzyl*iso*thiouronium salt,* m.p. 183°, is obtained by the action of sodium sulphite on bromomethyl-cyclohexane and by the catalytic hydrogenation of **cyclohex-1-enylmethane-sulphonic acid,** S-*benzyl*iso*thiouronium salt,* m.p. 173·5°; this latter acid is formed by the action of sulphur trioxide on methylenecyclohexane (*R. T. Arnold* and *J. F. Dowdall,* J. Amer. chem. Soc., 1948, **70,** 2590).

6. Nitro- and Amino-compounds

(a) Nitro-compounds

Substances of this type with the nitro group attached directly to the ring are generally made from the hydrocarbon by direct nitration or from the cyclohexyl halide by treatment with silver nitrite. Reduction gives the corresponding amine.

Nitrocyclohexane, b.p. 109°/40 mm., n_D^{20} 1·4612, is prepared by the action of nitric acid on cyclohexane at 100–200°/2–10 at. [*R. M. Cavenaugh* and *W. M. Nagle,* U.S.P. 2,343,534 (1944); *S. Nametkin,* Ber., 1909, **42,** 1372]. It is also formed by the action of silver nitrite on iodocyclohexane (*N. Kornblum* and *C. Teitelbaum,* J. Amer. chem. Soc., 1952, **74,** 3076). It dissolves readily in alkali, from which it may be regenerated by the action of urea in aqueous acetic acid (*N. Kornblum* and *G. E. Graham,* J. Amer. chem. Soc., 1951, **73,** 4041). Nitro-cyclohexane couples in alkaline solution with diazotised *p*-nitroaniline to furnish the p-*nitrobenzeneazo*-derivative, m.p. 95°.

1-Nitro-1-methylcyclohexane, b.p. 110°/40 mm., n_D^{20} 1·4598, is obtained by nitration of methylcyclohexane with nitric acid or almuminium nitrate (*S. Nametkin,* Chem. Ztbl., 1910, II, 1377). A by-product of this reaction is this isomeric side-chain nitro-compound *cyclohexylnitromethane,* b.p. 124°/40 mm., n_D^{20} 1·4705.

Cyclohex-1-enylnitromethane, b.p. 118°/25 mm., n_D^{20} 1·4838 is prepared by the interaction of cyclohexanone and nitromethane in the presence of methyl-amine or piperidine (*H. B. Fraser* and *G. A. R. Kon,* J. chem. Soc., 1934, 604; *H. J. Dauben et al.,* J. Amer. chem. Soc., 1951, **73,** 2359; *D. V. Nightingale et al.,* J. org. Chem., 1952, **17,** 1004). If sodium ethoxide, sodium hydroxide or diethyl-amine be employed as condensing agent, the product is 1-*(nitromethyl)cyclo-hexan*-1-*ol,* b.p. 133°/19 mm., n_D^{20} 1·4875 (*C. A. Grob* and *W. von Tscharner,*

Helv., 1950, **33**, 1070; *T. F. Wood* and *R. J. Cadorin*, J. Amer. chem. Soc., 1951, **73**, 5504; *F. F. Blicke et al.*, *ibid.*, 1952, **74**, 2925; *H. J. Dauben et al.*, *loc. cit.*).

1:2-**Dinitrocyclohexane,** b.p. 110°/1 mm., is produced together with 2-*nitrocyclohexan*-1-*ol*, b.p. 92°/1 mm., m.p. 48° by the addition of dinitrogen tetroxide to cyclohexene (*H. Baldock et al.*, J. chem. Soc., 1949, 2627).

(*b*) *Amines*

(*i*) *Ring amines*

Primary cyclohexylamines may be prepared by the catalytic hydrogenation of anilines or their acyl derivatives, by the catalytic hydrogenation of cyclohexanones in the presence of ammonia and by the chemical reduction of cyclohexanone oximes and nitrocyclohexanes. They may also be obtained by the Leuckart reaction i.e. by heating cyclohexanones with ammonium formate or formamide, and by the Hofmann degradation of cyclohexanecarboxyamides. Most of these methods furnish the corresponding dicyclohexylamine as by-product. Secondary amines may be obtained in the conventional manner from halogenocyclohexanes and primary amines, and these, by alkylation, furnish tertiary amines. For a discussion of the steric course of the reaction between nitrous acid and ring-substituted primary cyclohexylamines see *J. A. Mills*, J. chem. Soc., 1953, 260.

Cyclohexylamine (*aminocyclohexane, hexahydroaniline*), b.p. 135°, *acetyl* deriv., m.p. 104°, *benzoyl* deriv., m.p. 147°, is prepared by the catalytic hydrogenation of aniline (*P. Sabatier*, Compt. rend., 1904, **138**, 457; *A. Skita* and *W. Berendt*, Ber., 1919, **52**, 1519; *J. A. Bertsch*, U.S.P. 2,184,070 [1939]; *R. H. Baker* and *R. D. Schultz*, J. Amer. chem. Soc., 1947, **69**, 1250. For review see *T. S. Carswell* and *H. L. Morrill*, Ind. Eng. Chem., 1937, **29**, 1247). It is also obtainable by reduction of cyclohexanoneoxime (*W. H. Lycan et al.*, Org. Synth., Coll. Vol. II, 1943, 319) or of nitrocyclohexane and by the catalytic hydrogenation of cyclohexanone-hydrazone and -ketazine (*A. Mailhe*, Compt. rend., 1922, **174**, 465).

A by-product of these preparative methods is the secondary amine *dicyclohexylamine*, b.p. 145°/30 mm. (for review see *T. S. Carswell* and *H. L. Morrill*, *loc. cit.*). This amine has the unusual property of forming well-defined addition complexes with cyclohexanols in the cold. Thus the *adduct* from cyclohexanol itself has m.p. 48°, that from 2-methylcyclohexanol, m.p. 60°, that from cyclohexane-1:2-diol, m.p. 66°, that from the 1:3-diol, m.p. 66° and that from the 1:4-diol, m.p. 91° (*C. F. Winans*, J. Amer. chem. Soc., 1939, **61**, 3591).

N-Cyclohexyl-methylamine, b.p. 145°, *-ethylamine*, b.p. 164°, and *-dimethylamine*, b.p. 165°, are formed by the catalytic hydrogenation of the corresponding alkylanilines. *Cyclohexyltrimethylammonium bromide* (I), m.p. 281° (dec.), is obtained by the action of methyl bromide on this last amine and also by catalytic hydrogenolysis of 2:3-*dibromocyclohexyltrimethylammonium bromide*, m.p. 152° (dec.). This latter salt is produced by the action of bromine on *cyclohex-2-enyltrimethylammonium bromide* (II), m.p. 180° (dec.), itself obtained by the interaction of trimethylamine and 1-bromocyclohex-2-ene. The direct production of (I) from (II) by catalytic hydrogenation is not possible, the predominating reaction under these conditions being hydrogenolysis to trimethylamine hydrobromide (*D. R. Howton*, J. Amer. chem. Soc., 1947, **69**, 2555).

1-*Amino*-1-*methylcyclohexane*, b.p. 143°, *benzoyl* deriv. m.p. 101°, is formed by the reduction of 1-nitro-1-methylcyclohexane and by the Hofmann degradation of 1-methylcyclohexane-1-carboxyamide (*S. S. Nametkin*, Chem. Ztbl., 1910, II, 1377).

2-*Amino*-1-*methylcyclohexane*, cis-, b.p. 154°, *benzoyl* deriv., m.p. 110°, trans-, b.p. 150°, *benzoyl* deriv., m.p. 151° is made by the catalytic hydrogenation of *o*-acetotoluidide followed by hydrolysis; in acid solution this process leads mainly to the *cis*-isomer whilst in neutral solution the *trans*-isomer is the predominant product (*A. Skita*, Ber., 1923, **56**, 1014; Ann., 1923, **427**, 266). The *trans*-isomer is also the major product of the sodium and alcohol reduction of 2-methylcyclohexanoneoxime whilst the Leuckart reaction on 2-methylcyclohexanone yields approximately equal amounts of the geometric isomers (*D. S. Noyce* and *F. W. Bachelor*, J. Amer. chem. Soc., 1952, **74**, 4577). The pure isomers may be procured by the Schmidt degradation of *cis*- and *trans*-2-methylcyclohexane-1-carboxylic acid (*W. G. Dauben* and *E. Hoerger*, *ibid.*, 1951, **73**, 1504). 3-*Amino*-1-*methylcyclohexane*, cis-, b.p. 153·4°, *benzoyl* deriv., m.p. 98°, trans-, b.p. 152·5°, *benzoyl* deriv., m.p. 127°, and 4-*amino*-1-*methylcyclohexane*, cis-, b.p. 153·7, *benzoyl* deriv., m.p. 116°, trans-, b.p. 151·9, *benzoyl* deriv., m.p. 180° are obtained by similar means (*A. Skita, loc. cit.*).

For other homologues of this series see *M. Mousseron et al.*, Bull. Soc. chim. Fr., 1947, [v], **14**, 843, 868.

cis-1-**Amino-2-chlorocyclohexane,** *hydrochloride*, m.p. 186°, *benzoyl* deriv., m.p. 154°, is produced by the action of phosphorus pentachloride on *trans*-1-aminocyclohexan-2-ol (*G. E. McCasland et al.*, J. Amer. chem. Soc., 1949, **71**, 637; 1950, **72**, 2190; *E. E. van Tamelen* and *R. S. Wilson*, *ibid.*, 1952, **74**, 6299. On being heated with Grignard reagents the compound rearranges to cyclohexanone.

trans-1:2-**Diaminocyclohexane,** b.p. 80°/12 mm., m.p. 14·8° is obtained by the sodium and alcohol reduction of cyclohexane-1:2-dionedioxime (*F. M. Jaeger* and *J. A. van Dijk*, Proc. Koninkl. Nederland. Akad. Wetenschap., 1936, **39**, 384). It has been resolved via the *d*-tartrate (*F. M. Jaeger* and *L. Bijkerk*, *ibid.*, 1937, **40**, 12). The diamine forms complexes with many metallic salts.

The same 1:3-**diaminocyclohexane,** b.p. 198°, *picrate*, m.p. 265°, is obtained by the Curtius degradation of both *cis*- and *trans*-cyclohexane-1:3-dicarboxylic acids. The same compound is formed by reduction of *m*-nitroaniline together with an *isomeric* 1:3-diaminocyclohexane, b.p. 204°, *picrate*, m.p. 254° (*A. Skita* and *R. Roessler*, Ber., 1939, **72**, 461).

1:4-**Diaminocyclohexane,** b.p. 88°/18 mm., m.p. 73°, *picrate*, m.p. 275° (dec.), is obtained by reduction of cyclohexane-1:4-dione dioxime and *p*-nitroaniline and also by the Curtius degradation of cyclohexane-1:4-dicarboxylic acid (*T.*

Curtius, J. pr. Chem., 1915 [ii], **91**, 34; *C. Sly*, U.S.P. 2,175,003 (1940); *K. Hosino*, J. chem. Soc. Japan, 1941, **62**, 190).

(ii) Ring hydroxyamines

trans-2-**Aminocyclohexan-1-ol,** m.p. 68°, *hydrochloride*, m.p. 177°, is produced by the action of ammonia on 1:2-epoxycyclohexane and *trans*-2-chlorocyclohexane-1-ol (*L. Brunel*, Ann. Chim., 1905, **6**, 213; *A. E. Osterberg* and *E. C. Kendall*, J. Amer. chem. Soc., 1920, **42**, 2616) and by the reduction of cyclohexan-1-ol-2-one oxime (*N. A. B. Wilson* and *J. Read*, J. chem. Soc., 1935, 1269).

cis-2-**Aminocyclohexan-1-ol,** m.p. 72°, *hydrochloride*, m.p. 185°, is obtained by the catalytic hydrogenation of *o*-acetamidophenol followed by hydrolysis of the product (*G. E. McCasland et al.*, J. Amer. chem. Soc., 1949, **71**, 637). The geometrical configuration of these hydroxyamines has been established by their mode of preparation and by employment of their derivatives in stereospecific reactions (*G. E. McCasland et al., loc. cit.; ibid.*, 1951, **73**, 2190, 3923; *W. S. Johnson* and *E. N. Schubert*, *ibid.*, 1950, **72**, 2187; *G. Fodor* and *J. Kiss*, *ibid.*, 1950, **72**, 3495; Research, 1951, **4**, 382). Thus the reaction of thionyl chloride with trans-2-*benzamidocyclohexan*-1-*ol*, m.p. 169°, produces the *cis*-oxazoline (I) whilst the cis-*isomer*, m.p. 193°, furnishes *trans*-1-benzamido-2-chlorocyclohexane (II), both processes being accompanied by a Walden inversion.

HO — NH O — C — Ph $\xrightarrow[-H_2O]{SOCl_2}$ N O — C — Ph

(I)

Ph·CO·NH OH $\xrightarrow{SOCl_2}$ Cl — Ph·CO·NH

(II)

Treatment of the *trans*-aminoalcohol with nitrous acid furnishes exclusively cyclopentanealdehyde whilst the *cis*-isomer under these conditions yields a mixture of this aldehyde and cyclohexanone (*G. E. McCasland*, J. Amer. chem. Soc., 1951, **73**, 2293).

For homologous aminoalcohols see *M. Mousseron* and *R. Granger*, Bull. Soc. chim. Fr., 1947, [v], **14**, 850; *E. Furber* and *H. Brückner*, Ber., 1939, **72**, 995.

A 3-**aminocyclohexane**-1:2-**diol** of unknown configuration, *hydrobromide*, m.p. 167–168°, *N-nitrobenzoyl* deriv., m.p. 183° (dec.) has been obtained by the action of ammonia on 1-ethoxy-2:3-epoxycyclohexane followed by fission of the resulting 1-*ethoxy*-3-*aminocyclohexan*-1-*ol*, m.p. 132–134°, with hydrobromic acid (*G. E. McCasland*, J. Amer. chem. Soc., 1952, **74**, 3429).

A meso 1:5-**diaminocyclohexane**-2:3:4-**triol** has been obtained by degradation of the antibiotic neomycin A (*F. A. Kuehl et al., ibid.*, 1951, **73**, 881).

Aminocyclohexanepentols *(inosamines)* are formed by the reduction of the corresponding inosose oximes or phenylhydrazones (*H. E. Carter et al.*, J. biol. Chem., 1948, **175**, 683; *L. Anderson* and *H. A. Lardy*, J. Amer. chem. Soc., 1950, **72**, 3141; *G. E. McCasland, ibid.*, 1951, **73**, 2295; *T. Posternak*, Helv., 1950, **33**, 1597). Thus *scyllo*inososeoxime gives two epimeric aminocyclohexanepentols termed *inosamine-SA*, *hexa-acetyl* deriv., m.p. 260–261°, and *inosamine-SB*, *hexa-acetyl* deriv., m.p. 299–301°. Reduction of *dl-epi*inososeoxime gives only one of the expected epimers, *inosamine-EA*, *hexa-acetyl* deriv., m.p. 192–194°. On being treated with nitrous acid inosamine-SB gives *meso*inositol (p. 167) and inosamine-SA furnishes *scyllo*inositol (*T. Posternak, loc. cit.*). Inosamine-SB has been elegantly synthesised from 6-nitro-6-deoxy-D-glucose (III) which, under the influence of sodium hydroxide, undergoes smooth cyclisation to the nitrodeoxyinositol (IV); catalytic reduction of this product yields inosamine-SB (*J. M. Grosheintz* and *H. O. L. Fischer*, J. Amer. chem. Soc., 1948, **70**, 1476, 1479; *H. Straube-Rieke et al., ibid.*, 1953, **75**, 694; *T. Posternak, loc. cit.*).

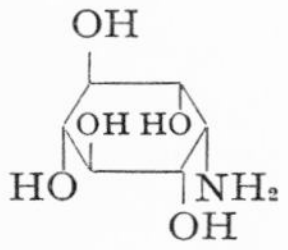

Inosamine-SA 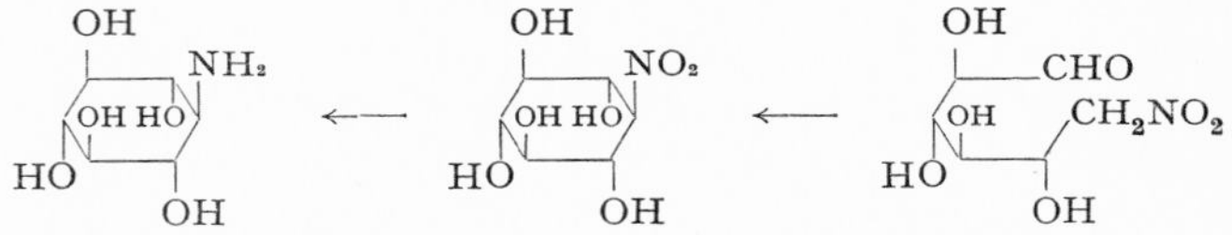   Inosamine-SB ← (IV) ← (III)

Streptidine, a strong base obtained by acid hydrolysis of streptomycin (cf. Vol. I, p. 1216), has been shown to be the 1:3-*diguanidinocyclohexane*-2:4:5:6-*tetrol* [V; R = NH·C(NH$_2$):NH] corresponding in configuration to *scyllo*inositol (p. 167). Alkaline hydrolysis yields the corresponding 1:3-diamino-compound, streptamine (V; R = NH$_2$) (for review see *R. U. Lemieux* and *M. L. Wolfrom*, Adv. Carb. Chem., **3**, 337).

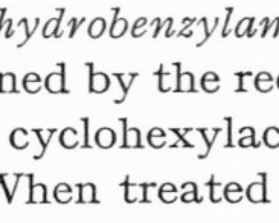

(V)

(iii) Exocyclic amines

Cyclohexylmethylamine *(hexahydrobenzylamine)*, $C_6H_{11}CH_2NH_2$, b.p. 163°, *benzoyl* deriv., m.p. 108°, is obtained by the reduction of cyclohexyl cyanide and by the Hofmann degradation of cyclohexylacetamide (*O. Wallach*, Ann., 1907, **353**, 298, 326; 1918, **414**, 229). When treated with nitrous acid it undergoes to some extent ring enlargement to cycloheptanol.

β-Cyclohexylethylamine, b.p. 189°, is formed by the reduction of cyclohexyl-acetonitrile (*O. Wallach*, Ann., 1907, **353**, 297; *E. Waser* and *E. Brauchli*, Helv., 1924, **7**, 756).

For other exocyclic amines see *B. L. Zenitz et al.*, J. Amer. chem. Soc., 1947, **69**, 1117; *M. Mousseron et al.*, Bull. Soc. chim. Fr., 1947, [v], **14**, 843.

The most important cyclohexanols with a side-chain amino-group are the 1-aminomethylcyclohexan-1-ols which may be obtained by the reduction of cyclohexanone cyanohydrins (*B.Tchoubar et al.*, Compt. rend., 1937, **205**, 54; 1941, **212**, 195; Bull. Soc. chim. Fr., 1949, **16**, 160, 164, 169) or 1-nitromethylcyclohexanols. By treatment with nitrous acid they undergo ring enlargement to cycloheptanones. Thus the parent member, **1-aminomethylcyclohexan-1-ol**, *hydrochloride*, m.p. 214°, *picrate*, m.p. 168–170°, yields cycloheptanone by this reaction. For 1-aminomethylcyclohexan-2-ols see *M. Mousseron et al.*, Compt. rend., 1948, **226**, 1909.

7. Aldehydes

Some members of this class occur naturally as terpene aldehydes e.g. phellandral and perillaldehyde (Vol. IIB).

Preparation. The best method of obtaining ring aldehydes is by employing the Diels-Alder condensation between a diene and an $\alpha\beta$-unsaturated aldehyde. This procedure leads to cyclohex-3-enealdehydes which may readily be catalytically hydrogenated to the saturated aldehyde e.g.

$$CH_2{=}CH{-}CH{=}CH_2 + CH_2{=}CH{\cdot}CHO \longrightarrow \text{(cyclohex-3-ene)}{-}CHO \xrightarrow{H_2} \text{(cyclohexane)}{-}CHO$$

The use of an unsymmetrical diene in this reaction usually gives only one position isomer although two are theoretically possible (Ref. 10, Table 11).

Cyclohex-1-enealdehydes are prepared by bromination of cyclohexanealdehydes and subsequent dehydrobromination of the 1-bromocyclohexanealdehydes formed (Refs. 5, 6, Table 11). They may also be obtained by lithium aluminium hydride reduction of 2-alkoxymethylenecyclohexan-1-ones, a reaction involving an anionotropic rearrangement followed by the elimination of the elements of the relevant alcohol (*P. Seifert* and *H. Schinz*, Helv., 1951, **34**, 728) e.g.

$$\text{(2-CHOR=, 1-one)} \xrightarrow{LiAlH_4} \text{(2-CHOR=, 1-OH)} \longrightarrow \text{(cyclohexene)}{-}CH(OR)(OH) \xrightarrow{-ROH} \text{(cyclohex-1-ene)}{-}CHO$$

Less satisfactory methods of obtaining the aldehydes include (a) heating the calcium salts of the corresponding carboxylic acids with calcium formate

(*A. Franke* and *F. Sigmund*, Monatsh., 1925, **46**, 61), (b) oxidation of the corresponding hydroxymethylcyclohexanes, (c) reduction and subsequent hydrolysis of the corresponding diphenylamidines, which are themselves obtained from the corresponding carboxylic acids (*G. Merling*, Ber., 1908, **41**, 2064), (d) hydrolysis and decarboxylation of the corresponding glycidic esters (*G. Darzens*, Compt. rend., 1906, **142**, 714; ref. 8, Table 11) and (e) hydrolysis of the acetals obtained from the interaction of cyclohexylmagnesium halides and ethyl orthoformate.

Some representative ring aldehydes are given in Table 11.

(a) Saturated aldehydes

Cyclohexanealdehyde *(cyclohexylformaldehyde, hexahydrobenzaldehyde)* occurs in heavy acetone oil (*H. Pringsheim*, Angew. Chem., 1927, **40**, 1392). It is best prepared by the catalytic hydrogenation of cyclohex-3-enealdehyde (ref. 6, Table 11) and has also been obtained by the above-mentioned general methods (*H. Adkins*, J. Amer. chem. Soc., 1933, **55**, 2992; *N. D. Zelinsky* and *J. Gutt*, Ber., 1907, **40**, 3050; *C. E. Wood* and *M. A. Combey*, J. Soc. chem. Ind., 1923, **42**, 429; *G. Darzens*, Compt. rend., 1906, **142**, 714). In addition it is formed by the dehydration of 1-hydroxymethylcyclohexan-1-ol (*O. Wallach*, Ann., 1906, **347**, 331), by the reaction of diazomethane with cyclohexanone in the presence of piperidine (*F. Mosettig* and *A. Burger*, J. Amer. chem. Soc., 1930, **52**, 3456) and by the hydrolysis of its *enol acetate*, b.p. 72°/15 mm.; this latter compound is a by-product in the reaction of lead tetraacetate with methylenecyclohexane (*M. Mousseron et al.*, Compt. rend., 1947, **224**, 1230).

Cyclohexanealdehyde readily forms a *dimer (metahexahydrobenzaldehyde)*, m.p. 202°. It undergoes photolysis in sunlight to carbon monoxide and cyclohexane. With formaldehyde and alcoholic alkali 1:1-di(hydroxymethyl)cyclohexane is produced (p. 179). The aldehyde condenses with acetophenone to yield *hexahydrobenzylideneacetophenone*, m.p. 59° (*J. Frezouls*, Compt. rend., 1912, **154**, 1707).

Other saturated ring aldehydes are obtained by analogous methods and possess similar properties.

(b) Unsaturated aldehydes

Cyclohex-1-enealdehyde is formed by the hydrolysis of methylenecyclohexane nitrosochloride (*O. Wallach*, Ann., 1908, **359**, 292) and also from cyclohexan-1-one-2-glyoxylic acid by the following route (*P. A. Plattner* and *L. M. Jampolsky*, Helv., 1943, **26**, 687).

$CO \cdot CO_2H$, O $\xrightarrow{Ac_2O}$ OAc, O, O $\longrightarrow$ OAc, O, O $\xrightarrow{\text{Pyrolysis}}$ CHO

TABLE 11

CYCLOHEXANE- AND CYCLOHEXENE-ALDEHYDES

Compound	B.p.°/mm.	Deriv.	m.p.°	Ref.
(i) Saturated				
Cyclohexanealdehyde	63/24	(d)	172	6
trans-2-Methylcyclohexanealdehyde	62/11	(s)	155	1
3-Methylcyclohexanealdehyde	95/35	(s)	175·5	2
2:6-Dimethylcyclohexanealdehyde	83/17	(d)	130	5
3:3:5-Trimethylcyclohexanealdehyde	53/4	(s)	132	3
2:2:6-Trimethylcyclohexanealdehyde (dihydrocyclocitral)	115/13	(d)	149	4
2:2:4:6-Tetramethylcyclohexanealdehyde	95/18	(d)	159	5
(ii) Unsaturated				
Cyclohex-1-enealdehyde	70/13	(d)	220	6
Cyclohex-3-enealdehyde	52/13	(s)	154	7
2-Methylcyclohex-1-enealdehyde	103/27	(d)	191	6,8
6-Methylcyclohex-1-enealdehyde	68/10	(d)	179	9
2-Methylcyclohex-3-enealdehyde	75/25	(d)	142	10
6-Methylcyclohex-3-enealdehyde	75/22	(s)	168	1,10
3:6-Dimethylcyclohex-3-enealdehyde	93/25	(s)	180	1
2:6-Dimethylcyclohex-3-enealdehyde	78/17	(d)	167	1,10
2:4:6-Trimethylcyclohex-3-enealdehyde	82/12	(s)	183	1
2:6:6-Trimethylcyclohex-1-enealdehyde (β-cyclocitral)	108/24	(s)	167	4,11
2:6:6-Trimethylcyclohex-2-enealdehyde (α-cyclocitral)	95/20	(s)	206	4,11
2:2:4:6-Tetramethylcyclohex-3-enealdehyde	92/13	(d)	228	5
Cyclohexa-1:3-dienealdehyde	79/20	(s)	182	2
6-Methylcyclohexa-1:3-dienealdehyde	90/21	(s)	201	12,13
2-Methylcyclohexa-1:4-dienealdehyde	66/2	(d)	219	16
4:6:6-Trimethylcyclohexa-1:3-dienealdehyde	86/9	(s)	213	14
2:6:6-Trimethylcyclohexa-1:3-dienealdehyde (safranal)	70/1	(s)	175	15
2:4:6:6-Tetramethylcyclohexa-1:3-dienealdehyde	80/0·2	(d)	195	16,17
2:4:6:6-Tetramethylcyclohexa-1:4-dienealdehyde	75/2	(d)	178	16
2-Butyl-4:6:6-trimethylcyclohexa-1:4-dienealdehyde	100/1	(d)	141	16

(s) Semicarbazones (d) 2:4-Dinitrophenylhydrazones

[1] *O. Diels* and *K. Alder*, Ann., 1929, **470**, 62.
[2] *A. Skita*, Ann., 1923, **431**, 16.
[3] *H. Barbier*, Helv., 1940, **23**, 519.
[4] *H. Schinz et al.*, Helv., 1951, **34**, 265.
[5] *J. C. Lunt* and *F. Sondheimer*, J. chem. Soc., 1950, 2957.
[6] *I. M. Heilbron et al.*, J. chem. Soc., 1949, 737.
[7] *O. Diels* and *K. Alder*, Ann., 1928, **460**, 98.
N. A. Chayanov, J. gen. Chem. U.S.S.R., 1938, **8**, 460.
[8] *D. R. Howton*, J. org. Chem., 1947, **12**, 379.
[9] *W. S. Rapson* and *R. H. Shuttleworth*, J. chem. Soc., 1940, 636.
[10] *H. L. Holmes et al.*, Canad. J. Res., 1948, **26B**, 248.
[11] *H. B. Henbest et al.*, J. chem. Soc., 1952, 1154.
[12] *W. Langenbeck et al.*, Ber., 1942, **75**, 232.
[13] *F. G. Fischer et al.*, Ber., 1937, **70**, 370.

[14] *F. G. Fischer* and *K. Löwenberg*, Ann., 1932, **494**, 263.
[15] *R. Kuhn* and *A. Winterstein*, Ber., 1934, **67**, 354.
[16] *J. C. Lunt* and *F. Sondheimer*, J. chem. Soc., 1950, 3361.
[17] *J. Schmitt*, Ann., 1941, **547**, 256.

The only practicable preparative method, however, involves the bromination of cyclohexanealdehyde followed by dehydrobromination (ref. 6). Homologues may be similarly obtained (refs. 3, 5, 6; *H. Barbier*, Helv., 1940, **23**, 793).

The 2:6:6-trimethyl-homologue, *β-cyclocitral* (I) is best prepared, together with the isomeric α-cyclocitral (II), by the cyclisation of citralanil with sulphuric acid (refs. 4, 11, Table 11).

Me Me CHO Me (I)   Me Me CHO Me (II)

Cyclohex-3-enealdehyde may be obtained from cyclohex-3-enylmagnesium bromide and ethyl orthoformate (*W. Sobecki*, Ber., 1910, **43**, 1040) but is much more conveniently prepared by the reaction between acrolein and butadiene. The aldehyde and its similarly prepared homologues have characteristic leafy odours (refs. 1, 7). They may readily be reduced to saturated aldehydes and react with Grignard compounds to form secondary alcohols [*M. Naef et Cie*, F.P. 672,025 (1929)].

The small number of cyclohexa-1:4-dienealdehydes known are prepared by the Diels-Alder reaction between dienes and acetylenic aldehydes (ref. 16) e.g.

$Me_2C{=}CH{-}C(Me){=}CH_2$ + $Me{-}C{\equiv}C{-}CHO$ ⟶ (Me Me, CHO, Me, Me cyclohexadiene) $\xrightarrow{H_2}$ (Me Me, CHO, Me, Me cyclohexene)

They undergo selective catalytic hydrogenation to produce good yields of cyclohex-1-enealdehydes.

Cyclohexa-1:3-dienealdehyde is produced by the action of sodium carbonate on anhydroecgonine dibromide (*R. Willstätter*, Ber., 1898, **31**, 1545), by treating 2-acetoxycyclohex-3-enealdehyde with sodium acetate (*O. Wichterle* and *M. Hudlicky*, Coll. Czech. chem. Comm., 1947, **12**, 564, 572) and by the action of acid on 2-diethylaminocyclohex-3-enealdehyde (ref. 12, Table 11).

2:6:6-*Trimethylcyclohexa*-1:3-*dienealdehyde (safranal)* is obtained by acid hydrolysis of the naturally-occurring glucoside, picrocrocin, the bitter principle of saffron (ref. 15); it has been synthesised in small yield by the selenium dioxide oxidation of β-cyclocitral (*R. Kuhn* and *F. Wendt*, Ber., 1936, **69**, 1549). This aldehyde has been shown to play a remarkable role as an androtermone in controlling the sexual characteristics of the hermaphroditic green alga *Chlamy-*

domonas eugametos f. *synoica* causing the cells to become male even at a dilution corresponding to ten molecules per cell (*R. Kuhn et al.*, Ber., 1939, **72**, 1702). Homologues of safranal have been obtained (refs. 16, 17, Table 11).

(c) Hydroxyaldehydes

The reaction between 1-acetoxybutadiene and acrolein yields *2-acetoxycyclohex-3-enealdehyde*, b.p. 113°/5 mm., *semicarbazone*, m.p. 162° (*O. Wichterle* and *M. Hudlicky, loc. cit.*); with sodium acetate it gives cyclohexa-1:3-dienealdehyde (see above). 2-Alkoxybutadienes condense with unsaturated aldehydes to give 4-alkoxycyclohex-3-enealdehydes (*H. Fiesselmann*, Ber., 1942, **75**, 881) e.g. *4-methoxycyclohex-3-enealdehyde*, b.p. 95°/13 mm., *2:4-dinitrophenylhydrazone*, m.p. 163°.

Enzymatic hydrolysis of picrocrocin with emulsin yields *4-hydroxy-2:6:6-trimethylcyclohex-1-enealdehyde* (*4-hydroxy-β-cyclocitral*), b.p. ca. 80°/10^{-3} mm., $[\alpha]_D^{20}$ −87°, *thiosemicarbazone*, m.p. 191°; it may be readily dehydrated to safranal and, like this latter compound, possesses termonic activity (*R. Kuhn* and *E. Löw*, Ber., 1941, **74**, 219).

(d) Aminoaldehydes

2-Dimethylaminomethylcyclohexanealdehyde, b.p. 62°/1 mm., *picrate*, m.p. 169°, *2:4-dinitrophenylhydrazone*, m.p. 147° is formed by the hydrolysis and decarboxylation of the corresponding glycidic ester (ref. 8, Table 11).

2-Diethylaminocyclohex 3-enealdehyde, b.p. 90–93°/3 mm., is obtained by condensing acrolein with 1-diethylaminobutadiene; by acid treatment it loses diethylamine to give cyclohexa-1:3-dienealdehyde (ref. 12, Table 11).

(e) Side-chain aldehydes

These compounds are prepared by the standard methods, i.e., by controlled oxidation of side-chain primary alcohols, by the action of ethyl orthoformate on Grignard reagents derived from side-chain halogen compounds and by the hydrolysis of glycidic esters derived from side-chain ketones.

By these routes may be obtained **β-cyclohexylpropionaldehyde,** b.p. 85°/16 mm., *semicarbazone*, m.p. 133° (*F. Sigmund*, Monatsh., 1929, **52**, 187; *A. Skita*, Ber., 1915, **48**, 1693). Aldehydes of the general formula $C_6H_{11}\cdot(CH_2)_2\cdot CHR\cdot CHO$, made by the glycidic ester method are used in perfumery [*A. Knorr* and *A. Weissenhorn*, G.P. 501,627 (1929)].

Cyclohexylideneacetaldehyde, b.p. 85°/16 mm., *semicarbazone*, m.p. 205° and *cyclohexenylacetaldehyde*, b.p. 62°/16 mm., *semicarbazone*, m.p. 186°, are obtained by the ozonolysis of 1-allylcyclohexan-1-ol [*J. B. Aldersley et al.*, J. chem. Soc., 1938, 545; 1940, 10; *I. M. Heilbron et al.*, B.P. 512,465 (1938)]. The first aldehyde is also produced in minute amount as a by-product in the rearrangement of 1-ethynylcyclohexan-1-ol to 1-acetylcyclohex-1-ene by means of formic acid (*J. D. Chanley*, J. Amer. chem. Soc., 1948, **70**, 244).

α-**Cyclohexenylpropionaldehyde** (*Δ*[1]*-tetrahydrohydratropic aldehyde*), b.p. 90–93°/15 mm., is obtained by the glycidic ester method (*G. Darzens*, Compt. rend., 1910, **151**, 758).

The important side-chain aldehyde, *γ*-(2:6:6-**trimethylcyclohex-1-enyl**)-*α*-**methylcrotonaldehyde** ("C_{14} aldehyde"; III), b.p. 92°/0·015 mm., *semicarbazone*, m.p. 157°, prepared from *β*-ionone by the glycidic ester method, is an important starting material for the synthesis of vitamin A and the carotenes (see p. 367) (*I. M. Heilbron et al.*, J. chem. Soc., 1942, 727; 1946, 500; 1949, 1516; *O. Isler et al.*, Helv., 1947, **30**, 1911; *N. A. Milas et al.*, J. Amer. chem. Soc., 1948, **70**, 1584).

Me Me Me
$-CH_2 \cdot CH{=}C(Me) \cdot CHO$
Me

(III)

8. Ketones

(a) Saturated ring ketones

(i) Cyclohexanones

Since cyclohexanones are among the most easily accessible hydroaromatic derivatives and serve as starting materials for the preparation of many other compounds, their preparation and properties have been studied in considerable detail. Representatives of the series occur naturally as terpenes e.g. menthone and carvomenthone.

Preparation. They may be prepared by the partial catalytic hydrogenation of phenols (see p. 126); the controlling factors which favour the formation of cyclohexanones have been discussed by *A. C. Whitaker* (J. Amer. chem. Soc., 1947, 69, 2414). Another frequently used preparative method involves the oxidation or dehydrogenation of cyclohexanols; this may be achieved by chromium trioxide, by metallic copper at 300° (*P. Sabatier* and *J. B. Senderens*, Compt. rend., 1903, **136**, 983) and by nickel at 250° (*A. S. Houghton* and *H. E. McHutt*, U.S.P. 2,303,550 [1942]). Cyclohexanones have also been obtained by heating the calcium or barium salts or the anhydrides of the corresponding pimelic acids; cyclisation of pimelic esters by the Dieckmann method or of pimelonitriles by the Thorpe procedure followed by hydrolysis of the *β*-keto-ester or *β*-imino-nitrile produced also furnishes the ketones. Cyclohexanones with one or more *α*-hydrogen atoms react with sodamide and alkyl halides to form the corresponding 2-alkylcyclohexanone and the process may be continued until all such hydrogen atoms are substituted. Other methods of formation include the reduction of cyclohexenones, the dehydration of cyclohexane-1:2-diols and the dehydrochlorination of *cis*-2-chlorocyclohexan-1-ols.

Some representatives of the cyclohexanone series are shown in Table 12. For terpenoids of this series see Vol. II B.

TABLE 12

CYCLOHEXANONES

Compound	B.p.°/mm.	Semicarbazone m.p.°	Ref. (p. 194)
Cyclohexanone	156 (m.p. –40·5°)	166	1, 2, 3
2-Methylcyclohexanone	166 (m.p. –14·4°)	197	4, 5, 6, 7, 33
3-Methylcyclohexanone	169 (m.p. –73·5°)	191·4	7, 8, 9, 26
4-Methylcyclohexanone	171 (m.p. –40·6°)	193	7, 8, 11, 31
2:2-Dimethylcyclohexanone	173 (m.p. –20·5°)	202	13, 14 15, 16, 17
3:3-Dimethylcyclohexanone	174	195	18
3:4-Dimethylcyclohexanone	187	185	19, 31
trans-2:4-Dimethylcyclohexanone	177	193	4, 19, 31
trans-2:5-Dimethylcyclohexanone	175	168	4, 19, 20 21, 22, 31
2:6-Dimethylcyclohexanone	174	198 (*trans*) 190 (*cis*)	21, 22, 23, 33
cis-3:5-Dimethylcyclohexanone	179	198	25, 31
trans-3:5-Dimethylcyclohexanone	64/15	194	25
4:4-Dimethylcyclohexanone	73/14 (m.p. 38°)	204	24
3-Ethylcyclohexanone	190	183	26, 31
2:4:4-Trimethylcyclohexanone	191		27
2:4:6-Trimethylcyclohexanone	188	217	31
2:2:6-Trimethylcyclohexanone	178 (m.p. –31·8°)	211	28, 33
2:2:5-Trimethylcyclohexanone (Pulenone)	184	177	12
2:3:5-Trimethylcyclohexanone	194	174	31
3:3:5-Trimethylcyclohexanone (Dihydro*iso*phorone)	54/11	202	29
2-*n*-Propylcyclohexanone	84/13	134	30
4-*n*-Propylcyclohexanone	212	180	10
3-*iso*Propylcyclohexanone	205	190	26, 32
2:2:6:6-Tetramethylcyclohexanone	185 (m.p. 11·2°)		33
2-*tert.*-Butylcyclohexanone	62·4/4	183	34
3-*tert.*-Butylcyclohexanone	220	206	26, 34
4-*tert.*-Butylcyclohexanone	(m.p. 49°)	213	34
2-Methyl-6-*tert.*-butylcyclohexanone	99/20		35
3-Methyl-6-*tert.*-butylcyclohexanone	103/20		35
4-Methyl-2-*tert.*-butylcyclohexanone	214	160	31
4-Methyl-2-benzylcyclohexanone	170/17	174	36
5:5-Dimethyl-3-phenylcyclohexanone	(m.p. 47°)	165	37
cis-2:6-Dibenzylcyclohexanone	(m.p. 122°)		38
trans-2:6-Dibenzylcyclohexanone	(m.p. 55°)		38

[1] *T. W. Richards* and *J. W. Shipley*, J. Amer. chem. Soc., 1916, **38**, 996.
[2] E. I. du Pont, U.S.P. 2,015,751 (1935).
[3] *G. Vavon* and *A. L. Berton*, Bull. Soc. chim. Fr., 1925, [iv], **37**, 296.
[4] *M. Tiffeneau et al.*, Compt. rend., 1943, **216**, 856.
[5] *A. I. Vogel* and *M. P. Oommen*, J. chem. Soc., 1930, 768.
[6] *H. Hopff*, Ber., 1932, **65**, 483.
[7] *G. Chiurdoglu*, Bull. Soc. chim. Belg., 1938, **47**, 241.
[8] *P. Sabatier* and *A. Mailhe*, Compt. rend., 1905, **140**, 352.
[9] *F. K. Signaigo* and *P. L. Cramer*, J. Amer. chem. Soc., 1933, **55**, 3326.
[10] *H. E. Ungnade* and *A. Ludutsky*, J. org. Chem., 1945, **10**, 29.
[11] *A. Einhorn* and *H. Ehret*, Ann., 1897, **295**, 186.
[12] *R. Cornubert* and *R. Humeau*, Bull. Soc. chim. Fr., 1931, [iv], **49**, 1469.
[13] *J. L. Simonsen et al.*, J. chem. Soc., 1938, 774.
[14] *W. S. Johnson* and *H. Posvic*, J. Amer. chem. Soc., 1945, **67**, 504.
[15] *H. Meerwein* and *W. Unkel*, Ann., 1910, **376**, 152.
[16] *A. Haller* and *R. Cornubert*, Compt. rend., 1920, **170**, 700.
[17] *J. D. Chanley*, J. Amer. chem. Soc., 1948, **70**, 244.
[18] *G. Blanc*, Compt. rend., 1907, **144**, 143.
[19] *P. Sabatier* and *A. Mailhe*, Compt. rend., 1906, **142**, 553.
[20] *A. Kötz*, Ann., 1907, **357**, 202.
[21] *A. Skita*, Ber., 1923, **56**, 2235.
[22] *J. von Braun*, Ber., 1927, **60**, 2442.
[23] *N. D. Zelinsky*, Ber., 1895, **28**, 781.
[24] *R. F. Miller* and *R. Adams*, J. Amer. chem. Soc., 1936, **58**, 787.
[25] *A. Skita* and *W. Faust*, Ber., 1939, **72**, 1127.
[26] *F. C. Whitmore* and *G. W. Pedlow*, J. Amer. chem. Soc., 1941, **63**, 758.
[27] *O. Wallach*, Ann., 1906, **346**, 256.
[28] *H. Masson*, Compt. rend., 1912, **154**, 517.
[29] *H. Pringsheim* and *J. Bondi*, Ber., 1925, **58**, 1414.
[30] *G. Vavon*, Bull. Soc. chim. Fr., 1927, [iv], **41**, 1638.
[31] *H. E. Ungnade* and *A. D. McLaren*, J. org. Chem., 1945, **10**, 29.
[32] *F. Siefert*, G.P. 389,815 (1921).
[33] *B. A. Hems et al.*, J. chem. Soc., 1952, 1094.
[34] *L. Schmerling*, J. Amer. chem. Soc., 1947, **69**, 1121.
[35] *A. C. Whitaker*, *ibid.*, 1947, **69**, 2414.
[36] *A. R. Poggi et al.*, Gazz., 1942, **72**, 16.
[37] *G. F. Woods*, J. Amer. chem. Soc., 1947, **69**, 2549.
[38] *P. Anziani et al.*, Compt. rend., 1946, **223**, 358.

Properties of cyclohexanones. These compounds closely resemble the aliphatic ketones, reacting in similar fashion with e.g. hydroxylamine, phenylhydrazines, semicarbazide, hydrogen cyanide and sodium bisulphite. The effect of ring substitution on the velocity of formation and hydrolysis of cyclohexanone oximes has been discussed by *A. R. Poggi et al.* (Gazz., 1942, **72**, 2, 262; 1943, **73**, 241). The action of Grignard compounds yields tertiary alcohols and the Reformatsky reaction furnishes cyclohexan-1-ol-1-acetic esters. The ketones react with phosphorus pentachloride to produce the unstable 1:1-dichlorocyclohexanes which readily lose hydrogen chloride to yield 1-chlorocyclohex-1-enes (p. 156). By treatment with sodium acetate-acetic anhydride or *iso*propenyl acetate cyclohexanones give the corresponding enol acetate (*M. Mousseron et al.*, Bull. Soc. chim. Fr., 1947, [v], 14,

598; *H. J. Hagemeyer* and *D. C. Hull,* Ind. Eng. Chem., 1949, **41**, 2920)

Cyclohexanones may be readily reduced to cyclohexanols by standard methods (see p. 157); milder reducing agents such as aluminium amalgam produce the corresponding 1:1′-dihydroxydicyclohexyl (p. 295). Oxidation may be carried out in several ways. Dehydrogenation with copper and manganese chromite at 350–600° furnishes phenols (*E. P. Bartlett* and *E. Field,* U.S.P. 2,291,584 [1942]). Selenium dioxide oxidation produces the corresponding cyclohexane-1:2-dione. More drastic oxidation processes result in ring scission. Thus nitric acid and potassium permanganate both furnish the corresponding adipic acid whilst both organic and inorganic peracids (e.g. perbenzoic and persulphuric acids) yield ε-lactones. The action of hydrogen peroxide on cyclohexanones gives peroxides the nature of which depends on the reaction conditions (see p. 197).

Acid rearrangement of cyclohexanone oximes leads to ε-lactams (*O. Wallach,* Ann., 1900, **312**, 173; 1906, **346**, 266); this type of Beckmann rearrangement has been studied with substituted cyclohexanone oximes (ref. 31, Table 12).

Substitution of cyclohexanones occurs at the two methylene groups vicinal to the carbonyl group. Thus bromine and chlorine react readily to produce 2-halogenocyclohexanones. Reaction with alkyl halides (generally the iodide) in the presence of sodamide yields alkyl ketones containing from one to four alkyl groups in the positions α to the carbonyl group (*K. von Auwers,* Ber., 1915, **48**, 1226; *R. Cornubert* and *A. Haller,* Compt. rend., 1925, **181**, 81; Bull. Soc. chim. Fr., 1927, [iv], **41**, 367, 894; for other refs., see ref. 33, Table 12). Cyclohexan-1-one-2-carboxylic acids are formed by treatment of cyclohexanones with sodamide followed by carbon dioxide (*W. H. Perkin et al.,* J. chem. Soc., 1910, **97**, 1746). Cyclohexanones undergo the Claisen condensation in the expected fashion e.g. ethyl acetate in the presence of sodium furnishes 2-acetylcyclohexanones and oxalic esters and sodium alkoxides produce cyclohexan-1-one-2-glyoxylic esters. Such 2-acylcyclohexanones are also produced by the action of acid anhydrides on cyclohexanones in the presence of boron trifluoride (*J. T. Adams* and *C. R. Hauser,* J. Amer. chem. Soc., 1945, **67**, 284). Benzaldehyde condenses readily with cyclohexanones to form 2-benzylidene- and 2:6-dibenzylidene derivatives (*O. Wallach,* Chem. Ztbl., 1908, I, 638; *R. Cornubert et al.,* Compt. rend., 1926, **183**, 294; Bull. Soc. chim. Fr., 1931, [iv], **49**, 1229, 1238, 1460).

Alkyl formates react with the cyclohexanones under the influence of sodium or sodium alkoxides to give 2-hydroxymethylenecyclohexanones. Alkylation of the sodio-derivatives of these latter compounds with methyl iodide gives almost exclusively the C-methyl derivative of type (I) whilst higher alkyl halides yield predominantly O-alkyl derivatives such as (II).

(I) (II)

These two complementary reactions have been ingeniously utilised both for direct methylation of a cyclohexanone (inter al., *H. K. Sen* and *K. Mondal*, J. Indian chem. Soc., 1928, 5, 609; *J. W. Cornforth* and *R. Robinson*, J. chem. Soc., 1949, 1855) and to provide a blocking group for one vicinal methylene group of the ketone. This latter use may be illustrated by the following series of reactions (*W. S. Johnson* and *H. Posvic*, J. Amer. chem. Soc., 1945, **67**, 504; 1947, **69**, 1561).

The 2-hydroxymethylenecyclohexanones react with many ketonic reagents to furnish bicyclic heterocyclic compounds; thus hydroxylamine yields isoxazoles e.g.

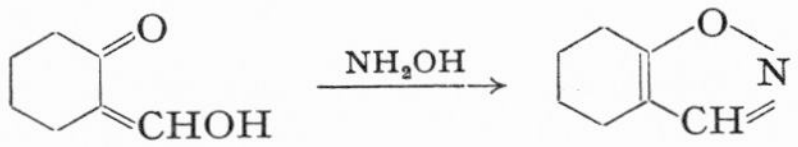

Sodium methoxide reacts with isoxazoles of this type to give 2-cyanocyclohexan-1-ones (*W. S. Johnson* and *W. E. Shelberg*, J. Amer. chem. Soc., 1945, **67**, 1745). Similarly hydrazine and semicarbazide yield bicyclic pyrazoles (*J. D. Riedel*, G.P. 266,405 [1912]).

Cyclohexanone, the simplest hydroaromatic ketone, an oil with a peppermint-like odour, has been detected in wood spirit and occurs with its homologues in heavy acetone oil. It may be prepared by the general methods described on p. 192; other methods of formation include the action of carbon dioxide on the Grignard compound of pentamethylene dibromide (*V. Grignard* and *G. Vignon*, Compt. rend., 1907, **144**, 1358) and the zinc-acetic acid reduction of nitrocyclohexane (*V. B. Markovnikov*, Ann., 1898, **302**, 18).

Properties. The catalytic hydrogenation or chemical reduction of cyclohexanone yields cyclohexanol (*inter al.*, *M. Mousseron et al.*, Bull. Soc. chim. Fr., 1947, **14**, 598) whilst drastic oxidation, commonly with nitric acid, furnishes adipic acid (Vol. I, p. 982). Selenium dioxide oxidation of cylohexanone gives cyclohexane-1:2-dione (*H. L. Riley et al.*, J. chem. Soc., 1932, 1875); oxidation with pervanadic acid furnishes cyclohexane-1:4-dione together with adipic acid and adipaldehydic acid as by-products (*W. Treibs*, Ber., 1939, **72**, 1194). Electrochemical oxidation is discussed by *F. Pirrone* (Gazz., 1936, **66**, 244). Hydrogen peroxide reacts with cyclohexanone to give a complex series of peroxy-compounds. With aqueous or ethereal hydrogen peroxide the ketone gives first the *cyclohexane hydroxyhydroperoxyperoxide* (I), m.p. 76°, and then the *bishydroperoxyperoxide* (II), m.p. 82°, *dibenzoate*, m.p. 92–93°. Hydrolysis of (I) furnishes cyclohexanone and the *bishydroperoxide* (III), *dibenzoate*, m.p. 96° (dec.) (*R. Criegee et al.*, Ann., 1950, **565**, 7; Fortschr. chem. Forschg., 1949/50, **1**, 508; *N. A. Milas et al.*, J. Amer. chem. Soc., 1939, **61**, 2430; *W. Cooper* and *W. H. T. Davison*, J. chem. Soc., 1952, 1180). Dehydration of (I) with acetic anhydride or sulphuric acid produces a small yield of the *bisperoxide* (IV), m.p. 132–133°, which is more easily obtainable directly from cyclohexanone by treatment with a mixture of hydrogen peroxide, acetic anhydride and sulphuric acid (*W. Dilthey et al.*, J. pr. Chem., 1940, [ii], **154**, 219; *M. Stoll* and *W. Scherrer*, Helv., 1930, **13**, 142). The reaction of cyclohexanone with hydrogen peroxide in the presence of hydrochloric acid gives the *trisperoxide* (V), m.p. 92°; this compound may also be obtained by the action of cyclohexanone on (II) in the presence of anhydrous copper sulphate (*R. Criegee et al., loc. cit.*).

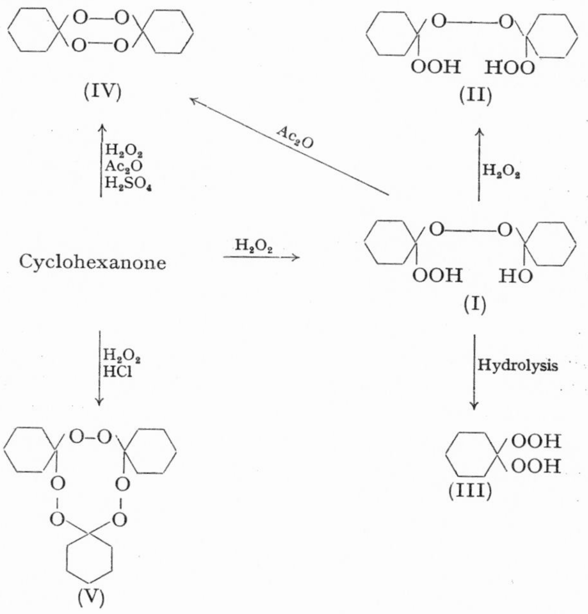

The action of persulphuric acid and organic peracids on cyclohexanone leads to ε-caprolactone; the process has been studied kinetically (*S. L. Friess*, J. Amer. chem. Soc., 1949, **71**, 2571; *P. Karrer* and *O. Haab*, Helv., 1949, **32**, 973).

Cyclohexanone gives the usual ketonic derivatives e.g. the 2:4-*dinitrophenylhydrazone*, m.p. 160°. The *oxime*, m.p. 88°, (Org. Synth., Coll. Vol. II, p. 76) undergoes the Beckmann rearrangement to furnish ε-caprolactam. The *phenylhydrazone*, m.p. 77°, loses ammonia by treatment with mineral acids to give tetrahydrocarbazole (Vol. IV). The action of hydrazine hydrate produces the *hydrazone*, b.p. 195°, and the *azine*, m.p. 37° (*A. Mailhe*, Bull. Soc. chim. Fr., 1922, [iv], **31**, 340). With an excess of hydrazoic acid cyclohexanone yields cardiazole, a bicyclic compound containing a tetrazole ring (*K. F. Schmidt*, Ber., 1924, **57**, 704; *F. R. Benson*, Chem. Reviews, 1947, **41**, 49). In the presence of acid catalysts cyclohexanone reacts with α-glycols to form cyclic acetals; the process has been used for the purification of such glycols (*Henkel et Cie*, G.P., 519,470 [1927]; *M. Kühn*, J. pr. Chem., 1940 [ii], **156**, 103). Cyclohexanone condenses with cyanoacetic ester in the presence of sodium ethoxide or ammonium acetate to give cyclohexylidenecyanoacetic ester which undergoes hydrolysis and decarboxylation to cyclohex-1-enylacetonitrile (*S. F. Birch* and *G. A. R. Kon*, J. chem. Soc., 1923, **123**, 2444; *A. C. Cope et al.*, J. Amer. chem. Soc., 1941, **63**, 3452). Sodio-acetoacetic ester reacts in similar fashion to yield cyclohex-1-enylacetoacetic ester (*G. A. R. Kon et al.*, J. chem. Soc., 1928, 1638). In the presence of potassium *tert.*-butoxide cyclohexanone and succinic ester undergo the Stobbe condensation with the formation of 1-(cyclohex-1′-enyl)-succinic mono-ester (*W. S. Johnson et al.*, J. Amer. chem. Soc., 1948, **70**, 3021).

Chlorination and bromination occur readily to give the 2-halogenocyclohexanones (p. 199). In the presence of an alkaline catalyst cyclohexanone condenses with four molecules of acrylonitrile to furnish 2:2:6:6-tetra(β-cyanoethyl)cyclohexanone, m.p. 165° (*H. A. Bruson*, U.S.P. 2,329,432 [1943]). The action of benzaldehyde produces the 2-*mono-* and 2:6-*di-benzylidenecyclohexanones*, m.p. 54·6° and 117°, with intermediate formation of the 2-*mono-* and 2:6-*di-α-hydroxybenzylcyclohexanones*, m.p. 102° and 162° respectively (*O. Wallach*, Ber., 1907, **40**, 71; Chem. Ztbl., 1908, I, 638; *D. Vorländer* and *K. Kunze*, Ber., 1926, **59**, 2081; *R. Cornubert et al.*, Bull. Soc. chim. Fr., 1938, [v], **5**, 509, 1490; 1939, **6**, 163, 275; Compt. rend., 1939, **208**, 1409). The acid- or alkali-catalysed self-condensation of cyclohexanone produces mainly cyclohexylidenecyclohexanone (see under dicyclohexyls, p. 294) together with lesser quantities of dicyclohexylidenecyclohexanone and dodecahydrotriphenylene (*C. Mannich*, Ber., 1907, **40**, 153; *K. Kunze*, Ber., 1926, **59**, 2085). Nitrous acid produces from cyclohexanone the 1:3-dioxime of cyclohexane-1:2:3-trione (*W. Borsche*, Chem. Ztbl., 1909, II, 1549).

2-**Methylcyclohexan**-1-**one** may be prepared by the methylation of cyclohexanone and by the oxidation of 2-methylcyclohexan-1-ol. It is also formed by the action of carbon monoxide on cyclohexane in the presence of aluminium chloride (*H. Hopff*, Ber., 1932, **65**, 483) and by the reduction of 2-hydroxymethylenecyclohexan-1-one. The *d*-ketone has been obtained by the oxidation of the corresponding 2-methylcyclohexan-1-ol (*M. Mousseron et al.*, Bull. Soc. chim. Fr., 1947, [v], **14**, 598).

3-**Methylcyclohexan**-1-**one** occurs naturally in pennyroyal oil and in Japanese peppermint oil (*R. E. Kremers*, J. biol. Chem., 1921, **50**, 31); the dextrorotatory isomer has been obtained by the degradation of pulegone (*F. Tiemann* and *R.

Schmidt, Ber., 1897, **30**, 23; J. pr. Chem., 1900, [ii], **61**, 477). Oxidation with nitric acid gives a mixture of α- and β-methyladipic acids.

4-**Methylcyclohexan**-1-**one** is prepared by the oxidation of 4-methylcyclohexan-1-ol. It is also formed by the distillation of γ-methylpimelic acid with calcium oxide (ref. 11, Table 12) and by the oxidative decarboxylation of 4-methylcyclohexan-1-ol-1-carboxylic acid with concentrated sulphuric acid (*W. H. Perkin*, J. chem. Soc., 1906, **89**, 836).

2:2-**Dimethylcyclohexanone** is prepared from 2-methylcyclohexanone by direct methylation admixed with the isomeric 2:6-dimethylcompound from which it is separated by fractional distillation. The pure ketone may be obtained by performing the methylation in conjunction with a blocking group (see p. 196). It is also formed by the dehydration of 1-(α-hydroxy*iso*propyl)cyclopentan-1-ol, a pinacol rearrangement with concomitant ring enlargement occurring (ref. 15). 2:6-**Dimethylcyclohexanone** occurs as an inseparable mixture of the *cis*- and *trans*-isomers but the corresponding derivatives may be isolated as separate entities e.g. the *oximes*, cis-, m.p. 79° and trans-, m.p. 118°; regeneration from these derivatives yields the same mixture of geometric isomers (*R.Cornubert et al.*, Bull. Soc. chim. Fr., 1945, [v], **12**, 367).

3:5:5-**Trimethylcyclohexanone** *(dihydro*iso*phorone)* occurs in heavy acetone oil and is also obtained by the chromium trioxide oxidation of the corresponding cyclohexanol. For a description of a series of derived compounds see *H. Barbier* (Helv., 1940, **23**, 519). 2:4:4-**Trimethylcyclohexanone,** also found in heavy acetone oil, is obtained by reduction of the corresponding unsaturated ketone (ref. 29). 2:2:5-**Trimethylcyclohexanone** *(pulenone)* was first obtained as an optically active isomer by a complex degradation process from the terpene pulegone; the racemic compound has been synthesised (*K. Auwers* and *M. Hessenland*, Ber., 1908, **41**, 1814; ref. 12, Table 12).

(ii) Halogenated cyclohexanones

Chlorination of cyclohexanone occurs readily to give 2-**chlorocyclohexanone,** m.p. 23°, b.p. 90°/14 mm. (*M. S. Newman*, Org. Synth., 1945, **25**, 22). 3-**Chlorocyclohexanone,** b.p. 92°/14 mm., is obtained by the addition of hydrogen chloride to cyclohexenone (*A. Kötz* and *F. Grethe*, J. pr. Chem., 1909, **80**, 503). The chlorination of irradiated cyclohexanol produces 2:3:5:6-*tetrachlorocyclohexanone*, m.p. 84°, which readily loses hydrogen chloride on being heated to give 2:6-dichlorophenol (*O. Hassel* and *K. Lunde*, Acta Chem. Scand., 1950, **4**, 200).

2-**Bromocyclohexanone,** b.p. 89°/4 mm., is prepared by the direct bromination of cyclohexanone (*A. Kötz*, Ann., 1907, **358**, 195). The use of two mols. of bromine gives 2:6-**dibromocyclohexanone,** m.p. 106–107° which may be dehydrobrominated with collidine to give phenol (*F. Galinowsky*, Ber., 1943, **76**, 230). Further bromination produces a *tetrabromocyclohexanone*, m.p. 119°, which readily loses hydrogen bromide to give 2:6-dibromophenol; by analogy with the above tetrachloro-derivative it is probably the 2:3:5:6-tetrabromo-compound.

(*F. Bodroux* and *F. Taboury*, Compt. rend., 1912, **154**, 1509; *O. Hassel* and *K. Lunde*, *loc. cit.*).

For homologous halogenated cyclohexanones see *M. Godchot* and *P. Bedos*, Bull. Soc. chim. Fr., 1926, [iv], **39**, 83; Compt. rend., 1925, **180**, 295; 1925, **181**, 919; *M. Mousseron et al.*, *ibid.*, 1947, **224**, 1230; 1946, **223**, 909; 1939, **208**, 1500; Bull. Soc. chim. Fr., 1946, [v], **13**, 628; 1947, **14**, 606.

The interaction of α-halogenated cyclohexanones with strong bases such as alcoholic potassium hydroxide and sodium ethoxide results in ring contraction, the corresponding cyclopentanecarboxylic acid being formed; this process is sometimes termed the *Favorsky* rearrangement (*A. Favorsky* and *V. Boshowsky*, Bull. Soc. chim. Fr., 1915, [iv], **18**, 615; *M. Jackman et al.*, J. Amer. chem. Soc., 1948, **70**, 498; *R. B. Loftfield*, *ibid.*, 1951, **73**, 4707; for review see *R. Jacquier*, Bull. Soc. chim. Fr., 1950, **17**, D35).

(iii) Hydroxycyclohexanones

Cyclohexan-2-ol-1-one *(adipoin)* is prepared by hydrolysis of 2-chlorocyclohexanone with aqueous potassium carbonate (*A. Kötz et al.*, Ann., 1913, **400**, 55; *P. D. Bartlett* and *G. F. Woods*, J. Amer. chem. Soc., 1940, **62**, 2933). It is also obtained by the intramolecular acyloin condensation of dimethyl adipate (*J. C. Sheehan et al.*, *ibid.*, 1950, **72**, 3376). The freshly prepared compound is a mobile liquid, b.p. 71°/7 mm., but soon solidifies to a *dimer* with the hemi-acetal constitution (I) *(idem, ibid.)*. Both monomer and dimer reduce Fehling's solution and give a 2:4-*dinitrophenylosazone*, m.p. 221° (dec.).

HO O O OH

(I)

Cyclohexan-3-ol-1-one, b.p. 95°/1 mm., *benzoate*, m.p. 61–62°, is a very labile compound, readily losing water to give cyclohexenone. It is prepared by oxidation of the monoacetate of cyclohexane-1:3-diol followed by hydrolysis of the resulting 3-*acetoxycyclohexanone*, b.p. 118°/11·5 mm. (*K. Dimroth* and *K. Resin*, Ber., 1942, **75**, 322).

Cyclohexan-4-ol-1-one, b.p. 98°/0·5 mm., 2:4-*dinitrophenylhydrazone*, m.p. 151°, is best prepared by the hydrolysis of its *benzoate*, m.p. 63°, which is readily obtainable by the chromium trioxide oxidation of the monobenzoate of cyclohexane-1:4-diol (*E. R. H. Jones* and *F. Sondheimer*, J. chem. Soc., 1949, 615; *L. N. Owen* and *P. A. Robins*, *ibid.*, 320; *J. B. Aldersley et al.*, *ibid.*, 1940, 10; *K. Dimroth et al.*, Ber., 1939, **72**, 2043; 1942, **75**, 317).

2-**Methylcyclohexan-2-ol-1-one,** b.p. 87°/16 mm., *semicarbazone*, m.p. 203°, is obtained by the action of methylmagnesium iodide on cyclohexane-1:2-dione (*J. W. Butz et al.*, J. org. Chem., 1947, **12**, 122; *N. A. B. Wilson* and *J. Read*, J. chem. Soc., 1935, 1269).

3:3:6:6-**Tetramethylcyclohexan**-2-**ol**-1-**one**, m.p. 29°, b.p. 77°/6 mm. is the product of subjecting dimethyl *aaa′a′*-tetramethyladipate to the acyloin condensation (*N. J. Leonard* and *P. M. Mader*, J. Amer. chem. Soc., 1950, **72**, 5388).

Controlled oxidation of *meso*inositol with nitric acid gives a pentahydrocyclohexanone, epi**inosose**, m.p. 200° (dec.), *semicarbazone*, m.p. 207°, *pentabenzoate*, m.p. 144° (*T. Posternak*, Helv., 1936, **19**, 1333). Its configuration has been shown to be (II) (*idem, ibid.*, 1946, **29**, 1991). Sodium amalgam reduction of the compound gives a mixture of *epi*inositol and *meso*inositol. Microbiological oxidation of *meso*inositol with *Acetobacter suboxydans* results in the attack of a different hydroxyl group with the formation in high yield of *scyllo*inosose (III), m.p. 202° (dec.), *phenylhydrazone*, m.p. 184° (dec.), *pentabenzoate*, m.p. 188° and 286° (dimorphs). Reduction gives a mixture of *meso*- and *scyllo*inositol (*A. J. Kluyver* and *A. G. J. Boezaardt*, Rec. Trav. chim., 1939, **58**, 956; *T. Posternak*, Helv., 1941, **24**, 1045; 1942, **25**, 746).

*epi*Inosose (II)

*scyllo*Inosose (III)

(*iv*) *Aminocyclohexanones*

2-Dialkylaminomethylcyclohexan-1-ones are readily obtainable from cyclohexanones by the Mannich reaction. Thus cyclohexanone, formaldehyde and dimethylamine hydrochloride give the *hydrochloride*, m.p. 140°, of 2-**dimethylaminomethylcyclohexan**-1-**one**, $NMe_2 \cdot CH_2 \cdot C_6H_9{:}O$, b.p. 94°/11·5 mm., *picrate*, m.p. 147°, 2:4-*dinitrophenylhydrazone*, m.p. 207° (*K. Dimroth et al.*, Ber., 1940, **73**, 1399; *D. R. Howton*, J. org. Chem., 1947, **12**, 379). Pyrolysis of the hydrochloride gives the highly unstable 2-methylenecyclohexanone (*C. Mannich*, Ber., 1941, **74**, 554). The free base reacts with diethyl malonate with elimination of dimethylamine to produce diethyl 2-ketocyclohexylmethylmalonate (*C. Mannich* and *W. Koch*, Ber., 1942, **75**, 803).

2-(*β*-**Dimethylaminoethyl**)**cyclohexanone**, $NMe_2 \cdot CH_2 \cdot CH_2 \cdot C_6H_9{:}O$, b.p. 112°/12 mm., *picrate*, m.p. 119°, is obtained by the condensation of *β*-dimethylaminoethyl chloride with sodium ethyl cyclohexan-1-one-2-carboxylate followed by hydrolysis and decarboxylation (*R. Grewe*, Ber., 1943, **76**, 1072; *W. E. Doering* and *S. J. Rhoads*, 1951, **73**, 3082).

(*v*) *Cyclohexanediones*

The introduction of a second carbonyl group into the cyclohexane ring has a profound effect on the enolisation of the first carbonyl. Thus, whilst cyclohexanone itself shows no enolic characteristics (although derivatives of the enol form are known) cyclohexane-1:2-dione and its homologues have been shown to exist completely in the mono-enolic form (I) and show weakly acidic properties (p*K* ca. 10) (*G. Schwarzenbach* and *C. Wittwer,* Helv., 1947, **30,** 663; *H. S. French* and *M. E. T. Holden,* J. Amer. chem. Soc., 1945, **67,** 1239; *G. W. Wheland,* J. chem. Phys., 1933, **1,** 735). The compounds are sometimes referred to as **"diosphenols"**, this being the name originally given to the first known compound of this type, 3-methyl-5-*iso*propylcyclohexane-1:2-dione (buchucamphor) (*O. Wallach,* Ann., 1924, **437,** 148). Cyclohexane-1:3-diones are also completely enolised as in (II) and possess an acidity (p*K* ca. 5) comparable to that of a carboxylic acid, with which they may be considered vinylogous (*A. R. Blout et al.,* J. Amer. chem. Soc., 1946, **68,** 566; *R. B. Woodward* and *A. R. Blout, ibid.,* 1943, **65,** 562; *H. Bastron et al.,* J. org. Chem., 1943, **8,** 515; *G. Schwarzenbach et al.,* Helv., 1940, **23,** 1147, 1191). Cyclohexane-1:4-diones show no enolic properties.

O O
—OH —OH
(I) (II)

Cyclohexane-1:2-**dione,** m.p. 38°, b.p. 97°/25 mm., *phenylurethane,* m.p. 124°, was first obtained by the action of aqueous potassium hydroxide on 2:6-dibromocyclohexanone (*O. Wallach,* Ann., 1924, **437,** 173). It may be conveneintly prepared by the oxidation of cyclohexanone with selenium dioxide (*E. G. Rauh et al.,* J. org. Chem., 1945, **10,** 199; *H. L. Riley et al.,* J. chem. Soc., 1932, 1875; *C. H. Hach et al.,* Org. Synth., 1952, **32,** 35). Further oxidation of the dione produces adipic acid. Heating the dione with aqueous alkali results in a rearrangement of the benzilic type to cyclopentan-1-ol-1-carboxylic acid. The *dioxime* (*nioxime*), m.p. 188°, forms sparingly soluble coloured salts with the transition metals, especially nickel (*O. Wallach, loc. cit.*; *E. G. Rauh et al., loc. cit.*; *T. A. Geissman* and *M. J. Schatter,* J. org. Chem., 1946, **11,** 771).

Homologous cyclohexane-1:2-diones are similarly prepared and have analogous properties e.g. 3-*methyl-*, m.p. 65° and 4:4:5-*trimethylcyclohexane-*1:2-*dione,* m.p. 94° (*O. Wallach, loc. cit.*; *E. R. Buchman* and *H. Sargent,* J. org. Chem., 1942, **7,** 148); 3:3:6:6-*tetramethylcyclohexane-*1:2-*dione,* m.p. 114°, which is incapable of enolisation, is obtained by oxidation of the corresponding hydroxyketone (p. 201).

Cyclohexane-1:3-**dione** *(dihydroresorcinol),* m.p. 104°, *dioxime,* m.p. 156°, is prepared from resorcinol by sodium amalgam reduction (*G. Merling,* Ann., 1894, **278,** 28) or by catalytic hydrogenation (*R. B. Thompson,* Org. Synth., 1947, **27,** 21). It may also be obtained by the intramolecular Claisen condensation of ethyl γ-acetylbutyrate (*D. Vorländer,* Ann., 1897, **294,** 270). It is almost insoluble in ether but dissolves readily in water, alcohols, esters and chloroform; with ferric chloride a purple colour is obtained. Its acid strength approximates to that of acetic acid and ethers of the enol form may be made by direct esterification with alcohols and mineral acids or by treatment with diazomethane (cf. *R. H. Frank* and *H. K. Hall*, J. Amer. chem. Soc., 1950, **72**, 1645); these derivatives are also procurable by treatment of the silver salt with alkyl iodides (*G. F. Woods* and *I. W. Tucker*, J. Amer. chem. Soc., 1948, **70**, 2174). Reaction of the sodium or potassium salt with alkyl halides gives a mixture of the enol ether with the isomeric 2-alkylcyclohexane-1:3-dione, the proportions of the two products varying with the experimental conditions and the nature of the alkyl halide (for detailed study of this reaction see *H. Stetter* and *W. Dierichs*, Ber., 1952, **85**, 61). Cyclohexane-1:3-dione reacts readily with aldehydes to form condensation products of the type

O O
—CH(R)—
O O

which may be employed for the characterisation of aldehydes. Hydrogen cyanide reacts with both carbonyl groups of the diketone to form 1:3-dicyanocyclohexane-1:3-diol (*G. Merling*, Ann., 1894, **278**, 20). The action of phosphorus trichloride gives 3-chlorocyclohex-2-en-1-one and phosphorus pentachloride produces 1:3-dichlorocyclohexa-1:3-diene. Bromination gives 2-*bromocyclohexane*-1:2-*dione*, m.p. 166° (dec.) (*G. Merling, loc. cit.*). With alkalis (e.g. barium hydroxide) the dione is smoothly cleaved to γ-acetylbutyric acid (*D. Vorländer*, Ann., 1897, **294**, 253); this facile reaction has been employed for the preparation of substituted aliphatic keto-acids from substituted cyclohexane-1:3-diones (*H. Stetter* and *W. Dierichs, loc. cit.*; Ber., 1952, **85**, 61, 290, 1061; *H. Lettré* and *A. Jahn, ibid.*, 346). Ring fission also takes place with sodium hypobromite with the formation of bromoform and glutaric acid.

Homologues of cyclohexane-1:3-dione are generally obtained by the intramolecular cyclisation of δ-keto-esters; these latter compounds are available by the interaction of sodiomalonic ester and $\alpha\beta$-unsaturated ketones or sodioacetoacetic ester and $\alpha\beta$-unsaturated esters. Thus the most familiar homologue, 5:5-**dimethylcyclohexane**-1:3-**dione** (5:5-*dimethyldihydroresorcinol; methone;* **dimedone**), m.p. 148–150° (dec.) is obtained by a condensation between sodiomalonic ester and mesityl oxide (*R. L. Shriner* and *H. R. Todd*, Org. Synth., Coll., Vol. II, 200).

CH_3–CO–CH=C(Me)Me + $CH_2(CO_2Et)_2$ $\xrightarrow{\text{NaOEt}}$ O, O, CO_2Et, Me Me $\xrightarrow{\text{Hydrolysis}}$ O, O, Me Me

Dimedone

Dimedone has been much used for the characterisation of aldehydes with which it condenses in the same manner as its parent compound (see above) (*D. Vor-*

länder, Z. anal. Chem., 1929, **77**, 241; *G. Klein* and *H. Linse*, Chem. Ztbl., 1930, I, 2085). Its properties exactly parallel those of the parent dione as detailed above. Bromination of dimedone can be adjusted to give the 2-*bromo*-, m.p. 175°, 4-*bromo*-, m.p. 150°, 2:2-*dibromo*-, m.p. 151°, 2:4-*dibromo*-, m.p. 150·5°, 4:6-*dibromo*-, m.p. 146°, 2:4:6-*tribromo*-, m.p. 175° (dec.) or 2:2:4:6-*tetrabromo*-derivative, m.p. 111° (*E. R. Blout et al.*, J. Amer. chem. Soc., 1946, **68**, 566; *T. Voitila*, C.A., 1939, **33**, 7742). Catalytic hydrogenation of dimedone employing platinised charcoal gives mainly 3:3-dimethylcyclohexan-1-ol and a little 1:1-dimethylcyclohexane (*J. P. Wibaut* and *H. P. L. Gitsels*, Rec. Trav. chim., 1941, **60**, 577); Raney nickel gives the same product together with 5:5-dimethylcyclohexane-1:3-diol (*T. Henshall*, J. Soc. Chem. Ind., 1943, **62**, 127; *J. M. Sprague* and *H. Adkins*, J. Amer. chem. Soc., 1934, **56**, 2669). Clemmensen reduction results in ring contraction to yield, among other products, 2:4:4-trimethylcyclopentanone (*A. N. Dey* and *R. P. Linstead*, J. chem. Soc., 1935, 1063).

For other homologous cyclohexane-1:3-diones see *D. Vorländer*, Ann., 1906, **345**, 206; 1902, **322**, 239; 1897, **294**, 253; *W. Borsche*, Ber., 1909, **42**, 4496; *A. W. Crossley et al.*, J. chem. Soc., 1902, **81**, 675; 1908, **93**, 629; 1915, **107**, 608; *C. Gilling*, *ibid.*, 1913, **103**, 2029; *A. J. Boyd et al.*, 1920, **117**, 1383; *E. Friedmann*, J. pr. Chem., 1936, [ii], **146**, 65, 71, 79; *R. H. Frank* and *H. K. Hall*, J. Amer. chem. Soc., 1950, **72**, 1645; *H. Stetter* and *W. Dierichs*, *loc. cit.*

Cyclohexane-1:4-**dione** *(tetrahydrobenzoquinone)*, m.p. 79·5°, b.p. 132°/20 mm., *dioxime*, m.p. 192°, is best prepared by heating ethyl cyclohexane-2:5-dione-1:4-dicarboxylate (ethyl succinosuccinate; p. 245) with water at 200° (*J. R. Vincent et al.*, J. org. Chem., 1939, **3**, 603). It reacts normally with sodium bisulphite, hydrogen cyanide and phenylhydrazine and forms bis-acetals with alcohols. It is very readily converted to benzenoid derivatives. Thus mild oxidising agents convert it to benzoquinone, the action of phosphorus pentachloride yields *p*-dichlorobenzene and condensation with benzaldehyde produces benzylhydroquinone (*R. Stolle*, Ber., 1904, **37**, 3486). Reaction with diazomethane produces 1:7-4:8-*diepoxy*-1:4-*dimethylcyclohexane*

H_2C O O CH_2

m.p. 106–108° (*J. R. Vincent et al.*, *loc. cit.*). The dioxime reacts with chlorine to form the deep blue 1:4-*dichloro*-1:4-*dinitrosocyclohexane*, m.p. 108°, which, by treatment with acetic acid-hydrogen chloride, is transformed into a colourless *isomer*, m.p. 128–130° (dec.); the two compounds are regarded as geometrical isomers (*O. Piloty* and *H. Steinbock*, Ber., 1902, **35**, 3101). Homologous 1:4-diketones, e.g. 2:5-*dimethylcyclohexane*-1:4-*dione*, m.p. 93°, are obtained in similar fashion (*A. von Baeyer*, Ber., 1892, **25**, 2122).

(vi) Cyclohexanetriones

Catalytic hydrogenation of pyrogallol furnishes *dihydropyrogallol* (I), m.p. 114°, *monoacetate*, m.p. 155·5°, a typical enediol (*B. Pecherer et al.*, J. Amer. chem.

Soc., 1948, **70**, 2587). It behaves as a monobasic acid and is readily oxidised by iodine to **cyclohexane-1:2:3-trionedihydrate** (II), m.p. 106°, *bisphenylhydrazone*, m.p. 132·5°, *trisphenylhydrazone*, m.p. 186°, from which it is re-formed by the action of hydrogen sulphide. Treatment of the trione (II) with acetic anhydride furnishes pyrogallol triacetate.

(I) $\underset{H_2S}{\overset{I_2}{\rightleftarrows}}$ (II) $\xrightarrow{Ac_2O}$ pyrogallol triacetate

2:2-**Dimethylcyclohexane-1:3:5-trione** (*filicinic acid)*, m.p. 215°, is a hydrolysis product of many fern tannins e.g. filicic acid, albaspidin and flavaspidic acid. It has been synthesised by the ring closure of ethyl 1:1-dimethylpentane-2:4-dione-1:3:5-tricarboxylate (*A. Robertson* and *W. F. Sandrock*, J. chem. Soc., 1933, 1617).

The continued methylation of phloroglucinol yields 2:2:6:6-*tetramethylcyclohexane*-1:3:5-*trione*, m.p. 192°, 2:2:4:6:6-*pentamethylcyclohexane*-1:3:5-*trione*, m.p. 114°, 2:2:4:4:6:6-*hexamethylcyclohexane*-1:3:5-*trione*, m.p. 80° (*A. Spitzer*, Monatsh., 1890, **11**, 104, 287; *R. Reisch*, *ibid.*, 1899, **20**, 493; *C. R. Hauser et al.*, J. Amer. chem. Soc., 1939, **61**, 3567; 1942, **64**, 2461).

Cyclohexanehexone (triquinoyl), see Vol. III.

A series of polyhalogenated cyclohexanones has been obtained by the continued action of chlorine and bromine on benzenoid compounds. Thus chlorination of resorcinol yields 2:2:4:4:5:6:6-*heptachlorocyclohexane*-1:3-*dione*, m.p. 50°, b.p. 170°/25 mm. (*T. Zincke*, Ber., 1891, **24**, 912) whilst chlorination of phloroglucinol produces *hexachlorocyclohexane*-1:3:5-*trione*, m.p. 48°, b.p. 268° (*T. Zincke* and *O. Kegel*, Ber., 1889, **22**, 1473). The action of bromine on phloroglucinol gives the strongly acidic *pentabromocyclohexane*-1:3:5-*trione*, *monohydrate*, m.p. 119° (dec.); further bromination produces *hexabromocyclohexane*-1:3:5-*trione*, m.p. 147° (*idem*, *ibid.*, 1890, **23**, 1729; 1891, **24**, 912). Tri- and tetra-chlorocyclohexane-1:2:4:5-tetrones are obtained from chloranilic acid and chlorine; the corresponding bromo-derivatives are similarly produced from bromanilic acid and bromine (*H. Landolt*, Ber., 1892, **25**, 845). Many of these polyhalogenated ketones may be decomposed by hydrolysis into highly halogenated aliphatic compounds.

(b) Unsaturated ring ketones

(i) Cyclohexenones

Cyclohexenones are found, together with the saturated ketones, in heavy acetone oil (*H. Pringsheim*, Angew. Chem., 1927, 40, 1390). They may be prepared synthetically by the dehydration of cyclohexan-2-ol-1-ones, by the dehydrohalogenation of 2-halogenocyclohexan-1-ones, and by the oxidation of cyclohexenes either by chromium trioxide (ref. 6; Table 13), selenium dioxide or gaseous oxygen. A frequent preparative procedure involves the cyclisation of aliphatic 1:5-diketones; these latter are usually not isolated but cyclised *in situ*. There are three processes of this type available. The first consists in the condensation of acetoacetic ester with alkylidene di-iodides or, better, with aldehydes in the presence of piperidine; the resulting 1:5-diketone (I) undergoes smooth self-condensation with the formation of the corresponding cyclohexenonedicarboxylic ester (II) hydrolysis and decarboxylation of which furnishes the cyclohexenone (*E. Knoevenagel et al.*, Ann., 1894, **281**, 25; 1895, **288**, 321; 1896, **289**, 131; 1897, **297**, 113; *P. Rabe*, Ann., 1904, **332**, 22; *E. C. Horning et al.*, J. org, Chem., 1944, **9**, 547; J. Amer. chem. Soc., 1946, **68**, 384):

$Me{\cdot}CO{\cdot}CH(CO_2Et){\cdot}CHR{\cdot}CH(CO_2Et){\cdot}CO{\cdot}Me$ (I) ⟶ (II) (cyclohexenone with O, CO_2Et, Me, R, CO_2Et) ⟶ cyclohexenone (O, Me, R)

In another procedure the interaction of a Mannich base quaternary salt with an acetoacetic ester is used to obtain the required 1:5-diketone (*A. Downes et al.*, Australian J. Science, 1948, **10**, 147). The method was devised by *R. Robinson, A. C. du Qeu* and *F. J. McQuillin* for the synthesis of a ketomethyloctalin from 2-methylcyclohexanone (J. chem. Soc., 1937, 53). The general scheme may be formulated as follows:

$R^1{-}CO{-}CH(R^2){-}CH_2NMe_3I$ + $R^4{\cdot}CH_2{\cdot}CO{\cdot}C(Na)(CO_2Et)R^3$ ⟶ $R^1{-}CO{-}CH(R^2){-}CH_2{-}C(R^3)(CO_2Et){-}CO{-}CH_2R^4$ ⟶ cyclohexenone (R^1, R^2, R^4, O, CO_2Et, R^3) ⟶ cyclohexenone (R^1, R^2, R^4, O, R^3)

A third method involves the reaction of sodioacetoacetic ester with a β-chloroketone (*J. Décombe*, Compt. rend., 1937, **205**, 680):

$EtO_2C{\cdot}CH_2{\cdot}CO{\cdot}CH_3$ + $CH_2Cl{\cdot}CH_2{\cdot}CO{\cdot}R$ ⟶ $EtO_2C{\cdot}CH(CO{\cdot}CH_3){\cdot}CH_2{\cdot}CH_2{\cdot}CO{\cdot}R$ ⟶ cyclohexenone (EtO_2C, O, R) ⟶ cyclohexenone (O, R)

Another preparation of cyclohexenones involves the lithium aluminium hydride reduction of 3-ethoxycyclohex-2-en-1-ones (ethyl ethers of cyclohexane-1:3-diones) (refs. 14, 23, Table 13); the action of Grignard reagents on these latter compounds furnishes 3-substituted cyclohex-2-en-1-ones (ref. 19, Table 13):

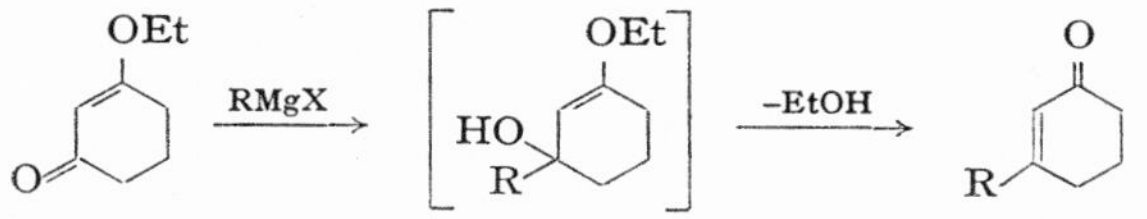

Acid hydrolysis of the 1-alkoxycyclohexa-1:4-dienes obtained by the reduction of phenol ethers (p. 126) furnishes cyclohexenones (*A. J. Birch*, Quarterly Reviews, 1950, 4, 69; J. chem. Soc., 1944, 430; 1946, 593; 1947, 1270); tertiary aromatic amines and pyridines may be employed in similar fashion.

Other methods of formation of cyclohexenones include the dechlorination of 3-chlorocyclohex-2-en-1-ones by zinc-potassium iodide (ref. 21; *A. W. Crossley* and *N. Renouf*, J. chem. Soc., 1907, **91**, 63) and the dehydrochlorination of cyclohexene nitrosochlorides with sodium ethoxide or sodium acetate followed by hydrolysis of the resulting oxime.

Some cyclohexenones are shown in Table 13.

Properties of cyclohexenones. Catalytic hydrogenation or sodium-alcohol reduction of cyclohexenones give the corresponding cyclohexanone; Ponndorf reduction produces the cyclohexenols. Reduction with sodium amalgam in acid solution results in the condensation of two cyclohexenone molecules to form dicyclohexyl derivatives; thus 3-methylcyclohex-2-en-1-one gives 1:1′-dimethyl-3:3′-diketodicyclohexyl. Cyclohexenones react normally with semicarbazide and 2:4-dinitrophenylhydrazine; hydroxylamine gives the expected oxime in the first instance but further reaction then ensues with the formation of a hydroxylamino-oxime, e.g.

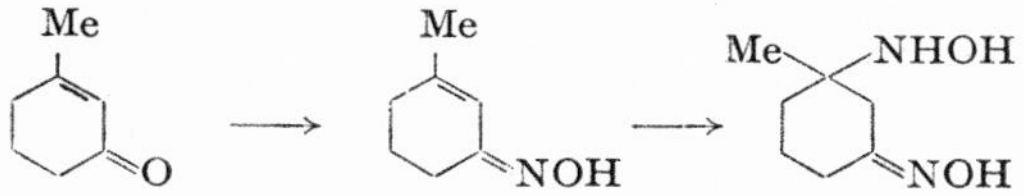

In acid media the oximes readily undergo a dehydration-aromatisation with the formation of the corresponding anilines, the process being known as the Wolff rearrangement (*L. Wolff*, Ann., 1902, **322**, 351; *W. Semmler*, Ber., 1892, **25**, 3352); the action of polyphosphoric acid, however, results in a normal Beckmann rearrangement, the $\alpha\beta$-unsaturated caprolactam being formed (*E. C. Horning et al.*, J. Amer. chem. Soc., 1952, **74**, 5153), e.g.

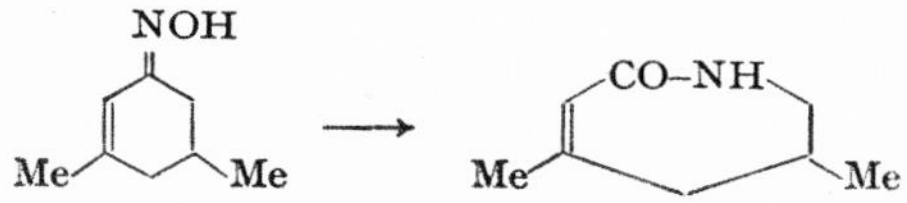

TABLE 13

CYCLOHEXENONES

Compound	B.p.°/mm.	Semicarbazone m.p.°	Ref.
Cyclohex-2-enone	63/14	161	1, 2, 3
Cyclohex-3-enone		147	4
2-Methylcyclohex-2-enone	54/8	205	6, 7, 8, 9
3-Methylcyclohex-2-enone	95/23	201	1, 6, 7, 10, 11
4-Methylcyclohex-2-enone	175	189	12, 13
5-Methylcyclohex-2-enone	60/8	176	1, 12, 14
6-Methylcyclohex-2-enone	172	178	12
2:6-Dimethylcyclohex-2-enone	82/14	211	7, 13
2:3-Dimethylcyclohex-2-enone	96/14	222	11, 15
3:4-Dimethylcyclohex-2-enone	95/15	193	13, 16
3:5-Dimethylcyclohex-2-enone	211	177	1, 11, 17, 18
5:5-Dimethylcyclohex-2-enone	75/15	192·5	21
3-Ethylcyclohex-2-enone	56/0·8	160 (a)	19
3:5:5-Trimethylcyclohex-2-enone (*iso*phorone)	89/10	182	See text
3-Propylcyclohex-2-enone	60/0·4	156 (a)	19
4-*iso*Propylcyclohex-2-enone (cryptone)	99/10	185 (dec.)	20
3-Methyl-2-ethylcyclohex-2-enone	85/9	194	11
3-Methyl-5-ethylcyclohex-2-enone	102/9		18
3-Methyl-6-ethylcyclohex-2-enone	98/12		16
4-Methyl-3-ethylcyclohex-2-enone	104/15		16
3-Methyl-5-*n*-propylcyclohex-2-enone	113/9		18
3-Methyl-5-*iso*propylcyclohex-2-enone	115/12	167	18
4-Methyl-2:6-di-*tert*.-butylcyclohex-2-enone	(m.p. 40°)		22
3-Phenyl-5:5-dimethylcyclohex-2-enone	(m.p. 54·5°)	oxime m.p. 157	23

(a) 2:4-Dinitrophenylhydrazones

[1] *A. J. Birch*, J. chem. Soc., 1947, 1270.
[2] *K. Dimroth* and *K. Resin*, Ber., 1942, **75**, 322.
[3] *P. D. Bartlett* and *G. F. Woods*, J. Amer. chem. Soc., 1940, **62**, 2933.
[4] *A. J. Birch*, J. chem. Soc., 1946, 593.
[5] *C. Mannich*, Ber., 1941, **74**, 554.
[6] *F. C. Whitmore* and *G. W. Pedlow*, J. Amer. chem. Soc., 1941, **63**, 758.
[7] *M. Mousseron et al.*, Compt. rend., 1947, **224**, 1230.
[8] *L. W. Butz et al.*, J. org. Chem., 1947, **12**, 122.
[9] *W. W. Rinne et al.*, J. Amer. chem. Soc., 1950, **72**, 5759.
[10] *O. Wichterle et al.*, C.A., 1948, **42**, 8162.
[11] *L. I. Smith* and *G. F. Rouault*, J. Amer. chem. Soc., 1943, **65**, 631.
[12] *A. Kötz* and *H. Steinhorst*, Ann., 1911, **379**, 17.
[13] *A. J. Birch*, J. chem. Soc., 1944, 430.
[14] *J. P. Blanchard* and *H. L. Goering*, J. Amer. chem. Soc., 1951, **73**, 5863
[15] *E. Bergmann* and *A. Weizmann*, J. org. Chem., 1939, **4**, 266.
[16] *J. Decombe*, Compt. rend., 1937, **205**, 680.
[17] *E. C. Horning et al.*, Org. Synth., 1947, **27**, 24.
[18] *E. C. Horning et al.*, J. org. Chem., 1944, **9**, 547.
[19] *G. F. Woods et al.*, J. Amer. chem. Soc., 1949, **71**, 2028.

[20] *J. L. Simonsen et al.*, J. chem. Soc., 1931, 1366.
[21] *R. L. Frank* and *H. K. Hall*, J. Amer. chem. Soc., 1950, **72**, 1654.
[22] *A. C. Whitaker, ibid.*, 1947, **69**, 2414.
[23] *G. F. Woods, ibid.*, 1947, **69**, 2549.

A similar aromatisation to anilines occurs when cyclohexenone azines are heated under reflux with palladised charcoal in triethylbenzene (*E. C. Horning et al., ibid.*, 1947, 69, 1907). Cyclohexenone dibromides readily lose hydrogen bromide to form phenols (*A. D. Petrov*, Ber., 1930, 63, 898). This dehydrogenation may be carried out directly from the cyclohexenone by heating with palladised charcoal or sulphur (*E. C. Horning et al.*, J. Amer. chem. Soc., 1945, 67, 1421; 1947, 69, 1359).

Cyclohex-2-en-1-one, *oxime*, m.p. 75°, *hydroxylamino-oxime*, m.p. 50°, is best prepared by the pyrolytic dehydration of cyclohexan-2-ol-1-one over alumina (ref. 3, Table 13) or by the chromic acid oxidation of cyclohexene (ref. 6). Other methods of formation include the dehydrohalogenation of 2-chloro- and 2-bromo-cyclohexan-1-one with organic bases, the oxygenation of cyclohexene in the presence of colloidal osmium (*A. Kötz et al.*, J. pr. Chem., 1909, [ii], **80**, 491; 1925, [ii], **111**, 373) and the chromium trioxide oxidation of cyclohex-2-en-1-ol (*C. Courtot*, Bull. Soc. chim. Fr., 1929, [iv], **45**, 286). With Grignard reagents the ketone gives a mixture of the 1:2- (III) and 1:4- (IV) adducts, the relative proportions depending on the nature of the reagent employed; thus ethylmagnesium bromide gives mainly the 1:2-adduct whilst *tert.*-butylmagnesium bromide yields predominantly the 1:4-addition product (ref. 6).

Michael condensation of the ketone with sodiomalonic ester proceeds normally to produce 3-ketocyclohexylmalonic ester (ref. 3). Cyclohexenone reacts very sluggishly with dienes although possessing the necessary characteristics of a dienophile (ref. 6).

RMgBr → (III) + (IV)

2-Methylcyclohex-2-en-1-one has been studied because of its potentialities for steroid synthesis. It may be obtained by the selenium dioxide oxidation of 1-methylcyclohex-1-ene (ref. 8) or by the dehydrohalogenation of 2-bromo-2-methylcyclohexan-1-one with 2:4-dinitrophenylhydrazine (ref. 9). The ketone is also formed from the nitrosochloride of 1-methylcyclohex-1-ene (*H. Meerwein*, Ann., 1908, **359**, 303).

3-Methylcyclohex-2-en-1-one is prepared by the acid hydrolysis and decarboxylation of its 4-carbethoxy-derivative (ref. 11) or by the oxidation of 1-methylcyclohex-1-ene with chromium trioxide in acetic acid (ref. 6). It is also obtainable together with its 6-carbethoxy-derivative by the sulphuric acid cyclisation of

3-carbethoxy-6-chlorohept-5-en-2-one, [Me·CCl:CH·CH_2·CH(CO_2Et)·COMe] which is readily prepared from 1:3-dichlorobut-2-ene and sodioacetoacetic ester (ref. 10). The bromine addition compound decomposes spontaneously to HBr and *m*-cresol. On treatment with potassium hydroxide the ketone gives an aldol-like *polymer*, m.p. 113°. The *oxime*, m.p. 89°, is converted to *m*-toluidine by the action of hot acetic acid.

5-Methylcyclohex-2-en-1-one has been obtained by the quinoline dehydrochlorination of the mixed stereoisomeric 2-chloro-5-methylcyclohexan-1-ones formed by chlorination of 3-methylcyclohexan-1-one (*M. Godchot* and *P. Bedos*, Bull. Soc. chim. Fr., 1926, [iv], **39**, 83). It is also formed by the reduction of 2:4-dimethylpyridine by sodium and alcohol in liquid ammonia in the following manner (ref. 1, Table 13):

Me, Me, N → [Me, Me, N] → [Me–CH(CH$_2$·CO·Me)(CH$_2$·CHO)] → Me, O

5:5-Dimethylcyclohex-2-en-1-one is obtained by the zinc dust reduction of the corresponding 3-chloro-derivative (ref. 21, Table 13).

3:5:5 **Trimethylcyclohex-2-en-1-one** (iso*phorone*, iso*acetophorone*) a condensation product of acetone (Vol. I, p. 513) is a constituent of heavy acetone oil. It is prepared by the condensation of mesityl oxide with acetoacetic ester with subsequent hydrolysis and decarboxylation. Catalytic hydrogenation or sodium in alcohol reduction furnishes 3:5:5-trimethylcyclohexan-1-ol (dihydro*iso*phorol). The addition of hydrogen cyanide to *iso*phorone proceeds normally to give 3-cyano-3:5:5-trimethylcyclohexanone (*W. F. Whitmore* and *C. W. Roberts*, J. org. Chem., 1948, **13**, 31). The interaction of methylmagnesium bromide with *iso*phorone furnishes 1:1:3:5-tetramethylcyclohexa-2:4-diene (*J. Schmitt*, Ann., 1941, **547**, 256) but in the presence of ferric chloride this reaction results in the isomerisation of the *iso*phorone to 3:5:5-trimethylcyclohex-3-en-1-one (*M. S. Kharasch* and *P. O. Tawney*, J. Amer. chem. Soc., 1945, **67**, 128). *iso*Phorone forms two isomeric *oximes*, m.p. 78° and 100°, both of which rearrange to 3:4:5-trimethylaniline on being heated with hydrochloric acid (*J. Bredt* and *R. Rübel*, Ann., 1898, **299**, 165; *L. Wolff*, Ann., 1902, **322**, 379).

Besides *iso*phorone, the condensation products of acetone contain the so-called xylitones, $C_{12}H_{18}O$, which are probably formed by condensation of a further molecule of acetone with *iso*phorone. Different xylitones seem to be obtained according to the condensing agent used (e.g. sodium ethoxide, hydrogen chloride or lime) and yet another form is derived from *iso*phorone and sodioacetoacetic ester.

2-iso**Propylcyclohex-2-en-1-one** is obtained as the *oxime*, m.p. 72°, by the treatment of 1-*iso*propylcyclohex-1-ene nitrosochloride with sodium acetate or piperidine (*O. Wallach*, Ann., 1908, **360**, 69).

The laevorotatory isomer of 4-*iso*propylcyclohex-2-en-1-one (*cryptone*) occurs in pine-needle oil and eucalyptus oil (*H. Wienhaus*, Chem. Ztbl., 1930, I, 137; *P. A. Berry et al.*, J. chem. Soc., 1937, 986; ref. 20, Table 13). It is formed, together with 4-*iso*propylidenecyclohexanone, when sabinaketone and nopinone are heated with dilute sulphuric acid, and also by the autoxidation of β-phellandrene. Cryptone readily polymerises especially in the presence of alkali. Ponndorf reduction yields cryptol (p. 172) and electrolytic reduction furnishes one isomer of the optically inactive dihydrocryptol. Methylmagnesium iodide converts it, with loss of water, into α-phellandrene (*H. Meerwein*, Ann., 1908, **359**, 270).

5-iso**Propylcyclohex**-2-**en**-1-**one** and its 3-*methyl*-derivative have been used as respiratory and circulatory stimulants under the name of "*hexetone*" (*E. Knoevenagel*, Ber., 1893, **26**, 1089; *R. Gottlieb*, Chem. Ztbl., 1924, I, 1232). Their physiological action seems to be associated with the presence of the *iso*propyl group in the 3-position to the carbonyl group (*E. Wedekind*, Angew. Chem., 1925, **38**, 315). The compounds have been resolved (*R. Wegler* and *W. Frank*, Chem. Ztbl., 1936, I, 53).

(ii) Halogenated cyclohexenones

3-Halogenocyclohex-2-en-1-ones are obtained by the action of phosphorus trihalides on the corresponding cyclohexane-1:3-diones. In this way are prepared 3-**chlorocyclohex**-2-**en**-1-**one,** b.p. 104°/24 mm., 3-**bromocyclohex**-2-**en**-1-**one,** b.p. 133°/25 mm., 3-**chloro**-5:5-**dimethylcyclohex**-2-**en**-1-**one,** b.p. 105°/20 mm., and 3-**chloro**-2-**methyl**-5-iso**propylcyclohex**-2-**en**-1-**one,** b.p. 124·5°/11 mm. The compounds readily undergo hydrolysis to the parent 1:3-diones; by reduction with zinc and methanolic potassium iodide they are dehalogenated to cyclohexenones (*A. W. Crossley et al.*, J. chem. Soc., 1903, **83**, 110, 498; 1907, **91**, 63; 1908, **93**, 629; ref. 21, Table 13).

Polyhalogenated cyclohexenones are produced by the exhaustive halogenation of aromatic compounds such as phenols, anilines and hydroxybenzoic acids. They are in general unstable and show a ready tendency to aromatise, e.g. reduction gives halogenophenols (*T. Zincke et al.*, Ber., 1890, **23**, 3777; 1892, **25**, 2688; 1894, **27**, 547; Ann., 1892, **267**, 16; *H. Biltz*, Ber., 1904, **37**, 4003). Thus the α- and β-**heptachlorocyclohexenones** (A) m.p. 98° and (B) m.p. 80° are produced by the chlorination of *m*-chloroaniline and three **octachlorocyclohexenones,** α-, m.p. 108°, β-, m.p. 90° and γ-, m.p. 88°, are obtained by the chlorination of pentachlorophenol or tetrachloro-*m*-hydroxybenzoic acid in acetic acid. **Hexachlorocyclohex**-3-**en**-1:2-**dione** (C), *dihydrate* m.p. 93° (dec.) is similarly prepared from catechol or *o*-aminophenol hydrochloride; it is reduced by stannous chloride to tetrachloro-*o*-benzoquinone. Chlorination of resorcinol gives **pentachlorocyclohex**-5-**en**-1:3-**dione** (D) m.p. 92°, b.p. 160°/25 mm.; similar treatment of 3:5-dihydroxybenzoic acid produces **hexachlorocyclohex**-5-**en**-1:3-**dione,** m.p. 115°, b.p. 159°/14 mm. **Hexachlorocyclohex**-2-**en**-1:4-**dione,** m.p. 89°, b.p. 184°/45 mm., is formed by chlorination of *p*-aminophenol hydrochloride.

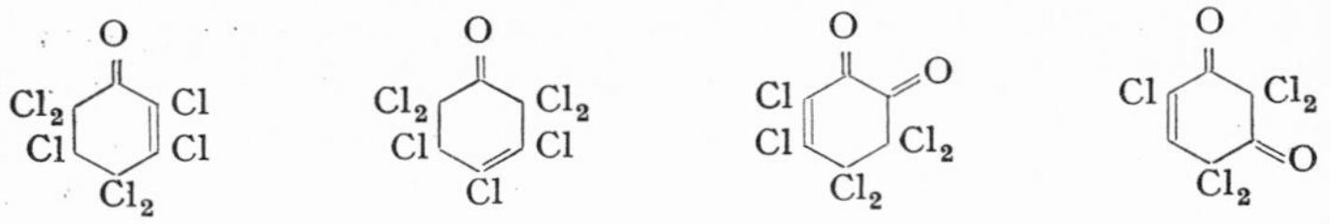

(A) (B) (C) (D)

(iii) Cyclohexadienones

Neither of the two possible simple compounds of this structure i.e. cyclohexa-2:4-dien-1-one and cyclohexa-2:5-dien-1-one, exists; they represent tautomeric forms of phenol. When however this aromatisation is blocked by the presence of a *gem.*-disubstituted carbon atom such compounds become capable of preparation.

Thus by the further chlorination of 1:3:5-trichlorophenol a **tetrachlorocyclohexadienone** [(I) or (II)], m.p. 122°, is formed (*T. Zincke*, Ber., 1894, **27**, 546) and, by heating heptachlorocyclohexenone, there is obtained a **hexachlorocyclohexadienone** [(III) or (IV)], m.p. 106° (*E. Barral*, Bull. Soc. chim. Fr., 1895, [iii], **11**, 557).

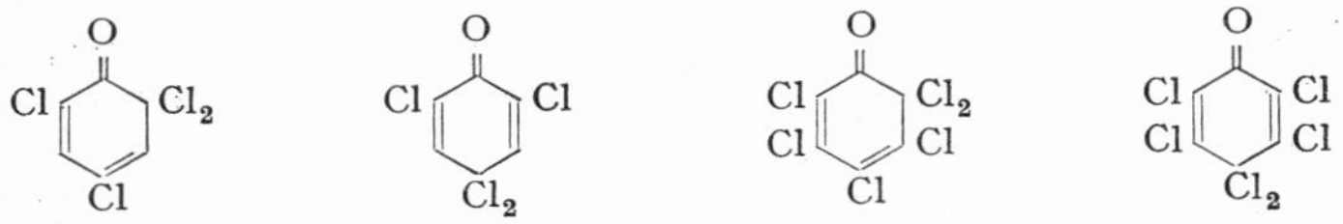

(I) (II) (III) (IV)

Derivatives of the two cyclohexadienones are represented by compounds of the general formulae (V), (VI) and (VII).

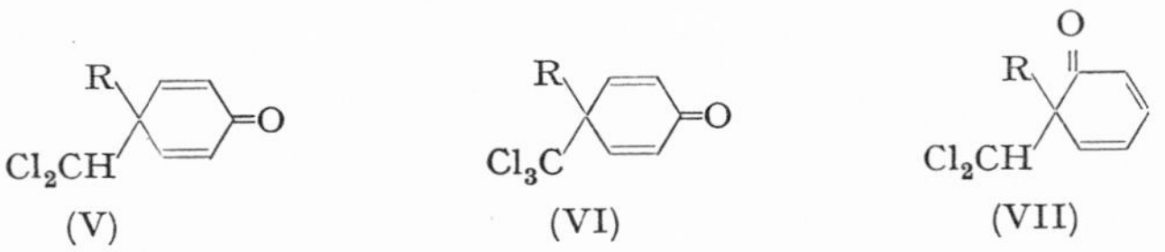

(V) (VI) (VII)

Types (V) and (VII) are formed as by-products in the reaction of chloroform and alkali with *p*- and *o*-alkylated phenols respectively. Type (VI) is obtained by the action of carbon tetrachloride and aluminium chloride on *p*-alkylated phenols. The best-studied compounds of this series are **4-methyl-4-dichloromethylcyclohexa-2:5-dien-1-one** (V; R = Me) m.p. 55° and **4-methyl-4-trichloromethylcyclohexa-2:5-dien-1-one** (VI; R = Me) m.p. 105°, *oxime* m.p. 134°, both obtained from *p*-cresol and **2-methyl-2-dichloromethylcyclohexa-3:5-dien-1-one** (VII; R = Me) m.p. 33°, b.p. 113°/9 mm., prepared from *o*-cresol. These substances are insoluble in alkali, give normal ketonic derivatives and are reduced by zinc-acetic acid to the original phenols with the formation of methylene dichloride or chloroform (*K. Auwers et al.*, Ann., 1907, **352**, 219;

1921, **425**, 280; Ber., 1903, **36**, 1861; 1915, **48**, 1357, 1371; 1916, **49**, 2389; 1922, **55**, 2167; *H. Lindemann*, Ann., 1923, **431**, 270; *T. Zincke* and *F. Schwabe*, Ber., 1908, **41**, 897). By treatment with phosphorus pentachloride the dienone (V; R = Me) is converted into 5-chloro-1-methyl-2-dichloromethylbenzene (IX) probably via the tetrachloride (VIII) followed by migration of the methyl group (*J. E. Driver*, J. Amer. chem. Soc., 1924, **46**, 2090).

Me, Cl_2CH ... =O —PCl_5→ [Me, Cl_2CH ... Cl_2] (VIII) ⟶ Cl_2CH (Me) ... Cl (IX)

With Grignard reagents the dienones of type (V) and (VI) yield tertiary alcohols, e.g. (X) which readily lose water to form compounds of the "semi-benzene" type (XI) (see p. 150); these latter substances readily rearrange into true benzene derivatives (XII).

Me, Cl_2CH, OH, CH_2R (X) ⟶ Me, Cl_2CH ... =CHR (XI) ⟶ Me ... $CHR{\cdot}CHCl_2$ (XII)

The Reformatsky reaction (e.g. with zinc and ethyl α-bromopropionate) proceeds in an exactly analogous manner.

The dienones of type (VII) behave differently with Grignard reagents, 1:4-addition taking place. Thus the dienone (VII; R = Me) reacts with methylmagnesium iodide to give 2:5-**dimethyl**-2-**dichloromethylcyclohex**-3-**en**-1-**one** (*dichloro-βγ-pulenenone*; XIII) b.p. 124°/15 mm. By treatment with sulphuric acid (XIII) rearranges into the conjugated ketone 2:5-**dimethyl**-2-**dichloromethylcyclohex**-5-**en**-1-**one** (*dichloro-αβ-pulenenone*, XIV), m.p. 41°, b.p. 151°/15 mm. This latter compound (XIV) undergoes ring fission with alcoholic potassium hydroxide with the transient formation of the acid (XV) which then cyclises with loss of HCl, the product on further loss of HCl giving first the dihydrobenzoic acid (XVI) and then 1:4-dimethylcyclohexa-1:3-diene (XVII). By the employment of *iso*propylmagnesium iodide at the start of this series of reactions α-terpinene has been synthesised (*K. Auwers* and *R. Hinterseber*, Ber., 1915, **48**, 1358).

O, Me, Cl_2CH, Me (XIII) —H_2SO_4→ O, Me, Cl_2CH, Me (XIV) —KOH→ [Me HO_2C—CH=CMe, CH, Cl_2CH CH_2—CH_2] (XV)

⟶ Me (Cl CO_2H) Me ⟶ Me (CO_2H) Me (XVI) ⟶ Me ... Me (XVII)

2:2:4:6-**Tetramethylcyclohexa**-3:5-**dien**-1-**one,** b.p. 95°/16 mm., 2:4-*dinitrophenylhydrazone* m.p. 234°, is obtained by the selenium dioxide oxidation of the corresponding diene (*J. Schmitt,* Ann., 1941, **547,** 256). Application of the Darzens reaction to the ketone furnishes the corresponding aldehyde (p. 188).

(c) Semicyclic and exocyclic unsaturated ring ketones

2-**Methylenecyclohexan**-1-**one,** *semicarbazone* m.p. 160°, is formed by the pyrolysis of 2-dimethylaminomethylcyclohexan-1-one hydrochloride *in vacuo* (*C. Mannich,* Ber., 1941, **74,** 554). It rapidly dimerises at room temperature to the compound (I).

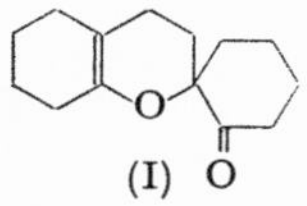

(I)

It may be catalytically hydrogenated to 2-methylcyclohexan-1-one and reacts with methylmagnesium iodide to give 1-methyl-2-methylenecyclohexan-1-ol.

4-iso**Propylidenecyclohexan**-1-**one,** b.p. 54°/1 mm., *semicarbazone* m.p. 201°, 2:4-*dinitrophenylhydrazone* m.p. 132° is formed by the oxidation of sabinene with chromyl chloride (*G. G. Henderson et al.,* J. chem. Soc., 1922, **121,** 2721). It is best prepared by heating γ-carboxy-γ-*iso*propenylpimelic acid with barium carbonate (*R. L. Frank* and *J. B. McPherson,* J. Amer. chem. Soc., 1949, **71,** 1387).

2-**Allylcyclohexan**-1-**one,** b.p. 94°/16 mm., *oxime,* m.p. 71°, may be prepared by the direct allylation of cyclohexanone in the presence of sodamide or by the action of allyl bromide on ethyl cyclohexanone-2-carboxylate followed by hydrolysis and decarboxylation of the product (*R. Cornubert,* Compt. rend., 1914, **158,** 1900; *R. Grewe,* Ber., 1943, **76,** 1072; *C. A. VanderWerf* and *L. V. Lemmerman,* Org. Synth., 1948, **28,** 8).

(d) Exocyclic hydroaromatic ketones

This class of substance includes the important perfumes irone and the ionones which are discussed in Vol. II B.

The saturated exocyclic ketones are produced by general methods e.g. the oxidation of the corresponding secondary alcohols, the treatment of acid chlorides with cadmium dialkyls and the hydrolysis and decarboxylation of α-alkylcyclohexylglycidic esters (*W. A. Yarnell* and *E. S. Wallis,* J. org. Chem., 1939, **4,** 270). Unsaturated ketones are obtained by the addition of acyl chlorides to cyclohexenes, by the rearrangement of 1-ethynylcyclohexan-1-ols and by the addition of dienes to $\alpha\beta$-unsaturated ethylenic and acetylenic ketones.

A series of saturated and unsaturated exocyclic hydroaromatic ketones is shown in Table 14. Exocyclic ketones containing other functional groups are described in the text.

TABLE 14

EXOCYCLIC HYDROAROMATIC KETONES

Compound	B.p.°/mm.	Semicarbazone m.p.°	Ref.
Acetylcyclohexane	63/12	175	1,2
1-Acetyl-1-methylcyclohexane	70/13	186	3
trans-1-Acetyl-2-methylcyclohexane	65/10	178·5	4,5,6
cis-1-Acetyl-2-methylcyclohexane	68/10	182	6
1-Acetyl-3-methylcyclohexane	77/13	160 (A) 196 (B)	4,5,7
1-Acetyl-4-methylcyclohexane	74/12		4,5
Cyclohexylacetone	196	166	8
1-Propionyl-3-methylcyclohexane	208	111 (A) 136 (B)	7
1-Acetyl-2-phenylcyclohexane	164/11	190	9
1-Acetylcyclohex-1-ene	201	221 (dec.)	10,11
1-Acetylcyclohex-3-ene	187	165	12
1-Acetyl-2-methylcyclohex-1-ene	90/17	227	13,14,15,16
1-Acetyl-2-methylcyclohex-2-ene	80/12	155	13,14,15,16
1-Acetyl-5-methylcyclohex-1-ene	105/15	188	7
1-Acetyl-6:6-dimethylcyclohex-1-ene	116/47	201·5	9
1-Acetyl-4:4-dimethylcyclohex-1-ene	102/12	218	22
1-Acetyl-2:6:6-trimethylcyclohex-1-ene	90/20		17
1-Propionyl-5-methylcyclohex-1-ene	113/15	145	7
Cyclohex-1-enylacetone	83/12	145	18
Cyclohex-2-enylacetone	197	164	19
Cyclohexylideneacetone	89/12·5	180	18
1-Acetylcyclohexa-1:4-diene	95/20	200	14,20,21
1-Acetyl-2-methylcyclohexa-1:4-diene	82/8	155 (d)	14
1-Acetyl-2:5-dimethylcyclohexa-1:4-diene	103/20	177	20
1-Acetyl-3:4-dimethylcyclohexa-1:4-diene	128/20	226	20

(d) 2:4-dinitrophenylhydrazone

[1] *C. D. Nenitzescu* and *J. P. Cantuniari*, Ann., 1934, **510**, 277.
[2] *N. D. Zelinsky* and *E. M. Tarassowa*, Ann., 1934, **508**, 115.
[3] *H. Meerwein* and *J. Schäfer*, J. pr. Chem., 1922, **104**, 306.
[4] *G. Darzens*, Compt. rend., 1907, **144**, 1123.
[5] *T. van Woerden*, Rec. Trav. chim., 1926, **45**, 124.
[6] *R. B. Turner*, J. Amer. chem. Soc., 1950, **72**, 878.
[7] *M. Mousseron et al.*, Bull. Soc. chim. Fr., 1947, **14**, 598.
[8] *C. Hell* and *O. Schaal*, Ber., 1909, **42**, 2230.
[9] *C. D. Nenitzescu* and *I. G. Gavat*, Ann., 1935, **519**, 265.
[10] *J. D. Chanley*, J. Amer. chem. Soc., 1948, **70**, 244.
[11] *G. Darzens*, Compt. rend., 1910, **150**, 707.
[12] *E. C. Britten et al.*, U.S.P. 2,301,515 (1942).
[13] *R. B. Turner* and *D. M. Voitle*, J. Amer. chem. Soc., 1951, **73**, 1403.
[14] *E. A. Braude et al.*, J. chem. Soc., 1949, **607**, 1890.
[15] *N. C. Deno* and *H. Chafetz*, J. Amer. chem. Soc., 1952, **74**, 3940.
[16] *K. Dimroth* and *O. Lüderitz*, Ber., 1948, **81**, 242.
[17] *H. B. Henbest* and *G. Woods*, J. chem. Soc., 1952, 1150.
[18] *G. A. R. Kon et al.*, J. chem. Soc., 1928, 1630.

[19] *M. Mousseron* and *F. Winternitz*, Compt. rend., 1943, **217**, 428.
[20] *A. Petrov*, C.R. Acad. Sci. U.S.S.R., 1946, **53**, 527.
[21] *E. R. H. Jones* and *K. Bowden*, J. chem. Soc., 1946, 52.
[22] *H. B. Henbest*, J. chem. Soc., 1952, 1154.

Acetylcyclohexane (*hexahydroacetophenone, cyclohexyl methyl ketone*) is best prepared by the hydrolysis and decarboxylation of 1-acetyl-1-carbethoxy cyclohexane or by the catalytic hydrogenation of 1-acetylcyclohex-1-ene. The Beckmann rearrangement of the oxime is discussed by *I. Manta* and *G. Pamfil* (Bull. Soc. chim. Fr., 1923, [iv], **51**, 1005). The rearrangement of a series of brominated derivatives of this ketone by alkaline reagents has been studied (*R. B. Wagner* and *J. A. Moore*, J. Amer. chem. Soc., 1949, **71**, 3214; 1950, **72**, 974). Thus 1-*bromoacetyl*-1-*bromocyclohexane*, m.p. 20°, by treatment with sodium methoxide yields methyl cyclohexylideneacetate, 1-*acetyl*-1:2-*dibromocyclohexane*, m.p. 48°, with the same reagent furnishes methyl cyclohexenylacetate whilst 1-*dibromoacetyl*-1-*bromocyclohexane*, m.p. 74°, reacts with potassium hydroxide to form α-bromocyclohexylideneacetic acid.

1-**Acetylcyclohexan**-1-**ol,** b.p. $46^{\circ}/10^{-6}$ mm., *semicarbazone* m.p. 222°, is obtained by the action of methyl-lithium on cyclohexan-1-ol-1-carboxylic acid. The action of bromine gives the 1-*bromoacetyl*-compound, b.p. $70^{\circ}/10^{-6}$ mm., which, on hydrolysis, furnishes 1-*hydroxyacetylcyclohexan*-1-*ol*, m.p. 89° (*R. B. Wagner* and *J. A. Moore*, J. Amer. chem. Soc., 1950, **72**, 1874; *J. D. Billimoria* and *N. F. Maclagan*, J. chem. Soc., 1951, 3067).

Other saturated exocyclic ketones are generally prepared by the glycidic ester method or by the chromium trioxide oxidation of the corresponding exocyclic secondary alcohol.

1-**Acetylcyclohex**-1-**ene,** *oxime* m.p. 99°, 2:4-*dinitrophenylhydrazone*, m.p. 203°, is obtained by the addition of acetyl chloride to cyclohexene in the presence of aluminium chloride or stannic chloride (*H. Wieland* and *L. Bettag*, Ber., 1922, **55**, 2246; *N. D. Zelinsky*, Ann., 1934, **508**, 115; ref. 11, Table 14; see also *F. Ebel* and *M. W. Goldberg*, Helv., 1927, **10**, 677). It may also be prepared by the rearrangement of 1-ethynylcyclohexan-1-ol with formic acid or phosphorus pentoxide (*inter al.*, ref. 10; *J. H. Saunders*, Org. Synth., 1949, **29**, 1). These methods also serve for the preparation of homologues (*L. Ruzicka et al.*, Helv., 1931, **14**, 1151; *J. Colonge* and *E. Duroux*, Bull. Soc. chim. Fr., 1940, [v], **7**, 459; *D. Nightingale et al.*, J. org. Chem., 1948, **13**, 357). By treatment with sodamide the ketone gives rise to two stereoisomeric dimers of structure (I) (*E. R. H. Jones* and *H. P. Koch*, J. chem. Soc., 1942, 393).

2 COMe ⟶ O CO (I) Me

1-**Acetylcyclohex**-3-**ene** and its 6-*methyl*-homologue are formed by the diene addition of vinylacetylene to butadiene and isoprene respectively and subsequent hydration of the triple bond (ref. 12, Table 14).

The action of acetyl chloride on 1-methylcyclohex-1-ene in the presence of aluminium chloride or the formic acid rearrangement of 2-methyl-1-ethynylcyclohexan-1-ol gives an equilibrium mixture of 1-acetyl-2-methylcyclohex-1-ene and 1-acetyl-2-methylcyclohex-2-ene which may be separated by means of their semicarbazones. The latter isomer may be obtained in a pure state by the zinc chloride catalysed addition of acetyl chloride to 1-methylcyclohex-1-ene (ref. 15). The atypical light absorption of the former isomer in the ultra-violet has been the subject of considerable study and speculation (refs. 13, 14, 16).

Cyclohex-1-enylacetone (II) and the isomeric **cyclohexylideneacetone** (III) are

$CH_2·CO·CH_3$ (II) $=CH·CO·CH_2$ (III)

formed as an equilibrium mixture by the hydrolysis and decarboxylation of ethyl cyclohexenylacetoacetate. They may also be obtained by the action of methylzinc iodide on cyclohex-1-enyl- and cyclohexylidene-acetyl chloride respectively. The pure ketones may be regenerated from their respective semicarbazones without equilibration by means of dilute sulphuric acid (ref. 18, Table 14).

1-**Acetylcyclohexa**-1:4-**dienes** (2:5-*dihydroacetophenones*) are obtained by the addition of dienes to methyl ethynyl ketone. Thus butadiene, 1:4-dimethylbutadiene and 2:3-dimethylbutadiene give respectively the parent compound, and the 2:5- and 3:4-dimethyl homologues (refs. 20, 21). These compounds are very readily dehydrogenated to the corresponding acetophenone.

For many unsaturated exocyclic ketones allied in structure to vitamin A see *I. M. Heilbron, E. R. H. Jones et al.*, J. chem. Soc., 1942, 727; 1946, 866; 1949, 287, 737, 742, 1516, 1823, 2023, 2028, 3120; 1950, 633; *O. Isler et al.*, Helv., 1947, **30**, 1911; *J. F. Arens* and *D. A. van Dorp*, Rec. Trav. chim., 1946, **65**, 338; 1947, **66**, 759; *H. H. Inhoffen* and *F. Bohlmann*, Fortschr. chem. Forschg., 1949/50, **1**, 175).

2-**Acetylcyclohexan**-1-**one**, b.p. 111°/18 mm., is obtained by the condensation of ethyl acetate with cyclohexanone. Its reactions are those of a typical 1:3-diketone e.g. alkaline hydrolysis gives acetylcaproic acid and alkylation occurs with sodium and alkyl iodides (*G. Leser*, Compt. rend., 1905, **141**, 1032; Bull. Soc. chim. Fr., 1901, [iii], **25**, 196). Homologues are similarly prepared (*H. K. Sen* and *U. Bose*, J. Indian chem. Soc., 1927, **4**, 51).

2-**Acetylcyclohexane**-1:3:5-**trione**, m.p. 218°, is prepared by the condensation of acetonitrile with phloroglucinol in the presence of hydrogen chloride and also by the zinc chloride-catalysed rearrangement of monoacetylphloroglucinol; the corresponding di- and tri-acetates undergo a similar isomerisation (*G. Heller*, Ber., 1912, **45**, 418; 1915, **48**, 1286).

Several acylcyclohexane-diones and -triones occur naturally. **Angustione** (2-*acetyl*-4:4:6-*trimethylcyclohexane*-1:3-*dione*; IV), b.p. 129°/15 mm., and **dehydroangustione** (2-*acetyl*-4:4-*dimethyl*-6-*methylenecyclohexane*-1:3-*dione*; V), b.p. 127°/11 mm. are constituents of the oil of *Backhousia angustifolia* from which they may be separated by fractional crystallisation of their imines (*J. L. Simon-*

sen et al., J. chem. Soc., 1930, 1184; 1931, 286; *A. J. Birch, ibid.*, 1951, 3026). Many essential oils of the genus *Leptospermum* contain **leptospermone** (1-iso-*valeryl*-3:3:5:5-*tetramethylcyclohexane*-2:4:6-*trione*; VI), b.p. 146°/10 mm. (*L. H. Briggs et al.*, J. chem. Soc., 1938, 1193; 1945, 706; 1948, 383). More complex examples of this type of structure are **albaspidin** (VII), m.p. 148°, and **flavaspidic acid** (VIII), α-form m.p. 92°, β-form m.p. 156°, which are both constituents of male fern (*R. Böhm*, Ann., 1898, **302**, 171; 1899, **307**, 250; 1901, **318**, 230; 1903, **329**, 310; *A. J. Birch*, J. chem. Soc., 1951, 3026). The two most

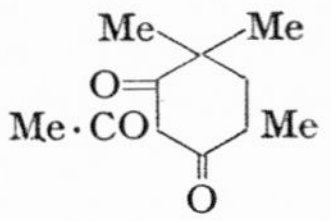

Angustione (IV) Dehydroangustione (V) Leptospermone (VI)

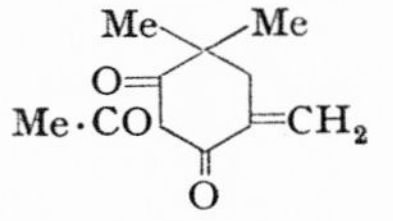

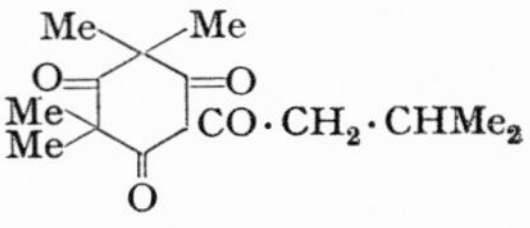

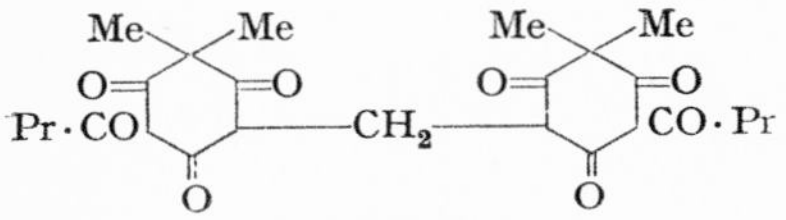

Albaspidin (VII) Flavaspidic acid (VIII)

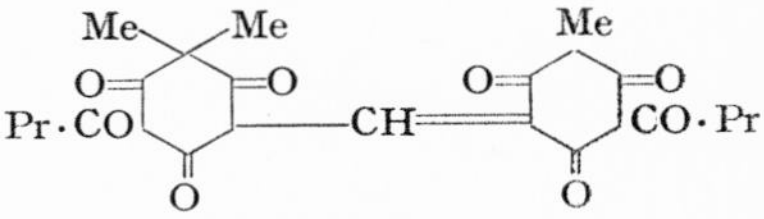

important naturally-occurring compounds of this type are humulone and lupulone, the two bitter, acidic constituents of the resin of the hop, *Humulus lupulus*.

Humulone (I; see scheme on p. 219) $C_{21}H_{30}O_5$, yellow crystals, m.p. 55°, $[\alpha]_D$ −232°, is an unsaturated compound, readily attacked by permanganate and yielding a tetrabromide. Zerewitinoff estimation shows that three of the oxygen atoms are present as hydroxyl groups; these latter are enolic giving yellow salts and a reddish-purple colouration with ferric chloride. Carbonyl reagents are without effect on humulone. On catalytic hydrogenation a remarkable fission and aromatisation occurs; an uptake of six atoms of hydrogen takes place, *iso*pentane is split out and the benzenoid *humulohydroquinone* (II), $C_{16}H_{24}O_5$, m.p. 125° (*tetrabenzoate*, m.p. 168°) is obtained. On oxidation this latter furnishes *humuloquinone* (III) red needles, m.p. 64°; on treatment with alkali this quinone undergoes a benzilic acid type of rearrangement with concomitant ring contraction to yield the cyclopentane derivative *dihydrohumulic* acid (IV) $C_{15}H_{24}O_4$, m.p. 126°. A similar contraction takes place when the quinone is treated with hypobromite, iso*humulic acid* (V), $C_{15}H_{22}O_4$, m.p. 143° being produced; an isomer of the latter acid, *humulic acid* (VI), $C_{15}H_{22}O_4$, m.p. 93°, is formed by the action of alkali on humulone itself, together with *iso*butaldehyde and acetic acid.

The key to the structure of *iso*humulic acid (V), known to be a cyclopentane-1:3:4-trione derivative, was provided by alkaline fission which took place in two ways to give (a) 4-methylpentan-2-one, 4-methylpentane-1-carboxylic acid and oxalic acid and (b) 6-methylheptan-2-one, 2-methylpropane-1-carboxylic acid and oxalic acid. Since one of the alkyl residues of humulic acid gives acetone on ozonolysis the following formulae are allotted to *iso*humulic acid (V) and humulic acid (VI):

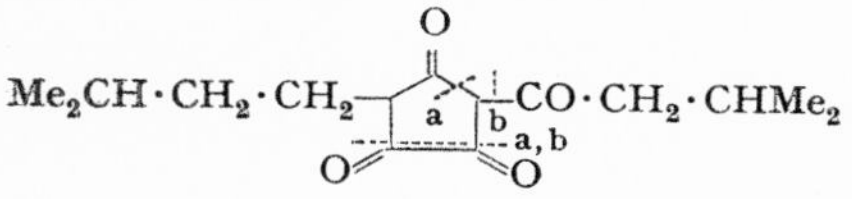

$Me_2CH \cdot CH_2 \cdot CH_2$—[ring: O; a; b; a, b; O; O]—$CO \cdot CH_2 \cdot CHMe_2$

(V)

$Me_2C{:}CH \cdot CH_2$—[ring: O; OH; O]—$CO \cdot CH_2 \cdot CHMe_2$

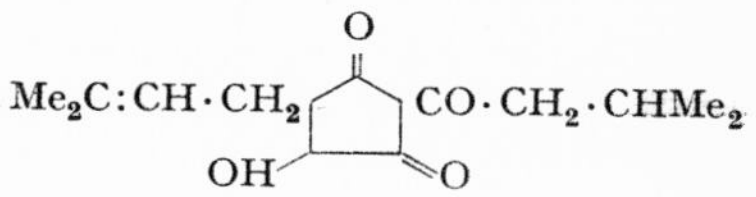

(VI)

The above degradations may be summed up as follows:

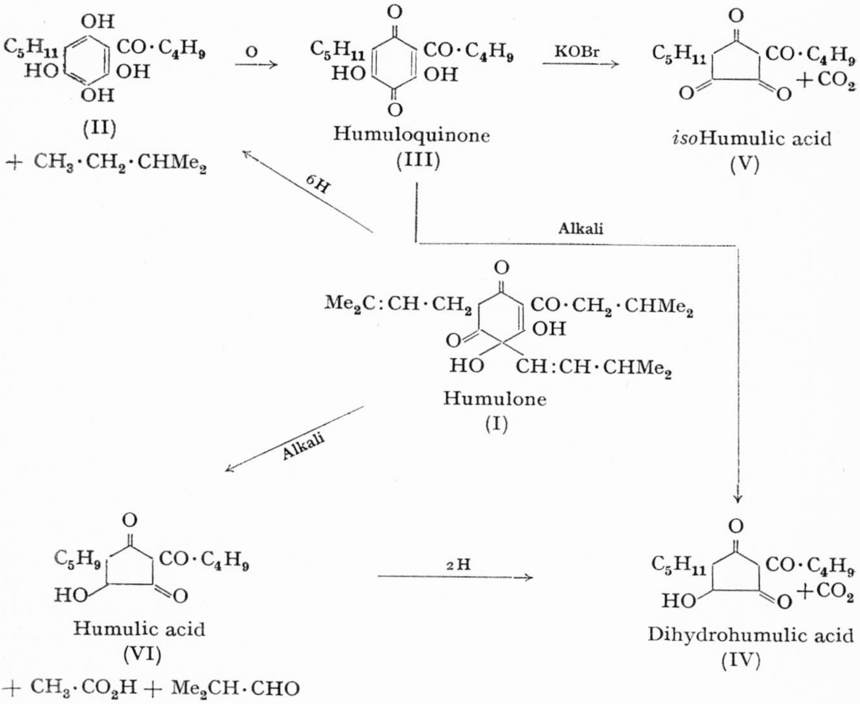

C_5H_{11}, HO, OH, OH, $CO \cdot C_4H_9$, OH

(II)

$+ CH_3 \cdot CH_2 \cdot CHMe_2$

$\xrightarrow{O}$

C_5H_{11}, HO, O, O, $CO \cdot C_4H_9$, OH

Humuloquinone

(III)

$\xrightarrow{KOBr}$

C_5H_{11}, O, O, O, $CO \cdot C_4H_9$ $+ CO_2$

*iso*Humulic acid

(V)

6H

Alkali

$Me_2C{:}CH \cdot CH_2$, O, O, HO, $CO \cdot CH_2 \cdot CHMe_2$, OH, $CH{:}CH \cdot CHMe_2$

Humulone

(I)

Alkali

C_5H_9, HO, O, O, $CO \cdot C_4H_9$

Humulic acid

(VI)

$+ CH_3 \cdot CO_2H + Me_2CH \cdot CHO$

$\xrightarrow{2H}$

C_5H_{11}, HO, O, O, $CO \cdot C_4H_9$ $+ CO_2$

Dihydrohumulic acid

(IV)

(*H. Wieland et al.*, Ber., 1925, **58**, 102; 1926, **59**, 2352; *W. Wöllmer*, Ber., 1916, **49**, 780).

Lupulone, $C_{26}H_{38}O_4$, m.p. 92°, is also unsaturated, adding bromine and immediately decolourising permanganate; it also has the properties of an enol. The determination of its constitution has been considerably simplified by its conversion into known derivatives of humulone. On catalytic hydrogenation eight atoms of hydrogen are absorbed, *iso*pentane is eliminated and a phloroglucinol derivative (*tribenzoate*, m.p. 165°) is formed. This latter compound is oxygen sensitive and yields on oxidation a quinol, *tetrahydrohumulone* $C_{21}H_{34}O_5$, m.p. 84°; the phloroglucinol derivative may be reformed by Clemmensen reduction. Alkaline fission of tetrahydrohumulone yields the cyclopentane derivative *dihydrohumulic* acid (IV) a side-chain being eliminated as 3-methylbutane-1-carboxylic acid. These reactions of lupulone can be expressed by the following constitution:

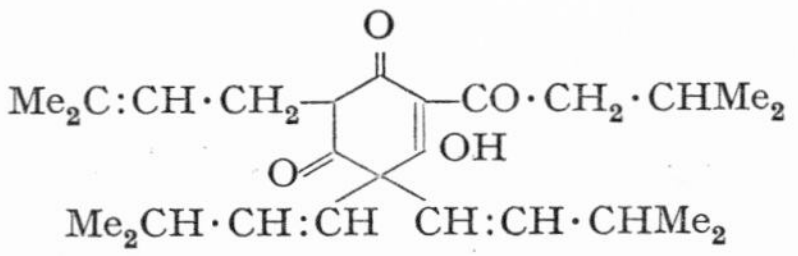

O

$Me_2C{:}CH{\cdot}CH_2$— —$CO{\cdot}CH_2{\cdot}CHMe_2$

OH

O

$Me_2CH{\cdot}CH{:}CH$ $CH{:}CH{\cdot}CHMe_2$

Lupulone

Later work has indicated that a slight modification of the above structures for humulone and lupulone might be necessary, the *iso*pent-1-enyl groups ($Me_2CH{\cdot}CH{:}CH{\cdot}$) being replaced by *iso*pent-2-enyl groups ($Me_2C{:}CH{\cdot}CH_2{\cdot}$) (*M. Verzele* and *F. Govaert*, Bull. Soc. chim. Belg., 1949, **58**, 432; J. chem. Soc., 1952, 3313; *A. H. Cook* and *G. Harris*, *ibid.*, 1950, 1873; *G. A. Howard et al.*, *ibid.*, 1952, 1902, 1906; *W. Riedl*, Chem. Ber., 1952, **85**, 692; *J. F. Carson*, J. Amer. chem. Soc., 1952, **74**, 4615).

9. Carboxylic acids

The hydroaromatic acids fall naturally into two classes, i.e. those in which the carboxyl groups are attached directly to the ring and those with exocyclic carboxyl groups. In the following text the exocyclic carboxylic acids immediately follow the ring carboxylic acids of the same functional type, e.g. cyclohexyl fatty acids follow cyclohexanecarboxylic acids, cyclohexenyl fatty acids follow cyclohexenecarboxylic acids etc.

(a) Monocarboxylic acids

(i) Cyclohexanecarboxylic acids (hexahydrobenzoic acids)

The old term "naphthenic acids" for these compounds is misleading and should be avoided (see p. 114). The most important method of preparation involves the reduction of benzoic acids; this may be carried out by catalytic hydrogenation or by treatment with metallic sodium and higher alcohols (e.g. amyl alcohol) the former process being much the more convenient. The acids may also be obtained by the reduction of cyclohexenecarboxylic acids, by the action of carbon dioxide on cyclohexylmagnesium halides and by the decarboxylation of cyclohexane-1:1-dicarboxylic acids.

The properties of the cyclohexanecarboxylic acids resemble closely those of the aliphatic monocarboxylic acids. For dissociation constants of members of the series see *N. D. Zelinsky*, Chem. Ztbl., 1909, I, 531; *H. L. Lochte* and *P. Brown*, J. Amer. chem. Soc., 1950, **72**, 4279. The velocity of esterification has been investigated by *B. W. Bhide* and *J. J. Sudborough* (J. Indian Inst. Science, 1925, **A8**, 89).

Physical properties of many of these acids with literature references are collected in Table 15.

TABLE 15

CYCLOHEXANECARBOXYLIC ACIDS

Compound	M.p.°	Amide m.p.°	Ref.
Cyclohexanecarboxylic acid	31 (b.p. 232°)	186	1,2,3, 4,7
1-Methylcyclohexane-1-carboxylic acid	39 (b.p. 234°)	69	5
cis-2-Methylcyclohexane-1-carboxylic acid	(b.p. 119°/11 mm.)	156	6
trans-2-Methylcyclohexane-1-carboxylic acid	52 (b.p. 99°/2 mm.)	182	6,7
3-Methylcyclohexane-1-carboxylic acid	(b.p. 245°)	156	8
cis-4-Methylcyclohexane-1-carboxylic acid	13 (b.p. 135°/20 mm.)	178	9
trans-4-Methylcyclohexane-1-carboxylic acid	113 (b.p. 246°)	221	10
2:4-Dimethylcyclohexane-1-carboxylic acid A	77 (b.p. 156°/40 mm.)	190	11
B	(b.p. 252°)	142	11
1:3-Dimethylcyclohexane-1-carboxylic acid A	44	84·5	12
B	90	73	12
3:5-Dimethylcyclohexane-1-carboxylic acid A	65	141	13
B	67	160	13
2^c:6^t-Dimethylcyclohexane-1^c-carboxylic acid	81		14
2^c:6^c-Dimethylcyclohexane-1^c-carboxylic acid	88	185	14
2^t:6^t-Dimethylcyclohexane-1^c-carboxylic acid	104	217	14
1:2:2-Trimethylcyclohexane-1-carboxylic acid	180	165	15
2:2:6-Trimethylcyclohexane-1-carboxylic acid A	75		16
B	83	191	16
1-*iso*Propylcyclohexane-1-carboxylic acid	105		15
cis-4-*iso*Propylcyclohexane-1-carboxylic acid	(b.p. 133°/2·5 mm.)	85 (a)	9
trans-4-*iso*Propylcyclohexane-1-carboxylic acid	94	108 (a)	9
1-Phenylcyclohexane-1-carboxylic acid	124	96	17,18
cis-2-Phenylcyclohexane-1-carboxylic acid	77	80	19
trans-2-Phenylcyclohexane-1-carboxylic acid	108	136	19

(a) *p*-Bromophenacyl ester

[1] *H. Gilman* and *R. H. Kirby*, Org. Synth., Coll. Vol. I, p. 364.
[2] *A. Einhorn* and *A. Meyerberg*, Ber., 1894, **27**, 2829.
[3] *A. E. Grey* and *C. S. Marvel*, J. Amer. chem. Soc., 1925, **47**, 2799.

[4] *N. D. Zelinsky*, Ber., 1902, **35**, 2688.
[5] *J. Gutt*, Ber., 1907, **40**, 2069.
[6] *A. K. MacBeth et al.*, J. chem. Soc., 1949, 1011.
[7] *A. Skita*, Ann., 1923, **431**, 18.
[8] *W. H. Perkin* and *G. Tattersall*, J. chem. Soc., 1905, **87**, 1091; *M. Mousseron et al.*, Bull. Soc. chim. Fr., 1947, **14**, 605.
[9] *A. K. MacBeth et al.*, J. chem. Soc., 1939, 1245; 1940, 808.
[10] *G. H. Keats*, *ibid.*, 1937, 2003.
[11] *W. H. Perkin et al.*, *ibid.*, 1897, **71**, 173; 1901, **79**, 356.
[12] *M. Godchot* and *G. Cauquil*, Compt. rend., 1938, **206**, 297.
[13] *N. D. Zelinsky*, Ber., 1902, **35**, 2689.
[14] *T. L. Jacobs et al.*, J. Amer. chem. Soc., 1951, **73**, 4505.
[15] *B. Shive et al.*, *ibid.*, 1941, **63**, 2979.
[16] *B. Shive et al.*, *ibid.*, 1942, **64**, 385.
[17] *A. W. Weston*, *ibid.*, 1946, **68**, 2345.
[18] *M. Rubin* and *H. Wishinsky*, *ibid.*, 1946, **68**, 828.
[19] *C. D. Gutsche*, *ibid.*, 1948, **70**, 4150.

Cyclohexanecarboxylic acid *(hexahydrobenzoic acid)* may be prepared by the catalytic hydrogenation of benzoic acid or by the action of carbon dioxide on cyclohexylmagnesium halides (refs. 1, 3, 4, 7, Table 15). It is also formed by the catalytic hydrogenation of the cyclohexenecarboxylic acids and by the decarboxylation of cyclohexane-1:1-dicarboxylic acid. It gives rise to the usual carboxylic derivatives e.g. the *methyl ester*, b.p. 183°, the *anhydride*, b.p. 171°/14 mm., *anilide*, m.p. 131°. The *phenyl ester*, b.p. 164°/21 mm., readily undergoes the Claisen rearrangement to give cyclohexyl *o*-hydroxyphenyl ketone (*S. Skraup* and *W. Beifuss*, Ber., 1927, **60**, 1070). The *chloride*, b.p. 101°/52 mm., may be prepared by the usual thionyl chloride process and is also formed by an interesting photochemical reaction between oxalyl chloride and cyclohexane (*M. S. Kharasch* and *H. C. Brown*, J. Amer. chem. Soc., 1940, **62**, 454). The *nitrile, cyclohexyl cyanide*, b.p. 184°, is formed by the action of cyanogen on cyclohexylmagnesium chloride (*M. Mousseron* and *F. Winternitz*, Bull. Soc. chim. Fr., 1948, **15**, 79; *V. Grignard et al.*, Ann. chim., 1915, **4**, 28). Electrolysis of potassium cyclohexanecarboxylate produces mainly cyclohexylcyclohexanecarboxylate, dicyclohexyl and dicyclohexyl ether (*F. Fichter* and *A. Petrovitch*, Helv., 1940, **23**, 806; 1941, **24**, 253).

trans-2-**Methylcyclohexane-1-carboxylic acid** *(hexahydro-*o*-toluic acid)* is produced by the catalytic reduction of *o*-toluic acid using platinic oxide in glacial acetic acid or by the decarboxylation of the 1:1-dicarboxylic acid (refs. 6, 7). The cis-isomer is obtained by the catalytic hydrogenation of *o*-toluic acid employing Raney nickel in sodium hydroxide solution.

A mixture of the stereoisomers of 3-**methylcyclohexane-1-carboxylic acid** is formed by the action of carbon dioxide on 3-methylcyclohexyl magnesium chloride. The optically active acids are produced in this way from the optically active chloride (ref. 6; *M. Mousseron et al.*, Bull. Soc. chim. Fr., 1947, **14**, 868; 1948, **15**, 79).

The isomeric 4-**methylcyclohexane-1-carboxylic acids,** cis-p-*bromophenacyl ester*, m.p. 100°, trans-p-*bromophenacyl ester*, m.p. 135°, are obtained from *p*-toluic acid by the two catalytic hydrogenation procedures described above for the 2-methylisomers (refs. 9, 10, Table 15).

Isomer A (probably *cis*) of 2:2:6-**trimethylcyclohexane-1-carboxylic acid** is formed by the catalytic hydrogenation of α-cyclogeranic acid (p. 227). By treatment with hot concentrated hydrochloric acid this acid rearranges to isomer B (probably *trans*) which is identical with an acid, $C_{10}H_{18}O_2$, isolated from Californian petroleum (ref. 16).

1:2:2-**Trimethylcyclohexane-1-carboxylic acid** is obtained by the reduction of dibromocampholide (ref. 15).

1-iso**Propylcyclohexane-1-carboxylic acid,** *anilide*, m.p. 102°, is formed by the Clemmensen reduction of 1-*iso*propylcyclohexan-2-one-1-carboxylic ester (ref. 15).

1-Phenylcyclohexane-1-carboxylic acid is produced by the hydrolysis of its *nitrile*, b.p. 127°/3 mm., which is obtained by the condensation of pentamethylene dibromide with benzyl cyanide in the presence of sodamide. A series of basic esters, e.g. the 2-*diethylaminoethyl ester*, b.p. 157°/2 mm., have been prepared and examined for antispasmodic properties (ref. 17).

Halogenated cyclohexanecarboxylic acids

1-Chlorocyclohexane-1-carboxylic acid, b.p. 138°/13 mm., *amide*, m.p. 118°, is formed by the hydrolysis of its *chloride*, b.p. 96°/18 mm., itself prepared by the chlorination of cyclohexanecarboxylic chloride (*C. C. Price* and *M. Schwarz*, J. Amer. chem. Soc., 1940, **62**, 2895).

cis- and trans-2-**Chlorocyclohexyl cyanide** (absolute configuration not allocated) m.p. −5°, b.p. 112°/14 mm., and m.p. 22° are produced by the action of phosphorus pentachloride on 1-cyanocyclohexan-2-ol and by the addition of hydrogen chloride to cyclohex-1-enyl cyanide (*M. Mousseron et al.*, Bull. Soc. chim. Fr., 1948, **15**, 79; Compt. rend., 1948, **226**, 91). Both isomers are converted by aqueous sodium hydroxide to cyclohex-1-ene-1-carboxyamide.

1-Chloro-3-methylcyclohexane-1-carboxylic acid, *methyl ester*, b.p. 98°/20 mm., is obtained by the action of phosphorus pentachloride on the corresponding 1-hydroxy-acid (*M. Mousseron et al.*, Bull. Soc. chim. Fr., 1947, **14**, 605).

1-Bromocyclohexane-1-carboxylic acid, m.p. 63°, and the homologous 2-*methyl-*, m.p. 97°, 3-*methyl-*, m.p. 118° and 142°, and 4-*methyl*-derivative, m.p. 71°, are all obtained by the bromination of the acid chloride of the corresponding cyclohexanecarboxylic acid (*W. Sernov*, Ber., 1899, **32**, 1167; *F. P. Mazza* and *G. Mase*, Gazz., 1927, **57**, 308).

trans-2-**Bromocyclohexane-1-carboxylic acid,** m.p. 109°, is produced by the addition of hydrogen bromide to cyclohex-1-ene-1-carboxylic acid. 3-**Bromocyclohexane-1-carboxylic acid,** m.p. 65°, is formed by the action of hydrobromic acid on the lactone of cylohexan-3-ol-1-carboxylic acid (1:3-cyclohexanolide) (*E. J. Boorman* and *R. P. Linstead*, J. chem. Soc., 1935, 258).

The addition of bromine to cyclohex-1-ene-1-carboxylic acid yields 1:2-**dibromocyclohexanecarboxylic acid,** m.p. 142°. Similar treatment of the 2-ene-acid furnishes 2:3-**dibromocyclohexane-1-carboxylic acid,** m.p. 166°; on being heated with aqueous sodium carbonate the latter acid forms a *bromolactone* m.p. 67° (*O. Aschan,* Ann., 1892, **271,** 231).

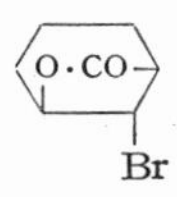

Aminocyclohexanecarboxylic acids

These acids are prepared by the hydrogenation of the corresponding aminobenzoic acids and by the reduction of the oximes of cyclohexanonecarboxylic acids. The 1-amino-1-carboxylic acids are produced from cyclohexanones by the Strecker synthesis.

1-**Aminocyclohexane-1-carboxylic acid,** m.p. 335°, is obtained by the action of ammonium cyanide on cyclohexanone followed by hydrolysis of the aminonitrile formed (*A. Skita* and *R. Levi,* Ber., 1908, **41,** 2925).

2-**Aminocyclohexane-1-carboxylic acid,** m.p. 274° (dec.), and the 3-*amino*-compound, m.p. 269°, are obtained by the sodium and alcohol reduction of anthranilic acid and *m*-aminobenzoic acid respectively (*A. Einhorn et al.,* Ann., 1897, **295,** 187; 1901, **319,** 324; Ber., 1894, **27,** 2470; *L. Orthner* and *R. Hein,* Biochem. Z., 1933, **262,** 461). The hydrogenation of *p*-aminobenzoic acid gives 4-**aminocyclohexane-1-carboxylic acid,** subliming above 330°; on being heated it gives the *lactam* (is*onortropinone*), m.p. 192° (*J. Houben* and *A. Pfau,* Ber., 1894, **27,** 2831). For the metabolism of these acids see *K. Bernhard,* Z. physiol. Chem., 1938, **256,** 59).

2-**Dimethylaminomethylcyclohexane-1-carboxylic acid,** m.p. 155°, is obtained by air oxidation of the corresponding aldehyde (p. 191) (*D. R. Howton,* J. org. Chem., 1947, **12,** 379).

4-*Amino-1-phenylcyclohexane-1-carboxylic acid, hydrochlorides,* m.p. 253° and 203°, is prepared by hydrogenation of the oxime of 1-phenylcyclohexan-4-one-1-carboxylic acid (*M. Rubin* and *H. Wishinsky,* J. Amer. chem. Soc., 1946, **68,** 828).

(ii) Cyclohexyl fatty acids

Cyclohexylacetic acid, m.p. 33°, b.p. 112°/3 mm., *amide,* m.p. 168°, is obtained by the reduction of sodium mandelate (*V. Ipatiev* and *G. Rasuvajev,* Ber., 1926, **59,** 306) and by catalytic hydrogenation of phenylacetic acid or cyclohexylideneacetic acid (*R. Adams* and *J. R. Marshall,* J. Amer. chem. Soc., 1928, **50,** 1970). It is also formed by the action of carbon dioxide on cyclohexylmethylmagnesium bromide and by the decarboxylation of cyclohexylmalonic acid (*J. Gutt,* Ber., 1907, **40,** 2067).

2:2-**Dimethylcyclohexylacetic acid,** b.p. 153°/17 mm., p-*phenylphenacyl ester,* m.p. 87°, is obtained by hydrogenation of the dehydration product of 2:2-dimethylcyclohexan-1-ol-1-acetic ester; the acid may be resolved by cinchonidine and *l*-ephedrine (*J. L. Simonsen et al.,* J. chem. Soc., 1938, 774).

2-**Cyclohexylpropane-1-carboxylic acid,** $C_6H_{11}\cdot CH(CH_3)\cdot CH_2\cdot CO_2H$, b.p. 161°/14 mm., *amide*, m.p. 123°, is produced by the catalytic hydrogenation of *β*-methylcinnamic acid (*B. L. Zenitz et al.*, J. Amer. chem. Soc., 1947, **69**, 1117).

cis-2-**Phenylcyclohexylacetic acid,** m.p. 169°, *amide*, m.p. 142°, is formed by the hydrogenation of 2-phenylcyclohex-1-enylacetic acid. The trans-*isomer*, m.p. 114°, *amide*, m.p. 127°, is produced by the Arndt-Eistert homologation (Vol. I, p. 575) of *trans*-2-phenylcyclohexane-1-carboxylic acid (*C. D. Gutsche*, J. Amer. chem. Soc., 1948, **70**, 4151).

For other representatives of this series see *R. B. Moffett et al.*, J. Amer. chem. Soc., 1947, **69**, 1854; *R. Adams et al.*, *ibid.*, 1926, **48**, 2391; 1928, **50**, 1970; *M. Mousseron et al.*, Bull. Soc. chim. Fr., 1947, **14**, 605.

Aminocyclohexyl fatty acids

(–)-*α*-**Aminocyclohexylacetic acid,** *hydrochloride*, m.p. 270° (dec.) is formed by the hydrogenation of (–)-phenylglycine (*H. Reiblen* and *L. Knöpfle*, Ann., 1936, **523**, 208).

A mixture of the geometrical isomers of 4-*acetamidocyclohexylacetic acid*, cis-, m.p. 187°, trans-, m.p. 235°, is obtained by the catalytic hydrogenation of *p*-acetamidophenylacetic acid (*E. Ferber* and *H. Bendix*, Ber., 1939, **72**, 839).

Racemic *β*-**cyclohexylalanine,** *benzoyl deriv.*, m.p. 183·5°, is obtained as its *acetyl* deriv., m.p. 178°, by the catalytic hydrogenation of *α*-acetamidocinnamic acid (*D. Shewin* and *H. M. Herbst*, J. Amer. chem. Soc., 1939, **61**, 2471). The (–)-*isomer*, *acetyl* deriv., m.p. 199°, is produced by the catalytic hydrogenation of tyrosine (*E. Waser* and *E. Bräuchli*, Helv., 1924, **7**, 740; *K. Bernhard*, Z. physiol. Chem., 1938, **256**, 49).

(iii) Cyclohexenecarboxylic acids (tetrahydrobenzoic acids)

These acids are produced by the controlled reduction of benzoic acids or cyclohexadienecarboxylic acids, by the dehydration of cyclohexanolcarboxylic acids and by the dehydrobromination of bromocyclohexanecarboxylic acids. Cyclohex-3-ene-1-carboxylic acids are readily available by the Diels-Alder condensation between dienes and *αβ*-unsaturated acids.

Some representatives of this series are shown in Table 16 (p. 226).

Cyclohex-1-ene-1-carboxylic acid, *amide*, m.p. 128°, is best prepared by hydrolysis of the *nitrile*, b.p. 81°/14 mm., which is obtained by the thionyl chloride dehydration of cyclohexanone cyanohydrin (refs. 2, 3, Table 16; see also *M. Mousseron* and *F. Winternitz*, Bull. Soc. chim. Fr., 1948, **15**, 79). It is also formed by the dehydrobromination of 1-bromocyclohexane-1-carboxylic acid and the rearrangement of cyclohex-2-ene-1-carboxylic acid with alcoholic alkali (*W. Braren* and *E. Buchner*, Ber., 1900, **33**, 3455).

Cyclohex-2-ene-1-carboxylic acid, *amide*, m.p. 144°, is produced by the sodium amalgam reduction of benzoic acid. Treatment of the acid with 50% sulphuric acid yields the lactone of cyclohexan-3-ol-1-carboxylic acid (ref. 3). The corresponding unsaturated *nitrile*, b.p. 89°/17 mm., is obtained by the action of potassium cyanide on 3-bromocyclohex-3-ene (*M. Mousseron* and *F. Winternitz*, *loc. cit.*).

TABLE 16

CYCLOHEXENECARBOXYLIC ACIDS

Compound	B.p.°/mm.	M.p.°	Ref.
Cyclohex-1-ene-1-carboxylic acid	240	38	1, 2, 3
Cyclohex-2-ene-1-carboxylic acid	122/10	7	3
Cyclohex-3-ene-1-carboxylic acid	237	13	4, 5, 6
2-Methylcyclohex-1-ene-1-carboxylic acid		88	7, 8
2-Methylcyclohex-2-ene-1-carboxylic acid	142/20		8, 9
2-Methylcyclohex-3-ene-1-carboxylic acid	139/20		9, 10
2-Methylcyclohex-4-ene-1-carboxylic acid	135/12	68	11, 12
cis-2-Methylcyclohex-5-ene-1-carboxylic acid	145/20		11
trans-2-Methylcyclohex-5-ene-1-carboxylic acid	163/50	62	11
2-Methylcyclohex-6-ene-1-carboxylic acid		79	13
3-Methylcyclohex-1-ene-1-carboxylic acid	130/7	26	3
3-Methylcyclohex-2-ene-1-carboxylic acid	123/7		3
3-Methylcyclohex-3-ene-1-carboxylic acid	184/100		14
3-Methylcyclohex-4-ene-1-carboxylic acid	145/20		15
3-Methylcyclohex-5-ene-1-carboxylic acid	143/20		15
3-Methylcyclohex-6-ene-1-carboxylic acid	160/25	60	16, 17
4-Methylcyclohex-1-ene-1-carboxylic acid		134	16, 18
4-Methylcyclohex-3-ene-1-carboxylic acid		99	16, 19
2:6-Dimethylcyclohex-1-ene-1-carboxylic acid		91·5	20
2:6-Dimethylcyclohex-4-ene-1-carboxylic acid	160/28	93·4	20
2:4:6-Trimethylcyclohex-3-ene-1-carboxylic acid	134/14	98	12
2:6:6-Trimethylcyclohex-1-ene-1-carboxylic acid (β-Cyclogeranic acid)		94	21
2:6:6-Trimethylcyclohex-2-ene-1-carboxylic acid (α-Cyclogeranic acid)	138/11	106	22
2:6:6-Trimethylcyclohex-3-ene-1-carboxylic acid		76 (A) 84 (B)	23
2:6:6-Trimethylcyclohex-4-ene-1-carboxylic acid	123/6	102	24

[1] *O. Aschan*, Ann., 1892, **271**, 267.
[2] *L. Ruzicka* and *W. Brugger*, Helv., 1926, **9**, 402.
[3] *E. J. Boorman* and *R. P. Linstead*, J. chem. Soc., 1935, 258.
[4] *W. H. Perkin* and *G. Tattersall*, J. chem. Soc., 1907, **91**, 490.
[5] *W. Sobecki*, Ber., 1910, **43**, 1039.
[6] *H. Fiesselmann*, Ber., 1942, **75**, 881.
[7] *F. W. Kay* and *W. H. Perkin*, J. chem. Soc., 1905, **87**, 1068.
[8] *M. Mousseron et al.*, Compt. rend., 1946, **223**, 36.
[9] *W. H. Perkin*, J. chem. Soc., 1911, **99**, 727.
[10] *H. L. Holmes et al.*, Canad. J. Res., 1948, **26B**, 248.
[11] *W. H. Perkin*, J. chem. Soc., 1911, **99**, 741.
[12] *O. Diels* and *K. Alder*, Ann., 1929, **470**, 62.
[13] *F. P. Mazza* and *G. Mase*, Gazz., 1927, **57**, 300.
[14] *W. H. Perkin et al.*, J. chem. Soc., 1908, **93**, 1886; 1913, **103**, 2233.
[15] *W. H. Perkin*, *ibid.*, 1910, **97**, 2129.
[16] *W. H. Perkin* and *G. Tattersall*, *ibid.*, 1905, **87**, 1091.
[17] *B. D. W. Luff* and *W. H. Perkin*, *ibid.*, 1910, **97**, 2147. *K. Auwers*, Ann., 1923, **432**, 98.
[18] *W. H. Perkin et al.*, J. chem. Soc., 1905, **87**, 645; 1906, **89**, 844; 1911, **99**, 534.
[19] *A. N. Meldrum* and *W. H. Perkin*, J. chem. Soc., 1908, **93**, 1424; *E. Lehmann* and *W. Paasche*, Ber., 1935, **68**, 1069.

[20] *R. W. Hufferd* and *W. A. Noyes*, J. Amer. chem. Soc., 1921, **43**, 931.
[21] *F. Tiemann*, Ber., 1900, **33**, 3712, 3723.
[22] *K. Bernhauer* and *R. Forster*, J. pr. Chem., 1936, [ii], **147**, 199; *L. Ruzicka* and *H. Schinz*, Helv., 1940, **23**, 959.
[23] *G. Merling et al.*, Ber., 1908, **41**, 2066; Ann., 1909, **366**, 174.
[24] *G. Merling*, G.P., 175,587 (1906).

Cyclohex-3-ene-1-carboxylic acid, is prepared by the dehydrobromination of 3- and 4-bromocyclohexane-1-carboxylic acids (ref. 4), by the carboxylation of cyclohex-3-enylmagnesium bromide (ref. 5) and by the addition of butadiene to acrylic acid (ref. 12; *M. Naef & Cie.*, F.P. 672,025 [1929]; *F. X. Werber et al.*, J. Amer. chem. Soc., 1952, **74**, 532); this last method serves for the preparation of homologues. The acid is also formed by the oxidation of the corresponding aldehyde (ref. 6). By heating with alkali under pressure it is converted into pimelic acid (*idem, ibid.*).

The numerous methylcyclohexenecarboxylic acids (tetrahydrotoluic acids) were prepared by *W. H. Perkin* and his co-workers (refs. 7 to 19, Table 16) by the dehydrobromination of bromomethylcyclohexanecarboxylic acids and by the dehydration of cyclohexanolcarboxylic acids. The acids have been used for the synthesis of many terpenes, e.g. sylvestrene, carvestrene, dipentene, α-terpineol and several menthenols.

Cyclisation of geranic acid with anhydrous formic acid gives a mixture of α-**cyclogeranic acid,** 2:6:6-*trimethylcyclohex-2-ene-1-carboxylic acid, amide,* m.p. 121°, and β-cyclogeranic acid, the corresponding -1-*ene-1-carboxylic acid, amide,* m.p. 202° (ref. 22; *C. A. Vodoz* and *H. Schinz*, Helv., 1950, **33**, 1047, 1313; *L. Ruzicka et al.*, Helv., 1950, **33**, 1510). The constitution of the α-acid is confirmed by its oxidation which gives first α-acetyl-ββ-dimethyladipic acid and ββ-dimethyladipic acid (*F. Tiemann*, Ber., 1898, **31**, 828; ref. 21, Table 16).

The action of potassium cyanide on 1:2-dichlorocyclohex-2-ene furnishes 1-*cyano-2-chlorocyclohex-2-ene*, b.p. 127°/15 mm., which, on alkaline hydrolysis, furnishes 2-**chlorocyclohex-1-ene-1-carboxylic acid,** m.p. 106°, *amide*, m.p. 182° (*M. Mousseron* and *F. Winternitz*, Bull. Soc. chim. Fr., 1948, **15**, 79).

(iv) Cyclohexenyl fatty acids

The most important acids of this type are those obtained by the dehydration of cyclohexan-1-ol-1-acetic acids or esters; if the dehydration be performed with phosphorus pentoxide or potassium bisulphate cyclohex-1-enylacetic acids are formed whilst acetic anhydride or formic acid produces the corresponding cyclohexylideneacetic acid (*G. A. R. Kon, R. P. Linstead et al.*, J. chem. Soc., 1926, 2733; 1927, 357, 1548, 2582; 1929, 1278, 2146).

In this manner is obtained **cyclohex-1-enylacetic acid,** m.p. 13°, b.p. 112°/3 mm., *amide*, m.p. 153° (above refs.). By permanganate oxidation 1-acetylcyclopent-1-ene is formed by cyclisation and decarboxylation of the initially produced heptan-2-one-7-al-1-carboxylic acid (*W. H. Perkin* and *O. Wallach*, Ber., 1909, **42**, 145). Similarly prepared homologues include 4-*methyl*-, m.p. 41°, b.p.

138°/14 mm., *amide*, m.p. 156° (*W. H. Perkin et al.*, 1908, **93**, 1943) and 5-*methyl-cyclohex*-1-*enylacetic acid*, b.p. 149°/26 mm. (*M. Mousseron et al.*, Bull. Soc. chim. Fr., 1947, **14**, 605).

Other cyclohexenyl fatty acids are generally prepared by the usual homologation reactions e.g. the reaction of cyclohexenylalkyl halides with sodiomalonic ester (*inter al.*, *C. D. Nenitzescu* and *V. Przemetzky*, Ber., 1941, **74**, 676; *R. B. Moffett et al.*, J. Amer. chem. Soc., 1947, **69**, 1854).

Cyclohexylideneacetic acid, m.p. 92°, *amide*, m.p. 148°, is prepared by the acetic anhydride dehydration of cyclohexan-1-ol-1-acetic acid (above refs.; cf. also *H. Schmid* and *P. Karrer*, Helv., 1948, **31**, 1067). It is also formed by oxidation of the corresponding aldehyde (*J. D. Chanley*, J. Amer. chem. Soc., 1948, **70**, 244) and by the alkaline rearrangement of 1-bromoacetyl-1-bromocyclohexane (p. 216). Treatment of the methyl ester with N-bromosuccinimide gives *methyl 2-bromocyclohexylideneacetate*, b.p. 97°/1·2 mm., which has been employed in Reformatsky reactions (*H. Schmid* and *P. Karrer*, *loc. cit.*).

4-**Methylcyclohexylideneacetic acid,** m.p. 66°, is of special theoretical interest as its structure contains no element of symmetry although it possesses no asymmetric carbon atom. It can therefore be resolved by brucine to give the optical enantiomorphs, m.p. 53°, $[\alpha]_D \pm 81°$ (see Vol. I, p. 109).

2:2-**Dimethylcyclohexylideneacetic acid,** m.p. 92°, is prepared in a manner analogous to the parent compound (*J. D. Chanley*, *loc. cit.*; *G. H. Elliott* and *R. P. Linstead*, J. chem. Soc., 1938, 776).

β-**Cyclohexylacrylic acid,** m.p. 58°, b.p. 154°/11 mm., *amide* m.p. 159°, is obtained by the condensation of cyclohexanealdehyde with malonic acid in the presence of pyridine and also by hypobromite oxidation of hexahydrobenzylideneacetone (*S. S. G. Sircar*, J. chem. Soc., 1928, 54).

Cyclohexylpropiolic acid, $C_6H_{11}{\cdot}C{:}C{\cdot}CO_2H$, b.p. 153°/13 mm., *amide* m.p. 104°, is obtained by the action of carbon dioxide on the sodium salt of cyclohexylacetylene (*W. Jegorova*, Chem. Ztbl., 1912, I, 1010). *Cyclohexyltetrolic acid*, m.p. 75°, is produced similarly from 3-cyclohexylpropyne (*B. de Resseguier*, Bull. Soc. chim. Fr., 1910, [iv], **7**, 431). For other acetylenic acids of this type see *M. Mousseron et al.*, Compt. rend., 1943, **217**, 155; Bull. Soc. chim. Fr., 1946, [v], **13**, 239; *M. Bourguel*, Ann. chim., 1925, **3**, 325.

(v) Cyclohexadienecarboxylic acids (dihydrobenzoic acids)

Cyclohexa-1:3-diene-1-carboxylic acid, m.p. 94°, *dibromide*, m.p. 167°, is obtained by the silver oxide oxidation of the corresponding aldehyde (*W. Langenbeck et al.*, Ber., 1942, **75**, 232; *A. Einhorn et al.*, Ber., 1890, **23**, 2886; 1893, **26**, 454). **Cyclohexa-1:4-diene-1-carboxylic acid,** m.p. 123°, is formed by the condensation of butadiene with propiolic acid (*K. Alder* and *K. H. Backendorf*, Ber., 1938, **71**, 2199). A *cyclohexadienecarboxylic acid*, m.p. 73°, of undetermined constitution is produced by the dehydrobromination of 2:3-dibromocyclohexane-1-carboxylic acid (*O. Aschan*, Ber., 1891, **24**, 2622).

2-**Methylcyclohexa**-2:6-**diene**-1-**carboxylic acid,** (4:5-*dihydro*-o-*toluic acid*), m.p. 175°, is formed by the phosphorus and hydriodic acid reduction of the corresponding dihydrophthalide (*F. P. Mazza* and *A. Calò*, Gazz., 1927, **57**, 315).

2:5-**Dimethylcyclohexa**-1:5-**diene**-1-**carboxylic acid,** m.p. 42°, is produced by the action of alkali on dichloro-$\alpha\beta$-pulenenone (p. 213) (*K. Auwers* and *M. Hessenland*, Ber., 1908, **41**, 1822).

2:6:6-**Trimethylcyclohexa**-2:4-**diene**-1-**carboxylic acid,** m.p. 111°, is obtained by hydrolysis of its *ethyl ester*, b.p. 103°/12 mm., which is produced by dehydration of ethyl 4-hydroxy-2:6:6-trimethylcyclohex-2-ene-1-carboxylate (*O. Jeger* and *G. Büchi*, Helv., 1948, **31**, 134).

The so-called *dehydroperillic acid*, m.p. 83°, occurring in the Washington cedar (*Thuja plicata*) was once thought to be a cyclohexadiene derivative but is now known to be 4:4-dimethylcyclohepta-2:5:7-triene-1-carboxylic acid (*J. Gripenberg*, Acta chem. Scand., 1949, **3**, 1137; 1952, **6**, 690, 854); it has therefore been renamed *thujic acid*.

Cyclohexadienyl fatty acids, the position of the double bonds being undetermined, are obtained by the reaction of cyclohexenones with zinc and ethyl bromoacetate. Thus 3-*methylcyclohexadienyl*-1-*acetic acid*, m.p. 171°, is formed from 3-methylcyclohex-2-en-1-one and the 3:5-*dimethyl*-acid, m.p. 151°, b.p. 170°/15 mm., from the corresponding ketone (*O. Wallach* and *H. Bötticher*, 1902, **323**, 139).

(b) Hydroxymonocarboxylic acids

(i) Hydroxycyclohexanecarboxylic acids

Cyclohexan-1-ol-1-carboxylic acid, m.p. 110°, 3:5-*dinitrobenzoate*, m.p. 165–168°, is conveniently prepared by acid hydrolysis of the corresponding *nitrile* (*cyclohexanone cyanohydrin*), m.p. 28°, b.p. 63°/10^{-6} mm., which is itself obtained by the action of hydrogen cyanide on cyclohexanone (*J. D. Billimoria* and *N. F. Maclagan*, J. chem. Soc., 1951, 3067). Homologous acids of this type are similarly prepared (cf. *B. Tchoubar* and *C. Collin*, Bull. Soc. chim. Fr., 1947, [v], **14**, 680; *M. Godchot*, Compt. rend., 1936, **203**, 1042).

Cyclohexan-2-ol-1-carboxylic acids (*hexahydrosalicylic acids*) cis- m.p. 78°, trans- m.p. 111°, may be obtained by the catalytic hydrogenation of salicylic acid (*N. L. Edson*, J. Soc. chem. Ind., 1934, **53**, 138). They are also produced by hydrolysis of their *ethyl esters*, b.p. 118°/18 mm. and 132°/25 mm., which are themselves prepared from ethyl cyclohexan-2-one-1-carboxylate by catalytic hydrogenation and sodium amalgam reduction respectively (*J. Pascual et al.*, J. chem. Soc., 1949, 1943). The trans-*nitrile*, m.p. 46°, is formed by the action of potassium cyanide on trans-2-chlorocyclohexan-1-ol (*M. Mousseron et al.*, Compt. rend., 1948, **226**, 91, 1909). The **cyclohexan-3-ol-1-carboxylic acids,** cis- m.p. 133°, trans- m.p. 120°, and the **cyclohexan-4-ol-1-carboxylic acids,** cis- m.p. 152°, trans- m.p. 148°, are obtained by exactly analogous methods (*N. R. Campbell* and *J. H. Hunt*, J. chem. Soc., 1950, 1379; *R. H. Leven* and *J. H. Pendergrass*, J. Amer. chem. Soc., 1947, **69**, 2436; *P. A. Plattner et al.*, Helv., 1944, **27**, 793; *N. L. Edson, loc. cit.; A. Windaus et al.*, Ber., 1922, **55**, 3981).

2:6:6-**Trimethylcyclohexan**-4-**ol**-1-**carboxylic acid** (4-*hydroxydihydrocyclogeranic acid*) possesses three asymmetric carbon atoms and therefore exists in four racemic modifications all of which are obtainable by the reduction of *iso*phoronecarboxylic ester with sodium and alcohol; cis-α, m.p. 145°, trans-α, m.p. 155°; cis-β, m.p. 158°, trans-β, m.p. 38°. Dehydrating agents convert all the isomers into 2:6:6-trimethylcyclohex-3-ene-1-carboxylic acid (*G. Merling* and *R. Welde*, Ann., 1909, **366**, 151).

Cyclohexane-3:4:5-**triol**-1-**carboxylic acid** (*dihydroshikimic acid*), m.p. 176–178°, is formed by the reduction of shikimic acid (p. 231) (*H. O. L. Fischer* and *G. Dangschat*, Helv., 1934, **17**, 1200).

Quinic acid (**cyclohexane**-1^c:3^c:4^c:5^t-**tetrol**-1^t-**carboxylic acid**), m.p. 162°, *methyl ester* m.p. 120°, is an optically active acid obtained as a secondary product in the isolation of quinine from cinchona bark; it is present in many other plants (*E. O. von Lippmann*, Ber., 1901, **34**, 1159; *J. Herzig* and *H. Ortony*, Arch. Pharm., 1920, **258**, 91). Its spatial configuration (I) was established by *H. O. L. Fischer* and *G. Dangschat* (Ber., 1932, **65**, 1009; Angew. Chem., 1932, **45**, 431; for review see *H. G. Fletcher*, Adv. Carb. Chem., **3**, 70). On distillation the acid breaks down into phenol, hydroquinone, benzoic acid and salicylaldehyde. Oxidation with manganese dioxide and sulphuric acid converts it into benzoquinone; hydriodic acid reduction yields benzoic acid. Treatment with caustic alkali gives protocatechuic acid which is also formed by the aerobic bacterial decomposition of calcium quinate. The action of periodic acid produces citric acid (*H. O. L. Fischer* and *G. Dangschat*, Helv., 1934, **17**, 1196). Reaction with acetone converts it into the iso*propylidene* derivative (II), m.p. 141°, of *quinolactone*, m.p. 198°. (II) gives a *benzoyl* derivative m.p. 140°, which may be hydrolysed by hot dilute mineral acid to quinolactone (quinide). This lactone may also be obtained directly from quinic acid by heating to 220° (*idem*, Ber., 1921, **54**, 781; 1927, **60**, 485; *F. P. Mazza*, Gazz., 1927, **57**, 292; *J. F. Eijkman*, Ber., 1891, **24**, 1296). Quinic acid forms a depside with caffeic acid, 3-caffeylquinic acid (chlorogenic acid), m.p. 206–207°, which occurs in coffee beans and in the milky sap of *Ficus elastica* and *Castilloa elastica* (*H. O. L. Fischer* and *G. Dangschat*, Ber., 1932, **65**, 1037; *W. Höpfner*, Chem.-Ztg., 1932, **56**, 991; *C. Griebel*, *ibid.*, 1933, **57**, 353, 875).

OH, HO, OH, CO_2H, OH

Quinic acid
(I)

Me_2C–O, O, OH, O, CO

*iso*Propylidenequinolactone
(II)

Cyclohexane-1:2:3:4:5-**pentol**-1-**carboxylic acid** (*dihydroxydihydroshikimic acid*), m.p. 156°, is obtained by the hydrolysis of shikimic acid dibromide with barium hydroxide (*J. F. Eijkman*, Ber., 1891, **24**, 1294).

2-(*α-Hydroxyamyl*)*cyclohex*-2-*ene*-1-*carboxylic acid* (*sedanolic acid*), m.p. 89°, occurs as the lactone, *sedanolide*, b.p. 85°/17 mm., in the essential oil of celery (*G. Ciamician* and *P. Silber*, Ber., 1897, **30**, 498, 1420).

Shikimic acid (*cyclohex*-1-*ene*-3:4:5-*triol*-1-*carboxylic acid*), m.p. 184°, is found in the fruit of *Illicium religiosum* (*H. O. L. Fischer* and *G. Dangschat*, Helv., 1934, **17**, 1200; 1935, **18**, 1206; 1937, **20**, 705).

(*ii*) *Hydroxycyclohexyl fatty acids*

The action of zinc and α-bromo-fatty acid esters on cyclohexanones gives acids of this type. In this manner are prepared **cyclohexan-1-ol-1-acetic acid,** m.p. 63°, and the 4-*methyl*-, m.p. of the geometrical isomers 141° and 90°, and 2:2-*dimethyl*-homologue, m.p. 99° (*O. Wallach*, Ann., 1906, **347**, 328; 1908, **360**, 26; 1909, **365**, 261; *F. Becherer*, Helv., 1925, **8**, 184). Dehydration gives the corresponding cyclohexenyl or cyclohexylidene fatty acids (p. 228).

The action of sodiomalonic ester on cyclohexene oxide, followed by hydrolysis and decarboxylation of the product yields the *lactone*, f.p. –1·2°, b.p. 119°/6 mm., of trans-**cyclohexan-2-ol-1-acetic acid,** m.p. 106°, which is obtained by alkaline hydrolysis. Chromic acid oxidation of the *trans*-acid gives cyclohexan-2-one-1-acetic acid, which by catalytic hydrogenation furnishes the *lactone*, f.p. 14·8°, b.p. 112°/16 mm., of the corresponding *cis*-acid. The *trans*-lactone reacts with ammonia to form the corresponding trans-*amide*, m.p. 152°, but the *cis*-lactone remains unaffected by this treatment (*M. S. Newman* and *C. A. VanderWerf*, J. Amer. chem. Soc., 1945, **67**, 233). 2-*Ethoxycyclohexyl*-1-*acetic acid*, b.p. 166°/20 mm., *amide* m.p. 119°, is formed by the catalytic hydrogenation of 2-*ethoxy-cyclohex*-5-*enyl*-1-*acetic acid*, b.p. 160°/20 mm., *amide* m.p. 116°, which is itself produced by the action of sodiomalonic ester on 2:3-dibromo-1-ethoxy-cyclohexane (*M. Mousseron* and *P. Brun*, Bull. Soc. chim. Fr., 1947, [v], **14**, 616).

Cyclohexylglycollic acid (*hexahydromandelic acid*), $C_6H_{11}\cdot CH(OH)\cdot CO_2H$, m.p. 166°, is obtained by the hydrolysis of cyclohexanealdehyde cyanohydrin (*N. D. Zelinsky*, Ber., 1908, **41**, 2677). It is also formed by the catalytic hydrogenation of *cyclohex*-1-*enylglycollic acid*, m.p. 126°, itself produced by the action of alkali on cyclohex-1-enylglyoxal (*J. D. Chanley*, J. Amer. chem. Soc., 1948, **70**, 244).

Hexahydroatrolactic acid, $C_6H_{11}\cdot CMe(OH)\cdot CO_2H$, m.p. 101·5°, is obtained by the hydrogenation of atrolactic acid (*K. Freudenberg et al.*, Ann., 1933, **501**, 217).

Cyclohexanones react with α-halogeno-esters in the presence of sodium ethoxide to yield epoxy-esters, e.g. cyclohexanone and ethyl bromoacetate furnish *ethyl α*:1-*epoxycyclohexylacetate*, b.p. 128°/17 mm. Such products are valuable synthetic intermediates as hydrolysis and decarboxylation furnish the corresponding aldehyde or ketone (*inter al.*, *G. Darzens et al.*, Compt. rend., 1906, **142**, 714; 1907, **144**, 1123; 1910, **151**, 758; *H. Barbier*, Helv., 1940, **23**, 519; *D. R. Howton*, J. org. Chem., 1947, **12**, 379; see aldehydes, p. 188).

Azafrin, a polyene hydroxycyclohexyl fatty acid, is considered with the carotenoids (p. 388).

(c) *Ketocarboxylic acids*

(i) *Ketocyclohexanecarboxylic acids*

Cyclohexan-2-one-1-carboxylic acids are made by the careful hydrolysis of the esters which are prepared by the Dieckmann cyclisation of pimelic esters and by the condensation of cyclohexanones with oxalic esters with subsequent pyrolytic elimination of carbon monoxide from the resulting cyclohexan-2-one-1-glyoxylic esters (*A. Kötz* and *A. Michels*, Ann., 1906, **350**, 210; *H. R. Snyder et al.*, Org. Synth., Coll. Vol. II, 532). The acids are also formed by the action of sodamide and carbon dioxide on cyclohexanones (*W. H. Perkin et al.*, J. chem. Soc., 1910, **97**, 1764. These compounds are cyclic analogues of the aliphatic β-keto-acids and esters and possess exactly analogous properties.

Cyclohexan-2-one-1-carboxylic acid, m.p. 82°, readily decarboxylates at the melting-point. It may be obtained by hydrolysis of the *ethyl ester*, b.p. 107°/11 mm., which is prepared by the above general methods; it is a highly enolised substance (*W. Dieckmann*, Ber., 1922, **55**, 2470; for infra-red absorption see *N. J. Leonard et al.*, J. Amer. chem. Soc., 1952, **74**, 4070). Action of dilute mineral acids causes a typical ketonic decomposition to cyclohexanone; with hot alcoholic potassium hydroxide the ester undergoes fission to pimelic acid (*N. Ivanoff*, Bull. Soc. chim. Fr., 1948, **15**, 660). With sodium or sodium alkoxides a sodio-derivative is produced which reacts readily with alkyl halides; thus methyl iodide gives *ethyl 1-methylcyclohexan-2-one-1-carboxylate*, b.p. 108°/11 mm., and allyl bromide produces the 1-*allyl*-analogue, *semicarbazone* m.p. 137° (*R. Grewe*, Ber., 1943, **76**, 1072). The parent ester reacts with hydrazine to give a bicyclic pyrazolone and with ammonia to produce *ethyl 2-aminocyclohex-1-ene 1-carboxylate*, m.p. 74° (*W. Dieckmann*, Ann., 1901, **317**, 93).

The homologous *ethyl 4-methylcyclohexan-2-one-1-carboxylate*, b.p. 123°/13 mm., is of interest since, by alkylation with *iso*propyl iodide and subsequent hydrolysis, it furnishes menthone (*A. Einhorn* and *L. Klages*, Ber., 1901, **34**, 3793).

Cyclohexan-3-one-1-carboxylic acid, m.p. 74°, is prepared by the dichromate oxidation of the corresponding hydroxy-acid and is also formed by the partial decarboxylation of cyclohexan-3-one-1:4-dicarboxylic acid (*W. H. Perkin et al.*, J. chem. Soc., 1907, **91**, 491; 1905, **87**, 852). A series of methyl 5-alkyl-1-methylcyclohexan-2-one-1-carboxylates has been prepared by the action of sodium cyanide on the bisulphite compounds of the corresponding cyclohexenones with subsequent methanolysis of the resulting 1-cyano-5-alkyl-1-methylcyclohexan-3-ones (*W. F. Whitmore* and *C. W. Roberts*, J. org. Chem., 1948, **13**, 31).

Cyclohexan-4-one-1-carboxylic acid, m.p. 68°, is produced by the action of acetic anhydride on pentane-1:3:5-tricarboxylic acid followed by distillation. It has been used for the synthesis of α-terpineol and dipentene (*W. H. Perkin,*

J. chem. Soc., 1904, **85**, 424; *P. A. Plattner et al.*, Helv., 1944, **27**, 793). Homologues of this acid are easily obtained by catalytic hydrogenation of the corresponding Δ^2-unsaturated esters (see below) followed by hydrolysis (*A. Skita*, Ber., 1909, **42**, 1627). In this way is prepared 2:2:6-**trimethylcyclohexan-4-one-1-carboxylic acid** (*dihydroisophoronecarboxylic acid*), *α-form*, m.p. 127°, *ethyl ester* m.p. 44°, b.p. 125°/9 mm., *β-form* m.p. 119°, *ethyl ester* b.p. 137°/12 mm. (*G. Merling* and *R. Welde*, Ann., 1909, **366**, 141).

2:3-**Dimethylcyclohexan-4-one-1-carboxylic acid,** m.p. 132°, appears to be identical with the keto-acid obtained by the action of concentrated sulphuric acid on santenequinone (*R. N. Chakravarti*, J. Indian chem. Soc., 1944, **21**, 319).

1-*Phenylcyclohexan-4-one-1-carboxylic acid*, m.p. 119°, *oxime* m.p. 156°, *methyl ester* m.p. 77°, is obtained by Dieckmann cyclisation and subsequent hydrolysis of methyl γ-carbomethoxy-γ-phenylpimelate (*M. Rubin* and *H. Wishinsky*, J. Amer. chem. Soc., 1946, **68**, 828).

Ethyl 1-acetylcyclohexane-1-carboxylate, b.p. 245°, is obtained from pentamethylene dibromide and sodio-acetoacetic ester; alkaline hydrolysis furnishes acetylcyclohexane. The 2-methyl-homologue is similarly formed (*J. von Braun*, Ber., 1907, **40**, 3943; *P. C. Freer* and *W. H. Perkin*, Ber., 1888, **21**, 735).

Cyclohexan-2-one-1-acetic acid, m.p. 74°, is obtained by oxidation of the corresponding hydroxy-acid (p. 231). By treatment with acetic anhydride it forms the isomeric *lactones* (I) f.p. 31·2°, b.p. 136°/6 mm., and (II), f.p. −37·4°, b.p. 117°/6 mm. By heating with piperidine each of the pure isomers is equilibrated to 93% of (I). The isomers show a striking difference in chemical properties. Thus lactone (II) reacts with bromine, reduces silver nitrate and forms a *benzylidene* derivative, m.p. 168°, while lactone (I) undergoes none of these reactions. Catalytic hydrogenation of (I) produces the lactone of *cis*-cyclohexan-2-ol-1-acetic acid, while (II) under these conditions undergoes hydrogenolysis to cyclohexaneacetic acid (*M. S. Newman* and *C. A. VanderWerf*, J. Amer. chem. Soc., 1945, **67**, 233).

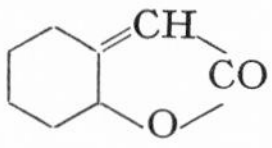

(I) Lactones of cyclohexan-2-one-1-acetic acid (II)

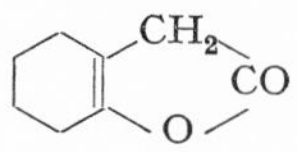

Cyclohexan-3-one-1-acetic acid, m.p. 81°, is obtained by the Michael addition of malonic ester to cyclohex-2-en-1-one followed by hydrolysis and decarboxylation (*P. D. Bartlett* and *G. F. Woods*, *ibid.*, 1940, **62**, 2933).

β-**Cyclohexan-2-one-1-propionic acid,** m.p. 65°, b.p. 180°/15 mm., is obtained by the condensation of ethyl β-chloropropionate with cyclohexanone in the presence of lithium (*C. D. Nenitzescu* and *V. Przemetzky*, Ber., 1941, **74**, 676) and by the interaction of diethyl malonate and 2-dimethylaminomethylcyclohexan-1-one in the presence of sodium ethoxide followed by hydrolysis and decarboxylation (*C. Mannich* and *W. Koch*, Ber., 1942, **75**, 803).

(ii) Ketocyclohexenecarboxylic acids

Cyclohex-3-en-2-one-1-carboxylic acid (*$\Delta^{1:3}$-dihydrosalicyclic acid*), readily decarboxylates on warming. It is obtained by treating cyclohex-2-en-1-one with sodium and carbon dioxide or by condensing the same ketone with diethyl oxalate followed by pyrolytic elimination of carbon monoxide and hydrolysis (*A. Kötz* and *T. Grethe*, J. pr. Chem., 1909, [ii], **80,** 506).

Cyclohex-6-en-2-one-1-carboxylic acid (*$\Delta^{2:6}$-dihydrosalicylic acid*) m.p. 128°, is obtained by hydrolysis of its *ethyl ester*, b.p. 103°/12 mm., which is formed by the aniline dehydrobromination of ethyl 1-bromocyclohexan-2-one-1-carboxylate. On being heated with soda-lime the acid decarboxylates forming cyclohex-2-en-1-one (*idem, ibid.*).

Ethyl 2-methylcyclohex-2-en-4-one-1-carboxylate (*"Hagemann's ester"*) b.p. 144°/15 mm., *semicarbazone* m.p. 167°, is best prepared by the condensation of formaldehyde with ethyl acetoacetate in the presence of piperidine, followed by selective decarbethoxylation with sodium ethoxide (*L. I. Smith* and *G. F. Rouault*, J. Amer. chem. Soc., 1943, **65,** 631; see also *E. Bergmann* and *A. Weizmann*, J. org. Chem., 1939, **4,** 266; for the course of the reaction and further refs. see p. 206). The ester is also formed by the interaction of sodio-acetoacetic ester and 1-diethylaminobutan-3-one (*C. Mannich* and *J. Fourneau*, Ber., 1938, **71,** 2090). Reaction of the ester with alkyl halides in the presence of sodium alkoxides has been shown to lead exclusively to the production of 3-substituted esters (*A. Kötz et al.*, Ber., 1911, **44,** 466; Ann., 1913, **400,** 77; *P. Rabe* and *E. Pollack*, Ber., 1912, **45,** 2926; *J. A. Hogg*, J. Amer. chem. Soc., 1948, **70,** 161). Hydrolysis and decarboxylation of the esters gives 3-methylcyclohex-2-en-1-one (p. 208). Homologous esters of the same type are prepared by analogous methods (*E. C. Horning et al.*, J. org. Chem., 1944, **9,** 547; Org. Synth., 1947, **27,** 24).

Ethyl 4-methylcyclohex-3-en-2-one-1-carboxylate, b.p. 141°/7 mm., *phenylhydrazone*, m.p. 123°, is obtained by the sulphuric acid cyclisation of ethyl α-(3-chlorocrotyl)acetoacetate (*O. Wichterle et al.*, Coll. Czech. chem. Comm., 1948, **13,** 300).

Ethyl 2:6:6-trimethylcyclohex-2-en-4-one-1-carboxylate (*ethyl isophoronecarboxylate*) b.p. 140°/10 mm., is produced by the reaction between ethyl sodioacetoacetate and ethyl *iso*propylideneacetoacetate. Hydrolysis leads to *iso*phorone and reduction gives a mixture of the stereoisomeric hydroxydihydrocyclogeranic acids (p. 230).

6-*Valerylcyclohex-1-ene-1-carboxylic acid* (*sedanonic acid*), m.p. 113°, occurs in celery oil (*G. Ciamician* and *P. Silber*, Ber., 1897, **30,** 503, 1419) and in the essential oil of the Chinese drug *Cnidium officinale* (*Y. Murayama* and *J. Hagaki*, Chem. Ztbl., 1923, III, 252).

Ethyl 5:5-dimethylcyclohex-1-en-3-one-1-acetate, b.p. 171°/22 mm., *semicarbazone* m.p. 157°, is produced by the condensation of 3-chlorocyclohex-2-en-1-one with ethyl sodiomalonate with concomitant elimination of one carbethoxy-group (*A. W. Crossley* and *C. Gilling*, J. chem. Soc., 1909, **95,** 19; cf. also *idem, ibid.*, 1910, 97, 526; *J. C. Bardhan et al., ibid.*, 1951, 3197).

For *methyl* 1-*methylcyclohex*-3-*ene*-2:4-*dione*-1-*carboxylate*, b.p. 69·5°/0·5 mm. and its use as a dienophile see *L. H. Sarett et al.*, J. Amer. chem. Soc., 1952, **74**, 1401.

(*d*) *Dicarboxylic acids*

(*i*) *Cyclohexanedicarboxylic acids*

Cyclohexane-1:1-dicarboxylic acid, m.p. 179·5° (dec.), *diamide*, m.p. 261°, is obtained by the hydrolysis of its ester, which is produced by the action of pentamethylene dibromide on sodiomalonic ester (*A. I. Vogel*, J. chem. Soc., 1929, **123**, 1487; *A. W. Dox* and *L. Yoder*, J. Amer. chem. Soc., 1921, **43**, 1366). The acid chloride is formed by the action of diphosgene at elevated temperature on cyclohexane or, better, on cyclohexanecarboxylic chloride (*M. S. Kharasch et al.*, *ibid.*, 1942, **64**, 2975). The free acid decarboxylates readily on being heated. Homologous acids of the same type are similarly prepared.

Cyclohexane-1:2-, 1:3- and 1:4-dicarboxylic acids (hexahydrophthalic acids) are most conveniently prepared by hydrogenation of the corresponding phthalic ester. They may also by obtained by the action of ethylene, trimethylene and tetramethylene dibromides on the sodio-derivatives of ethane-1:1:2:2-, propane-1:1:3:3- and butane-1:1:4:4-tetracarboxylic esters respectively followed by hydrolysis and decarboxylation (e.g. *L. Goldsworthy*, J. chem. Soc., 1931, 482). Both geometrical isomers of each of the acids are known.

Hydrogenation with Raney nickel at 175°/100 at. of methyl phthalate yields after hydrolysis a mixture of the cis- and trans-**cyclohexane**-1:2-**dicarboxylic acids** (*C. C. Price* and *M. Schwarcz*, J. Amer. chem. Soc., 1940, **62**, 2733). A similar mixture is also produced by the decarboxylation of cyclohexane-1:1:2:2-tetracarboxylic acid (*L. J. Goldsworthy*, *loc. cit.*). The pure cis-*acid*, m.p. 192°, *anhydride*, m.p. 32°, b.p. 145°/18 mm., is best prepared by the catalytic hydrogenation of *cis*-cyclohex-4-ene-1:2-dicarboxylic anhydride followed by hydrolysis (*E. F. Jenkins* and *E. J. Costello*, J. Amer. chem. Soc., 1946, **68**, 2733). It may also be obtained from the mixed acids by treatment with hot acetic anhydride whereby the pure *cis*-anhydride is formed. The pure trans-*acid*, m.p. 221°, *anhydride*, m.p. 143°, is obtained by hydrolysis of its *diethyl ester*, b.p. 135°/10 mm., which is prepared by treating the mixed esters with ethanolic potassium hydroxide (*C. C. Price* and *M. Schwarcz*, *loc. cit.*; see also *W. Hückel* and *E. Goth*, Ber., 1925, **58**, 449). The *trans*-acid is also formed by oxidation of decalin-1:3-dione (*G. A. R. Kon* and *M. Qudrat-I-Khuda*, J. chem. Soc., 1926, 3071).

The *cis*-acid is more soluble in water than the *trans*-isomer and is transformed into the latter by hot concentrated hydrochloric acid. The *trans*-acid has been resolved by means of its quinine salt into enantiomorphs, m.p. 179–183°, $[\alpha]_D$ ±18·5° (*A. Werner* and *H. E. Conrad*, Ber., 1899, **32**, 3046). The *cis*-acid, being a meso structure is non-resolvable, but its anilic acid is asymmetric and has been resolved via the cinchonidine salt (*R. Stoermer* and *H. J. Steinbeck*, Ber., 1932, **65**, 413). The *cis*-acid undergoes oxidative decarboxylation to cyclohexene when heated with lead dioxide (*W. von E. Doering et al.*, J. Amer. chem. Soc., 1952, **74**, 4370).

Cyclohexane-1:3-dicarboxylic acid *(hexahydroisophthalic acid)* may be obtained as a mixture of geometrical isomers by catalytic hydrogenation of dimethyl *iso*phthalate (*A. Skita* and *R. Rössler*, Ber., 1939, **72**, 265; *F. Ramirez* and *J. W. Sargent*, J. Amer. chem. Soc., 1952, **74**, 5785; *H. Smith* and *F. P. Byrne*, *ibid.*, 1950, **78**, 4406). The isomers are separated by the action of ammonia on the mixed calcium salts, that of the *cis*-acid being the less soluble.

The cis-*acid* has m.p. 167° and the trans-*isomer*, m.p. 150°; both acids by treatment with acetyl chloride give the cis-*anhydride*, m.p. 187°. The trans-*acid* has been resolved via the strychnine salt into the optical enantiomorphs, m.p. 134°, $[\alpha]_D \pm 23°$ (*J. Böeseken* and *A. E. J. Peek*, Rec. Trav. chim., 1925, **44**, 841).

Cyclohexane-1:4-dicarboxylic acid *(hexahydroterephthalic acid)* is obtained as a mixture of geometrical isomers by the catalytic hydrogenation of methyl terephthalate (*G. Wittig* and *H. Pook*, Ber., 1937, **70**, 2485; *F. Fichter* and *T. Holbro*, Helv., 1938, **21**, 141; *P. C. Guha* and *G. D. Hazra*, C.A., 1940, **34**, 2822). The *cis*-acid is also formed by the ozonolysis of bicyclo[2:2:2]oct-2-ene-2:3-dicarboxylic acid (*O. Diels* and *K. Alder*, Ann., 1930, **478**, 149) and by the degradation of dicyclohexadiene (p. 348). The isomers may be separated by treatment with chloroform in which the *cis*-acid is soluble, the *trans*-acid remaining undissolved.

The cis-*acid* has m.p. 171°, *dimethyl ester*, m.p. 5°, b.p. 132°/10 mm. and the trans-*acid*, m.p. 309°, *dimethyl ester*, m.p. 71°; the *cis*-isomer is converted to the *trans* by the action of hot concentrated hydrochloric acid.

(ii) Cyclohexenedicarboxylic acids

The cyclohexene-1:2-dicarboxylic acids (tetrahydrophthalic acids) were first investigated in detail by *A. von Baeyer* (Ann., 1890, **258**, 145; 1892, **269**, 145; hereafter referred to as refs. 1 and 2 respectively) and his conclusions have been corrected and amplified by *K. Alder* and *M. Schumacher* (Ann., 1949, **564**, 96; hereafter termed ref. 3).

CO_2H CO_2H (I) CO_2H CO_2H (II) CO_2H CO_2H (III) CO_2H CO_2H (IV)

Cyclohex-1-ene-1:2-dicarboxylic acid (Δ^1-*tetrahydrophthalic acid*, I), m.p. 120°, is obtained as its *anhydride*, m.p. 74°, by melting cyclohex-2-ene-1:2-dicarboxylic acid or by heating this latter acid with acetic anhydride (refs. 1, 3). The anhydride is also formed by the pyrolytic dehydration of cyclohexan-1-ol-1:2-dicarboxylic acid (*W. Hückel* and *U. Lampert*, Ber., 1934, **67**, 1811). A method of formation which confirm its structure involves the partial catalytic hydrogenation of cyclohexa-1:4-diene-1:2-dicarboxylic acid or anhydride (ref. 3; *K. Alder* and *K. H. Backendorf*, Ber., 1938, **71**, 2199).

Cyclohex-2-ene-1:2-dicarboxylic acid (*Δ^2-tetrahydrophthalic acid*, II), m.p. 215°, *anhydride*, m.p. 79°, is the main product of the sodium amalgam reduction of phthalic acid or of cyclohexa-2:6-diene-1:2-dicarboxylic acid (ref. 1). A more convenient preparation involves the electrochemical reduction of phthalic acid (*F. Fichter* and *C. Simon*, Helv., 1934, **17**, 1218; see also *G. A. R. Kon* and *B. L. Nandi*, J. chem. Soc., 1933, 1631). It is also formed by the alkali-induced isomerisation of the Δ^1-acid (refs. 1, 3) and by the partial catalytic hydrogenation of cyclohexa-2:4-diene-1:2-dicarboxylic acid (ref. 3).

The two geometrical isomers of **cyclohex-3-ene-1:2-dicarboxylic acid** (*Δ^3-tetrahydrophthalic acid*, III) were first obtained by the high temperature sodium amalgam reduction of cyclohexa-2:6-diene-1:2-dicarboxylic acid (ref. 1). Baeyer regarded them as the Δ^4-acids but this was disproved by their unequivocal synthesis from butadiene-1-carboxylic acid and acrylic acid (*K. Alder et al.*, Ann., 1949, **564**, 79). This procedure gives the cis-*acid*, m.p. 174°, *anhydride*, m.p. 59° at room temperature but at higher temperatures a considerable quantity of the trans-*acid*, m.p. 218°, *anhydride*, m.p. 140°, is formed; the acids are separated by fractional crystallisation from ethyl acetate.

The *anhydride*, m.p. 104°, of cis-**cyclohex-4-ene-1:2-dicarboxylic acid** (*Δ^4-tetrahydrophthalic acid*, IV), m.p. 166°, is very readily obtained by the diene synthesis employing butadiene and maleic anhydride (ref. 3; *O. Diels* and *K. Alder*, Ann., 1928, **460**, 113; *E. F. Jenkins* and *E. J. Costello*, J. Amer. chem. Soc., 1946, **68**, 2733). The trans-*acid*, m.p. 172°, *anhydride*, m.p. 188°, is obtained by the interaction of butadiene and fumaryl chloride followed by hydrolysis of the adduct (ref. 3); employment of fumaronitrile in like manner furnishes the trans-*dinitrile*, m.p. 125° (*K. Ziegler et al.*, Ann., 1942, **551**, 1). Homologous acids of the same type are obtained by the condensation of substituted maleic anhydrides with substituted butadienes (*O. Diels* and *K. Alder*, Ber., 1929, **62**, 2087; *K. Ziegler et al., loc. cit.*).

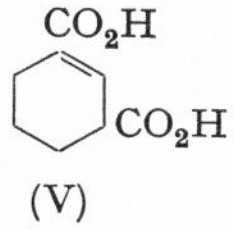

CO_2H / CO_2H (V) CO_2H / CO_2H (VI) CO_2H / CO_2H (VII)

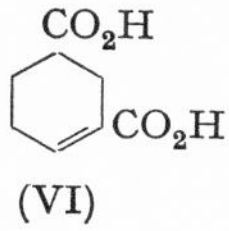

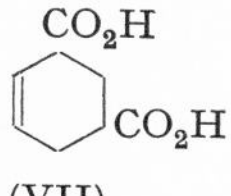

Cyclohex-1-ene-1:3-dicarboxylic acid (*Δ^1-tetrahydro*iso*phthalic acid*, V), m.p. 198°, is obtained by the dehydration of cyclohexan-2-ol-1:3-dicarboxylic acid with thionyl chloride and pyridine; it is not formed by the reduction of *iso*phthalic acid (*G. A. R. Kon* and *B. L. Nandi*, J. chem. Soc., 1933, 1628).

Cyclohex-3-ene-1:3-dicarboxylic acid (*Δ^3-tetrahydro*iso*phthalic acid*, VI), m.p. 244°, is obtained by the alkali-induced isomerisation of the Δ^4-acid.

cis-**Cyclohex-4-ene-1:3-dicarboxylic acid** (*$\Delta^{4(5)}$-tetrahydro*iso*phthalic acid*, VII), m.p. 165°, is the main product of the sodium amalgam reduction of iso*phthalic acid* (*W. H. Perkin* and *S. S. Pickles*, J. chem. Soc., 1905, **87**, 293; *E. H. Farmer* and *H. L. Richardson*, *ibid.*, 1926, 2172; 1927, 59); the *trans*-isomer is as yet unknown.

All the three tetrahydro*iso*phthalic acids give the same *anhydride*, m.p. 78°, of the cis-Δ^4-*acid* (for the bearing of Bredt's rule on this anhydride see *F. S. Fawcett*, Chem. Reviews, 1950, **47**, 256).

CO_2H CO_2H

CO_2H CO_2H

(VIII) (IX)

Cyclohex-2-ene-1:4-dicarboxylic acid (Δ^2-*tetrahydroterephthalic acid*, VIII) is obtained as a mixture of the geometrical isomers, cis-, m.p. 161°, trans-, m.p. 228° by the sodium amalgam reduction of either cyclohexa-1:3- or 1:5-diene-1:4-dicarboxylic acid (*A. von Baeyer*, Ann., 1889, **251**, 273). The *cis*-acid is much more soluble in water than the *trans*-isomer. The configurations have been confirmed by the resolution of the *trans*-acid (*W. H. Mills* and *G. H. Keats*, J. chem. Soc., 1935, 1373).

Cyclohex-1-ene-1:4-dicarboxylic acid (Δ^1-*tetrahydroterephthalic acid*, IX) subliming over 300°, is produced by heating the Δ^2-acid with alkali (*A. von Baeyer, loc. cit.*).

(iii) Cyclohexadienedicarboxylic acids

Six structurally isomeric cyclohexadiene-1:2-dicarboxylic acids are theoretically possible all of which are known, two only in the form of their anhydrides.

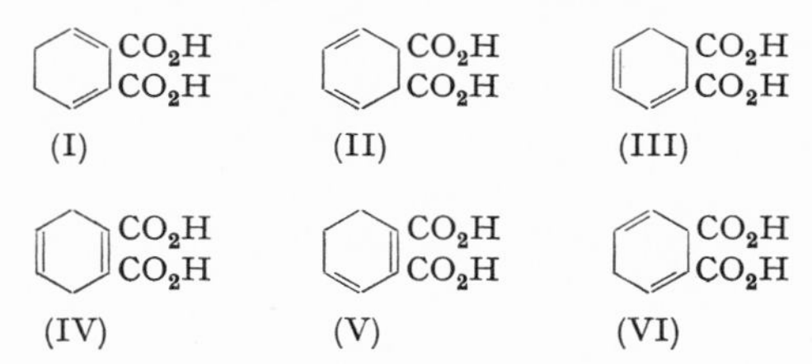

(I) (II) (III)

(IV) (V) (VI)

Cyclohexa-2:6-diene-1:2-dicarboxylic acid ($\Delta^{2:6}$-*dihydrophthalic acid*, I), m.p. 215°, *anhydride*, m.p. 83°, is obtained by the sodium amalgam reduction of phthalic acid in alkaline solution (*A. von Baeyer*, Ann., 1892, **269**, 152, 194). It is also formed by the alkali-induced isomerisation of the $\Delta^{2:4}$- and $\Delta^{3:5}$-acids. The *monoethyl ester*, m.p. 122°, is very conveniently prepared by the electrolytic reduction of potassium ethyl phthalate (*V. M. Rodionov* and *V. K. Zworykina*, Bull. Soc. chim. Fr., 1938, [v], **5**, 840).

trans-**Cyclohexa-3:5-diene-1:2-dicarboxylic acid** ($\Delta^{3:5}$-*dihydrophthalic acid*, II), m.p. 210°, is produced by the sodium amalgam reduction of phthalic acid in acetic acid solution and by electrolytic reduction (*C. Mettler*, Ber., 1906, **39**, 2941). Its configuration has been confirmed by its resolution (*A. Neville*, J. chem. Soc., 1906, **89**, 1744). Electrolysis of the sodium salt produces benzene (*E. A. Pasquinelli*, C.A., 1944, **38**, 5734). The acid is converted to the $\Delta^{2:6}$-isomer by treatment with hot alkali. Heating the *trans*-acid with acetic anhydride produces the *anhydride*, m.p. 99°, of the cis-*isomer*, m.p. 174°.

Cyclohexa-2:4-**diene**-1:2-**dicarboxylic acid** ($\Delta^{2:4}$-*dihydrophthalic acid*, III), m.p. 179° is obtained by the dehydrobromination of the $\Delta^{2:6}$-acid dihydrobromide with alcoholic potassium hydroxide. The acid is also produced by heating 3-acetoxycyclohex-4-ene-1:2-dicarboxylic anhydride (formed by interaction of 1-acetoxybutadiene and maleic anhydride) with concentrated hydrochloric acid (*W. Flaig*, Ann., 1950, **568**, 33). The action of acetic anhydride gives the *anhydride*, m.p. 103°.

Cyclohexa-1:4-**diene**-1:2-**dicarboxylic acid** ($\Delta^{1:4}$-*dihydrophthalic acid*, IV), m.p. 153°, *anhydride*, m.p. 147°, is formed by heating the $\Delta^{2:4}$-acid with acetic anhydride. A more convenient preparation of the acid is achieved by the Diels-Alder reaction between butadiene and acetylenedicarboxylic acid (*K. Alder* and *K. H. Backendorf*, Ber., 1938, **71**, 2199).

The *anhydride*, m.p. 59°, of **cyclohexa**-1:3-**diene**-1:2-**dicarboxylic acid** ($\Delta^{1:3}$-*dihydrophthalic acid*, V) is obtained by fractional crystallisation of the anhydride mixture produced by heating the crude product from the sodium amalgam reduction of sodium phthalate (*G. Abati et al.*, Gazz., 1906, **36**, 824, 834, 838, 848).

The *anhydride*, m.p. 74°, of **cyclohexa**-2:5-**diene**-1:2-**dicarboxylic acid** ($\Delta^{2:5}$-*dihydrophthalic acid*, VI) is produced by heating the $\Delta^{1:3}$-anhydride to 230° (*G. Abati et al.*, Chem. Ztbl., 1907, I, 886).

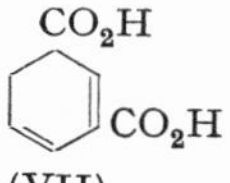

(VII) 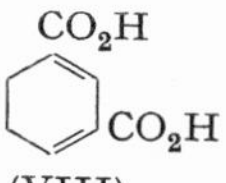 (VIII)

Cyclohexa-2:4-**diene**-1:3-**dicarboxylic acid** ($\Delta^{2:4}$-*dihydro*iso*phthalic acid*, VII), m.p. 255°, is formed by the dehydrobromination of 3:4-dibromocyclohexane-1:3-dicarboxylic acid (*W. H. Perkin* and *S. S. Pickles*, J. chem. Soc., 1905, **87**, 310).

Cyclohexa-1:3-**diene**-1:3-**dicarboxylic acid** ($\Delta^{1:3}$-*dihydro*iso*phthalic acid*, VIII), m.p. above 270°, is obtained by the dehydrobromination of 1:3-dibromocyclohexane-1:3-dicarboxylic acid (*W. Goodwin* and *W. H. Perkin*, *ibid.*, 1905, **87**, 853).

All the theoretically possible cyclohexadiene-1:4-dicarboxylic acids are known. They are solids melting at an indefinite temperature with the formation of terephthalic acid.

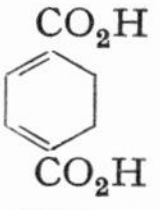

(IX) 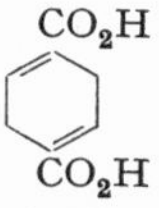 (X) 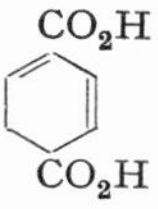 (XI) 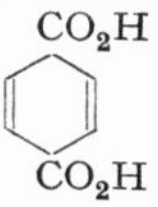 (XII)

Cyclohexa-1:3-**diene**-1:4-**dicarboxylic acid** ($\Delta^{1:3}$-*dihydroterephthalic acid*, IX), *dimethyl ester*, m.p. 85°, is obtained by the dehydrobromination of 1:4- or 2:3-

dibromocyclohexane-1:4-dicarboxylic acid (*A. von Baeyer*, Ann., 1889, **251**, 257; 1890, **258**, 1; *P. C. Guha* and *G. D. Hazra*, C.A., 1940, **34**, 2822).

Cyclohexa-1:4-diene-1:4-dicarboxylic acid ($\Delta^{1:4}$-*dihydroterephthalic acid*, X), *dimethyl ester*, m.p. 130°, is one of the products of the sodium amalgam reduction of terephthalic acid and is also formed by the alkali-induced isomerisation of the other cyclohexadiene-1:4-dicarboxylic acids (*A. von Baeyer, loc. cit.*). It may also be obtained by the dehalogenation of 2:5-*dichlorocyclohexa*-1:4-*diene*-1:4-*dicarboxylic acid*, m.p. 275°, with sodium amalgam (*S. Levy* and *A. Curchod*, Ber., 1889, **22**, 2112). The acid condenses with benzaldehyde to produce benzylterephthalic acid.

Cyclohexa-1:5-diene-1:4-dicarboxylic acid ($\Delta^{1:5}$-*dihydroterephthalic acid*, XI) is formed by the partial alkali-induced isomerisation of cyclohexa-2:5-diene-1:4-dicarboxylic acid (*A. von Baeyer, loc. cit.*).

A mixture of the geometrical isomers of **cyclohexa-2:5-diene-1:4-dicarboxylic acid** ($\Delta^{2:5}$-*dihydroterephthalic acid*, XII), trans-*dimethyl ester*, m.p. 77°, is obtained as one of the reduction products of terephthalic acid. On being heated with palladium black the ester disproportionates to methyl terephthalate and cyclohexane-1:4-dicarboxylate.

(iv) Exocyclic hydroaromatic dicarboxylic acids

In this group are included dicarboxylic acids in which one or both of the carboxyl groups are not attached to the cyclohexane nucleus. Acids of this type are very numerous and only a few members are discussed in detail.

Cyclohexylmalonic acid, m.p. 177°, decomposes on being heated into carbon dioxide and cyclohexylacetic acid. The acid is obtained by hydrolysis of the *ethyl ester*, b.p. 164°/20 mm., which is procured by the condensation of iodocyclohexane with ethyl sodiomalonate (*G. S. Hiers* and *R. Adams*, J. Amer. chem. Soc., 1926, **48**, 2385; *I. Vogel*, J. chem. Soc., 1928, 2023) or by the catalytic hydrogenation of ethyl cyclohexenylmalonate. Alkylation, hydrolysis and decarboxylation of the ester furnishes homologues of the acid (*R. B. Moffett et al.*, J. Amer. chem. Soc., 1947, **69**, 1854; see also *F. D. Gunstone* and *R. M. Heggie*, J. chem. Soc., 1952, 1354).

A series of cyclohexenylmalonic esters has been prepared by *R. B. Moffett et al. (loc. cit.)*; thus *ethyl cyclohexenylmalonate*, b.p. 87/0·1 mm., is obtained from 1:2-dibromocyclohexane and ethyl sodiomalonate.

Ethyl cyclohexylmethylmalonate, b.p. 136°/3 mm., and higher homologues are obtained by reaction of ethyl sodiomalonate with the relevant cyclohexylalkyl halide (*G. S. Hiers* and *R. Adams*, J. Amer. chem. Soc., 1926, **48**, 2385).

Cyclohexane-1-carboxylic-1-acetic acid, m.p. 133°, is obtained by the hypobromite oxidation of spiro[5:4]decane-1:3-dione (*C. K. Ingold et al.*, J. chem. Soc., 1923, **123**, 853). Homologues are described by *R. F. Hunter et al.* (*ibid.*, 1936, 416). The 4-methyl-homologue is produced by the action of potassium cyanide on 4-methylcyclohexylidenecyanoacetic ester followed by hydrolysis of the product; it is also obtainable by the oxidation of 4-methylcyclohexane-1-acetic-1-glyoxylic acid (*R. D. Desai, ibid.*, 1932, 1058). Claims that this acid exists in isomeric forms corresponding to the "boat" and "chair" forms of the cyclohexane nucleus have been refuted by later work (*S. Goldschmidt* and *E. Gräfinger*, Ber., 1935, **68**, 279; *R. F. Hunter et al.*, J. chem. Soc., 1936, 416).

Cyclohexane-1-carboxylic-2-acetic acid, cis- m.p. 146°, trans- m.p. 157°, is obtained by the catalytic hydrogenation of homophthalic acid; the *trans*-acid may be prepared by the Michael addition of diethyl malonate to ethyl cyclohex-1-ene-1-carboxylate followed by hydrolysis (*E. J. Boorman* and *R. P. Linstead*, J. chem. Soc., 1935, 258). The individual acids are also formed by the oxidation of *cis*- and *trans*-β-hydrindanone (see p. 320).

1-Methylcyclohexane-1-carboxylic-2-acetic acid, cis- m.p. 163°, trans- m.p. 175°, is obtained by the catalytic hydrogenation of *2-carboxy-2-methylcyclohexylideneacetic acid,* α-isomer m.p. 103·5°, β-form m.p. 170·5°, which is itself prepared by a Reformatsky reaction between 2-carboethoxy-2-methylcyclohexan-1-one and ethyl bromoacetate (*W. E. Bachmann* and *S. Kushner*, J. Amer. chem. Soc., 1943, **65**, 1963; *R. P. Linstead et al.*, J. chem. Soc., 1936, 470, 1937, 1140).

Cyclohexane-1-carboxylic-3-acetic acid, cis- m.p. 159°, *diamide* m.p. 286° (decomp.), trans- m.p. 134°, is obtained by the Arndt-Eistert homologation of the corresponding cyclohexane-1:3-dicarboxylic acid monomethyl ester (*F. Ramirez* and *J. W. Sargent*, J. Amer. chem. Soc., 1952, **74**, 5785). The *cis*-acid is also obtained by the catalytic hydrogenation of homo*iso*phthalic acid; distillation of its calcium salt gives bicyclo[3:2:1]octan-2-one (*G. Komppa et al.*, Ber., 1903, **36**, 3610; Ann., 1936, **521**, 242).

Cyclohexane-1-carboxylic-2-propionic acids, cis- m.p. 103°, trans- m.p. 143°, are obtained by the catalytic hydrogenation of hydrocinnamic-*o*-carboxylic acid and also by the oxidation of *cis*- and *trans*-β-decalone (p. 326). Heating with acetic anhydride converts both isomers into α-hydrindanone (*W. Hückel* and *E. Goth*, Ber., 1925, **58**, 449). cis-*Cyclohexane-1-carboxylic-2-butyric acid,* m.p. 94°, is formed by the catalytic hydrogenation of phenylene-1-carboxylic-2-butyric acid; hot hydrochloric acid converts it into the trans-*isomer,* m.p. 94°. Both isomers yield *trans*-α-decalone by cyclisation with acetic anhydride (*W. Hückel et al.*, Ber., 1923, **56**, 95; 1924, **57**, 1285; Ann., 1925, **441**, 37).

Cyclohexane-1:1-diacetic acid, m.p. 181°, is prepared by hydrolysis of the Guareschi imide obtained from cyclohexanone, ethyl cyanoacetate and ammonia (*A. I. Vogel et al.*, J. chem. Soc., 1934, 1758). It is also obtained by the addition of cyanoacetamide to cyclohex-1-enylacetonitrile followed by hydrolysis of the adduct (*S. F. Birch* and *G. A. R. Kon*, *ibid.*, 1923, **123**, 2440).

cis-**Cyclohexane-1:2-diacetic acid,** m.p. 163°, *anhydride* m.p. 52°, is obtained by catalytic hydrogenation of *o*-phenylenediacetic acid or by permanganate oxidation of *cis*-β-decalone and *cis*-Δ^2-octalin. The trans-*isomer,* m.p. 167°, *anhydride* m.p. 79°, is obtained by similar oxidation of the corresponding *trans*-compounds; its configuration is proved by its resolution into the optical enantiomorphs, m.p. 151° (*W. Hückel et al.*, Ann., 1927, **451**, 140, 159). Cyclisation of the two acids yields the corresponding *cis*- and *trans*-β-hydrindanone. **Cyclohexane-1-acetic-2-propionic acid,** cis- m.p. 109°, trans- m.p. 116°, is similarly obtained from phenylene-1-acetic-2-propionic acid; ring closure yields the *cis-* and *trans-β*-decalones (*W. Hückel* and *E. Goth*, Ber., 1925, **58**, 449).

Cyclohex-1-ene-1:2-diacetic acid, m.p. 122°, is obtained by the interaction of ethyl 1:2-dibromocyclohexane-1-acetate and ethyl sodiomalonate followed by hydrolysis (*J. W. Baker*, J. chem. Soc., 1925, **127**, 985).

Cyclohexylsuccinic acid, m.p. 150°, *anhydride* m.p. 42°, *imide* m.p. 164°, is obtained by the action of ethyl bromoacetate on ethyl cyclohexylcyanoacetate followed by hydrolysis (*R. D. Desai* and *G. S. Sahariya*, Brit. chem. Abstr., 1941, AII, 100).

The Stobbe condensation of cyclohexanone with diethyl succinate yields the *half-ester*, b.p. 156°/0·5 mm., of **cyclohex-1-enylsuccinic acid**; hydrolysis yields the free *acid*, m.p. 146°, together with the isomeric *cyclohexylidenesuccinic acid*, m.p. 180° (decomp.) (*W. S. Johnson et al.*, J. Amer. chem. Soc., 1948, **70**, 3021).

Addition of maleic anhydride to methylenecyclohexane followed by hydrolysis yields *cyclohex-1-enylmethylsuccinic acid*, the structure being established by permanganate oxidation (*R. T. Arnold* and *J. F. Dowdall*, *ibid.*, 1948, **70**, 2590).

(v) Hydroxycyclohexanedicarboxylic acids

Cyclohexan-1-ol-1:2-dicarboxylic acid, m.p. 130°, is formed by the hydrolysis of the cyanohydrin of cyclohexan-1-one-2-carboxylic acid (*W. Hückel* and *U. Lampert*, Ber., 1934, **67**, 1811). **Cyclohexan-1-ol-1:4-dicarboxylic acid,** cis- m.p. 169°, trans- m.p. 229°, is similarly obtained (*A. von Baeyer*, Ber., 1889, **22**, 2186; *W. H. Perkin*, J. chem. Soc., 1904, **85**, 421).

Cyclohexane-1:3-diol-1:3-dicarboxylic acid, m.p. 217° (dec.), *anhydride* m.p. 175°, is produced by the hydrolysis of the dicyanohydrin of cyclohexane-1:3-dione (*G. Merling*, Ann., 1894, **278**, 49). **Cyclohexane-1:4-diol-1:4-dicarboxylic acid,** m.p. 122°, is similarly obtained from the *dicyanohydrin*, m.p. 180° (dec.), of cyclohexane-1:4-dione (*N. D. Zelinsky*, Ber., 1907, **40**, 2890).

The *ethyl ester*, m.p. 136°, of **cyclohexane-2:5-diol-1:4-dicarboxylic acid** is formed by the sodium amalgam reduction of ethyl cyclohexane-2:5-dione-1:4-dicarboxylate (*R. Stollé*, Ber., 1900, **33**, 390).

The condensation of furan with maleic anhydride produces 3:6-*epoxycyclohex-4-ene-1:2-dicarboxylic anhydride*, m.p. 125°, which on catalytic hydrogenation furnishes the *anhydride*, m.p. 117°, of 3:6-**epoxycyclohexane-1:2-dicarboxylic acid,** *monohydrate* m.p. 123° (*O. Diels* and *K. Alder*, Ber., 1929, **62**, 554).

A naturally-occurring compound of this type, cantharidin, is contained in the genital glands of the so-called Spanish flies, which are really beetles of the genera *Lytta* and *Meloe* (*W. C. Colledge*, Pharm. J., 1910, **30**, 647; cf. *C. van Zijp*, Pharm. Weekbl., 1917, **54**, 295; 1922, **59**, 285; *F. Stern*, Chem. Ztbl., 1932, II, 557). It has vesicant properties and is a powerful kidney poison (*A. Ellinger*, Arch. Exp. Path., 1908, **58**, 424; *G. Forni*, Chem. Ztbl., 1915, I, 323). The oestrogenic action reported to be produced by subcutaneous injection (*F. Stern*, Arch. Exp. Path., 1932, **166**, 395) is probably due to the presence of traces of sex hormones.

Cantharidin, $C_{10}H_{12}O_4$, m.p. 218°, has been shown by titration to be an anhydride (*imide* m.p. 194°; *hydrazide* m.p. 118°) (*P. W. Danckwortt,* Arch. Pharm., 1914, **252,** 663; *H. Meyer,* Monatsh., 1897, **18,** 393; *J. Gadamer,* Arch. Pharm., 1922, **260,** 199) and on hydrolysis yields the dibasic *cantharidinic acid, dimethyl ester* m.p. 91° (*B. Homolka,* Ber., 1886, **19,** 1082); the fourth oxygen atom of the molecule is present as an ether group. Thermal degradation of cantharidin with phosphorus pentasulphide gives *o*-xylene whilst soda-lime distillation produces dihydro-*o*-xylene (*cantharene*) (*J. Piccard,* Ber., 1877, **10,** 1504; 1878, **11,** 2122; 1879, **12,** 577; 1886, **19,** 1404; *J. Gadamer,* Arch. Pharm., 1917, **255,** 315). Elimination of the ether oxygen via the dibromide $C_{10}H_{12}O_3Br_2$ produces *deoxycantharidinic acid,* $C_{10}H_{14}O_4$, m.p. 160–164°, which is readily converted to *deoxycantharidin* (I) $C_{10}H_{12}O_3$, m.p. 129° (*J. Gadamer,* Arch. Pharm., 1917, **255,** 290; 1914, **252,** 636; *S. Coffey,* Rec. trav. chim., 1923, **42,** 387, 1026). The structure of this latter compound as the *anhydride* of 1:2-*dimethylcyclohexane*-1:2-*dicarboxylic acid* has been demonstrated by its total synthesis from dimethylmaleic anhydride and butadiene followed by hydrogenation (*R. B. Woodward* and *R. B. Loftfield,* J. Amer. chem. Soc., 1941, **63,** 3167).

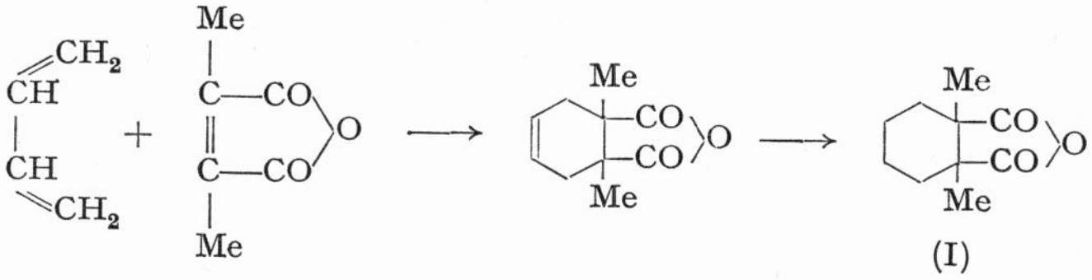

(I)

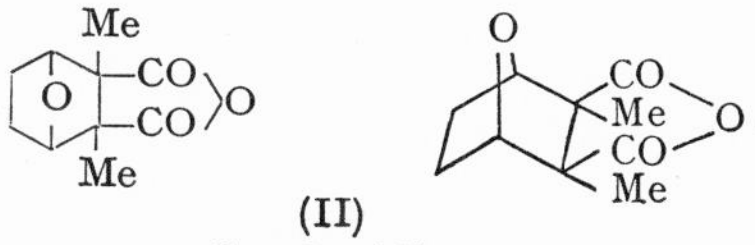

(II)
Cantharidin

The above reactions strongly suggest that cantharidin is 3:6-*epoxy*-1:2-*dimethyl*-1:2-*dicarboxylic anhydride* (II) and this receives convincing support from the catalytic fission of the compound with palladium at 280°, which leads, via dehydrocantharidin, to furan and dimethylmaleic anhydride (*F. von Bruchhausen* and *H. W. Bersch,* Arch. Pharm., 1928, **266,** 697). All attempts to reverse this reaction and to synthesise cantharidin by a Diels-Alder reaction between furan and dimethylmaleic anhydride followed by hydrogenation have ended in failure; the equilibrium furan + dimethylmaleic anhydride ⇄ dehydrocantharidin lies completely on the side of the cleavage products at the temperature required for addition. Even if condensation did occur the adduct would probably assume the endo-configuration and it has been shown that cantharidin possesses the *exo*-configuration (II) (*R. B. Woodward* and *R. B. Loftfield, loc cit.*).

The total synthesis of cantharidin was eventually achieved from dimethylmaleic anhydride and 1:3-cyclohexadiene as shown in the following flow-sheet (*K. Ziegler, G. Schenk* and *E. W. Krockow,* Ann., 1942, **551,** 1).

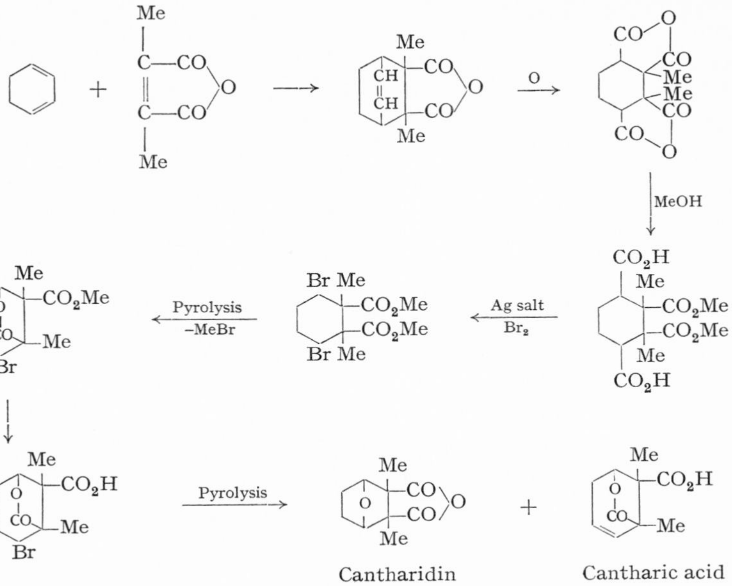

Cantharidin

Cantharic acid

The final remarkable pyrolysis stage furnishes only a small yield of cantharidin, the bulk of the product being *cantharic acid* m.p. 276°; this latter compound may be obtained from cantharidin by the action of bromine or chlorosulphonic acid (*H. Meyer*, Monatsh., 1898, **19**, 707; *J. Gadamer et al.*, Arch. Pharm., 1920, **258**, 171; 1922, **260**, 172).

A later attempt to render the synthesis stereospecific was unsuccessful (*K. Ziegler et al.*, Ann., 1950, **567**, 204) but this goal has now been achieved by the following most elegant process (*G. Stork et al.*, J. Amer. chem. Soc., 1951, **73**, 4501; 1953, **75**, 384).

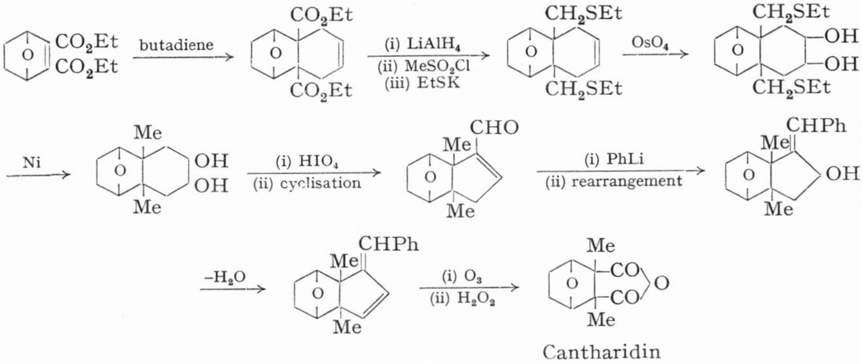

Cantharidin

(vi) Ketocyclohexanedicarboxylic acids

Cyclohexan-2-one-1:4-dicarboxylic acid, m.p. 120° (dec.) is obtained by the reduction of hydroxyterephthalic acid. It readily decarboxylates on being warmed with the formation of cyclohexan-1-one-3-carboxylic acid (*A. von Baeyer*, Ber., 1889, **22,** 2187).

Ethyl cyclohexan-6-one-1:3-dicarboxylate, b.p. 180°/20 mm., is formed by the Dieckmann cyclisation of ethyl pentane-1:3:5-tricarboxylate (*F. W. Kay* and *W. H. Perkin,* J. chem. Soc., 1906, **89,** 1640). *Ethyl cyclohexan-2-one-1:3-dicarboxylate,* keto form m.p. 88°, enol form b.p. 160°/12 mm., is similarly obtained from ethyl pentane-1:1:5:5-tetracarboxylate (*M. I. Ushakov,* C.A., 1929, **23,** 4678) and also by the condensation of trimethylene dibromide with ethyl acetonedicarboxylate in the presence of magnesium (*P. C. Guha* and *N. K. Seshadriengar,* Chem. Ztbl., 1935, II, 3906). Homologous esters are obtained in analogous fashion (*R. N. Chakravarti,* J. Indian chem. Soc., 1944, **21,** 319).

Homologous **cyclohex-2-en-1-one-4:6-dicarboxylic esters** are intermediates in the preparation of cyclohex-2-en-1-ones by the cyclisation of alkylidene-bisacetic esters (see p. 206) and have been isolated in some cases, e.g. *ethyl 3:5-dimethylcyclohex-2-en-1-one-4:6-dicarboxylate,* b.p. 190°/19 mm., 2:4-*dinitrophenyl hydrazone* m.p. 127° (*E. C. Horning et al.,* J. org. Chem., 1944, **9,** 547).

Cyclohexane-2:5-dione-1:4-dicarboxylic acid *(succinosuccinic acid)* is obtained by the careful alkaline hydrolysis of the ester; it is readily decarboxylated by heat to cyclohexane-1:4-dione (*A. von Baeyer* and *W. A. Noyes,* Ber., 1889, **22,** 2168). The *diethyl ester (succinosuccinic ester),* m.p. 126°, is readily preparable by the self-condensation of diethyl succinate in the presence of basic catalysts such as the alkali metals, their alkoxides, ammonia or secondary amines (*H. Liebermann,* Ann., 1914, **404,** 272; Org. Reactions, 1942, **1,** 283); other methods of formation include the reaction of basic catalysts with ethyl γ-halogenoaceto-acetate (*F. Herrmann,* Ann., 1882, **211,** 306; *W. Mewes,* Ann., 1888, **245,** 74; *R. Schönbrodt,* Ann., 1889, **253,** 182), and the reduction of ethyl 2:5-dihydroxy-terephthalate (*A. von Baeyer,* Ber., 1886, **19,** 432; *M. Sommelet* and *P. Couroux,* Bull. Soc. chim. Fr., 1921, [iv], **29,** 402). The compound behaves as a typical β-keto-ester and is strongly enolised. Thus it is readily soluble in aqueous alkalis to form canary-yellow salts and the disodio-derivative may be alkylated in the usual fashion with alkyl halides to form e.g. the 1:4-*diethyl derivative,* trans-, m.p. 65°, cis- a liquid. The ester is sparingly soluble in water and ether but dissolves readily in alcohol to give a blue fluorescent solution which gives a cherry-red colouration with ferric chloride. The extraordinary stability of the ester has prompted the suggestion that its structure is that of a "rigid *cis*-dienol", i.e. a cyclohexa-1:4-diene-2:5-diol-1:4-dicarboxylic ester in which hydrogen bonding occurs between the hydroxyl and ester groups (I) (*A. Hantzsch,* Ber., 1915, **48,** 772). As expected the ester reacts with ammonia to give the *diketimine,* represented as 2:5-*diaminocyclohexa*-1:4-*diene*-1:4-*dicarboxylic ester* (II), m.p. 178° and with hydrazine to yield the bispyrazolonocyclohexane. With hydroxylamine, however, the ester is oxidised and decarboxylated to form ethyl quinonedioximecarboxylate (*A. Jeanrenaud*, Ber., 1889, **22**, 1283). With ethyl orthoformate and acetic anhydride the ester yields *ethyl 1:4-di (diethoxymethyl)-cyclohexane-2:5-dione-1:4-dicarboxylate*, (III), m.p. 89° (*S. N. Naumova et al.*, Brit. chem. Abstr., 1940, AII, 47).

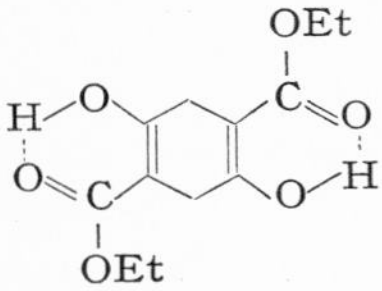

(I) 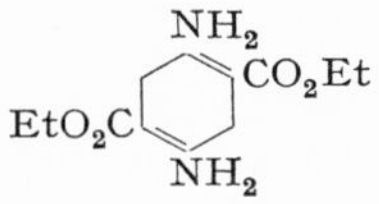 (II) 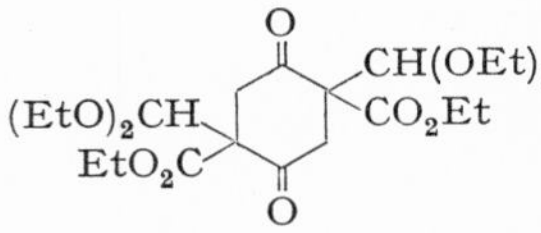 (III)

Ethyl cyclohexane-2:3-dione-1:4-dicarboxylate is obtained by the Claisen condensation of ethyl oxalate with ethyl adipate. With sodium ethoxide the ester undergoes ring contraction to give a cyclopentane derivative (p. 17). Hydrolysis with dilute sulphuric acid gives cyclohexane-1:2-dione. Bromination gives the 1-*bromo*-, m.p. 52°, and 1:4-*dibromo*-derivative, m.p. 86°, both of which aromatise on being heated *in vacuo*. With methyl iodide the sodio-derivative yields the 1-*methyl*-homologue, m.p. 50°, *oxime*, m.p. 48°; no dimethyl-derivative seems to be formed (*S. N. Naumova* and *L. S. Dedusenko*, Brit. chem. Abstr., 1940, AII, 47).

Methyl cyclohexane-3:6-dione-1:2-dicarboxylate, m.p. 57°, is obtained by the reduction of methyl 3:6-dihydroxyphthalate (*B. Helferich*, Ber., 1921, **54**, 155).

Methyl 1-methylcyclohex-3-en-2:4-dione-1:3-dicarboxylate, m.p. 75°, and -1:4-*dicarboxylate*, m.p. 43°, have been used as dienophiles (*R. E. Beyler* and *L. H. Sarett*, J. Amer. chem. Soc., 1952, **74**, 1397).

(e) Polycarboxylic acids

(i) Tricarboxylic acids

Methyl cyclohexane-1:3:5-tricarboxylate, b.p. 164°/2·5 mm., is obtained by the catalytic hydrogenation of methyl trimesate (*R. C. Fuson* and *C. H. McKeever*, J. Amer. chem. Soc., 1940, **62**, 2088).

1^t:3^t-**Dimethylcyclohexane**-1^c:2^t:3^c-**tricarboxylic acid,** m.p. 218° (dec.), *trimethyl ester*, m.p. 74·5°, is obtained by the nitric acid oxidation of abietic acid (for the most convenient method see *D. H. R. Barton* and *G. A. Schmeidler*, J. chem. Soc., 1948, 1197; 1949, S 232). The action of heat, acetyl chloride and concentrated hydrochloric acid all give the 1:3-*anhydride*, m.p. 178°.

The Diels-Alder condensation between sorbic acid and maleic anhydride gives the 2:3-*anhydride*, m.p. 174°, of **4-methylcyclohex-5-ene-1:2:3-tricarboxylic acid,** m.p. 198°, 1-*ethyl ester*, m.p. 118°. Catalytic hydrogenation of the acid gives **4-methylcyclohexane-1:2:3-tricarboxylic acid,** *monohydrate* m.p. 196° (*E. H. Farmer* and *F. L. Warren*, J. chem. Soc., 1928, 897; *O. Diels* and *K. Alder*, Ann., 1929, **470**, 92).

1-Methylcyclohexa-2:4-diene-1:3:5-tricarboxylic acid (*1:2-dihydro-1-methyltrimesic acid*) is formed by heating pyruvic acid with sodium hydroxide. When heated with concentrated sulphuric acid it loses carbon dioxide and hydrogen to form uvitic acid (5-methyl*iso*phthalic acid); on being fused it disproportionates into uvitic acid, a dihydrouvitic acid and several tetrahydrouvitic acids. Reduction with sodium amalgam furnishes a **1-methylcyclohexene-1:3:5-tricarboxylic acid,** m.p. 221° (dec.) (*L. Wolff* and *F. Heip*, Ann., 1899, **305**, 135).

The 1:4-*lactone*-2:3-*anhydride*, m.p. 297°, and the 2:4-*lactone*, m.p. 296° (changing in structure at 205°) of **2-methylcyclohexan-4-ol-1:2:3-tricarboxylic acid** are obtained as by-products in the Ziegler synthesis of cantharidin (p. 244).

Ethyl cyclohexan-4-one-1:3:5-tricarboxylate, b.p. 189°/ca. 10 mm., is obtained by the Dieckmann cyclisation of ethyl pentane-1:3:3:5-tetracarboxylate (*P. A. Plattner et al.*, Helv., 1944, **27**, 793).

Ethyl 1:4-dimethylcyclohexan-4-one-1:3:5-tricarboxylate, b.p. 170°/6 mm., is similarly produced (*R. N. Chakravarti*, J. Indian chem. Soc., 1944, **21**, 322).

Ethyl cyclohex-2-en-6-one-1:3-dicarboxylic-4-acetate, m.p. 82°, is produced by treating ethyl glutaconate with alcohol-free sodium ethoxide (*H. von Pechmann et al.*, Ber., 1904, **37**, 2113).

α-1-Carboxy-4-methylcyclohexylsuccinic acid (II) is obtained in two isomeric forms, m.p. 207° and 178°, by the hydrolysis of the complex nitrile (I) which is synthesised from 4-methylcyclohexanone cyanohydrin thus:

4-Me-cyclohexane-1-(NC)(OH) $\xrightarrow{CH_2CN\cdot CO_2Et}$ 4-Me-cyclohexane-1-(NC)-CH(CN)·CO_2Et $\xrightarrow{CH_2Br\cdot CO_2Et}$ cyclohexane-1-(NC)-C(CN)(CO_2Et)·$CH_2\cdot CO_2Et$ (I) $\longrightarrow$ cyclohexane-1-(HO_2C)-CH(CO_2H)·$CH_2\cdot CO_2H$ (II)

The 2-*methyl*-, m.p. 210° and 172°, and 3-*methyl*-analogue, m.p. 185° and 175°, are similarly procured (*R. D. Desai et al.*, J. chem. Soc., 1939, 84).

(*ii*) *Tetra*- and *hexa-carboxylic acids*

Esters of acids with two carboxyl groups attached to the same carbon atom are obtained by the action of dihalogenoalkanes on disodio-bismalonates, e.g.

$$CH_2\begin{cases}CH_2\cdot CNa(CO_2Et)_2\\ CH_2\cdot CNa(CO_2Et)_2\end{cases} \xrightarrow{CH_2I_2} \text{cyclohexane-1,1,3,3-}(CO_2Et)_2(CO_2Et)_2$$

In this way is obtained *ethyl cyclohexane-1:1:3:3-tetracarboxylate*, b.p. 245°/50 mm. The free acid readily loses carbon dioxide to give cyclohexane-1:3-dicarboxylic acid (*W. H. Perkin*, J. chem. Soc., 1891, **59**, 798, 990).

Ethyl cyclohexane-1:1:2:2-tetracarboxylate, b.p. 192°/11 mm., is obtained by the catalytic hydrogenation of **ethyl cyclohex-4-ene-1:1:2:2-tetracarboxylate,**

b.p. 151°/0·1 mm., which is itself produced by a Diels-Alder condensation between tetracarbethoxyethylene and butadiene (*K. Alder* and *H. F. Rickert*, Ber., 1939, **72**, 1983).

The condensation of ethyl *trans-trans*-muconate with maleic anhydride gives the 2:3-*anhydride*-1:4-*diethyl ester*, m.p. 188°, of **cyclohex-5-ene-1:2:3:4-tetracarboxylic acid,** m.p. 241° (dec.), *ethyl ester*, m.p. 75°. Catalytic hydrogenation of the acid furnishes **cyclohexane-1:2:3:4-tetracarboxylic acid** *(hexahydroprehnitic acid), monohydrate*, m.p. ca. 168° (*E. H. Farmer* and *F. L. Warren*, J. chem. Soc., 1929, 897).

Methyl cyclohexan-2-one-1:3:5:5-tetracarboxylate, m.p. 122°, is produced by the Dieckmann cyclisation of methyl pentane-1:1:3:3:5:5-hexacarboxylate (*H. Meerwein* and *W. Schürrmann*, Ann., 1913, **398**, 218).

Cyclohexane-1:2:3:4:5:6-hexacarboxylic acid *(hydromellitic acid)* is obtained by treating an ammoniacal solution of mellitic acid with sodium amalgam. The acid is unstable and does not crystallise well but, by treatment with hot concentrated hydrochloric acid, it is converted into a stable iso*hydromellitic acid, hexamethyl ester*, m.p. 125°. Both acids decompose on heating (*A. von Baeyer*, Ann., Suppl., 1872, **7**, 15; *J. van Loon*, Ber., 1895, **28**, 1272).

Chapter VI

Cycloheptane, Cyclo-octane and Macrocyclic Groups

R. A. RAPHAEL

1. Cycloheptane group

Cycloheptane compounds have in modern times acquired an increased interest as starting materials for the synthesis of azulenes and of compounds containing the cycloheptatrienolone (tropolone) system (see Vol. III). In nature seven-membered rings occur as part of the molecule of certain alkaloids (colchicine, cocaine etc.) and terpenes (guaiol, vetivone etc.). The synthesis of cycloheptane derivatives generally begins from cycloheptanone or its homologues.

TABLE 1

SATURATED AND UNSATURATED HYDROCARBONS OF THE CYCLOHEPTANE SERIES

Compound	B.p.°/mm.	*d*	*n*	Ref.
Cycloheptane (Suberane)	118–120 (m.p. –7·98°)	d_4^0 0·8275	n_D^{20} 1·4449	1
Methylcycloheptane	133–135	d_4^{20} 0·8052	n_D^{20} 1·4410	2
1:1:2-Trimethylcycloheptane	104–105/100	d_4^{20} 0·8243	n_D^{20} 1·4527	2
Cycloheptene	114·38/760	d_4^{20} 0·8254	n_D^{20} 1·4580	1
1-Methylcyclohept-1-ene	133–135/720	d_4^{22} 0·8243	n_D^{22} 1·4575	2
Methylenecycloheptane	138–140	d 0·824	n_D 1·4611	3
3:3:5-Trimethylcyclohept-1-ene	38/4		n_D^{20} 1·4498	4
1:4:4-Trimethylcyclohept-1-ene	35/4	d_{20} 0·8288	n_D^{20} 1·4593	4
Cyclohepta-1:3-diene	121·52/758 (m.p. –110·42°)			1
1-Vinylcyclohept-1-ene	48/12			5
1-Ethynylcyclohept-1-ene	78/35		n_D^{20} 1·4980	5, 6
Cyclohepta-1:3:5-triene	115·5/760 (m.p. –79·49°)		n_D^{20} 1·5243	1

[1] *E. P. Kohler et al.*, J. Amer. chem. Soc., 1939, **61**, 1057.
[2] *L. Ruzicka* and *C. F. Seidel*, Helv., 1936, **19**, 424.
[3] *O. Wallach*, Ann., 1906, **345**, 146.
[4] *H. Barbier*, Helv., 1940, **23**, 519, 524.
[5] *H. J. Backer* and *J. R. van der Bij*, Rec. Trav. chim., 1943, **62**, 561.
[6] *I. M. Heilbron et al.*, J. chem. Soc., 1949, 1827.

(a) Hydrocarbons

Physical properties of some saturated and unsaturated hydrocarbons of this group are given in Table 1, with references.

Cycloheptanes are available by reduction of the corresponding cycloheptene or cycloheptyl halide and by Kishner-Wolff reduction of the corresponding cycloheptanone (*L. Ruzicka et al.*, ref. 2; Helv., 1945, **28**, 395). Many of the chemical reactions of this group involve ring contraction leading to products containing a six-membered ring; thus dehydrogenation furnishes benzene derivatives (ref. 2). **Cycloheptane** itself may be isomerised to methylcyclohexane with hydriodic acid or aluminium chloride (*W. Markovnikov*, Ber., 1894, **27**, R. 47; *M. B. Turova–Pollak* and *F. P. Sidelkovskaya*, J. gen. Chem. U.S.S.R., 1941, **11**, 817) whilst exhaustive bromination in the presence of aluminium bromide furnishes pentabromotoluene.

Cycloheptene may be prepared by the dehydration of cycloheptanol with oxalic acid, naphthalene-β-sulphonic acid or alumina (ref. 1 and 2; *N. Rosanov*, Chem. Ztbl., 1924, I, 2426; 1930, II, 229; *H. Pines et al.*, J. Amer. chem. Soc., 1945, **67**, 2193), by the dehydrohalogenation of cycloheptyl halides or by the distillation of cycloheptyltrimethylammonium hydroxide (*R. Willstätter*, Ann., 1901, **317**, 218) and by the ring expansion of methylenecyclohexane or cyclohexylmethylamine (*L. Ruzicka* and *W. Brugger*, Helv., 1926, **9**, 399; *N. Rosanov*, *loc. cit.*). It combines with bromine to form an unstable dibromide and with phenyl azide to yield a triazole which undergoes a ring contraction on acid treatment (p. 19). With benzene and aluminium chloride cycloheptylbenzene is produced (*H. Pines et al.*, *loc. cit.*). High temperature isomerisation over silica results in the formation of dimethylcyclopentenes and methylcyclohexenes (*N. D. Zelinsky* and *J. D. Arbusov*, Brit. chem. Abstr., 1945, AII, 188).

Higher homologues of cycloheptene may be obtained by analogous methods. The selenium dioxide oxidation of some of these has been studied by *H. Barbier* (Helv., 1940, **23**, 524, 1477); the corresponding $\alpha\beta$-unsaturated ketone is produced.

Cyclohepta-1:3-diene, (*maleic anhydride adduct,* m.p. 110–111°), is prepared by the Hofmann elimination reaction on cycloheptenyltrimethylammonium hydroxide (*R. Willstätter*, Ann., 1901, **317**, 223; and ref. 1). The cyclic allene, *cyclohepta-1:2-diene,* b.p. 118–119°, d_4^{20} 0·8532 (formerly regarded as the cyclic acetylene) is obtained by the action of sodium on 1-chloro-2-bromocyclohept-1-ene (*A. E. Favorski*, C.A., 1936, **30**, 6337).

Cyclohepta-1:3:5-triene (*tropilidene*) (*maleic anhydride adduct,* m.p. 102–104°) is prepared from the 1:3-diene by bromine addition followed by quinoline dehydrobromination (*R. Willstätter*, *loc. cit.*; and ref. 1). It may also be obtained by the photolytic diazomethane ring expansion of benzene (*W. E. Doering* and *L. H. Knox*, J. Amer. chem. Soc., 1950, **72**, 2305; 1951, **73**, 828). Hot hydrobromic acid transforms its dibromide to benzyl bromide (*R. Willstätter*, Ann., 1901, **317**, 204; Ber., 1898, **31**, 1544). Unlike cyclopentadiene (p. 82) it does not react with Grignard compounds.

A *tetramethylcycloheptatriene,* b.p. 67–68°/11 mm., is obtained from eucarvone and methyl magnesium iodide, via the corresponding tertiary carbinol (*H. Rupe* and *W. Kerkovius*, Ber., 1911, **44**, 2702).

(b) Halogen compounds

Cycloheptyl chloride, b.p. 175°, d_0^0 1·0133, **bromide** 101·5°/40 mm., d_{15}^{18} 1·299, n_D^{22} 1·4996, and **iodide,** b.p. 92°/14 mm., d_{15}^{15} 1·572, are made by the usual metathetical reactions from cycloheptanol (*L. Ruzicka et al.*, Helv., 1945, **28,** 395; *W. Markovnikov,* Chem. Ztbl., 1903, I, 568; Ann. 1903, **327,** 63; J. pr. Chem., 1894, [ii], **49,** 417). They react in the expected metathetic fashion with the usual replacement reagents (*J. Loevenich et al.*, Ber., 1929, **62,** 3101).

1:2-*Dibromocycloheptane,* made by the addition of bromine to cycloheptene, is unstable; with anhydrous dimethylamine, 3-dimethylaminocyclohept-1-ene is formed together with 1-*bromocyclohept*-1-*ene,* b.p. 191°/760 mm. (*E. P. Kohler et al.*, J. Amer. chem. Soc., 1939, **61,** 1057).

Bromomethylcycloheptane, b.p. 80–82°/15 mm., is prepared from the carbinol by means of hydrobromic acid (*J. von Braun et al.*, Ber., 1926, **59,** 1081).

The action of phosphorus pentachloride on cycloheptanone yields 1-*chlorocyclohept*-1-*ene,* b.p. 58–59°/12 mm., d_4^{20} 1·0276, which readily reacts with bromine to form 1:2-*dibromo*-1-*chlorocycloheptane,* b.p. 105–108°/2 mm., d_4^0 1·7369. With alcoholic potassium hydroxide this polyhalide is converted to 2-*bromo*-1-*chlorocyclohept*-1-*ene,* b.p. 80–82°/2 mm., d_4^{20} 1·4916 (*A. E. Favorski,* C.A., 1936, **30,** 6337).

(c) Alcohols

Secondary ring alcohols, including **cycloheptanol** itself, are prepared by reduction of the corresponding ketones. Sodium in alcohol may be used but by far the most convenient procedure is catalytic hydrogenation (*M. Godchot et al.*, Compt. rend., 1920, **171,** 1378; 1930, **190,** 642; *E. P. Kohler et al.*, J. Amer. chem. Soc., 1939, **61,** 1057; *L. Ruzicka et al.*, Helv., 1945, **28,** 395). Their properties are typical for secondary alcohols. Reduction of cycloheptanol with hydriodic acid yields methylcyclohexane (*W. Markovnikov,* Ber., 1897, **30,** 1216). Dehydration of 2:2-dimethylcycloheptanol with zinc chloride leads to ring contraction (p. 13). The tertiary ring alcohols are obtained by the action of Grignard reagents on the corresponding ketones.

Some alcohols of the cycloheptane series, with properties and references, are given in Table 2.

3-*Ethoxycyclohept*-1-*ene,* b.p. 174°, is produced by the action of alcoholic KOH on 1:2-dibromocycloheptane (*R. Willstätter,* Ann., 1901, **317,** 223).

The exocyclic alcohol **cycloheptylcarbinol** is prepared by reacting formaldehyde with cycloheptylmagnesium bromide.

cis-**Cycloheptane**-1:2-**diol,** m.p. 46°, is prepared by hydroxylation of cycloheptene with permanganate; the *trans* isomer, m.p. 63°, is obtained by boiling

TABLE 2

ALCOHOLS OF THE CYCLOHEPTANE SERIES

Compound		B.p.°/mm.	n	Derivatives	Ref.
Cycloheptanol		186–187	n_D^{20} 1·4760	phenylurethane m.p. 85°	1
1-Methylcycloheptan-1-ol		183–185	n_D^{22} 1·4677		2
2-Methylcycloheptan-1-ol	*cis*	191/753	n_D^{15} 1·4762	phenylurethane m.p. 40–41°	3
	trans	194/768	n_D^{15} 1·4704	phenylurethane m.p. 59–60°	
4-Methylcycloheptan-1-ol		105/40		hydrogen phthalate m.p. 95–97°	4
Cycloheptylcarbinol		204/49	n_D^{20} 1·4685		5
2:2-Dimethylcycloheptan-1-ol		87/13	n_D^{20} 1·4748	phenylurethane m.p. 101°	6
1-Vinylcycloheptan-1-ol		80–84/11			7
1-Ethynylcycloheptan-1-ol		90/13 (m.p. 14°)	n_D^{22} 1·4880	3:5-dinitrobenzoate m.p. 108°	7, 8

[1] *H. Pines et al.*, J. Amer. chem. Soc., 1945, **67**, 2193.
[2] *O. Wallach*, Ann., 1906, **345**, 140.
[3] *M. Godchot* and *G. Cauquil*, Compt. rend., 1930, **190**, 642.
[4] *M. Qudrat-I-Khuda* and *S. K. Ghosh*, J. Indian chem. Soc., 1940, **17**, 19.
[5] *N. Rosanov*, Chem. Ztbl., 1930, II, 229.
[6] *H. Meerwein* and *J. Schäfer*, J. pr. Chem., 1922, [ii], **104**, 300.
[7] *H. J. Backer* and *J. R. van der Bij*, Rec. Trav. chim., 1943, **62**, 561.
[8] *I. M. Heilbron et al.*, J. chem. Soc., 1949, 1827.

cycloheptene oxide with dilute acid (*J. Böeseken* and *H. G. Derx*, Rec. Trav. chim. 1921, **40**, 530). The *trans* isomer has been resolved (*M. Godchot* and *M. Mousseron*, Compt. rend., 1934, **198**, 837). The properties of these two diols are interesting from the point of view of the fine structure of the cycloheptane ring. Unlike the corresponding cyclohexane-1:2-diols both isomers form cyclic *iso*propylidene ethers with acetone and boric acid complexes, thus indicating that configurations favourable to such ring formation (i.e. those leading to approximate coplanarity of the hydroxyl groups) are statistically preferred. Stuart models show that such a configuration is indeed possible for the chair form of the *trans*-diol but not for the boat form of the *trans*-diol or the boat and chair forms of the *cis*-diol (*P. H. Hermans* and *C. J. Maan*, Rec. Trav. chim., 1938, **57**, 643). The results can be interpreted by postulating an intramolecular movement of a vibratory nature which enables the hydroxyl groups to pass to positions favourable for complex formation (*J. Böeseken*, Rec. Trav. chim., 1939, **58**, 856); this concept can be illustrated very clearly if the more flexible Barton models be employed.*

* In these models the carbon atoms are represented by small precision-made tetrahedra each face of which contains a hole fitted with a locking screw. These are joined by steel rods of a length accurately representing the proportional bond lengths. The ends of these rods are grooved round the circumference in such a way that the locking screws, while ensuring a secure hold, allow freedom for rotation. In this way a very flexible representation of the molecule is achieved.

Cycloheptene oxide, b.p. 161°, is prepared from cycloheptene with perbenzoic acid; with ammonia it forms trans-2-*aminocycloheptan*-1-*ol,* m.p. 72–78°, *hydrochloride,* m.p. 115–116° (*M. Godchot,* Compt. rend., 1927, **184,** 208; 1933, **196,** 1680).

1-(**Hydroxymethyl**)**cycloheptan**-1-**ol,** m.p. 50°, is produced by permanganate hydroxylation of methylenecycloheptane; on dehydration with sulphuric acid it gives cycloheptanealdehyde (*O. Wallach,* Ann., 1906, **345,** 146). The *dimethyl ether,* b.p. 65°/1 mm., n_D^{20} 1·4530, d_4^{20} 0·9480 is obtained from cyclo-octatetraene dichloride by reaction with sodium methoxide followed by catalytic hydrogenation (*J. W. Reppe et al.,* Ann., 1948, **560,** 1; cf. p. 260).

(*d*) *Amines*

Cycloheptylamine, b.p. 169°/751 mm., a very strong base, is obtained from cycloheptanone oxime by reduction or by the Hofmann degradation from cycloheptanecarboxylic acid (*W. Markovnikov,* Ber., 1893, **26,** R. 813; J. pr. Chem., 1894, [ii], **49,** 423; *R. Willstätter,* Ann., 1901, **317,** 219). Methylation yields the *NN-dimethyl*-compound, b.p. 190°.

1-**Aminocyclohept**-2-**ene,** b.p. 166°/724 mm., *hydrochloride,* m.p. 172–174°, is obtained from the corresponding amide by Hofmann degradation. On methylation it gives the *NN-dimethyl*-compound, b.p. 188°/721 mm., *picrate,* m.p. 162–163° (*R. Willstätter,* Ann., 1901, **317,** 223) which may also be obtained by the action of dimethylamine on 1:2-dibromocycloheptane (*E. P. Kohler et al., loc. cit.*). 1-*Dimethylaminocyclohept*-3- and -4-*enes* are degradation products of tropine (*R. Willstätter,* Ann., 1901, **317,** 204).

Cycloheptylmethylamine, b.p. 193–195°, $d^{21.5}$ 0·8840, $n_D^{21.5}$ 1·4719, *hydrochloride,* m.p. 229–232°, is prepared by Hofmann degradation of the corresponding amide; it undergoes the Demjanov rearrangement (p. 11) with nitrous acid to give cyclo-octanol (*O. Wallach,* Ann., 1907, **353,** 327).

(*e*) *Aldehydes*

Cycloheptanealdehyde, b.p. 180°/11 mm., *semicarbazone,* m.p. 153–154°, is obtained by the action of sulphuric acid on 1-(hydroxymethyl)cycloheptan-1-ol or its dimethyl ether (see above).

2:2:6-*Trimethylcycloheptane*-1-*aldehyde,* b.p. 65–67°/4 mm., *semicarbazone,* m.p. 121°, is obtained by means of the Darzens reaction on the corresponding ketone (*H. Barbier,* Helv., 1940, **23,** 524).

Cyclohept-1-**ene**-1-**aldehyde,** *semicarbazone,* m.p. 203–204°, is formed from the nitrosochloride of methylenecycloheptane by elimination of HCl and hydrolysis of the resulting oxime (*O. Wallach,* Ann., 1906, **345,** 152).

3:3:4-*Trimethylcyclohept*-1-*ene*-1-*aldehyde,* b.p. 98°/11 mm., is prepared from

2:2:3-trimethylcycloheptan-1-one by the following procedure [*M. Naef & Co.*, F.P., 744,344 (1933)].

Me Me / —Me / =O $\xrightarrow{H \cdot CO_2Et}$ Me Me / —Me / =O / =CHOH $\xrightarrow[-H_2O]{H_2}$ Me Me / —Me / CHO

4:4-*Dimethylcyclohept*-1-*ene*-1-*aldehyde*, b.p. 76°/4 mm., *semicarbazone*, m.p. 196–200°, is formed by the selenium dioxide oxidation of 1:4:4-trimethylcyclohept-1-ene. 2:6:6-*Trimethylcyclohept*-1-*ene*-3-*aldehyde*, b.p. 72°/4 mm., *semicarbazone*, m.p. 194°, is obtained by the Darzens reaction on the corresponding ketone (*H. Barbier, loc. cit.*).

(*f*) *Ketones*

Some ketones of this series are given in Table 3.

TABLE 3

KETONES OF THE CYCLOHEPTANE SERIES

Compound	B.p.°/mm.	*n*	Derivatives	Ref.
Cycloheptanone	71/19	n_D^{15} 1·4365	semicarbazone m.p. 163° 2:4-dinitrophenylhydrazone m.p. 148°	1
2-Methylcycloheptanone	185–186/760		semicarbazone m.p. 129–131°	2
2:2-Dimethylcycloheptanone	191–192/770		oxime m.p. 83°	3
2:2:6-Trimethylcycloheptanone	58/4		semicarbazone m.p. 190–192°	4
3:3:5-Trimethylcycloheptanone	86–88/12	$n_D^{16.5}$ 0·4594	semicarbazone m.p. 196–197°	5
3:5:5-Trimethylcycloheptanone	87–88/12	$n_D^{18.5}$ 1·4590	semicarbazone m.p. 192–193°	5
Cyclohept-2-en-1-one	186–188		oxime m.p. 80–88°	6
2-Methylcyclohept-2-en-1-one	200–205		semicarbazone m.p. 162–163°	7
2:5:5-Trimethylcyclo-hept-2-en-1-one	66/4		semicarbazone m.p. 177° (also given as 195–196°)	8

[1] *A. I. Vogel*, J. chem. Soc., 1928, 2030.
[2] *O. Wallach*, Ann., 1906, **345**, 146.
[3] *M. Godchot*, Compt. rend., 1929, **188**, 794.
[4] *H. Barbier*, Helv., 1940, **23**, 519, 524.
[5] *M. Stoll and W. Scherrer*, Helv., 1940, **23**, 941.
[6] *A. Kötz*, Ber., 1911, **44**, 464; Ann., 1913, **400**, 72.
[7] *O. Wallach*, Ann., 1906, **345**, 145.
[8] *H. Barbier*, Helv., 1940, **23**, 524, 1477.

Cycloheptanone *(suberone)* has a peppermint odour; it is formed by the interaction of 1:4-dibromobutane and acetonedicarboxylic ester (*J. von Braun*, Ber., 1913, 46, 1792); by distilling calcium suberate; by distilling suberic acid with various catalysts (e.g. Fe-BaO; *A. I. Vogel*, J. chem. Soc., 1929, 171); and by the application of Ziegler's method (p. 271) to suberic dinitrile. The most convenient method of preparation is by the ring expansion of cyclohexanone with diazomethane (*E. Mosettig* and *A. Burger*, J. Amer. chem. Soc., 1930, **52**, 3456; *E. P. Kohler et al., ibid.*, 1939, **61**, 1017). With nitric acid the ring is split yielding pimelic acid; bromine furnishes *2:7-dibromocycloheptan-1-one*, m.p. 68° (*M. Godchot*, Compt. rend., 1922, **174**, 618). Cycloheptanone condenses readily with benzaldehyde to form 2:7-dibenzylidenecycloheptanones (for the stereoisomerism of these compounds see, *inter al., R. Cornubert et al.*, Bull. Soc. chim. Fr., 1938, [v], **5**, 1490). Its *oxime*, m.p. 23° undergoes the Beckmann rearrangement in the presence of sulphuric acid to give the cyclic lactam.

Homologues of cycloheptanone may be obtained by the cyclization of substituted suberic acids; the α-substituted ketones are produced by direct alkylation of the parent ketone.

Cyclohept-2-en-1-one is a degradation product of tropine and tropidine; it has been prepared by the dehydrohalogenation of 2-chloro- and 2-bromo-cycloheptan-1-one. It gives cycloheptanone on catalytic reduction and adipic acid on oxidation. Substituted cycloheptenones have been obtained by selenium dioxide oxidation of the corresponding cycloheptenes.

Cycloheptylideneacetone, b.p. 98°/10 mm., *semicarbazone*, m.p. 172–173°, and *cyclohept-1-enylacetone*, b.p. 95°/13 mm., *semicarbazone*, m.p. 128–129° (dec.), are prepared by the action of methylzinc iodide on the corresponding acid chlorides (*G. A. R. Kon et al.*, J. chem. Soc., 1929, 1435).

1-Acetylcyclohept-1-ene, b.p. 97°/16 mm., n_D^{25} 1·4900, light absorption λ_{max} 236 mμ, ε_{max} 10,500, *semicarbazone*, m.p. 197°, *2:4-dinitrophenylhydrazone*, m.p. 178°, is prepared by the rearrangement of 1-ethynylcycloheptan-1-ol with formic acid (*I. M. Heilbron et al.*, J. chem. Soc., 1949, 1827).

Eucarvone, 2:6:6-trimethylcyclohepta-2:4-diene-1-one, see Vol. II B.

The study of seven-membered ring ketones was stimulated by the suggestion of *M. J. S. Dewar* (Nature, 1945, **155**, 50, 141, 479) that the mould metabolic product stipitatic acid and the alkaloid colchicine are derivatives of the cyclohepta-2:4:6-trien-2-ol-1-one system for which the trivial name "tropolone" has been adopted. Because of their aromatic character, tropolone and related compounds are discussed in Vol. III.

(g) Carboxylic acids

Cycloheptanecarboxylic acid *(suberanecarboxylic acid)*, b.p. 139°/15 mm., *amide*, m.p. 195°, has been prepared synthetically via *cycloheptane-1:1-dicarboxylic acid* the ester of which is formed in small quantity by the reaction of

1:6-dibromohexane with sodiomalonic ester (*E. Haworth* and *W. H. Perkin*, J. chem. Soc., 1894, **65**, 591). Other ways of obtaining the acid are by treating cycloheptylmagnesium bromide with carbon dioxide and by reducing the various unsaturated acids.

On bromination the acid gives 1-bromocycloheptane-1-carboxylic acid which when dehydrobrominated furnishes *cyclohept-1-ene-1-carboxylic acid*, m.p. 54°, *amide*, m.p. 134–135°; this latter acid is also formed by the alkaline rearrangement of *cyclohept-2-ene-1-carboxylic acid*, m.p. 19°, *amide*, m.p. 158°. Both of these unsaturated acids have also been obtained by reducing cycloheptatriene-carboxylic acids or their dihydrobromides (*R. Willstätter*, Ann., 1901, **317**, 234).

There exist four **cycloheptatrienecarboxylic acids,** the isomerism being due to the differing position of the carboxyl group; *α*, m.p. 71°, *amide*, m.p. 129°; *β*, m.p. 56°, *amide*, m.p. 98°; *γ*, liquid, *amide*, m.p. 90°; δ, m.p. 32°, *amide*, m.p. 125°. All the acids result from the degradation of the alkaloid ecgonine (*R. Willstätter*, Ber., 1898, **31**, 2498); they have been obtained synthetically by the rearrangement of ethyl norcaradienecarboxylate (p. 315) (*W. Braren* and *E. Buchner*, Ber., 1900, **33**, 684). The acids combine with hydrogen bromide to form mono-, di- and tri-hydrobromides; energetic treatment with HBr results in rearrangement to *p*-toluic acid.

trans-**Cycloheptane**-1:2:4-**tricarboxylic acid,** m.p. 198–200°, is obtained by acid hydrolysis of its *triethyl ester*, b.p. 212–215°/30 mm. This latter is a by-product in the preparation of pentaethyl cycloheptane-1:1:2:4:4-penta-carboxylate from pentane-1:1:5:5-tetracarboxylic ester and ethyl *αβ*-dibromo-propionate (*L. J. Goldsworthy* and *W. H. Perkin*, J. chem. Soc., 1914, **105**, 2665).

Cycloheptane-1:1:3:3:5:6-**hexacarboxylic acid,** m.p. 177°, is prepared by hydrolysis of its *methyl ester*, m.p. 128°; this latter compound is obtained by ring fission of the complex tricyclic diketone (I).

CO_2Me ... (I) $\xrightarrow{NaOMe}$ ... i.e. ...

By the action of heat the hexacarboxylic acid is converted into *cycloheptane-1:3:5:6-tetracarboxylic acid*, m.p. 233°, *dianhydride*, m.p. 197–198° (*H. Meerwein*, J. pr. Chem., 1922, **104**, [ii], 199).

The reaction of ethyl bromoacetate with cycloheptanone under Reformatski conditions yields an equilibrium mixture of **cycloheptylideneacetic acid** (25%), m.p. 54°, *anilide*, m.p. 90–91°, *dibromide*, m.p. 125° and **cyclohept-1-en-1-acetic acid,** b.p. 153°/17 mm., *anilide*, m.p. 79–80°, *dibromide*, m.p. 102–103° (*G. A. R. Kon et al.*, J. chem. Soc., 1929, 1435). Reduction of these acids or of the 1-halo-1-acetic acids produces **cycloheptylacetic acid,** b.p. 165°/19 mm., *amide*, m.p. 148° (*O. Wallach*, Ann., 1907, **353**, 301).

1-Hydroxycycloheptane-1-carboxylic acid, m.p. 79°, is prepared from the reaction product of hydrogen cyanide with cycloheptanone and by the hydrolysis of 1-bromocycloheptane-1-carboxylic acid with barium hydroxide. Oxidation with lead peroxide smoothly regenerates the parent ketone. Concentrated hydrochloric acid or phosphorus pentachloride give 1-*chlorocycloheptane*-1-*carboxylic acid*, m.p. 43° (*R. Willstätter*, Ber., 1898, **31**, 2505; *A. Spiegel*, Ann., 1882, **211**, 117; *E. Buchner*, Ber., 1898, **31**, 2004).

1-*Aminocycloheptane*-1-*carboxylic acid*, m.p. 306–307°, *picrate*, m.p. 215–216° (dec.) is obtained by the application of the Strecker reaction to cycloheptanone (*N. Zelinsky* and *G. Stadnikov*, Ber., 1906, **39**, 1722).

Condensation of ethyl cyanoacetate with cycloheptanone yields *ethyl cycloheptylidenecyanoacetate*, b.p. 160°/12 mm. On reduction this gives the saturated ester, b.p. 149°/11 mm., which on hydrolysis furnishes *cycloheptylmalonic acid*, m.p. 164·5° (dec.) (*A. I. Vogel*, J. chem. Soc., 1928, 2013). The reaction of potassium cyanide with cycloheptylidenecyanoacetic ester followed by acid hydrolysis gives *cycloheptane*-1-*acetic*-1-*carboxylic acid*, m.p. 159°, *anhydride*, m.p. 16° (*A. I. Vogel*, *loc. cit.*).

Condensation of cycloheptanone with ethyl cyanoacetate in the presence of ammonia, followed by hydrolysis of the *αα-dicyanocycloheptane*-1 : 1-*diacetimide*, m.p. 203·5–204° (I) so formed, yields **cycloheptane-1 : 1-diacetic acid,** m.p. 156–157°, *anhydride*, m.p. 75–76°, *imide*, m.p. 177–178° (*G. A. R. Kon et al.*, J. chem. Soc., 1920, **117**, 639). The yield is small.

```
CH2·CH2·CH2\   /CH(CN)·CO\
|           \C/            NH   (I)
|           /C\            /
CH2  CH2·CH2/   \CH(CN)·CO/
```

Ethyl cycloheptan-1-*one*-2-*glyoxylate*, b.p. 146–148°/3 mm. is obtained from cycloheptanone and ethyl oxalate. It readily loses carbon monoxide to yield *ethyl cycloheptan*-1-*one*-2-*carboxylate*, b.p. 135–138°/22 mm. (*A. Kötz*, J. pr. Chem., 1913, [ii], **88**, 261; *R. H. F. Manske* and *L. C. Leitch*, Canad. J. Res., 1936, **14B**, 1).

Diethyl cyclohepta-1 : 2-*dione*-3 : 7-*dicarboxylate*, m.p. 71°, *phenylhydrazone*, m.p. 189–190°, *quinoxaline*, m.p., 142° is prepared by the condensation of ethyl pimelate with ethyl oxalate (*S. N. Naumov* and *A. N. Perminova*, Brit. chem. Abstr., 1940, AII, 48).

2. Cyclo-octane group

The cyclo-octane carbocyclic system *per se* has not been found in nature; the former hypothesis that the eight-membered ring occurs in the caoutchouc molecule has proved to be erroneous. An alkaloid occurring in pomegranate bark, *pseudo*pelletierine, has been found to incorporate this ring system in its structure and this substance has served as a starting material for the synthesis of many cyclo-octane derivatives. The later discovery that cyclo-octatetraene may be produced in quantity by the polymerisation of acetylene started intense activity in cyclo-octane chemistry, which should provide ample material for study, from both the theoretical and practical view-points, for many years to come. A review of eight-membered ring compounds has been provided by *L. E. Craig* (Chem. Reviews, 1951, **49**, 103).

(a) Hydrocarbons

Cyclo-octane, b.p. 148–149°/749 mm., m.p. 4·3°, d_4^{20} 0·8362, n_D^{20} 1·4581, has been obtained by the reduction of cyclo-octene (*L. Ruzicka* and *H. A. Boekenoogen,* Helv., 1931, **14**, 1319) or cyclo-octyl iodide (*L. Ruzicka et al.*, Helv., 1945, **28**, 395) and by Kishner-Wolff reduction of cyclo-octanone (*A. I. Vogel,* J. chem. Soc., 1929, 721; *N. D. Zelinsky* and *M. G. Freimann,* Ber., 1930, **63**, 1485). The best method of preparation is by complete hydrogenation of the readily available cyclo-octatetraene (*W. Reppe et al.*, Ann., 1948, **560**, 1). On oxidation with nitric acid it furnishes suberic acid (*R. Willstätter* and *T. Kametaka,* Ber., 1908, **41**, 1484).

Cyclo-octene, b.p. 143·8–144·5°/773 mm., n_D^{20} 1·4693 may be obtained by the dehydration of cyclo-octanol (*M. Godchot,* Compt. rend., 1927, **185**, 1202; *L. Ruzicka et al.*, Helv., 1931, **14**, 319; *E. P. Kohler et al.*, J. Amer. chem. Soc., 1939, **61**, 1057) and by the partial hydrogenation of cyclo-octatetraene (*W. Reppe, loc. cit.*); it is also formed from cycloheptylcarbinol by ring enlargement (*N. Rosanov,* Chem. Ztbl., 1930, II, 229). It has the expected ethylenic properties; on treatment with 80% sulphuric acid it dimerises to 1-cyclo-octylcyclo-oct-1-ene (*W. Reppe et al., loc. cit.*).

1-*Methylcyclo-oct-1-ene,* b.p. 158–160°, *nitrosochloride,* m.p. 107–108°, is obtained by distillation of the unstable tertiary alcohol derived from cyclo-octanone and methylmagnesium iodide (*M. Godchot, loc. cit.*).

Cyclo-octyne,

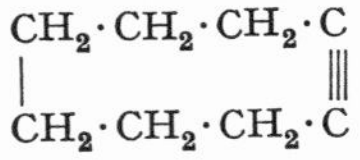

$$\begin{array}{l} CH_2\cdot CH_2\cdot CH_2\cdot C \\ | \qquad\qquad\qquad\quad ||| \\ CH_2\cdot CH_2\cdot CH_2\cdot C \end{array}$$

b.p. 72–76°/100 mm., n_α^{15} 1·4626, d_4^{15} 0·8440 has been made by the dehalogenation of 1-chloro-2-bromocyclo-oct-1-ene (*N. A. Domnin,* C.A., 1939, **33**, 1282).

1-*Vinylcyclo-oct-1-ene,* b.p. 76°/12 mm. is produced by the dehydration of 1-vinylcyclo-octan-1-ol (*H. J. Backer* and *J. R. van der Bij,* Rec. Trav. chim., 1943, **62**, 561).

A series of unsaturated compounds with eight-membered rings have been obtained by *R. Willstätter* and his collaborators by degradation of the alkaloid *pseudo*pelletierine (N-methylgranatonine; I) (Ber., 1905, **38**, 1979; 1908, **41**, 1482; 1911, **44**, 3423; 1913, **46**, 517). Their procedures are shown in the following diagram:

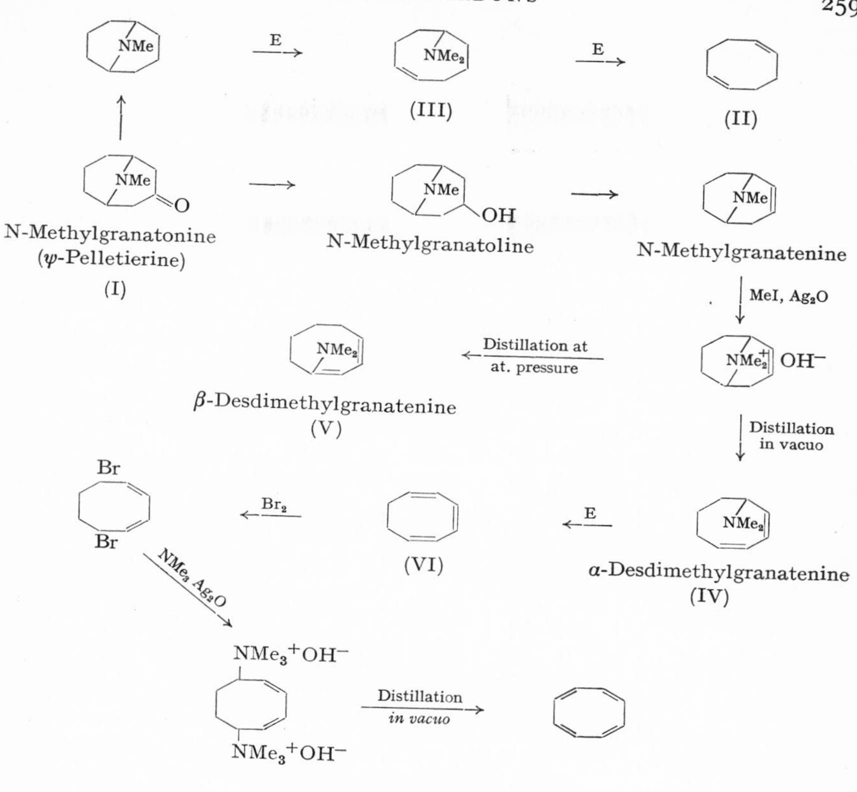

(E = Exhaustive methylation)

Cyclo-octa-1:5-diene (II), b.p. 148–149°, n_D^{25} 1·4905, d_4^{24} 0·8818, has been prepared by reducing a dimer of chloroprene (1:5- and/or 1:6-dichlorocyclo-octa-1:5-diene; see Chapter XI, p. 402) with sodium in liquid ammonia (*A. C. Cope* and *W. J. Bailey*, J. Amer. chem. Soc., 1948, **70**, 2305; *R. E. Foster* and *R. S. Scheiber*, *ibid.*, 1948, **70**, 2303). The hydrocarbon prepared from *pseudo*pelletierine as above contains about 20% of a bicyclo-octene. Its constitution is confirmed by hydrogenation to cyclo-octane and oxidation to succinic acid. The diene is described as a mobile oil of penetrating odour, readily polymerising to a *dimer*, m.p. 114° and an amorphous high melting *polymer*. Addition of hydrogen bromide yields a dibromocyclo-octane of undertermined constitution which on dehydrobromination furnishes another *cyclo-octadiene*, b.p. 143° which possesses a pleasant smell and shows no tendency to polymerise (*R. Willstätter* and *H. Veraguth*, Ber., 1907, **40**, 957).

Cyclo-octa-1:3:5-triene (VI) obtained as above is a somewhat unstable oil with a sweetish odour, b.p. 45°/18 mm., d_4^{25} 0·9042, n_D^{25} 1·5248, $\lambda_{max.}$ 2650 Å. (log $\varepsilon_{max.}$ 3·57).

Cyclo-octa-1:4:6-triene, b.p. 145–146°/760 mm., *maleic anhydride adduct,* m.p. 144–145°, is obtained by the decomposition with methanol of the lithium adduct of cyclo-octatetraene (*W. Reppe et al., loc. cit.*).

(For later work on unsaturated cyclo-octanes see *A. C. Cope et al.,* J. Amer. chem. Soc., 1950, **72,** 1123, 1128, 2510, 2515, 3399, 3405; 1952, **74,** 4867; *K. Ziegler et al.,* Ann., 1950, **567,** 1, 214.)

Cyclo-octatetraene. Willstätter's formulation of his degradation end-product as cyclo-octa-1:3:5:7-tetraene (VII) did not meet with complete acceptance and evidence was adduced to indicate that the substance might be styrene (*J. R. Vincent et al.,* J. org. Chem., 1939, **3,** 303; *S. Goldwasser* and *H. S. Taylor,* J. Amer. chem. Soc., 1939, **61,** 1260. For summary see *W. Baker,* J. chem. Soc., 1945, 258). The discovery that it is possible to prepare cyclo-octatetraene by the catalytic tetramerisation of acetylene (nickel cyanide in tetrahydrofuran at 60–70°/15–20 at. gives the optimum yield) made this hitherto rare substance available in commercial quantities (*W. Reppe et al., loc. cit.*; Experientia, 1949, **5,** 93. A full bibliography of the relevant patents is included in the latter review). A direct comparison of the products obtained by the Willstätter and Reppe methods fully confirmed their identity; the two products and their maleic anhydride adducts showed no mixed melting point depression and the ultra-violet and infra-red absorption curves were identical (*A. C. Cope* and *C. G. Overburger,* J. Amer. chem. Soc., 1947, **69,** 976; 1948, **70,** 1433). The following table compares the physical properties of the two products.

	Willstätter	Reppe
B.p./17 mm.	42·2–42·4°	42–42·5°
M.p.	–27°	–7°
d_4^0	0·943	0·9382
d_4^{20}	0·925	0·9206
n_D^{20}	1·5389	1·5290
M.R.	35·20	35·17

The difference in melting point is attributed to the presence of a small amount of styrene in the Willstätter product.

Cyclo-octatetraene has also been obtained from chloroprene dimer via cyclo-octa-1:5-diene (*A. C. Cope* and *W. J. Bailey, loc. cit.*).

(For benzocyclo-octatetraenes see *W. S. Rapson, R. G. Shuttleworth et al.,* J. chem. Soc., 1941, 487; 1943, 326; 1944, 71, 73; *S. Wawzonek,* J. Amer. chem. Soc., 1940, **62,** 745; *M. Fry* and *L. F. Fieser, ibid.,* 1940, **62,** 3489.)

Cyclo-octa-1:3:5:7-tetraene, the cyclic vinylogue of benzene, has always been regarded with considerable interest and a systematic investigation of its properties had been long awaited. The Reppe synthesis provided the requisite quantity of material for this task and it is now apparent that any previous speculation on the chemical behaviour of cyclo-octatetraene falls far short of the amazing properties actually observed for this protean molecule.

The double bonds in cyclo-octatetraene are typically olefinic, in striking contrast to those of benzene. The hydrocarbon is readily attacked by oxidising agents, halogens and dienophiles rapidly form adducts and polymerisation is easily induced.

The chemical reactions of cyclo-octatetraene may be conveniently divided into three classes based on the structure of the products produced.

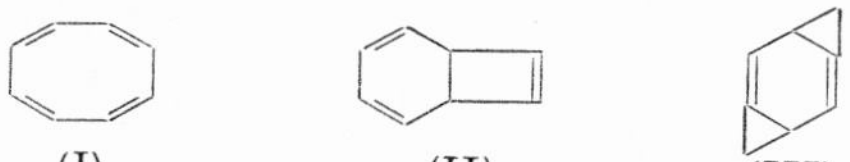

(I) (II) (III)

In conformity with structure (I) the hydrocarbon combines with four molecules of hydrogen on catalytic hydrogenation to yield cyclo-octane; interruption of the reduction after the uptake of three molecules of hydrogen furnishes an excellent yield of cyclo-octene. With hydrogen and carbon monoxide an "oxo" type of reaction taken place with the production of cyclo-octylcarbinol.

Even with excess of perbenzoic acid cyclo-octatetraene forms only a monoepoxide which on catalytic hydrogenation furnishes cyclo-octanol; in the presence of dilute mineral acid the epoxide rearranges to phenylacetaldehyde.

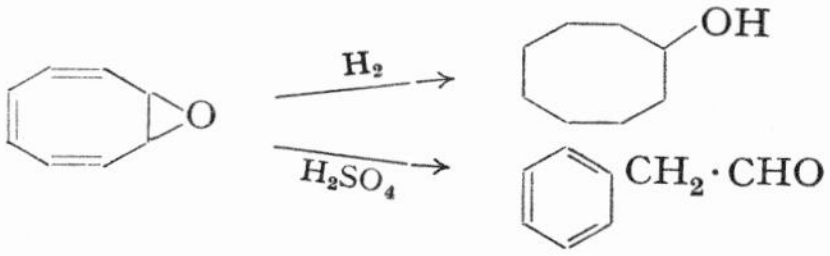

O $\xrightarrow{H_2}$ OH

$\xrightarrow{H_2SO_4}$ $CH_2 \cdot CHO$

The hydrocarbon reacts with lithium and sodium to form di-adducts; these compounds react with alcohols to form cyclo-octa-1:4:6-triene and with carbon dioxide to yield cyclo-octa-1:4:6-triene-3:8-dicarboxylic acid.

i.e. Li, Li $\xrightarrow{ROH}$

$\xrightarrow{CO_2}$ CO_2H, CO_2H

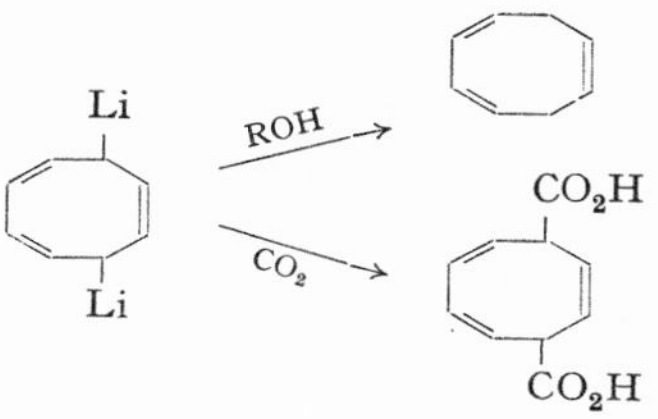

With sulphuryl chloride cyclo-octatetraene yields a dichloride (IV) which is undoubtedly a derivative of bicyclo[4:2:0]octa-1:3:5-triene (II); this is confirmed by its degradation to *cis*-hexahydrophthalic acid and *cis*-hexahydrophthalaldehyde.

Cyclo-octatetraene $\xrightarrow{SO_2Cl_2}$ (IV) $\xrightarrow{H_2}$

$\xleftarrow{HNO_3}$ $\xrightarrow{Pb(OAc)_4}$

More direct evidence for structure (IV) is provided by pyrolysis of the naphthoquinone adduct (V) when 1:2-dichlorocyclobut-3-ene (see p. 54) is formed.

(IV) + → (V) → +

This dicyclic formulation provides a convincing explanation of the fact that cyclo-octatetraene gives two dihalides, two tetrahalides, a hexahalide but no octahalide.

Intermediates possessing the carbon skeleton of type (II) account for the almost quantitative yield of benzoic acid obtained when cyclo-octatetraene is oxidized under various conditions and also for the production of phenylacetaldehyde on treating the hydrocarbon with aqueous mercuric sulphate; similarly hydrogen bromide yields α-bromoethylbenzene.

Cyclo-octatetraene $\xrightarrow{O}$ [ ] → $C_6H_5 \cdot CO_2H$

Cyclo-octatetraene $\xrightarrow[H_2O]{HgSO_4}$ [OH] → $C_6H_5 \cdot CH_2 \cdot CHO$

Cyclo-octatetraene $\xrightarrow{HBr}$ [Br] → $C_6H_5 \cdot CHBr \cdot CH_3$

In similar fashion dienophiles form only mono-adducts with cyclo-octatetraene and the products are derivatives of the ring system (II), e.g.

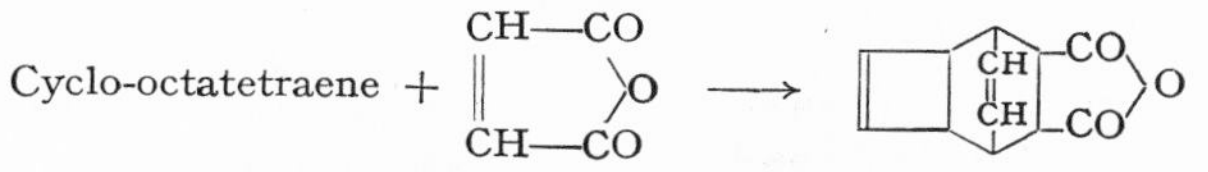

With alkaline hypochlorite cyclo-octatetraene reacts as though it were 1:2:4:5-dimethylenecyclohexa-2:5-diene (III) and terephthalaldehyde is produced. Similarly with chromium trioxide in glacial acetic acid it yields terephthalic acid.

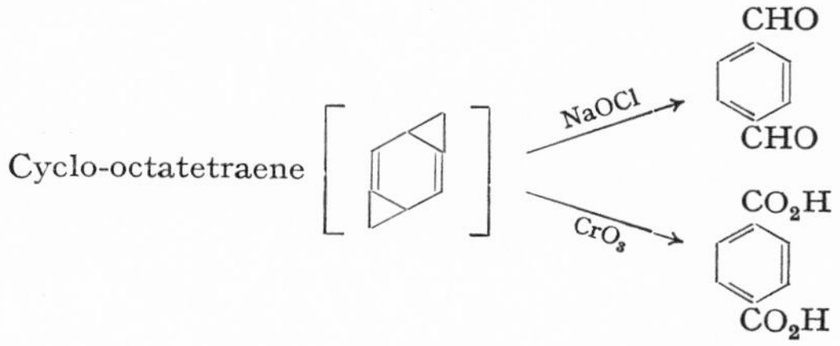

It should be realised that constitutions (II) and (III) do not represent tautomeric forms of cyclo-octatraene but are to be regarded solely as convenient mnemonic structures. Physical investigations on the fine structure of the cyclo-octatetraene molecule have led to conflicting results. Electron diffraction measurements indicate that the molecule is puckered with all the $C\langle^{C}_{C}$ angles 120^0 and all the C–C bonds of equal length (*O. Bastiansen et al.*, Nature, 1947, **160**, 128). From these data it is suggested that cyclo-octatetraene resonates to some extent, the resonance being damped to a degree conditioned by the amount of deviation from the planar model. This concept is in agreement with the calculated resonance energy (30 kcals./mol. as against 41 for benzene) and with the light absorption (*L. Pauling* and *J. Sherman*, J. chem. Phys., 1933, **1**, 679; *A. Maccoll*, Nature, 1946, **157**, 695).

On the other hand X-ray data suggest the presence of alternating single and double bonds of lengths 1·54 and 1·34 Å. respectively with little or no resonance (*H. S. Kaufman et al.*, Nature, 1948, **161**, 165) and this picture is borne out by Raman spectra evidence (*E. R. Lippincott* and *R. C. Lord*, J. Amer. chem. Soc., 1946, **68**, 1868) and diamagnetic susceptibility data (*R. C. Pink* and *A. R. Ubbelohde*, Nature, 1947, **160**, 502).

(For reviews, see *N. Campbell*, Annual Reports, 1947, **44**, 120; *J. W. Copenhaver* and *M. H. Bigelow*, "Acetylene and Carbon Monoxide Chemistry", New York, 1949.)

(b) Halogen compounds

Cyclo-octyl iodide, b.p. 106–107°/11 mm., d_4^{21} 1·498, is prepared by the action of hydriodic acid on the alcohol (*L. Ruzicka et al.*, Helv., 1945, **28**, 395).

1-**Chlorocyclo-oct-1-ene,** b.p. 77–78/19 mm., n_D^{20} 1·4928 has been obtained by the reaction of cyclo-octanone with phosphorus pentachloride (*N. A. Domnin*, C.A., 1939, **33**, 1282) or by the dehydrochlorination of 1:2-dichlorocyclo-octane with dimethylamine (*E. P. Kohler et al.*, J. Amer. chem. Soc., 1939, **61**, 1061); the corresponding *bromo*-compound, b.p. 97–98°/23 mm., n_D^{20} 1·5182, is produced by the latter method (*idem, ibid.*).

1:2-**Dichlorocyclo-octane,** b.p. 130·4–130·6°/25 mm., m.p. −5° n_D^{20}, 1·5061, is the product of the addition of chlorine to cyclo-octene (*idem, ibid.*).

Addition of bromine to 1-chlorocyclo-oct-1-ene followed by the action of KOH yields 1-*chloro-2-bromocyclo-oct-1-ene*, b.p. 96–100°/3 mm., n_a^{15} 1·5295, dehalogenation of which gives cyclo-octyne (p. 258).

1:5(6)-**Dichlorocyclo-octa-1:5-diene,** b.p. 88–89°/3 mm., n_D^{23} 1·5300, is formed by the thermal dimerisation of chloroprene (*A. C. Cope* and *W. J. Bailey*, J. Amer. chem. Soc., 1948, **70**, 2305; *R. E. Foster* and *R. S. Scheiber*, *ibid.*, 1948, **70**, 2303) and can also be isolated from chloroprene distillation residues (*J. L. Simonsen et al.*, J. chem. Soc., 1944, 101).

1:5-**Dichloro-4:8-diphenylcyclo-octa-1:5-diene,** m.p. 187–188°, is obtained by the action of phosphorus pentachloride on 4:8-diphenylcyclo-octa-1:5-dione (*S. Wawzonek*, J. Amer. chem. Soc., 1943, **65**, 839).

(c) *Alcohols*

Cyclo-octanol, m.p. 14–15°, b.p. 99°/16 mm., *phenylurethane*, m.p. 57°, p-*nitrobenzoate*, m.p. 64°, is best prepared by catalytic hydrogenation of cyclo-octanone (*L. Ruzicka et al.*, Helv., 1949, **32**, 256; 1945, **28**, 397; *E. P. Kohler et al.*, J. Amer. chem. Soc., 1939, **61**, 1061); it is also formed by the Demjanov ring expansion of cycloheptylmethylamine (*O. Wallach*, Ann., 1907, **353**, 318). The *acetate* may be obtained by the addition of acetic acid to cyclo-octene (*W. Reppe et al.*, Ann., 1948, **560**, 1).

2-**Methylcyclo-octan-1-ol** is known in two forms; (i), b.p. 100–101°/16 mm., n_D^{21} 1·4770, *hydrogen phthalate*, m.p. 104°, *phenylurethane*, m.p. 137°, obtained by catalytic hydrogenation of 2-methylcyclo-octan-1-one; (ii), b.p. 103–104°/16 mm., $n_D^{20.5}$ 1·4808, *hydrogen phthalate*, m.p. 119–120°, *phenylurethane*, m.p. 154° obtained by chemical reduction of the ketone (*M. Godchot* and *G. Cauquil*, C.A., 1934, **28**, 468). 2:2-**Dimethylcyclo-octan-1-ol,** b.p. 91–92°/6 mm., n_D^{20} 1·4798, *hydrogen phthalate*, m.p. 110–113°, *phenylurethane*, m.p. 147° (*idem, ibid.*) is obtained by chemical reduction of the ketone.

1-**Ethynylcyclo-octan-1-ol,** m.p. 41–42°, b.p. 104–106°/12 mm., p-*nitrobenzoate*, m.p. 111·5–112°, is made by action of potassium acetylide on cyclo-octanone (*H. J. Backer* and *J. R. van der Bij*, Rec. Trav. chim., 1943, **62**, 561).

Cyclo-octylcarbinol, b.p. 114–116°/22 mm., *phenylurethane*, m.p. 49–50°, is obtained by the action of nitrous acid on cyclo-octylmethylamine (*L. Ruzicka* and *W. Brugger*, Helv., 1926, **9**, 399) and by the reaction of cyclo-octene with carbon monoxide and hydrogen (*W. Reppe et al., loc. cit.*). β-**Cyclo-octylethyl alcohol,** b.p. 125–127°/12 mm., n_D^{21} 1·4818 is produced by the Bouveault-Blanc reduction of the corresponding ester (*L. Ruzicka* and *H. A. Boekenoogen*, Helv., 1931, **14**, 1319).

Cyclo-octene oxide, b.p. 76°/14 mm., m.p. 45°, is formed by the action of perbenzoic acid on cyclo-octene (*M. Godchot,* Compt. rend., 1931, **192,** 962; *W. Reppe et al., loc. cit.*). 7:8-**Epoxycyclo-octa**-1:3:5-**triene,** b.p. 73°/12 mm., n_D^{20} 1·5399, is obtained by the action of perbenzoic acid on cyclo-octatetraene; on warming with dilute sulphuric acid it rearranges to phenylacetaldehyde (*W. Reppe et al., loc. cit.*).

(d) Amines

Dimethylaminocyclo-octane, b.p. 110°/40 mm., n_D^{25} 1·4707, *methiodide,* m.p. 274–275°, is obtained by hydrogenation of any of the unsaturated dimethylamines described below. 1:4-*Bisdimethylaminocyclo-octane,* b.p. 105°/6 mm., n_D^{25} 1·4823, *bismethiodide,* m.p. 258–259° (dec.), is produced by hydrogenation of the corresponding diene.

5-**Dimethylaminocyclo-oct**-1-**ene** (III; p. 259), b.p. 89–92°/14·5 mm., *picrate,* m.p. 155°, *methiodide,* m.p. 264° (dec.) is one of the degradation products of *pseudo*pelletierine (*R. Willstätter* and *H. Veraguth,* Ber., 1905, **28,** 1975). 5-*Dimethylaminocyclo-octa*-1:3-*diene* (*α-desdimethylgranatenine*; IV; p. 259), b.p. 80°/12 mm., n_D^{25} 1·4988, *methiodide,* m.p. 274–275° (dec.) and 4-*dimethylaminocyclo-octa*-1:3-*diene* (*β-desdimethylgranatenine*; V; p. 259), b.p. 218–220°–722 mm., d_4^{20} 0·959 are further degradation products of *pseudo*pelletierine (*R. Willstätter* and *E. Wäser,* Ber., 1911, **44,** 3423; *A. C. Cope et al.,* J. Amer. chem. Soc., 1948, **70,** 1433, 2305).

5:8-**Bisdimethylaminocyclo-octa**-1:3-**diene,** the precursor of cyclo-octatetraene in the Willstätter synthesis, has b.p. 116°/8 mm., n_D^{25} 1·4990, *dipicrate,* m.p. 194·6–195·2° (dec.), *bismethiodide,* m.p. 173·4–174·1° (dec.) (*idem, ibid.*). It has also been obtained by reacting cyclo-octa-1:5-diene with two molecules of N-bromosuccinimide and treating the resulting dibromide with dimethylamine; the anionotropic rearrangement probably occurs at the bromination stage (*A. C. Cope* and *W. J. Bailey,* J. Amer. chem. Soc., 1948, **70,** 2305).

Cyclo-octylmethylamine, b.p. 90–94°/10 mm., *benzoyl* compound, m.p. 70°, is produced by the catalytic hydrogenation of cyclo-octanone cyanohydrin or its acetate (*L. Ruzicka et al.,* Helv., 1926, **9,** 402; 1943, **26,** 1631). The *hydroxycyclo-octylmethylamine* $C_8H_{14}(OH)CH_2NH_2$, m.p. 35°, *hydrochloride,* m.p. 232°, *benzoyl* compound, m.p. 133°, is obtained as a by-product.

(e) Aldehydes and Ketones

Cyclo-octanealdehyde, b.p. 76–78°/16 mm., n_D^{20} 1·4736, *semicarbazone,* m.p. 140° (not sharp) is the product of application of the Darzens reaction to cyclo-octanone (*L. Ruzicka* and *H. A. Boekenoogen,* Helv., 1931, **16,** 1319).

Cyclo-octanone *(azelaone),* b.p. 197–198°, m.p. 42°, *oxime,* m.p. 35–36°, *semicarbazone,* m.p. 168–169°, is prepared by distilling the calcium and thorium salts of azelaic acid (*L. Ruzicka* and *W. Brugger*, Helv., 1926, **9**, 339), by heating azelaic acid with Fe-BaO (*A. I. Vogel*, J. chem. Soc., 1929, 721), by the diazomethane ring expansion of cycloheptanone (*E. P. Kohler et al.*, J. Amer. chem. Soc., 1939, **61**, 1061) and by the Ziegler cyclisation of azelaic dinitrile. Oxidation of the ketone causes ring fission to suberic acid. Alkylated ketones are obtained by similar methods from alkylated azelaic acids (*M. Godchot* and *G. Cauquil*, Compt. rend., 1931, **192**, 962).

Cyclo-oct-3-en-1-one *(granatal)*, b.p. 73–74°/8 mm., d_4^{20} 0·990 is formed by the hydrochloric acid hydrolysis of β-desdimethylgranatenine (V; p. 259) (*R. Willstätter* and *E. Wäser*, Ber., 1911, **44**, 3534).

1-**Acetylcyclo-oct-1-ene,** b.p. 110°/16 mm., is produced by the interaction of cyclo-octene, acetyl chloride and stannic chloride; on hydrogenation it yields **acetylcyclo-octane,** *semicarbazone*, m.p. 180–181° (*L. Ruzicka* and *H. A. Boekenoogen, loc. cit.*).

Cyclo-octa-1:5-dione, b.p. 107–110°/14 mm., m.p. 20–24°, *disemicarbazone*, m.p. 186°, has been isolated as an ozonisation product of regenerated para-caoutchouc (*C. Harries*, Ber., 1913, **46**, 733, 2590).

2:6-**Diphenylcyclo-octa-1:5-dione** (II), m.p. 217–220°, *dioxime*, m.p. 148–150 , *monoenol acetate*, m.p. 123–124°, is prepared by the oxidation of the bicyclic compound (I); on reduction with zinc and acetic acid it yields the bicyclic pinacol (III) (*S. Wawzonek*, J. Amer. chem. Soc., 1943, **65**, 889).

(I) $\xrightarrow{O}$ (II) $\xrightarrow{H_2}$ (III)

(f) Carboxylic acids

Cyclo-octanecarboxylic acid, b.p. 150°/19 mm., *amide*, m.p. 191°, is prepared by oxidation of the corresponding carbinol (*L. Ruzicka* and *W. Brugger*, Helv., 1926, **9**, 399), and by treatment of cyclo-octylmagnesium bromide with carbon dioxide (*M. Godchot* and *G. Cauquil*, C.A. 1934, **28**, 468).

Application of the Reformatsky reaction to cyclo-octanone yields **cyclo-octenylacetic acid**, b.p. 135–137°/2 mm. which, on hydrogenation, gives **cyclo-octylacetic acid,** b.p. 130°/1 mm., n_D^{20} 1·4820 (*L. Ruzicka* and *H. A. Boekenoogen, loc. cit.*).

3. Macrocyclic compounds

Carbocyclic compounds containing nine or more carbon atoms in the ring are generally termed macrocyclic or many membered ring compounds. The conflict of the existence of such molecules with the tenets of the Baeyer strain theory and the subsequent resolution of the problem have already been discussed (p. 3). The correlation of the physical properties of the systems with their fine structure or "constellation" has also been dealt with (p. 7ff); chemical evidence for such constellations in the case of the macrocyclic ketones will be presented in the appropriate section (p. 273).

The foundation of the study of these cyclic systems was laid by the beautiful work of L. Ruzicka and his collaborators by which the constitutions of the natural odorants muscone and civetone were established as derivatives of cyclopentadecane and cycloheptadecane respectively. As discussion of the degradation and synthesis of these two natural products presupposes considerable acquaintance with the chemistry of macrocyclic compounds these topics are dealt with after the macrocyclic ketones.

The majority of the procedures for preparing macrocyclic compounds employ the aliphatic $\alpha\omega$-dicarboxylic acids as starting materials and it is fortunate that convenient preparative methods for these latter have been developed concurrently (*P. Chuit et al.*, Helv., 1926, **9**, 264, 1074; 1927, **10**, 114, 167; 1929, **12**, 463, 850, 1096).

(a) *Hydrocarbons*

A list of macrocyclic hydrocarbons, saturated and unsaturated, is given in Table 4, with references.

The saturated hydrocarbons are usually prepared: (1) by Clemmensen reduction of the ketones; (2) by the Kishner-Wolff reduction of the ketone semicarbazones; (3) by dehydration of the alcohols followed by reduction; (4) by reduction of the iodides.

Cyclodecane is obtained by a special procedure from decalin thus (*W. Hückel et al.*, Ann., 1929, **474**, 121; ref. 2, Table 4).

$\xrightarrow{O_3}$ OH $\longrightarrow$ $\xrightarrow{O_3}$ O O $\xrightarrow[\text{dioxime}]{\text{via}}$

Cycloundecane is made in similar fashion from bicyclo[5:4:0]undecane (ref. 3, Table 4).

Vigorous oxidation of these saturated hydrocarbons results in ring fission to produce the corresponding aliphatic $\alpha\omega$-dicarboxylic acids but otherwise their chemical inertness parallels that of the straight chain paraffins.

The few monoethylenic hydrocarbons known are produced by dehydration of the corresponding alcohols or by the action of nitrous acid on the vicinal amino-

TABLE 4

MACROCYCLIC HYDROCARBONS

Compound	M.p.°	B.p.°/mm.	d	n	Ref.
Cyclononane	9·7	69/14	$d_4^{15.2}$ 0·8534	n_D^{16} 1·4328	1
Cyclodecane	9·5	69/12	d_4^{20} 0·8575	n_D^{20} 1·4714	2
Cycloundecane	–7·3	91/12	d_4^{20} 0·8591		3
Cyclododecane	61		d_4^{20} 0·861		4
Cyclotridecane	23·5	128/20	d_4^{20} 0·861		4
Cyclotetradecane	54	131/11	d_4^{20} 0·863		4
Cyclopentadecane	61	147/12	d_4^{20} 0·860		4
Methylcyclo-pentadecane	–19	148/12	d_4^{20} 0·8576	n_D^{21} 1·4735	4
Cyclohexadecane	57	170/20	d_4^{20} 0·854		4
Cycloheptadecane	65		d_4^{20} 0·853		4
Cyclo-octadecane	72		d_4^{20} 0·853		4
Cyclodocosane	46		d_4^{20} 0·850		4
Cyclotricosane	49	177/0·4	d_4^{55} 0·8305		5
Cyclotetracosane	47				4
Cyclohexacosane	42		0·847		4
Cyclo-octacosane	48		0·846		4
Cyclononacosane	47		0·851		4
Cyclotriacontane	56		0·855		4
Cyclotridecene		122/10	d_4^{19} 0·870		8
Cyclopentadecene	37	122/2	0·872	n_D^{20} 1·4832	5
Cyclohexadecene		104/0·1			8
Cycloheptadecene	47	115/0·3			6
Cyclopentadecyne		158/14	d_4^{21} 0·8843	n_D^{21} 1·4910	7
Cycloheptadecyne		127/25	d_4^{22} 0·8840	n_D^{22} 1·4864	7

[1] *L. Ruzicka, P. A. Plattner* and *H. Wild*, Helv., 1945, **28**, 395.
[2] *P. A. Plattner* and *J. Hulstkamp*, Helv., 1944, **27**, 220.
[3] *P. A. Plattner*, Helv., 1944, **27**, 801.
[4] *L. Ruzicka et al.*, Helv., 1930, **13**, 1158.
[5] *L. Ruzicka* and *H. A. Boekenoogen*, Helv., 1931, **14**, 1319.
[6] *L. Ruzicka, H. Schinz* and *C. F. Seidel*, Helv., 1927, **10**, 695.
[7] *L. Ruzicka, M. Hürbin* and *H. A. Boekenoogen*, Helv., 1933, **16**, 498.
[8] *M. Stoll*, Helv., 1947, **40**, 1837.

alcohols (ref. 8). Addition of bromine to cyclopentadecene and cycloheptadecene followed by the action of alcoholic potash yields respectively 1-*bromocyclopentadec*-1-*ene*, b.p. 132°/0·25 mm. and 1-*bromocycloheptadec*-1-*ene*, b.p. 150°/0·5 mm., further dehydrobromination of which produces the cyclic acetylenes cyclopentadecyne and cycloheptadecyne (ref. 7). For references to later work on macrocyclic ethylenes and acetylenes see Chapter 1, p. 5.

The known macrocyclic halides are not numerous. *Iodocyclononane*, b.p.

81°/0·3 mm., $d_4^{16.2}$ 1·486, *iodocyclotridecane* and *iodocyclotetradecane* are obtained by the action of hydriodic acid on the alcohols (ref. 1, Table 4).

Few macrocyclic amines have been investigated. The 1:6-**diaminocyclodecanes,** two isomers, *α*, b.p. 145°/12 mm., m.p. 43–46°, *diacetyl,* m.p. 296°, *dipicrate,* m.p. 280–285° (dec.), and *β*, b.p. 145°/12 mm., m.p. 8–10°, *diacetyl,* m.p. 253°, *dipicrate,* m.p. 247–252° (dec.) are prepared by reduction of the corresponding dioxime (ref. 2); 1:6-**diaminocycloundecane,** b.p. 156–158°/12 mm., *diacetyl,* m.p. 252·5°, *dipicrate,* m.p. 233–235° is obtained similarly (ref. 3, Table 4) (cf. also *V. Prelog et al.*, Helv. 1950, **33**, 365).

(b) Alcohols

The alcohols, which are listed in Table 5, are best prepared by catalytic hydrogenation of the ketones with Raney nickel (ref. 1). **Cyclononanol** has been obtained by the Demjanov ring expansion of cyclo-octylmethylamine (*L. Ruzicka* and *W. Brugger,* Helv., 1926, **9,** 399). Cyclotridecanol, cyclopentadecanol cycloheptadecanol and cyclononadecanol are found in the secretion of the musk-rat, *Ondatra zibethicus, rivalicius* (*P. G. Stevens* and *J. L. E. Erickson,* J. Amer. chem. Soc., 1942, **64,** 144; 1945, **67,** 907). The diols are obtained by reduction of the corresponding diketones (ref. 3) or acyloins (ref. 2). The properties of these compounds are in no way different from those of ordinary secondary alcohols.

TABLE 5

MACROCYCLIC ALCOHOLS

Compounds	B.p.°/mm.	M.p.°	Derivative, m.p.°		Ref.
Cyclononanol	115/17		phenylurethane	47 and 54	1
Cyclodecanol	125/12	41	,,	83	1
Cycloundecanol	131/20	4	,,	58–59	1
Cyclododecanol		80	,,	128–129	1
Cyclotridecanol		60	,,	84–85	1
Cyclotetradecanol		80	,,	132–133	1
Cyclopentadecanol		81	,,	104	1
Cyclohexadecanol		80	,,	79–80	1
Cycloheptadecanol		81	,,	79	1
Cyclo-octadecanol		81	,,	88·5	1
Cyclononadecanol		89	,,	72	1
Cycloeicosanol		69	,,		1
Cyclononane-1:2-diol		112			2
Cyclodecane-1:2-diol		141·5			2
Cyclodecane-1:6-diol		*α* 151–153	dibenzoate	168	3
		β 146	,,	77	

[1] *L. Ruzicka et al.*, Helv., 1949, **32,** 256.
[2] *V. Prelog et al.*, Helv., 1947, **30,** 1741.
[3] *P. A. Plattner* and *J. Hulstkamp,* Helv., 1944, **27,** 211.

(c) Ketones

(i) Saturated ketones

TABLE 6

MACROCYCLIC KETONES

Compound	B.p.°/mm.	M.p.°	M.p.° of oxime	M.p.° of semicarbazone
Cyclononanone	95/12	34	79	182 (a)
Cyclodecanone	107/13	28	80	205 (b)
Cycloundecanone	108/12	10	81	204
Cyclododecanone	125/12	61	132	219 (c)
Cyclotridecanone	138/12	32	106	208
Cyclotetradecanone	155/12	52	114	198
Cyclopentadecanone (exaltone)	120/0·3	63	77	188
2-Methylcyclopentadecan-1-one	173/12			150
4-Methylcyclopentadecan-1-one	125/0·5	29		162
5-Methylcyclopentadecan-1-one	125/0·5			165
Cyclohexadecanone	138/0·3	64	64	180
Cycloheptadecanone	145/1		63	
Cyclo-octadecanone	158/0·3	72	49	184
Cyclononadecanone	160/0·3	72	58	
Cycloeicosanone	171/0·3	59	45	180
Cycloheneicosanone	177/0·3	46		
Cyclodocosanone		32		
Cyclotricosanone		39		
Cyclotetracosanone	238/0·4	36		
Cyclohexacosanone	212/0·3	42		
Cyclo-octacosanone	210/0·25	45		
Cyclononacosanone	220/0·1	47		
Cyclotricontanone		54		

M.p. of 2:4-dinitrophenylhydrazones (a) 136° (b) 167° (c) 153°.
(For references see following text.)

The ketones (Table 6) are the most important compounds of the macrocyclic series and serve as starting materials for most syntheses in this field. The methods of preparation may conveniently be discussed in historical order.

(1) *Ruzicka's method*. This consists in the pyrolysis *in vacuo* of the thorium, yttrium or cerium salts of the aliphatic αω-dicarboxylic acids; cyclic ketones containing one carbon atom less than the starting acid are produced. Two by-products are formed; the first, an aliphatic ketone, is readily removed by means of sodium bisulphite; the second is the symmetrical monocyclic diketone of twice the molecular weight which may readily be isolated by

$$\overline{(CH_2)_n\ CO} \longleftarrow (CH_2)_n(CO_2H)_2 \longrightarrow \overline{(CH_2)_n(CO)_2(CH_2)_n}$$

virtue of its high boiling point (*L. Ruzicka et al.*, Helv., 1926, 9, 389, 499; 715; 1928, 11, 496, 670; 1932, 15, 1459).

The technical modification of this process involves heating a mixture of the dicarboxylic acid with cerium or thorium oxide; in an alternative procedure the vapour of the acid is passed over either of these oxides [*M. Naef & Cie*, B.P. 235,540 (1924); 251,188 (1925)].

The yields obtained in this process are largely dependent on the size of the ring in the final product; thus the yields of C_7 and C_8 ketones are fair (20–40%) but those of the ketones in the range C_9–C_{13} are not more than 0·5%. From C_{13} upwards the yield improves, reaches a maximum (5%) for the C_{18} ketone and then falls again to a lower level (2%).

(2) *Ziegler's method*. In the preparation of macrocyclic compounds from dicarboxylic acids or their derivatives it is apparent that there exist two competing processes, the intramolecular reaction leading to the desired compound and the intermolecular reaction yielding polymeric products. An obvious device to suppress the latter in favour of the former is to carry out the condensation at high dilution in a homogeneous medium (*P. Ruggli*, Ann., 1912, **392**, 92; *G. M. Bennett*, Trans. Faraday Soc., 1941, **37**, 794). In 1933 K. Ziegler successfully worked out a technique applying this dilution principle.

$(CH_2)_n$ with $-CH_2CN$ / $-CH_2CN$ $\xrightarrow{LiN<^{Et}_{Ph}}$ $(CH_2)_n$ with $-CH_2CN$ / $-CHCN$ (Li) $\longrightarrow$ $(CH_2)_n$ with $-CH_2-C{=}NLi$ / $-CHCN$ $\xrightarrow{\text{Hydrolysis} -CO_2}$ $(CH_2)_n$ with $-CH_2-CO$ / $-CH_2$

The reactions involved are delineated in the above flow-sheet. An aliphatic $\alpha\omega$-dinitrile is treated with the ether-soluble lithium ethylanilide whereby a monolithium salt is produced which readily undergoes cyclisation to a ketiminonitrile salt; hydrolysis and decarboxylation then furnishes the macrocyclic ketone. In practice a solution of the dinitrile in ether is added extremely slowly to a boiling ethereal solution of the condensing agent; in this way the required high dilution is attained without the necessity of employing a large volume of solvent. The yields obtained by this process are as follows: C_7 95%, C_8 88%, C_9–C_{11} negligible, C_{12} 8%, C_{13} 15%, C_{14}–C_{25} ca. 60%. It is seen that even this refined procedure has a zone of minimum yield and does not lend itself to the preparation of compounds with nine to eleven carbon atoms in the ring (*K. Ziegler et al.*, Ann., 1933, **504**, 94; 1934, **512**, 164; 1934, **513**, 14; 1937, **528**, 114; Ber., 1934, **67A**, 139).

(3) *Hunsdiecker's method.* This procedure involves an intramolecular condensation of an ω-halogenoacylacetic ester to yield a cyclic β-keto-ester which on hydrolysis and decarboxylation furnishes the corresponding cyclic ketone, *e.g.*

$$(CH_2)_n\begin{cases}CO\cdot CH_2\cdot CO_2Et\\ CH_2Br\end{cases} \longrightarrow (CH_2)_n\begin{cases}CO\cdot CHCO_2Et\\ \quad\quad | \\ \quad\quad CH_2\end{cases} \longrightarrow (CH_2)_n\begin{cases}CO\cdot CH_2\\ \quad\quad | \\ \quad\quad CH_2\end{cases}$$

The reaction is carried out at high dilution in methyl ethyl ketone employing potassium carbonate as condensing agent. This method produces C_{14}–C_{17} ketones in good yield (*H. Hunsdiecker*, Ber., 1942, 75, 1190, 1197; *M. Stoll*, Helv., 1947, 30, 1401).

(4) *Diketen method.* When $\alpha\omega$-dicarboxylic acid chlorides are treated with ethereal triethylamine, $\alpha\omega$-diketens are formed which readily undergo intramolecular condensation to give a macrocyclic product with a constitution (I) analogous to a keten dimer (cf. Vol. I, p. 528). Alkaline hydrolysis of (I) gives the corresponding macrocyclic ketone, the diketone of double the molecular size and polymeric products; frequently the dione is the only isolatable product.

$$(CH_2)_n\begin{cases}CH_2\cdot COCl\\ CH_2\cdot COCl\end{cases} \longrightarrow (CH_2)_n\begin{cases}CH{=}CO\\ CH{=}CO\end{cases} \longrightarrow (CH_2)_n\begin{cases}CH\\ \| \\ C{-}O\\ | \quad | \\ CH{-}CO\end{cases}$$

(I)

$$(CH_2)_n\begin{cases}CH_2\\ | \\ CO\\ | \\ CH_2\end{cases} + \begin{matrix}CO\\ (CH_2)_{n+2}\quad(CH_2)_{n+2}\\ CO\end{matrix}$$

The yields by this method are generally superior to those obtained by the Ruzicka method but inferior to those of Ziegler and Hunsdiecker although it has the advantage of the latter in convenience (*A. T. Blomquist et al.*, J. Amer. chem. Soc., 1947, 69, 472; 1948, 70, 30, 34).

(5) *Acyloin method.* This procedure, worked out independently and simultaneously by *M. Stoll* and *V. Prelog*, is the method *par excellence* for obtaining macrocyclic compounds. The process involves heating a well stirred solution of an $\alpha\omega$-dicarboxylic ester in xylene with molten sodium. An

intramolecular acyloin condensation takes place to give cyclic α-hydroxy-ketones of type (I).

$$\begin{array}{l} \ulcorner CO_2Et \\ (CH_2)_n \\ \llcorner CO_2Et \end{array} \longrightarrow \begin{array}{l} \ulcorner\text{———}CO \\ (CH_2)_n \quad | \\ \llcorner\text{———}CHOH \end{array}$$

(I)

Use of a high dilution is quite unnecessary and the yields are spectacular; even in the minute yield region of the Ruzicka and Ziegler procedures (C_9–C_{13}) 40% yields of the cyclic acyloins are readily obtainable. Furthermore, the yield increases with increasing ring size of the product and reaches 96% for the C_{21} acyloin (*V. Prelog et al.*, Helv., 1947, **30**, 1741; *M. Stoll et al.*, Helv., 1947, **30**, 1815, 1822, 1837). The acyloins may be readily converted to the ketones either by direct reduction with zinc and acid, or by dehydration and subsequent hydrogenation of the αβ-unsaturated ketone produced (*idem, ibid.*).

This new technique undoubtedly represents the major single advance in this field; by its use the whole range of macrocyclic compounds has been made readily available for comparative study in a manner hitherto impossible.

Properties of the ketones

In view of their relationship to the natural odorants muscone and civetone it is interesting to note the following odour "spectrum" of the macrocyclic ketones. The odour of the ketones up to C_{12} is camphoraceous and that of the C_{13} ketone resembles cedar wood with a faint suggestion of musk. The C_{14} ketone smells distinctly of musk and this odour reaches its full strength in the C_{15} ketone; further enlargement of the ring results in a progressive weakening of the odour. Substitution of the ring has little effect on the odour (*L. Ruzicka et al.*, Helv., 1931, **14**, 1319).

The macrocyclic ketones react with the usual carbonyl reagents in the expected fashion. The oximes undergo the Beckmann rearrangement in acid medium to furnish cyclic amides or lactams (the so-called *iso*-oximes) which can be reduced to polymethylene imines by various reducing agents the best being lithium aluminium hydride (*L. Ruzicka et al.*, Helv., 1949, **32**, 544; 1935, **18**, 659; 1933, **16**, 1323).

$$\overbrace{(CH_2)_n\ C{=}NOH} \longrightarrow \begin{array}{l} \ulcorner\text{———}CO \\ (CH_2)_n \quad | \\ \llcorner\text{———}NH \end{array} \longrightarrow \begin{array}{l} \ulcorner\text{———}CH_2 \\ (CH_2)_n \quad | \\ \llcorner\text{———}NH \end{array}$$

Caro's acid reacts with the ketones to form macrocyclic lactones.

The question of the molecular fine structure of the macrocyclic ketones has been investigated by *V. Prelog* and his collaborators (for review see J. chem.

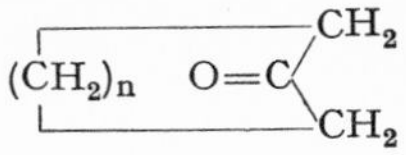

$(CH_2)_n$ O=C<(CH_2)(CH_2) (ring) (I) $(CH_2)_n$ (CH_2)(CH_2)>C=O (ring) (II)

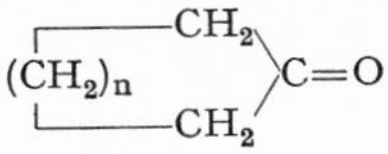

Soc., 1950, 420). From consideration of models it becomes apparent that the greater the number of energetically favourable *b* and *d* constellations (see p. 9) employed in the construction of a macrocyclic ketone the more tendency there is for the oxygen atom of the carbonyl group to assume a shielded position inside the ring as in (I); this "O-inside" structure is stabilised still further in the case of the medium-sized ring ketones by the formation of hydrogen bonds between the oxygen atom and the hydrogen atoms of the polymethylene chain. Conversely, if the ring be constituted from energetically unfavourable constellations the oxygen atom takes up an exposed position as in (II); this "O-outside" structure occurs in the small-ring ketones. These conceptions are well borne out when the course of certain condensation reactions of the cyclic ketones is studied.

A. 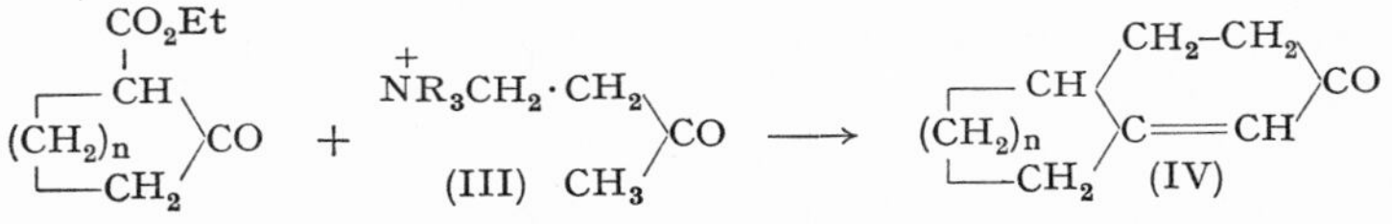 $(CH_2)_n$[CH(CO_2Et)–CO–CH_2] (ring) + $\overset{+}{N}R_3CH_2 \cdot CH_2$–CO–$CH_3$ (III) ⟶ $(CH_2)_n$[CH–C=CH–CO–CH_2–CH_2–; CH_2] (IV)

B. 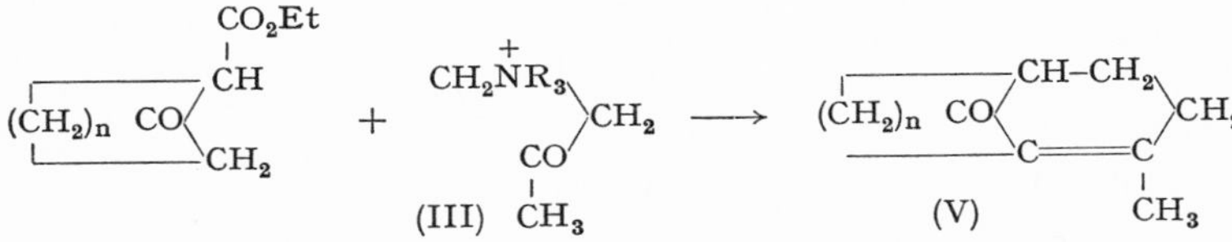 $(CH_2)_n$ CO<[CH(CO_2Et)][CH_2] (ring) + $CH_2\overset{+}{N}R_3$–CH_2–CO–CH_3 (III) ⟶ $(CH_2)_n$ CO<[CH–CH_2>CH_2][C=C(CH_3)] (V)

It has been found that the course of the reaction between the quaternary base of 4-diethylaminobutan-2-one and macrocyclic β-keto-esters is conditioned by the ring size of the latter compounds. The esters derived from cyclohexanone ($n = 3$) and cycloheptanone ($n = 4$) enter into the condensation in the expected fashion (Robinson-Mannich reaction) to yield fused ring ketones of type (IV) (Scheme A). These latter form the usual carbonyl derivatives and produce no acetic acid on chromic acid oxidation by the Kuhn-Roth procedure. On the other hand the products from the esters derived from cyclononanone ($n = 6$) to cyclopentadecanone ($n = 12$) inclusive do not react to form carbonyl derivatives and give one mol. of acetic acid on Kuhn-Roth oxidation. Examination of the properties of these "abnormal" products leads inescapably to the conclusion that they possess a bridged ring structure of type (V) (Scheme B), the lack of carbonyl reactivity being due to the highly sheltered position of the keto-group. In the case of cyclo-octanone both types of product are formed. It is seen that this clear-cut difference in reaction can be interpreted very successfully by the constellation concepts outlined above (*V. Prelog, L. Ruzicka et al.*, Helv., 1947, **30**, 1883; 1948, **31**, 92; 1950, **33**, 356).

A further point of interest with regard to the compounds of type (V) is their apparent conflict with the tenets of Bredt's rule. This states that derivatives of bicyclo[3:1:1]heptane and bicyclo[2:2:1]heptane with a double bond at the bridge head [e.g. (VI) and (VII)] are incapable of existence.

CH_2 (VI) CH_2 (VII) $(CH_2)_n$ CH_2 (VIII)

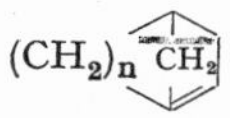

The above investigations show that the rule also holds for similarly constituted substance (VIII) when n = 3 or 4 but is no longer valid when n = 5 and upwards. A more general formulation of the Bredt rule may be derived from a consideration of the geometrical isomerism about the double bond with respect to the largest ring (n + 4 members in VIII). Thus it may be stated (R. Robinson) that the Bredt rule no longer holds when this ring is of sufficient size to accomodate a *trans* configuration about the double bond (for an interpretation in terms of molecular orbitals see *V. Prelog, M. Barman* and *M. Zimmerman*, Helv., 1949, **32**, 1284).

Further evidence for the occurrence of the large ring ketones in the constellation (I) is provided by the result of their reaction with nitromalonic dialdehyde.

$(CH_2)_n$ CO$<$(CH_2)(CH_2) (I) + OCH, OCH $>CHNO_2$ $\longrightarrow$ $(CH_2)_n$ HO–C$_6$H$_2$–NO_2 (IX)

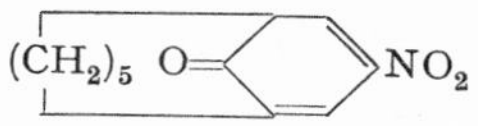

$(CH_2)_5$ O= NO_2 (X)

The higher ketones (cyclononanone to cyclotriacontanone) existing in constellation (I), condense readily with this reagent to give the meta-bridged nitrophenols of type (IX) (n = 6 to 27), while cyclohexanone and cycloheptanone yield no definite product. Cyclo-octanone furnishes compound (X) which shows no tendency to aromatize (*V. Prelog et al.*, Helv., 1947, **30**, 1465; 1948, **31**, 1325).

(ii) Unsaturated ketones

Ethylenic cyclic ketones such as *cyclohexadec-8-en-1-one*, m.p. 23° and *cyclo-octadec-9-en-1-one*, m.p. 38°, are obtained from the corresponding unsaturated dicarboxylic acids by the Ruzicka method (Helv., 1932, **15**, 1459). $\alpha\beta$-Unsaturated ketones are prepared by the dehydration of the α-hydroxy-ketones (acyloins). In this way are obtained *cyclodec-2-en-1-one*, b.p. 106–114°/14 mm., *cyclotridec-2-en-1-one*, b.p. 157–158°/17 mm., and *cyclopentadec-2-en-1-one*, b.p. 123–127°/0·13 mm., $n_D^{19.7}$ 1·4944 (*M. Stoll et al.*, Helv., 1947, **30**, 1837; 1948, **31**, 554). For cycloheptadec-9-en-1-one, see civetone, p. 278.

(iii) α-Hydroxy-ketones (α-ketols, acyloins)

TABLE 7

MACROCYCLIC α-HYDROXY-KETONES

Compound	B.p.°/mm.	M.p.°	M.p.° of oxime
Cyclononanolone (azeloin)	110–112/10	43	116–117
Cyclodecanolone (sebacoin)	124–127/10	38–39	100–102
Cycloundecanolone	100–105/0·12	29–33	119–120
Cyclododecanolone	106–109/0·09	78–79	131–132
Cyclotridecanolone (brassyloin)	126–139/0·2	45–46	98–99
Cyclotetradecanolone	116–124/0·15	84–85	123–124
Cyclopentadecanolone	123–139/0·02	57–58	110–111
Cyclohexadecanolone (thapsoin)	143–146/0·1	56–58	110–111
Cycloheptadecanolone	168–170/0·1	53–54	119–120
Cyclo-octadecanolone	155–160/0·15	59–60	
Cycloeicosanolone	210–225/0·3		

V. Prelog et al., Helv., 1947, **30**, 1741.
M. Stoll et al., Helv., 1947, **30**, 1815, 1822.

The elegant and convenient preparation in good yield of these cyclic acyloins (Table 7) has already been discussed (p. 272; cf. also *S. M. McElvain*, Org. Reactions, 1948, **4**, 263). These products are a fruitful source of many other types of macrocyclic compound; thus catalytic hydrogenation furnishes the corresponding α-glycols, oxidation yields the α-diketones and dehydration produces the αβ-unsaturated ketones which may readily be hydrogenated to the macrocyclic ketones themselves. Reduction of the oximes leads to the corresponding α-amino-alcohols. Oxidation of the acyloins with alkaline hydrogen peroxide or silver oxide regenerates the starting aliphatic αω-dicarboxylic acids.

(iv) Diketones

TABLE 8

MACROCYCLIC α-DIKETONES

Compound	M.p.°	M.p.° of bis-2:4-dinitro-phenylhydrazone	M.p.° of quinoxaline
Cyclononane-1:2-dione		250–251	66
Cyclodecane-1:2-dione	44	272 (dec.)	
Cyclododecane-1:2-dione	44	282	86
Cyclotetradecane-1:2-dione		284·5	
Cyclohexadecane-1:2-dione		243	

V. Prelog et al., Helv., 1947, **30**, 1741.

a-**Diketones** (Table 8) are formed as by-products in the acyloin synthesis and may also be obtained by oxidation of the acyloins themselves.

Symmetrical diketones of type

$$\begin{array}{ccc} & \ulcorner\text{---CO---}\urcorner & \\ (CH_2)_n & & (CH_2)_n \\ & \llcorner\text{---CO---}\lrcorner & \end{array}$$

are listed in Table 9.

TABLE 9

SYMMETRICAL MACROCYCLIC DIKETONES

	M.p.°	M.p.° of dioxime	Ref.
Cyclodecane-1:6-dione	100	231	1
Cycloundecane-1:6-dione	(b.p. 115°/0·1 mm.)	232–234 (dec.)	2
Cyclotetradecane-1:8-dione	147·5–148	234–235 (dec.)	3
Cyclohexadecane-1:9-dione	83–84	185–186	4
Cyclo-octadecane-1:10-dione	96–97	166–168	4
Cycloeicosane-1:11-dione	51		4
Cyclodocosane-1:12-dione	55–56		4
Cyclotetracosane-1:13-dione	64–65		4
Cyclohexacosane-1:14-dione	68–69		4
Cyclo-octacosane-1:15-dione	72–73		4
Cyclotriacontane-1:16-dione	78–79	130–131	4
Cyclodotriacontane-1:17-dione	77–78		4
Cyclotetratriacontane-1:18-dione	84		4

[1] *W. Hückel et al.*, Ann., 1929, **474**, 121; Ber., 1933, **66**, 563. *P. A. Plattner et al.*, Helv., 1944, **27**, 211, 220.
[2] *P. A. Plattner*, Helv. 1944, **27**, 801.
[3] *A. T. Blomquist* and *R. T. Spencer*, J. Amer. chem. Soc., 1948, **70**, 30.
[4] *L. Ruzicka et al.*, Helv. 1928, **11**, 496, 676; 1930, **13**, 1152; 1931, **14**, 1319.

The first member of the symmetrical series, cyclodecane-1:6-dione, is prepared from decalin by the special method outlined on p. 267; undecane-1:6-dione is obtained similarly from bicyclo[5:4:0]undecane. The remaining diketones are formed as the dimeric by-products in the Ruzicka, Ziegler and diketen methods of preparation of the macrocyclic ketones.

Muscone and Civetone

The animal secretions containing these two substances have been known for a very long time as they constitute the most valued perfumery fixative and blending agents of animal origin (cf. *T. F. West, H. J. Strausz* and *D. H. R. Barton*, "Synthetic Perfumes", Edward Arnold & Co., 1949, pp. 186 *et seq.*, 331 *et seq.*). The establishment of the constitution of these two substances as derivatives of the hitherto unknown class of macrocyclic compounds provided the initial stimulus for the further study of such systems.

(1) **Civetone** (cis-*cycloheptadec-9-en-1-one*)

The animal secretion civet is found in the anal sac of the civet cat; its characteristic odour is due in the main to the presence of two compounds, skatole and civetone. These two substances were first isolated from civet by *A. Sack* (Chem. Ztg., 1915, **39**, 538).

The constitution of civetone was elucidated by *L. Ruzicka* in the following manner (Helv., 1926, **9**, 230, 249, 339, 388, 499, 716; Chem. and Ind., 1935, **54**, 2). The presence of an ethylenic double bond and a carbonyl group in civetone ($C_{17}H_{30}O$) was readily shown by the usual methods. On catalytic hydrogenation it absorbed one mol. of hydrogen to form dihydrocivetone ($C_{17}H_{32}O$); this latter condensed readily with benzaldehyde thus indicating the presence of a ketomethylene group. Thus dihydrocivetone may be represented by the partial formula (I).

(I) $C_{15}H_{30}$ ring closed by —CO—CH_2— $\xrightarrow{\text{via oxime}}$ $C_{15}H_{30}$ ring closed by —CO—NH—CH_2— $\longrightarrow$ (II) $(CH_2)_{15}$ bearing —CO_2H and —CH_2NH_2

(I) $\xrightarrow{CrO_3}$ (III) $(CH_2)_{15}$ bearing —CO_2H and —CO_2H

The oxime of dihydrocivetone readily underwent the Beckmann rearrangement to give a cyclic amide which, on hydrolysis, produced 17-aminoheptadecanoic acid (II), containing the same number of carbon atoms. Chromic acid oxidation of dihydrocivetone furnished pentadecane-1:15-dicarboxylic acid (III) with the same number of carbon atoms. These two results demonstrated conclusively that not only was the keto group situated in a ring, but that this ring must be seventeen membered. Confirmation of this point was provided by oxidation of the Clemmensen reduction product of civetone, civetene (IV) when the same $\alpha\omega$-dicarboxylic acid was produced.

$$\text{CH=CH ring with } C_{15}H_{28}O \longrightarrow \text{CH=CH ring with } C_{15}H_{30}\ \text{(IV)} \longrightarrow HO_2C\text{—}(CH_2)_{15}\text{—}CO_2H$$

Final proof was provided by the synthesis of cycloheptadecanone and the demonstration of its identity with dihydrocivetone.

The position of the double bond in civetone was shown by permanganate oxidation when the symmetrical ketodicarboxylic acid (V) was produced.

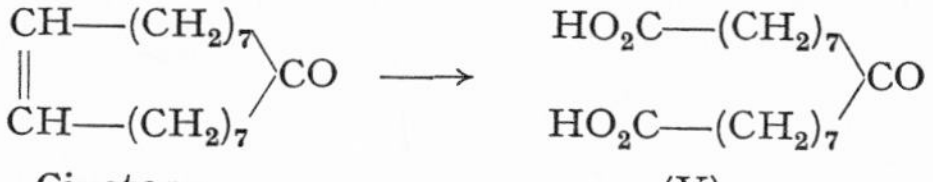

$$\begin{array}{l} CH{-}(CH_2)_7\diagdown \\ \| \qquad\qquad\quad CO \\ CH{-}(CH_2)_7\diagup \end{array} \longrightarrow \begin{array}{l} HO_2C{-}(CH_2)_7\diagdown \\ \qquad\qquad\qquad CO \\ HO_2C{-}(CH_2)_7\diagup \end{array}$$

Civetone (V)

Ruzicka has pointed out the similarity of the skeletal structures of civetone and oleic acid and has suggested that the latter acid might well be the biological precursor of the macrocyclic ketone. On this basis civetone might be expected to possess a *cis* configuration about the double bond; synthetic studies have fully confirmed this idea.

The first synthesis of *trans*-civetone was due to H. Hunsdiecker who effected the ring closure of compound VI (prepared from aleuritic acid, Vol. I, 1165) by the method already described (p. 272).

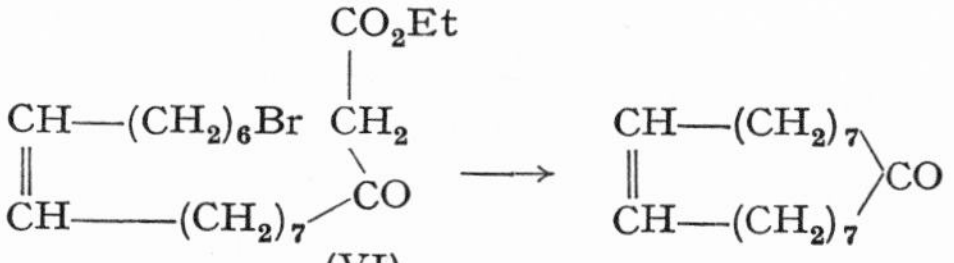

$$\begin{array}{l} \qquad\qquad\qquad\quad CO_2Et \\ \qquad\qquad\qquad\quad | \\ CH{-}(CH_2)_6Br\ \ CH_2 \\ \| \qquad\qquad\qquad\quad \diagdown \\ CH{-}(CH_2)_7{-}CO \end{array} \longrightarrow \begin{array}{l} CH{-}(CH_2)_7\diagdown \\ \| \qquad\qquad\quad CO \\ CH{-}(CH_2)_7\diagup \end{array}$$

(VI)

The product was not identical with the natural odorant and was almost certainly *trans*-civetone (*H. Hunsdiecker*, Ber., 1943, **76**, 142; cf. also *A. T. Blomquist* and *R. W. Holley*, J. Amer. chem. Soc., 1948, **70**, 36).

trans-Civetone has also been synthesized by the diketen method (p. 272) employing as starting material hexadec-8-ene-1:16-dicarboxylic acid (also prepared from aleuritic acid) (*A. T. Blomquist et al., ibid.*, 1948, **70**, 34).

The total synthesis of the natural *cis*-civetone was accomplished by *M. Stoll, J. Hulstkamp* and *A. Rouvé* (Helv., 1948, **31**, 543).

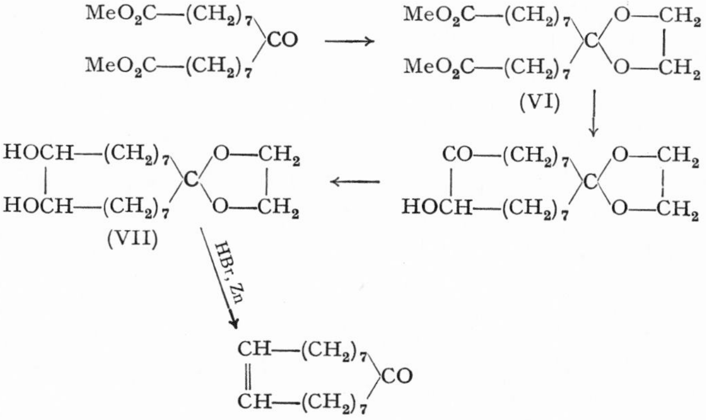

$$\begin{array}{l} MeO_2C{-}(CH_2)_7\diagdown \\ \qquad\qquad\qquad\quad CO \\ MeO_2C{-}(CH_2)_7\diagup \end{array} \longrightarrow \begin{array}{l} MeO_2C{-}(CH_2)_7\diagdown\ \diagup O{-}CH_2 \\ \qquad\qquad\qquad\quad C \qquad | \\ MeO_2C{-}(CH_2)_7\diagup\ \diagdown O{-}CH_2 \end{array}$$

(VI) $\downarrow$

$$\begin{array}{l} HOCH{-}(CH_2)_7\diagdown\ \diagup O{-}CH_2 \\ | \qquad\qquad\qquad\quad C \qquad | \\ HOCH{-}(CH_2)_7\diagup\ \diagdown O{-}CH_2 \end{array} \longleftarrow \begin{array}{l} CO{-}(CH_2)_7\diagdown\ \diagup O{-}CH_2 \\ | \qquad\qquad\qquad C \qquad | \\ HOCH{-}(CH_2)_7\diagup\ \diagdown O{-}CH_2 \end{array}$$

(VII)

$\downarrow$ HBr, Zn

$$\begin{array}{l} CH{-}(CH_2)_7\diagdown \\ \| \qquad\qquad\quad CO \\ CH{-}(CH_2)_7\diagup \end{array}$$

Pentadecan-8-one-1 : 15-dicarboxylic methyl ester was converted to its ethylene ketal (VI) which was then subjected to the acyloin condensation (p. 272). Reduction of the resulting acyloin furnished the glycol (VII) in the two stereoisomeric *erythro* and *threo* forms. Both modifications afforded a mixture of *cis*-civetone (30%) and *trans*-civetone (70%) on treatment with hydrogen bromide/acetic acid followed by zinc dust in alcohol. The two isomers were separated by fractional crystallisation of their ethylene ketals and the *cis*-compound proved to be identical with the natural ketone.

An elegant conversion of *trans*- to *cis*-civetone was recorded by the same authors. *trans*-Civetone ethylene ketal was treated with bromine to give the dibromide (VIII) which, on dehydrobromination with alcoholic potash, furnished the substituted acetylene (IX). Partial catalytic hydrogenation of the latter afforded cis-civetone ethylene ketal.

trans-Civetone ketal $\xrightarrow{Br_2}$ $BrCH—(CH_2)_7$ / $BrCH—(CH_2)_7$ >C< $O—CH_2$ / $O—CH_2$ (VIII)

↓ KOH

cis-Civetone ketal $\xleftarrow{H_2}$ $C—(CH_2)_7$ ≡ $C—(CH_2)_7$ >C< $O—CH_2$ / $O—CH_2$ (IX)

The properties of natural civetone and the synthetic materials are as follows:

	Natural civetone	*cis*-Civetone	*trans*-Civetone
M.p.	31–32°	31–32°	29–30°
d_4^{33}	0·917	0·915	0·913
$b_D^{33.4}$	1·4830	1·4827	1·4812
M.p. of ketal	21–22°	19–21°	49–50°
M.p. of semicarbazone	186–187°	186–187°	195–196°

(2) **Muscone** (l–3-*methylcyclopentadecanone*)

Muscone is the odoriferous principle of musk, used from times of antiquity as a perfume constituent. The natural musk is an animal secretion found in an abdominal sac of the male musk deer *(Moschus moschiferus)*.

The first isolation of a pure ketone from musk was achieved by *H. Wahlbaum* who gave it the name muscone (J. pr. Chem., 1906, [ii], 73, 488). Twenty years later the work was confirmed by *L. Ruzicka* who showed that the ketone was optically active and possessed the molecular formula $C_{16}H_{30}O$ (Helv., 1926, 9, 715, 1008).

An indirect lead to the structure of muscone was provided by the observation that synthetic cyclopentadecanone (exaltone) exhibited the strongest musk odour of the macrocyclic ketones and that methyl substitution in the ring had very little effect on this property (*L. Ruzicka et al.*, Helv., 1926, **9**, 249, 260). This suggested the possibility that muscone was the laevorotatory enantiomorph of one of the seven possible methylcyclopentadecanones. This was confirmed by the Clemmensen reduction of muscone to an optically inactive hydrocarbon $C_{16}H_{32}$ which was shown to be methylcyclopentadecane by direct comparison with a synthetic sample.

Vigorous chromic acid oxidation of muscone yielded two isomeric aliphatic dicarboxylic acids containing the same number of carbon atoms ($C_{16}H_{30}O_4$) together with the even-numbered straight chain $\alpha\omega$-dicarboxylic acids from succinic acid to decane-1:10-dicarboxylic acid. The formation of this last eliminated the possibility that muscone could be represented as 6-, 7- or 8-methylcyclopentadecan-1-one. Further, the formation of the two C_{16} dicarboxylic acids was evidence against the formulation of muscone as 2-methylcyclopentadecan-1-one, as this would have given a keto-acid which would have been readily oxidised further to a C_{15} acid. Again, *l*-2-methylcyclopentadecan-1-one would be expected to racemise very readily via the enol form, but muscone emerged unchanged from all racemisation procedures.

The structures 4- and 5-methylcyclopentadecan-1-one were eliminated by direct comparison of their semicarbazones with that of muscone. This left 3-methylcyclopentadecan-1-one as the only possible structure; confirmation of this was provided in the following manner.

$$\begin{array}{c}\mathrm{CH_2}\text{—}\mathrm{CO}\\ |\quad\quad |\\ \mathrm{Me}\text{—}\mathrm{CH}\quad\quad |\\ |\quad\quad |\\ (\mathrm{CH_2})_{11}\text{—}\mathrm{CH_2}\\ \text{Muscone}\end{array} \longrightarrow \begin{array}{c}\mathrm{CH_2}\text{—}\mathrm{CO}\\ |\quad\quad |\\ \mathrm{Me}\text{—}\mathrm{CH}\quad\quad |\\ |\quad\quad |\\ (\mathrm{CH_2})_{11}\text{—}\mathrm{C{=}CHPh}\\ \text{(IX)}\end{array} \longrightarrow \begin{array}{c}\mathrm{CH_2\cdot CO_2H}\\ |\\ \mathrm{Me}\text{—}\mathrm{CH}\\ |\\ (\mathrm{CH_2})_{11}\cdot\mathrm{CO_2H}\\ \text{(X)}\end{array}$$

Muscone reacted readily with benzaldehyde to yield a single benzylidene compound (IX), condensation taking place exclusively on the less sterically hindered methylene group. Ozonisation of (IX) followed by chromic acid oxidation produced *d*-2-methyltridecane-1:13-dicarboxylic acid (X) which was identified by comparison with a synthetic specimen (*L. Ruzicka et al.*, Helv., 1926, **9**, 715, 1015). The two $C_{16}H_{30}O_4$ acids obtained by oxidation of muscone itself were thus seen to be (X) and 1-methyltridecane-1:13-dicarboxylic acid.

The Ruzicka method (p. 270) for preparing macrocyclic ketones is not applicable to the synthesis of muscone. The first synthesis of *dl*-muscone was achieved by *K. Ziegler* and *K. Weber* (Ann., 1933, **504**, 94; 1934, **512**, 164) who effected the cyclisation of the corresponding branched chain $\alpha\omega$-dinitrile (p. 271). It is interesting that the semicarbazones of *dl*-muscone and natural *l*-muscone have the same melting point which shows no depression when the two are mixed;

it seems that the lone asymmetric centre in such a large molecule exerts very little effect on this property. Syntheses of *dl*-muscone have also been carried out employing the Hunsdiecker method (p. 272; Ber., 1942, **75**, 1190, 1197) and the diketen procedure (*A. T. Blomquist et al.*, J. Amer. chem. Soc., 1948, **70**, 34).

The $\alpha\beta$-unsaturated ketone, cyclopentadec-2-en-1-one, has been employed for two syntheses of *dl*-muscone.

In the first, Michael addition of diethyl malonate followed by hydrolysis and decarboxylation gave the acid (XI) which, on electrolysis, furnished among other products, 3-methylenecyclopentadecanone (XII) which on catalytic hydrogenation yielded *dl*-muscone (*L. Ruzicka* and *M. Stoll*, Helv., 1934, **17**, 1308).

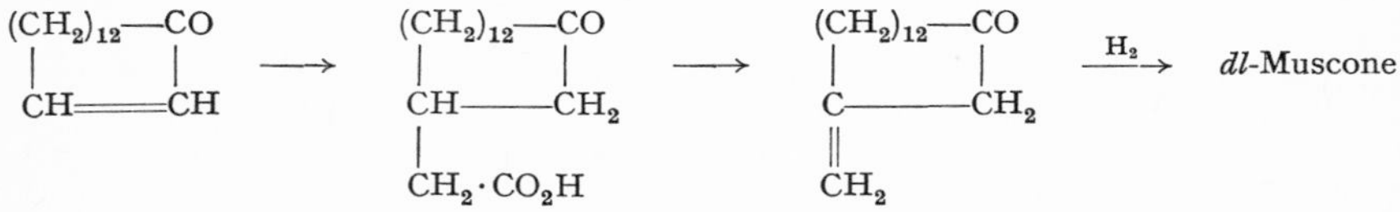

```
(CH2)12—CO           (CH2)12—CO           (CH2)12—CO      H2
|       |     ——→    |       |     ——→    |       |     ——→   dl-Muscone
CH=====CH            CH——————CH2          C———————CH2
                     |                    ‖
                     CH2·CO2H             CH2
                       (XI)                 (XII)
```

In the second, simpler procedure the unsaturated ketone was treated with methylmagnesium bromide in the presence of cuprous chloride; this latter catalyst tends to promote the 1:4-addition leading directly to *dl*-muscone as against the more usual 1:2-addition (*M. Stoll* and *H. Commarmont*, Helv., 1947, **30**, 554).

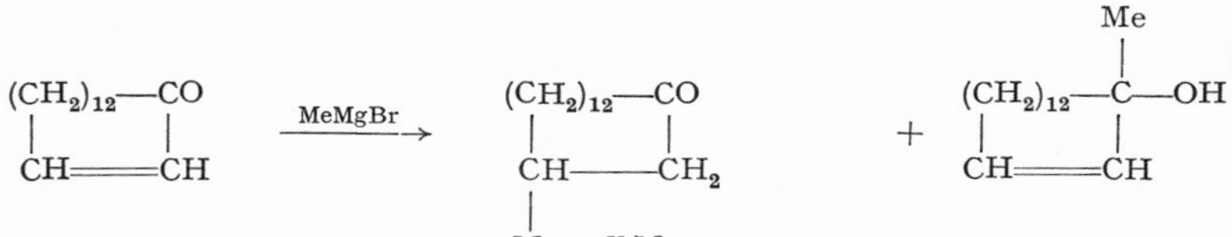

```
                                                                Me
                                                                |
(CH2)12—CO                    (CH2)12—CO                (CH2)12—C—OH
|       |      MeMgBr         |       |            +    |       |
CH=====CH      ——————→        CH——————CH2               CH=====CH
                              |
                              Me   dl-Muscone
                        (1:4-addition product)     (1:2-addition product)
                                 20%                        80%
```

A most elegant synthesis of *dl*-muscone which has technical potentialities is described by *M. Stoll* and *A. Rouvé* (Helv., 1947, **30**, 2019).

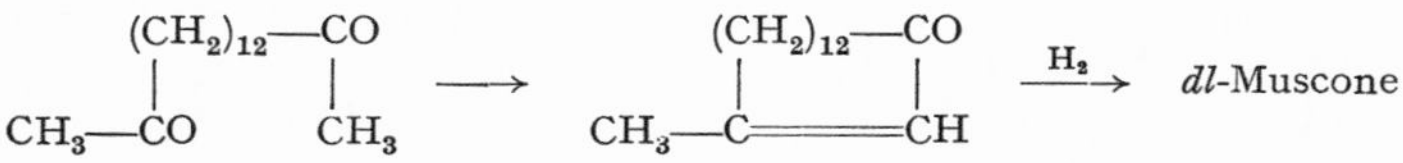

```
     (CH2)12—CO                  (CH2)12—CO       H2
     |       |       ——→         |       |      ——→   dl-Muscone
CH3—CO       CH3          CH3—C==========CH
      (XIII)                     (XIV)
                                  17%
```

Hexadecane-2:15-dione (XIII) when treated in ethereal solution with methylanilinomagnesium bromide was found to undergo an intramolecular aldol condensation with formation of the unsaturated ketone (XIV), hydrogenation of which furnished *dl*-muscone directly.

The properties of the natural (*l*) and synthetic (*dl*) ketones are as follows.

	l-muscone	*dl*-muscone
B.p.	$130^0/0\cdot5$ mm.	$132–134^0/0\cdot8$ mm.
d^{17}	$0\cdot9222$	
n_D^{17}	$1\cdot4802$	
M.p. of semicarbazone	134^0	$133–133\cdot5^0$
M.p. of phenylsemicarbazone		$170–171^0$
M.p. of oxime	46^0	
$[\alpha]_D$	$-13\cdot01^0$	0

Biogenesis of muscone and civetone

As has been briefly mentioned (p. 279) *L. Ruzicka* drew attention to the similarity in structure between civetone and oleic acid on the one hand and muscone and palmitic acid on the other, and put forward the suggestion that these two acids are in fact the biological precursors of the ketones (Helv., 1926, 9, 230, 1008).

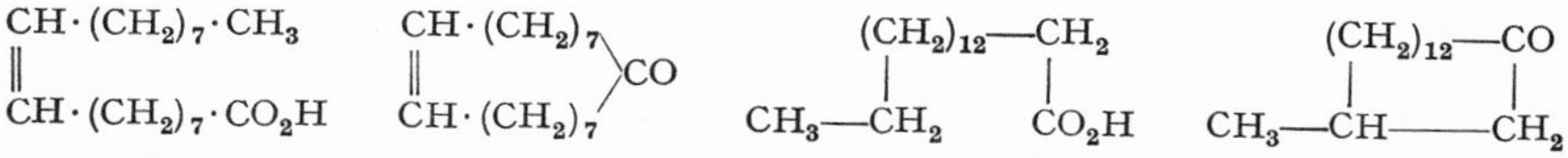

$CH\cdot(CH_2)_7\cdot CH_3$ ‖ $CH\cdot(CH_2)_7\cdot CO_2H$ — Oleic acid

$CH\cdot(CH_2)_7$ ‖ $CH\cdot(CH_2)_7$ >CO — Civetone

$(CH_2)_{12}—CH_2$ | $CH_3—CH_2$ CO_2H — Palmitic acid

$(CH_2)_{12}—CO$ | $CH_3—CH——CH_2$ — Muscone

P. G. Stevens has examined these hypotheses in the light of later knowledge of the *in vivo* reactions of the fatty acids (J. Amer. chem. Soc., 1945, 67, 907). The following flow-sheet shows his conception of the biological production of civetone from oleic acid.

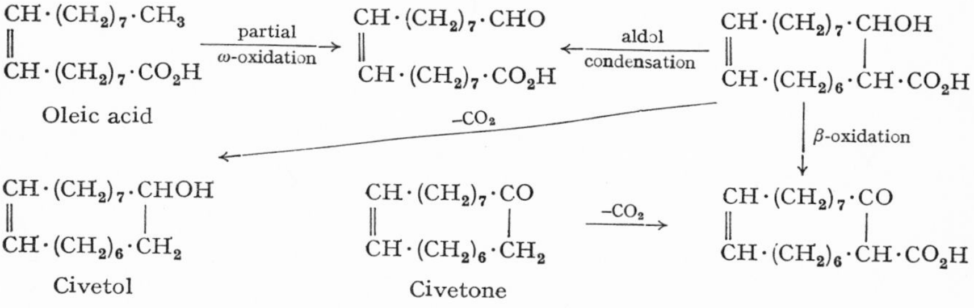

$CH\cdot(CH_2)_7\cdot CH_3$ ‖ $CH\cdot(CH_2)_7\cdot CO_2H$ (Oleic acid) —partial ω-oxidation→ $CH\cdot(CH_2)_7\cdot CHO$ ‖ $CH\cdot(CH_2)_7\cdot CO_2H$ ←aldol condensation— $CH\cdot(CH_2)_7\cdot CHOH$ ‖ $CH\cdot(CH_2)_6\cdot CH\cdot CO_2H$

—β-oxidation→ $CH\cdot(CH_2)_7\cdot CO$ ‖ $CH\cdot(CH_2)_6\cdot CH\cdot CO_2H$ —$-CO_2$→ $CH\cdot(CH_2)_7\cdot CO$ ‖ $CH\cdot(CH_2)_6\cdot CH_2$ (Civetone)

$CH\cdot(CH_2)_7\cdot CHOH$ ‖ $CH\cdot(CH_2)_6\cdot CH_2$ (Civetol) ←$-CO_2$— $CH\cdot(CH_2)_7\cdot CHOH$ ‖ $CH\cdot(CH_2)_6\cdot CH\cdot CO_2H$

This scheme receives support from the occurrence of civetol along with civetone in the animal extract.

The biogenesis of cyclotridecanol, cyclopentadecanol, cycloheptadecanol and cyclononadecanol (all obtained from the musk of the musk-rat) may be postulated in exactly analogous fashion and it has been demonstrated that there is indeed a striking correlation between the amounts of C_{14}, C_{16}, C_{18} and C_{20} fatty acids occurring in the rodent fat and the proportions of the macrocyclic alcohols found in the musk secretion (*P. G. Stevens, loc. cit.*).

The problem of the biogenesis of muscone is not so straightforward and Stevens considers that this ketone is derived from stearic acid (C_{18}) rather than from palmitic acid (C_{16}). The suggested process is as follows:

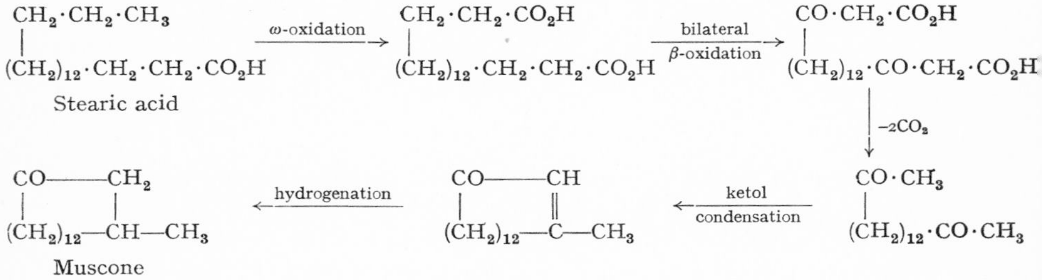

$$\begin{array}{l} CH_2\cdot CH_2\cdot CH_3 \\ | \\ (CH_2)_{12}\cdot CH_2\cdot CH_2\cdot CO_2H \end{array} \xrightarrow{\omega\text{-oxidation}} \begin{array}{l} CH_2\cdot CH_2\cdot CO_2H \\ | \\ (CH_2)_{12}\cdot CH_2\cdot CH_2\cdot CO_2H \end{array} \xrightarrow[\beta\text{-oxidation}]{\text{bilateral}} \begin{array}{l} CO\cdot CH_2\cdot CO_2H \\ | \\ (CH_2)_{12}\cdot CO\cdot CH_2\cdot CO_2H \end{array}$$

Stearic acid

$$\xrightarrow{-2CO_2} \begin{array}{l} CO\cdot CH_3 \\ | \\ (CH_2)_{12}\cdot CO\cdot CH_3 \end{array} \xrightarrow[\text{condensation}]{\text{ketol}} \begin{array}{l} CO\text{———}CH \\ |\qquad\quad \| \\ (CH_2)_{12}\text{—}C\text{—}CH_3 \end{array} \xrightarrow{\text{hydrogenation}} \begin{array}{l} CO\text{———}CH_2 \\ |\qquad\quad | \\ (CH_2)_{12}\text{—}CH\text{—}CH_3 \end{array}$$

Muscone

It will be recalled (see above) that the last two stages have since been accomplished *in vitro*. It is seen that, unlike the civetone biogenesis, this mechanism does not provide for prior carbinol formation and it is interesting to note that muscol does not accompany muscone in the animal secretion. The above scheme would appear more feasible than any hypothesis envisaging the rarely-occurring branched-chain fatty acids as precursors.

Certain androstenols have a musk-like odour and show a formal structural resemblance to civetone (see Vol. II B).

(d) Carboxylic acids

The macrocyclic acids have not been well investigated as a class. Civetone has been condensed with ethyl cyanoacetate to give (I), m.p. 65–68°; reduction and hydrolysis of this compound furnishes **cycloheptadecylacetic acid** (II), m.p. 26·5–28°, *amide*, m.p. 133–134·8° (*A. T. Blomquist* and *R. W. Holley*, J. Amer. chem. Soc., 1948, **70**, 36).

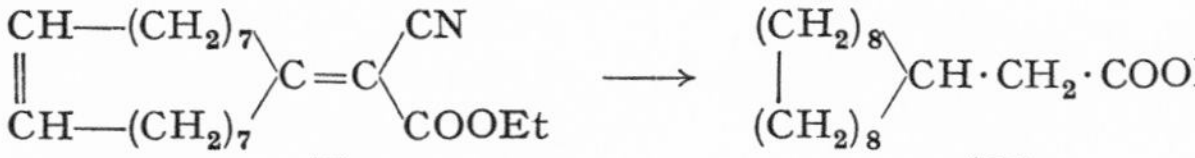

$$\underset{\text{(I)}}{\begin{array}{l} CH\text{—}(CH_2)_7 \\ \| \\ CH\text{—}(CH_2)_7 \end{array}\!\!\!\!> C=C <\!\!\begin{array}{l} CN \\ \\ COOEt \end{array}} \longrightarrow \underset{\text{(II)}}{\begin{array}{l} (CH_2)_8 \\ | \\ (CH_2)_8 \end{array}\!\!> CH\cdot CH_2\cdot COOH}$$

Dehydration, hydrogenation and hydrolysis of cycloheptadecanone cyanohydrin furnishes the non-crystalline **cycloheptadecanecarboxylic acid,** *amide*, m.p. 165–167° (*A. T. Blomquist* and *R. W. Holley, loc. cit.*).

Cyclic β-keto-esters are readily prepared by treating the ketones with **sodium** triphenylmethyl and carbonating the resulting sodium salt; esterification of the resulting β-keto-acids with diazomethane furnishes the corresponding **β-keto-esters** (*V. Prelog, L. Ruzicka et al.*, Helv., 1946, **29**, 1425; 1948, **31**, 92).

(e) *Benzenoid compounds*

A variety of derivatives of benzene are known in which two of the carbon atoms of the ring are joined by a polymethylene chain. Although formally they may be regarded as aromatic compounds they are conveniently discussed among the macrocyclic derivatives.

(i) *Ortho-substituted benzenes of the type*

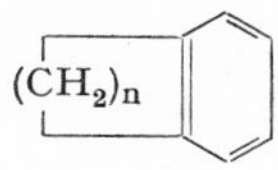

$(CH_2)_n$

The lower members of this series, hydrindane (n = 3), tetralin (n = 4) and benzsuberane (n = 5), are discussed in Vol. III.

Compounds of this type where n = 5, 6, 8, 10, 13 and 14 have been prepared by condensation of the appropriate α-hydroxymethylene ketone with acetone-dicarboxylic ester. The reaction proceeds as follows:

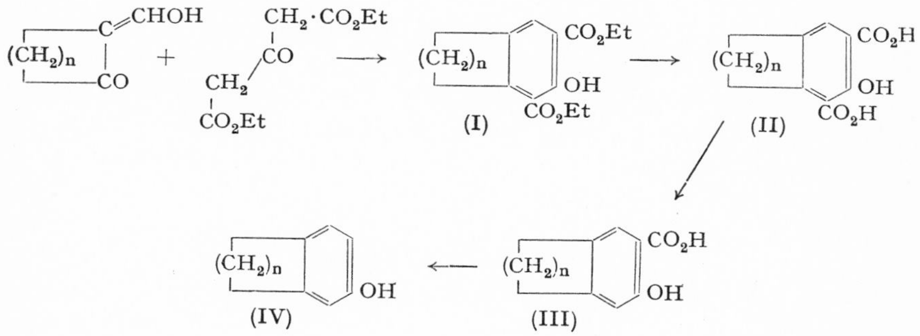

$(CH_2)_n$ C=CHOH / CO + $CH_2\cdot CO_2Et$ / CO / CH_2 / CO_2Et ⟶ $(CH_2)_n$ CO_2Et OH CO_2Et (I) ⟶ $(CH_2)_n$ CO_2H OH CO_2H (II)

$(CH_2)_n$ CO_2H OH (III) ⟶ $(CH_2)_n$ OH (IV)

The substituted phenolic ester (I) first formed is readily hydrolysed to the acid (II) which may be differentially decarboxylated to the substituted salicylic acid (III); further decarboxylation leads to the 3:4-polymethylenephenols (IV). These latter may be converted into the corresponding cyclohexanols, cyclohexanones and cyclohexanes by the usual procedures (*V. Prelog, L. Ruzicka* and *O. Metzler*, Helv., 1947, **30**, 1883).

The m.p. of the above phenolic compounds of differing ring sizes are as follows:

	n	5	6	8	10	13	14
I	m.p.°	55	77	81	105	88	81
II	m.p.°	226	252	215–218	232 (dec.)	208 (dec.)	205 (dec.)
III	m.p.°	204	213	230		196	
IV	m.p.°	72	53	78	70	68	71

An interesting series of catechol polymethylene ethers of the type

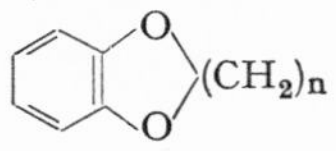

$(CH_2)_n$

where n = 2 to 10 has been described (*K. Ziegler et al.*, Ann., 1937, **528**, 162).

(ii) *Meta-substituted benzenes of the type*

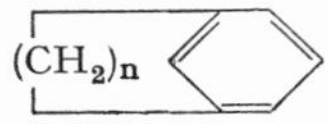

$(CH_2)_n$

The first substance of this kind to be described was 6:6′-(m-*phenylene*)*dihexyl ketone* (V), b.p. 205°/0·8 mm., n_D^{21} 1·5265, *semicarbazone*, m.p. 153–155°, obtained by heating the cerium salt of the corresponding dicarboxylic acid.

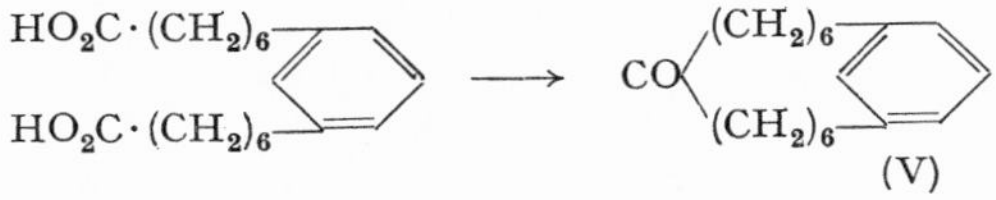

$HO_2C\cdot(CH_2)_6$ $HO_2C\cdot(CH_2)_6$ ⟶ CO $(CH_2)_6$ $(CH_2)_6$ (V)

(*L. Ruzicka et al.*, Helv., 1932, **15**, 1220).

Later a large number of 2:6-polymethylene-4-nitrophenols (VI) were obtained by the condensation of the macrocyclic ketones from cyclononanone upwards with nitromalonic dialdehyde (p. 275; *V. Prelog* and *K. Wiesner*, Helv., 1947, **30**, 1465).

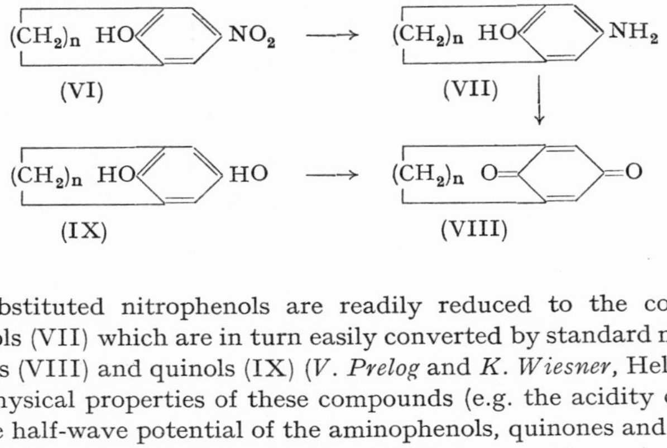

$(CH_2)_n$ HO NO_2 (VI) ⟶ $(CH_2)_n$ HO NH_2 (VII)

$(CH_2)_n$ HO HO (IX) ⟵ $(CH_2)_n$ O= =O (VIII)

These substituted nitrophenols are readily reduced to the corresponding aminophenols (VII) which are in turn easily converted by standard methods into the quinones (VIII) and quinols (IX) (*V. Prelog* and *K. Wiesner*, Helv., 1948, **31**, 870). The physical properties of these compounds (e.g. the acidity of the nitrophenols, the half-wave potential of the aminophenols, quinones and quinols and the position of the wave-length of maximum ultra-violet absorption) depend in a regular way on the size of the polymethylene chain joining the *meta*-positions; the theoretical implications of these phenomena have been fully discussed (*V. Prelog et al.*, Helv., 1948, **31**, 877, 1325).

The m.p. of the above benzene derivatives are as follows:

	n	6	7	9	19	11	12	13	14	15	17	18	27
VI	m.p.°	143	162	158·5	135	143·5	109	90	86	77	71	54	79·5
VII	m.p.°		138	83	82	93		88	114	123			
VIII	m.p.°		55	112	96	165	97	90	63	50			
IX	m.p.°				96	118	113	90	102				

Resorcinol ethers of the general type

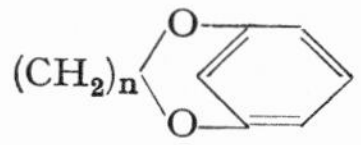

$(CH_2)_n$ O O

have been described (*A. Lüttringhaus* and *K. Ziegler*, Ann., 1937, **528**, 155, 185; 1934, **511**, 1).

(iii) *Para-substituted benzenes of the type*

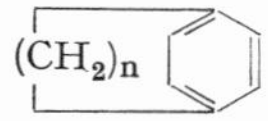

$(CH_2)_n$

For long no compound with a polymethylene chain joining the *para*-positions of the benzene ring had been reported; an unsuccessful attempt to obtain such a substance had been described by *L. Ruzicka et al.* (Helv. 1932, **15**, 1220). Later work, however, has resulted in the formation of such compounds by employing a Diels-Alder condensation between a macrocyclic diene and maleic anhydride with subsequent dehydrogenation of the adduct. In this way 3:6-*decamethylene-phthalic anhydride* (X; n = 10), m.p. 107°, and the 3:6-*tetradecamethylene*-compound (X; n = 14), m.p. 118° have been obtained (*D. M. MacDonald et al.*, Canad., J. Res., 1950, **28B**, **453**, 561; *idem*, Nature, 1950, **166**, 225).

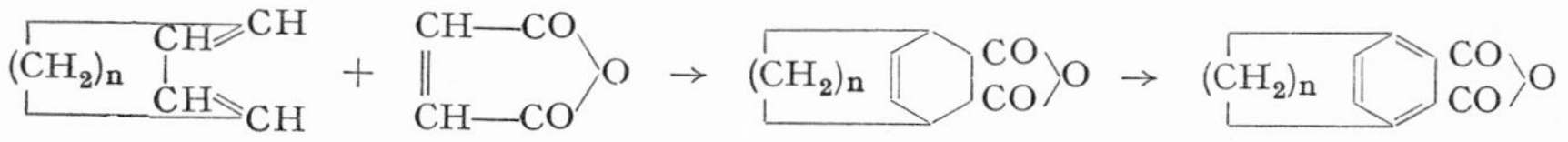

$(CH_2)_n$ CH=CH, CH=CH + CH—CO, CH—CO >O → $(CH_2)_n$ CO, CO >O → $(CH_2)_n$ CO, CO >O

(X)

For analogous compounds with two benzene rings, the so-called *paracyclophanes*, see *D. J. Cram* and *H. Steinberg* (J. Amer. chem. Soc., 1951, **73**, 5691).

Hydroquinone ethers of the type (XI) (n = 8 and 10) have been prepared by *A. Lüttringhaus* (Ann., 1937, **528**, 181) who goes into some detail concerning the geometry of such systems.

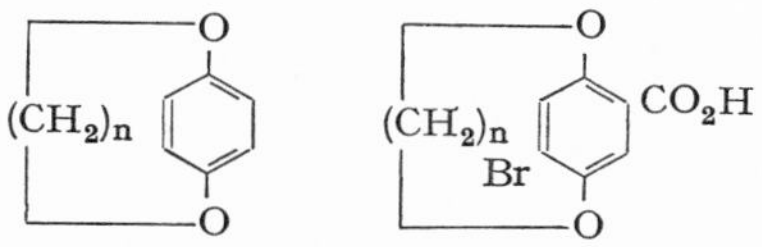

O $(CH_2)_n$ O O $(CH_2)_n$ CO_2H Br O

(XI) (XII)

Interesting compounds of this class are the similarly constituted polymethylene ethers of 4-bromogentisic acid (XII). When n = 10 the *acid*, m.p. 114·5°, is resolvable via the strychnine salt into two highly stable enantiomorphs, m.p. 154°, $[\alpha]_D^{17}$ −37·2° (acetone) and m.p. 154° $[\alpha]_D^{17}$ +37·5°; when n = 12, however, the acid cannot be resolved. The resolvability of the former compound is due to the fact that the handle-like outer ring is of sufficiently small dimensions to prevent free rotation of the rigid aromatic nucleus around the axis of union; when n = 12 unhindered rotation is possible and the compound is non-resolvable. Substances exhibiting this phenomenon have been termed "ansa" compounds (*A. Lüttringhaus* and *H. Gralheer*, Naturwiss., 1940, **28**, 255; Ann., 1941, **550**, 67; cf. also *R. Adams* and *N. Kornblum*, J. Amer. chem. Soc., 1941, **63**, 188).

Macrocyclic lactones: see Vol. I, p. 802.

Chapter VII

Polynuclear Alicyclic Compounds with Separate Ring Systems and Spiro Compounds

R. A. RAPHAEL

Polynuclear alicyclic compounds may be conveniently divided into four sub-groups:

(1) Compounds containing discrete rings which may either be joined directly as in (I) or by a carbon chain as in (II).

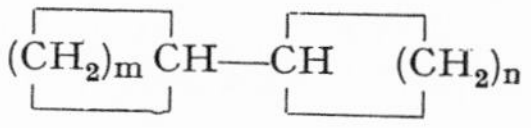

$$(CH_2)_m\,CH{-}CH\,(CH_2)_n \qquad (CH_2)_l\,CH\cdot(CH_2)_m\cdot CH\,(CH_2)_n$$

(I) 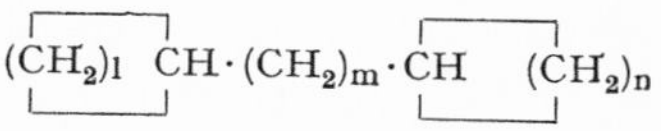 (II)

(2) Spiranes (from the Latin *spira*, a coil or twist) in which one carbon atom is common to two rings as in (III).

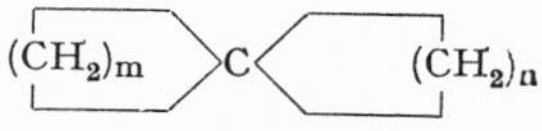

$$(CH_2)_m{>}C{<}(CH_2)_n$$

(III)

(3) Condensed ring systems, in which two carbon atoms are common to two rings as in (IV).

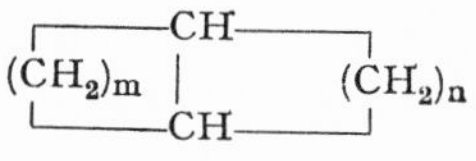

$$(CH_2)_m\;\begin{matrix}CH\\ |\\ CH\end{matrix}\;(CH_2)_n$$

(IV) (Chapter VIII)

(4) Bridged ring systems (V) in which two carbocyclic rings share three or more carbon atoms.

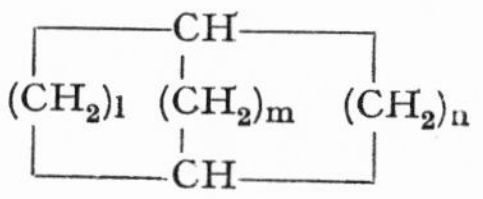

$$(CH_2)_l\;\begin{matrix}CH\\ |\\ (CH_2)_m\\ |\\ CH\end{matrix}\;(CH_2)_n$$

(V) (Chapter IX)

1. Rings united directly or by a carbon chain

Apart from one representative of the dicyclopentyl series which is found in petroleum, this type of compound is found in nature only in the carotenoid series (Chapter X) some members of which have molecules made up of two six-membered rings of the ionone type joined by a polyene hydrocarbon chain.

Synthetically, these polynuclear compounds are obtained by the following general procedures.

1. Application of Wurtz's method (*inter al.*, *W. Meiser*, Ber., 1899, **32**, 2054; *N. D. Zelinsky et al.*, Ber., 1933, **66**, 1422), e.g.

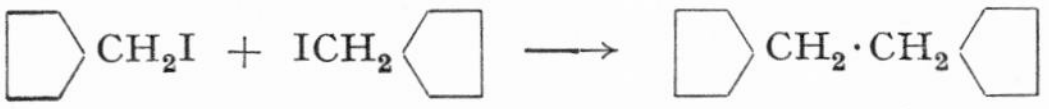

CH_2I + ICH_2 ⟶ $CH_2 \cdot CH_2$

2. The cyclic ketones are readily reduced to pinacols from which the polynuclear hydrocarbons are obtained by dehydration and reduction (*inter al.*, *N. D. Zelinsky* and *N. I. Schuikin*, Ber., 1929, **62**, 2180; *L. Ruzicka* and *H. A. Boekenoogen*, Helv., 1931, **14**, 1319), e.g.

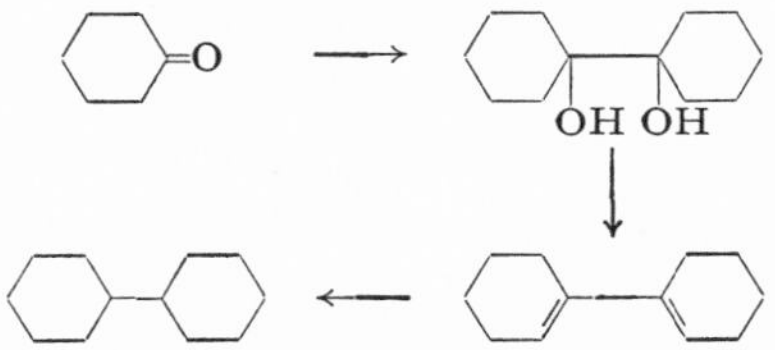

=O ⟶ OH OH

3. Cyclic ketones readily undergo a condensation of the aldol type under alkaline conditions giving products which are convenient starting materials for other bicyclic compounds of the same class (*inter al.*, *O. Wallach*, Ann., 1912, **389**, 169; *F. Taboury*, Compt. rend., 1919, **169**, 62; *M. Godchot*, Compt. rend., 1922, **174**, 618), e.g.

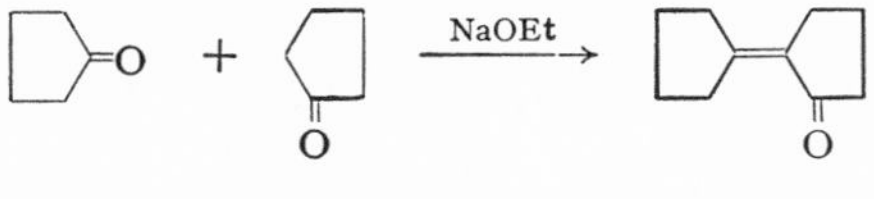

=O + O —NaOEt→ O

4. The reaction of cyclic Grignard compounds with cyclic ketones produces bicyclic compounds of the required type (*N. D. Zelinsky*, Chem. Ztbl., 1933, II, 1673), e.g.

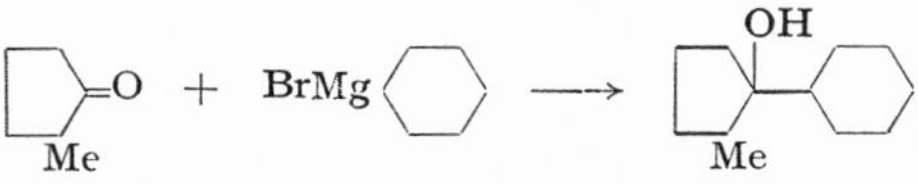

=O Me + BrMg ⟶ OH Me

5. Dicyclohexyl compounds are readily available by the catalytic reduction of the corresponding aromatic compounds e.g. diphenyl, diphenylmethane etc.

Nomenclature. The conventions used in the naming and numbering of these systems are as follows. If the two rings joined directly be of the same size, the compound may be named as the double radical [e.g. (I) is termed dicyclopentyl] the enumeration of the rings being as shown. Alternatively the structure may be regarded as a derivative of one of the rings; on this system, (I) would be cyclopentylcyclopentane. This latter method is always adopted when the rings are of unequal size, the compound being named as a derivative of the larger ring. Thus (II) is called cyclopropylcyclopentane, the dashed figures in the enumeration being reserved for the smaller ring. If the two rings be joined by a carbon chain the compound is regarded as a derivative of this chain, the carbon atoms of which are conveniently designated by Greek letters; the smaller ring is again enumerated by dashed figures. On this basis (III) is termed α-cyclohexyl-γ-cyclopentyl-β-methylpropane.

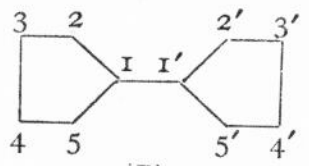

(I) 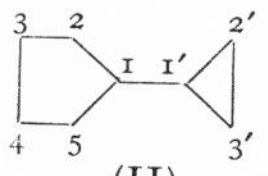 (II) 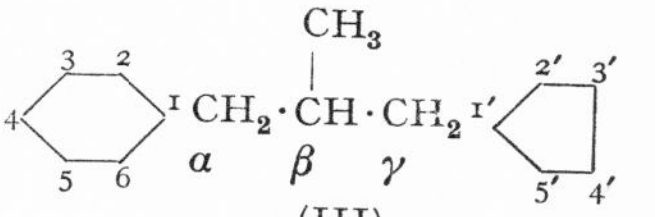 (III)

$CH_2 \cdot CH(CH_3) \cdot CH_2$ (α β γ)

(a) Dicyclopropyl compounds

Dicyclopropyl-2:2:3:2′:2′:3′-hexacarboxylic acid, m.p. 197°, is obtained by the hydrolysis of its *methyl ester*, m.p. 148°, which is prepared from $\alpha\alpha'$-dichloromuconic ester and sodiomalonic ester (*E. H. Farmer*, J. chem. Soc., 1923, **123**, 3332).

For phenyldicyclopropyls see *L. I. Smith* and *E. R. Rogier*, J. Amer. chem. Soc., 1951, **73**, 3831, 3837, 3840.

(b) Dicyclobutyl compounds

Dicyclobutyl ketone, $(C_4H_7)_2CO$, b.p. 104°/30 mm., *semicarbazone*, m.p. 129–130°, is prepared from cyclobutanecarboxylic acid by the usual ketone synthesis; on reduction it furnishes *dicyclobutylmethane*, b.p. 161°/743 mm. (*B. A. Kazanski* and *V. P. Golmov*, Brit. chem. Abstr., 1943, AII, 58).

(c) Dicyclopentyl compounds

Dicyclopentyl, b.p. 188–189.5°/744 mm. is obtained by the Wurtz method from cyclopentyl bromide (*W. Meiser*, Ber., 1899, **32**, 2054) or by Wolff-Kishner reduction of cyclopentylcyclopentanone (*N. D. Zelinsky*, Chem. Ztbl., 1931, I, 1098).

2:2′-*Dimethyldicyclopentyl*, m.p. 45.5–45.7°, b.p. 216.9°/760 mm. is produced by the action of aluminium chloride on dicyclohexyl (*M. Orchin* and *J. Feldman*, J. Amer. chem. Soc., 1946, **68**, 2737).

3:3'-*Dimethyldicyclopentyl*, b.p. 213–214°, occurs in petroleum and is formed when carbazole is reduced with phosphorus and hydriodic acid (*J. Schmidt* and *A. Sigwart*, Ber., 1912, **45**, 1779).

The action of cyclopentylmagnesium bromide on 3-chlorocyclopent-1-ene yields cyclopentylcyclopent-2-ene, b.p. 185–186°/760 mm., n_D^{20} 1.4760 (*G. E. Goheen*, J. Amer. chem. Soc., 1941, **63**, 744).

αβ-Dicyclopentylethane, b.p. 206–207°, is prepared by the action of sodium on cyclopentylmethyl iodide (*N. D. Zelinsky et al.*, Ber., 1933, **66**, 1422).

(For further dicyclopentyls see *J. von Braun et al.*, Ber., 1937, **70**, 1750; *H. Suida* and *A. Gemassmer*, Ber., 1939, **72**, 1168; *N. D. Zelinsky et al., loc. cit.* For polycyclopentyls of the type

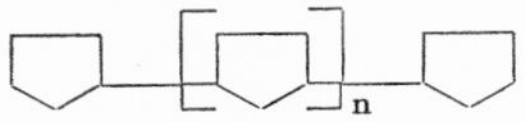

see *J. von Braun* and *J. Reitz-Kopp*, Ber., 1941, **74**, 1105; *G. E. Goheen, loc. cit.*).

Cyclopentylcyclopentan-2-ol, cis-*form* m.p. 55°, b.p. 236°, *phenylurethane* m.p. 110°, trans-*form* m.p. 8.5°, b.p. 117°/12 mm., *phenylurethane* m.p. 93–94°, is obtained by reduction of the corresponding ketone and also as a by-product in the reduction of cyclopentanone (*O. Wallach*, Ann., 1912, **389**, 169; *M. Godchot*, Compt. rend., 1911, **153**, 1010; *N. D. Zelinsky*, Ber., 1929, **62**, 2180; Chem. Ztbl., 1931, I, 1098; *W. Hückel et al.*, Rec. Trav. chim., 1938, **57**, 555). On treatment with zinc chloride the *trans*-form is converted into $\Delta^{9:10}$-octalin (p. 329); the *cis*-form yields in addition a small amount of a different hydrocarbon, probably *cyclopentylcyclopent-1-ene* (*nitrosochloride* m.p. 111°) (*N. D. Zelinsky et al.*, Ber., 1926, **59**, 2580; *W. Hückel*, Ann., 1930, **477**, 131).

Dicyclopentyl-1:1'-diol, m.p. 107–108°, the pinacol of cyclopentanone, is obtained from the latter by reduction with sodium and moist ether. When the compound is dehydrated with sulphuric acid a rearrangement of the carbon skeleton occurs with the formation of the ketospirane

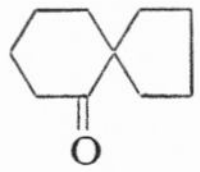

(*N. D. Zelinsky*, Ber., 1929, **62**, 2180).

Bis-(1-hydroxycyclopentyl)acetylene, m.p. 107–108° is obtained by the condensation of cyclopentanone with acetylenedimagnesiumbromide (*P. S. Pinkney* and *C. S. Marvel*, J. Amer. chem. Soc., 1937, **59**, 2669). On partial hydrogenation it furnishes the corresponding *ethylene glycol* m.p. 82–83°, and 129.6–130.6° (polymorphic forms) both of which on full hydrogenation yield *bis-4-hydroxy-cyclopentylethane*, m.p. 131.2–132.4° (*J. S. Salkind* and *I. M. Gverdsiteli*, J. gen. Chem. U.S.S.R., 1939, **9**, 855). *Bis-(1-hydroxycyclopentyl)diacetylene*, m.p. 133.2–134.2°, is prepared by the oxidative coupling of 1-ethynylcyclopentan-1-ol (*idem, ibid.*, 1939, **9**, 971). (For further information concerning the acetylenic glycols see A. W. Johnson "Acetylenic Compounds" Vol. I, E. Arnold and Co.).

2-**Ketodicyclopentyl,** m.p. −30°, b.p. 97°/10 mm., *semicarbazone* m.p. 208–210°, is obtained by the hydrogenation of cyclopentylidenecyclopentan-2-one (*O. Wallach*, Ann., 1912, **389**, 169). On reduction it furnishes the corresponding alcohol (see above) and oxidation yields 4-cyclopentylbutan-4-one-1-carboxylic acid. Reduction of its *oxime*, m.p. 82°, with sodium and alcohol gives trans-2-*aminodicyclopentyl*, b.p. 96–97°/20 mm., *acetyl* compound m.p. 116°; catalytic hydrogenation with platinum in glacial acetic acid yields the cis-*amine*, b.p. 108–111°/20 mm. *benzoyl compound* m.p. 128°. The action of nitrous acid on these amines causes complete inversion; the *cis*-amine produces the *trans*-carbinol (see above) whilst the *trans*-amine yields the *cis*-carbinol (*W. Hückel et al.*, Rec. Trav. chim., 1938, **57**, 555).

Cyclopentylidenecyclopent-2-one, b.p. 117–119°/12 mm., *oxime* m.p. 128°, 2:4-*dinitrophenylhydrazone* m.p. 228–229°, is prepared by the self-condensation of cyclopentanone under the influence of alkaline catalysts (*O. Wallach*, Ber., 1896, **29**, 2963; Ann., 1912, **389**, 179; *C. S. Marvel* and *L. A. Brooks*, J. Amer. chem. Soc., 1941, **63**, 2853). When the compound is methylated with sodium and methyl iodide, the double bond migrates into the ring and 2-keto-1-methylcyclohexylcyclohex-1′-ene is formed (*G. A. R. Kon* and *J. H. Nutland*, J. chem. Soc., 1926, 3101).

2:2′-**Diketodicyclopentyl,** m.p. 67–69°, *bis*-2:4-*dinitrophenylhydrazone* m.p. 230–240° (dec.), is prepared either by a double Dieckmann ring closure on the corresponding tetracarboxylic ester or by the action of iodine on the sodium salt of cyclopentan-2-one-1-carboxylic ester (*B. J. F. Hudson* and *R. Robinson*, J. chem. Soc., 1942, 691).

(*d*) *Cyclopentylcyclohexane compounds*

2-**Methylcyclopentylcyclohexane,** b.p. 224·4°, n_4^{20} 1·4705, may be obtained by isomerisation of dicyclohexyl under the influence of aluminium chloride (*M. Orchin* and *J. Feldman*, J. Amer. chem. Soc., 1946, **68**, 2737). It can also be synthesised from 2-methylcyclopentanone and cyclohexylmagnesium bromide via the corresponding carbinol (*N. D. Zelinsky*, Chem. Ztbl., 1933, II, 1673).

Cyclopent-1-enylcyclohexylmethane (I), b.p. 231–234°, is formed by the elimination of water from 2-hydroxydicyclohexyl with concomitant rearrangement; its constitution is confirmed by ozonisation (*W. Hückel et al.*, Ann., 1930, **477**, 106).

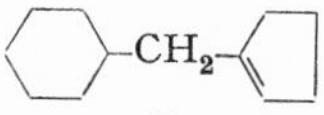

CH_2

(I) 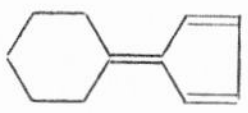 (II)

Condensation of cyclohexanone with cyclopentadiene gives *pentamethylenefulvene* (II), a bright yellow liquid, b.p. 78–80°/25 mm., *maleic anhydride adduct* m.p. 132° (*E. P. Kohler* and *J. Kable*, J. Amer. chem. Soc., 1935, **57**, 917. For diene syntheses with this compound see *R. B. Woodward* and *H. Baer*, *ibid.*, 1944, **66**, 645).

(e) Dicyclohexyl compounds

(i) Hydrocarbons

Dicyclohexyl, m.p. 2·5–3°, b.p. 100°/10 mm. has been prepared (a) by the catalytic hydrogenation of diphenyl or the dicyclohexenyls; (b) by the action of hydriodic acid on 2-hydroxydicyclohexyl; (c) by a Wurtz reaction on cyclohexyl iodide; (d) by the electrolysis of sodium cyclohexanecarboxylate (*O. Wallach*, Ber., 1907, **40**, 70; *W. Schrauth and K. Görig*, Ber., 1923, **56**, 1900; *W. Hückel et al.*, Ann., 1930, **477**, 106; *N. D. Zelinsky*, Chem. Ztbl., 1933, II, 1674; *F. Fichter* and *H. Petrovitch*, Helv., 1940, **23**, 806).

1-**Cyclohexylcyclohex**-1-**ene,** b.p. 234°, is prepared by the dehydration of cyclohexylcyclohexan-2-ol; 1-*cyclohexylcyclohex*-3-*ene* b.p. 237°, is obtained by a similar procedure (*W. Hückel et al.*, Ann., 1930, **477**, 106).

Cyclohexylidenecyclohexane, b.p. 236–237°, is prepared by Kishner-Wolff reduction of cyclohexylidenecyclohexanone (*N. D. Zelinsky*, Chem. Ztbl., 1933, II, 1673).

Dicyclohex-1-**enyl,** b.p. 120–125°/15 mm., is formed by the dehydration of cyclohexanone pinacol (*O. Wallach*, Ann., 1911, **381**, 112); with sulphur dioxide it forms a sulphone

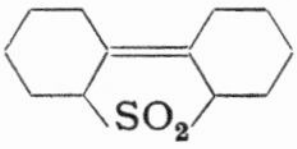

SO_2

m.p. 76–77° from which it may be regenerated by the action of heat (*O. Grummitt* and *C. Helber*, J. Amer. chem. Soc., 1941, **63**, 3236). *Dicyclohex*-2-*enyl*, b.p. 127°/30 mm. is prepared by the action of ethylmagnesium bromide on 3-chlorocyclohex-1-ene, when a Wurtz type of coupling takes place (*A. Berlande*, Compt. rend., 1941, **213**, 484).

The partly hydrogenated diphenyls in which one benzene ring is intact are discussed in Vol. III. For the preparation of a series of dicyclohexyl-substituted paraffins see *M. Tuot* and *M. Guyard*, Bull. Soc. chim. Fr., 1947, **14**, 1087.

Dehydration of the acetylenic glycol of cyclohexanone (see below) yields *dicyclohex*-1-*enylacetylene*, b.p. 126–128°/3 mm. n_D^{20} 1·5520, which on hydrogenation furnishes $\alpha\beta$-**dicyclohexylethane** b.p. 93–94°/2 mm., n_D^{20} 1·4765 (*C. S. Marvel et al.*, J. Amer. chem. Soc., 1936, **58**, 972). The diacetate of the corresponding ethylenic glycol loses acetic acid on heating with copper bronze to give the triene *$\alpha\beta$-dicyclohexenylethylene*, m.p. 29°, b.p. 110–115°/1 mm. (*G. N. Burkhardt* and *N. C. Hindley*, J. chem. Soc., 1938, 987).

(ii) Alcohols

2-**Hydroxyldicyclohexyl,** m.p. 52°, b.p. 136–138°/13 mm., *phenylurethane* m.p. 114°, is prepared from cyclohexanol by the action of solid potash and by catalytic hydrogenation of *o*-cyclohexylphenol, *o*-hydroxydiphenyl and cyclohexylidenecyclohexanone (*W. Hückel et al.*, Ann., 1930, **477**, 106; B.P.

397,883). 4-*Hydroxydicyclohexyl*, cis-*form* m.p. 105°, trans-*form* m.p. 84°, is prepared similarly.

Dicyclohexyl-1:1′-diol, m.p. 130°, is the pinacol of cyclohexanone from which it is prepared by reduction with sodium. The isomeric *dicyclohexyl-4:4′-diol*, m.p. 204–207°, is produced by catalytic hydrogenation of 4:4′-dihydroxydiphenyl (*N. D. Zelinsky*, Ber., 1901, **34**, 2801; *C. R. Waldeland et al.*, J. Amer. chem. Soc., 1933, **55**, 4234).

With acetylenedimagnesium bromide cyclohexanone yields the corresponding acetylene glycol, *bis-(1-hydroxycyclohexyl)acetylene*, m.p. 109° (*inter al.*, *G. N. Burkhardt* and *N. C. Hindley*, J. chem. Soc., 1938, 987). Partial hydrogenation produces *bis-(1-hydroxycyclohexyl)ethylene*, m.p. 152°. (For further acetylenic and ethylenic glycols of this type see *A. W. Johnson*, "Acetylenic Compounds" Vol. I, E. Arnold and Co.)

The hydrogenation of stilboestrol to give perhydrostilboestrols, which belong to this series, has been investigated by *H. E. Ungnade* and his co-workers (J. Amer. chem. Soc., 1947, **69**, 2629; 1945, **67**, 1617; J. org. Chem., 1945, **10**, 307).

(iii) Ketones

Saturation of cyclohexanone, either alone or in ether, with hydrogen chloride produces the chloro-compound (I). Treatment of this latter with pyridine or caustic soda yields *cyclohex-1′-enylcyclohexan-2-one* (II) b.p. 142–145°/15 mm., n_D^{60} 1·4918, *semicarbazone* m.p. 189–190° (*O. Wallach*, Ann., 1911, **381**, 97; *N. D. Zelinsky et al.*, Chem. Ztbl., 1933, II, 1674; *W. S. Rapson*, J. chem. Soc., 1941, 15; *H. Gault et al.*, Bull. Soc. chim. Fr., 1945, **12**, 952). If the chloro-ketone (I) be dehydrohalogenated with sodium methoxide in the cold, *1-cyclohexylidene-cyclohexan-2-one* (III), m.p. 57°, b.p. 105°/2 mm., n_D^{60} 1·5051, *semicarbazone* m.p. 180° (resolidifying and remelting at 186–188°) is produced (*J. Reese*, Ber., 1942, **75**, 384).

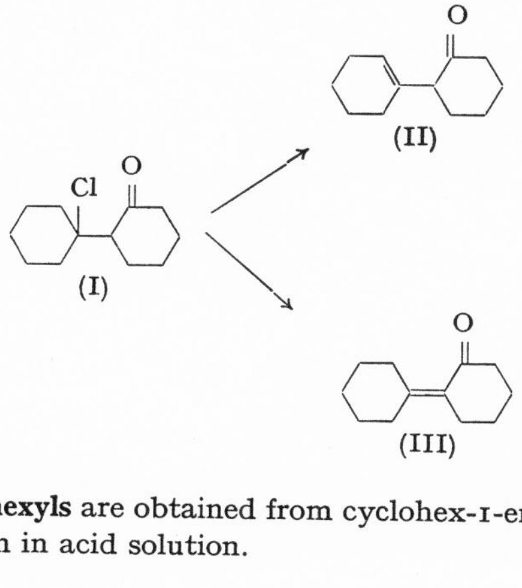

O
(II)
Cl O
(I)
O
(III)

3:3′-Diketodicyclohexyls are obtained from cyclohex-1-en-3-ones by reduction with sodium amalgam in acid solution.

(iv) Carboxylic acids

Electrolysis of the monomethyl ester of *trans*-cyclohexane-1:4-dicarboxylic acid yields **dimethyl dicyclohexyl-4:4′-dicarboxylate** m.p. 101° which on hydrolysis yields a free *acid* of wide m.p. range; this latter on heating with hydrochloric acid furnishes the stable trans-trans-*acid* m.p. 345°, *dimethyl ester* m.p. 117° (*F. E. Fichter* and *T. Holbro*, Helv., 1938, **21**, 141).

The **dicyclohexyl-2:2′-dicarboxylic acids** *(perhydrodiphenic acids)* have been the subject of a series of fundamental papers by R. P. Linstead and his collaborators who studied the catalytic hydrogenation of diphenic acid and its derivatives, and the stereochemical inversion of the products; the spatial configurations of the isomers produced were established by absolute methods (see *R. P. Linstead et al.*, J. Amer. chem. Soc., 1942, **64**, 1991, 2003, 2006, 2009; J. chem. Soc., 1939, 850).

Theoretically, perhydrodiphenic acid can exist in six inactive modifications, four of which are resolvable; all these isomers have been obtained except the optical enantiomorphs of one acid (the *cis-anti-trans*). The configurations and physical properties of the acids and their derivatives are shown in Table 1.

The convention employed for delineating and naming these acids is as follows. The molecule is written with the carboxyl groups together as shown. A black dot on an asymmetric carbon atom indicates that the hydrogen atom attached to that carbon is above the plane of the molecule while a normal junction shows that the hydrogen atom is situated below; a dot is always placed on carbon atom 1. The configuration about the carbon atoms C_1–C_2 and $C_{1'}$–$C_{2'}$ are designated *cis* and *trans* in the usual way while the "backbone" configuration about C_1–$C_{1'}$ is termed *syn* or *anti*. The acids thus fall into two convenient groups, the *syn*-series and the *anti*-series.

(f) Cyclohexylcycloheptane compounds

Cyclohexylcycloheptylmethane b.p. 273–274·5°/739 mm. is obtained by the hydrogenation of benzylcycloheptane; on dehydrogenation with platinised carbon it yields phenanthrene (*N. V. Elagina* and *N. D. Zelinsky*, C.r. Acad. Sci. U.R.S.S., 1941, **30**, 728).

(g) Dicycloheptyl compounds

Dicycloheptyl, b.p. 290°, has been made by Wurtz' method from cycloheptyl bromide.

Dicyclohept-1-enyl, b.p. 149–150°/19 mm., is prepared by the dehydration of cycloheptanone pinacol (*M. Godchot*, Compt. rend., 1928, **186**, 767).

TABLE 1

PERHYDRODIPHENIC ACIDS AND DERIVATIVES

Series	Structure	Form	Acid m.p.°	Anhydride m.p.°	Dimethyl ester m.p.°	Acid $[\alpha]_D$
syn series	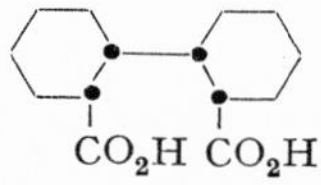 CO_2H CO_2H *cis-syn-cis*	*meso*	289°	147°	73°	—
	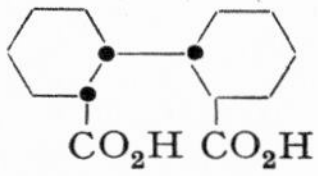 CO_2H CO_2H *cis-syn-trans*	*dl*	200°(174°*)	104°	14°	—
		d	170–174°			+75°
		l	171–174°			—75°
	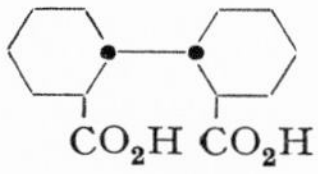 CO_2H CO_2H *trans-syn-trans*	*meso*	223°	106°	57°	—
anti series	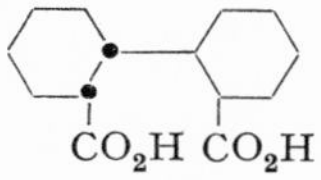 CO_2H CO_2H *cis-anti-cis*	*dl*	198°	100°(96°*)	44°	—
		d	238–240°			+43°
		l	238–240°			—45°
	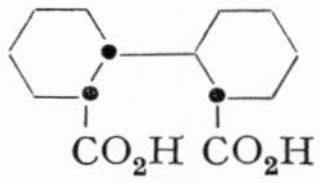 CO_2H CO_2H *cis-anti-trans*	*dl*	206°	93°		—
	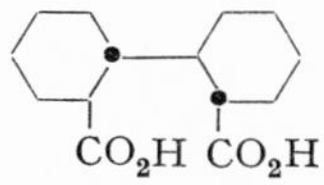 CO_2H CO_2H *trans-anti-trans*	*dl*	247°	242°	86°	—
		d	257–259°			+77.5°
		l	257–259°			—79°

* Unstable polymorph.

2-Hydroxydicycloheptyl, b.p. 158–161°/20 mm., *allophanate* m.p. 185°, is obtained by reduction of cycloheptylidenecycloheptanone (*M. Godchot,* Compt. rend., 1922, **174,** 618; 1928, **186,** 767).

1:1′-*Dihydroxydicycloheptyl,* cycloheptanone pinacol, m.p. 78°, is produced by reduction of cycloheptanone (*M. Godchot, loc. cit.*).

1:1′-*Dihydroxydicycloheptylacetylene,* m.p. 76–78° (*J. I. Iotsitch,* Bull. Soc. chim. Fr., 1908, [iv], **4,** 1203).

Cycloheptylidenecycloheptan-2-one, b.p. 143–145°/8 mm. is formed by the self-condensation of cycloheptanone (*M. Godchot, loc. cit.*).

(h) Dicyclo-octyl compounds

Dicyclo-octyl, b.p. 135–140°/1 mm., is obtained from the hydrogenation of *cyclo-octylcyclo-oct-1-ene,* b.p. 135–140°/2 mm. which is produced by treating cyclo-octene with 80% sulphuric acid (*W. Reppe et al.,* Ann., 1948, **560,** 41). The saturated hydrocarbon is also formed by the hydrogenation of *dicyclo-octa-1-enyl,* m.p. 37°, b.p. 115–116°/0·25 mm. which is prepared by the dehydration of *cyclo-octanone pinacol,* m.p. 94° (*L. Ruzicka* and *H. A. Boekenoogen,* Helv., 1931, **14,** 1319; *M. Godchot,* Compt. rend., 1927, **185,** 1202).

2. Spiranes

Logically the first representative of this series is allene (I) (Vol. I, p. 266). Increasing the number of ring members leads firstly to the methylene-cycloparaffins (II), which have been discussed in the monocyclic section, and finally to the spiranes proper (III).

$CH_2{=}C{=}CH_2$ (I) $(CH_2)_m{>}C{=}CH_2$ (II) $(CH_2)_m{>}C{<}(CH_2)_n$ (III)

$\genfrac{}{}{0pt}{}{a}{b}{>}C{<}\genfrac{}{}{0pt}{}{(CH_2)_m}{(CH_2)_m}{>}C{<}\genfrac{}{}{0pt}{}{(CH_2)_n}{(CH_2)_n}{>}C{<}\genfrac{}{}{0pt}{}{a}{b}$

(IV)

Although substituted spiranes of type IV have no asymmetric carbon atoms they possess no element of symmetry and are therefore resolvable (*W. H. Mills* and *C. R. Nodder,* J. chem. Soc., 1920, **117,** 1407; 1921, **119,** 2097; *P. Maitland* and *W. H. Mills, ibid.,* 1936, 987; *E. P. Kohler et al.,* J. Amer. chem. Soc., 1935, **57,** 1743; *H. J. Backer et al.,* Rec. Trav. chim., 1938, **57,** 761; Proc. Koninkl. Nederland. Akad. Wetenschap., 1928, **31,** 370; *S. E. Janson* and *W. J. Pope,* Proc. roy. Soc., 1936, **154A,** 53).

Nomenclature. Compounds of the spirane type may be named by describing each of the rings separately and joining the two terms by the particle "spiro". Thus the compound below may be designated cyclobutan-1-onespirocyclohex-5-ene-7-carboxylic acid. Another, more logical, method derives the root name from the number of carbon atoms in the nucleus; this is prefixed by "spiro" followed by figures in square brackets indicating the number of carbon atoms joined to the central "junction" carbon atom. On this system the compound below would be termed spiro[5:3]non-5-ene-1-one-7-carboxylic acid; this method has been generally adopted in this chapter.

The position of substituents is indicated by numbering the carbon atoms to which substituents can be attached, beginning with the smaller ring and ending with the "junction" carbon atom, e.g.

1 CO, 2 CH_2, 3 CH_2, 9 C, 8 CH_2—7 $CH\cdot CO_2H$, 6 CH, 5 CH—4 CH_2

Methods of formation

In general spiranes are prepared by applying the usual cyclisation methods to 1:1-disubstituted monocyclic compounds, e.g.

CH_2Br / CH_2Br $\xrightarrow{Na}$

$(CH_2)_n$ CHBr—CO, CH—O, CO_2H $\xrightarrow{KOH}$ $(CH_2)_n$ CO_2H, CO_2H, OH

Internal condensations of esters by Dieckmann's method and condensations with oxalic, malonic, succinic etc. esters may also be employed, e.g.

$(CH_2)_2\cdot CO_2Et$ / $CH_2\cdot CO_2Et$ $\longrightarrow$ =O

CO_2Et, CH_2, CH_2, CO_2Et + EtO_2C, EtO_2C $\longrightarrow$ CO_2Et, =O, =O, CO_2Et

The Guareschi imides derived from cyclic ketones, cyanoacetic ester and ammonia may be used for the preparation of spiranes in the following way:

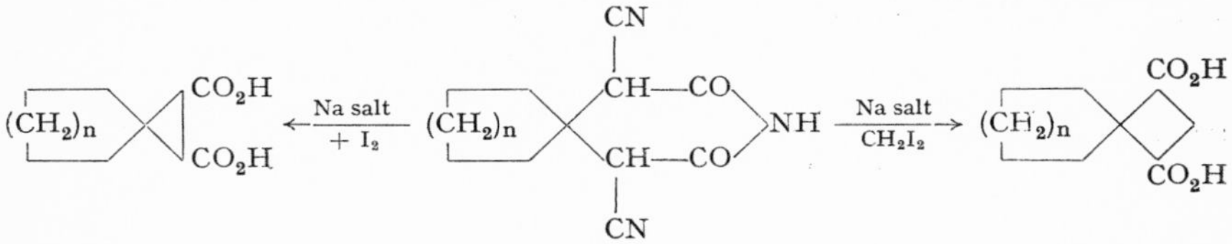

$$(CH_2)_n\text{C}(CO_2H)_2 \xleftarrow[+ I_2]{\text{Na salt}} (CH_2)_n\text{C}[CH(CN)CO]_2NH \xrightarrow[CH_2I_2]{\text{Na salt}} (CH_2)_n\text{-spiro-cyclobutane-}(CO_2H)_2$$

In isolated cases where benzenoid nuclei are involved a Friedel-Crafts type of reaction may be utilised, e.g.

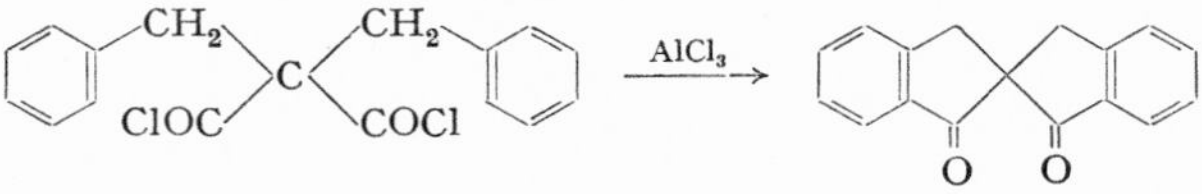

$$(C_6H_5CH_2)_2C(COCl)_2 \xrightarrow{AlCl_3} \text{spirobiindanedione}$$

A special method of obtaining spiranes is the pinacolin transformation of cyclic vicinal tertiary glycols. Thus both 1:1′-dihydroxydicyclopentyl (cyclopentanone pinacol) and decalin-9:10-diol on acid dehydration yield spiro [5:4] decan-5-one.

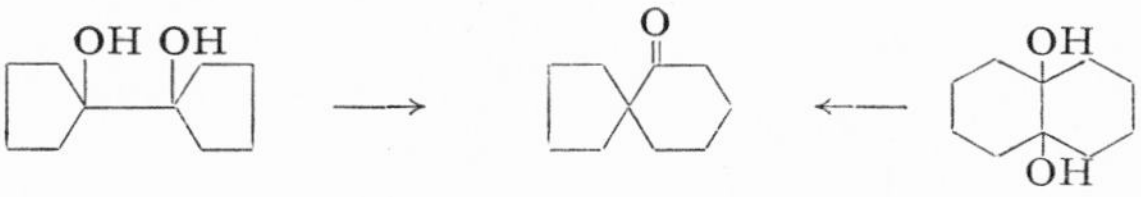

(a) Spiro [2:2] pentane group

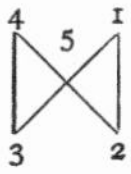

The simplest representative of the spirane class, **spiro**[2:2]**pentane**, m.p. −107·05°, b.p. 39·03°/760 mm., n_D^{20} 1·41220, d_4^{20} 0·7551, is obtained by the zinc debromination of pentaerythrityl tetrabromide or 1:1-di(bromomethyl)cyclopropane (*G. Gustavson*, J. pr. Chem., 1896, [ii], **54**, 97; *H. Fecht*, Ber., 1907, **40**, 3884; *N. D. Zelinsky*, Ber., 1913, **46**, 160. See later references). The constitution of this substance was a subject of disagreement for some time but physical investigations finally placed the correctness of its structure beyond doubt (*J. Goubeau* and *I. Sander*, Chem. Ber., 1949, **82**, 176; *V. A. Slabey*, J. Amer. chem. Soc., 1946, **68**, 1338; *M. J. Murray* and *E. H. Stevenson*, *ibid.*, 1944, **66**, 812; *F. Rogowski*, Ber., 1939, **72**, 2021).

On catalytic hydrogenation the substance undergoes ring fission to produce first 1:1-dimethylcyclopropane and then tetramethylmethane (*V. A. Slabey*, J. Amer. chem. Soc., 1947, **69**, 475). On treatment with potassium cyanide one ring only is opened to give, after hydrolysis, cyclopropane-1-carboxylic-1-propionic acid.

(b) Spiro [4:2] heptane group

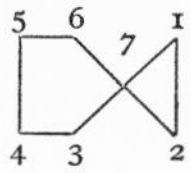

Spiro[4:2]heptane-1:2-dicarboxylic acid, trans-*form* m.p. 211°, *dianilide* m.p. 289°, is obtained by the action of alcoholic KOH on diethyl cyclopentane-1:1-bisbromoacetate, and from cyclopentanone by the Guareschi imide method. The cis-*form* m.p. 170°, *anilic acid* m.p. 191–192°, is obtained via the non-crystallline anhydride of the *trans*-acid (*J. F. Thorpe et al.*, J. chem. Soc., 1920, **117**, 1579; 1922, **121**, 1821).

Spiro[4:2]heptan-1-ol-1:2-dicarboxylic acid, cis-*form* m.p. 163°, is produced from cyclopentane-1:1-bisbromoacetic acid by reaction with methanolic potassium carbonate. In solution the acid is in equilibrium with *cyclopentane-1-acetic-1-glyoxylic acid*, m.p. 112° (*E. W. Lanfear* and *J. F. Thorpe*, J. chem. Soc., 1923, **123**, 1683).

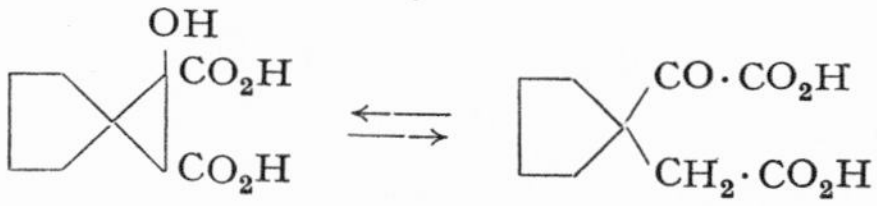

OH, CO_2H, CO_2H ⇌ $CO \cdot CO_2H$, $CH_2 \cdot CO_2H$

Spiro [4:2]heptane-3:6-dione-4:5-dicarboxylic acid, m.p. 161°, is made by the condensation of cyclopropane-1:1-dicarboxylic ester with succinic ester; alcoholic KOH regenerates the starting acids (*D. Radulescu*, Ber., 1909, **42**, 2770; 1911, **44**, 1018).

The *tetraethyl ester*, b.p. 245°/11 mm., of **spiro[4:2]heptane-1:2-dicarboxylic-1-malonic acid** is obtained by condensing cyclopentane-1:1-bisbromoacetic ester with sodiomalonic ester (*C. K. Ingold et al.*, J. chem. Soc., 1923, **123**, 3147):

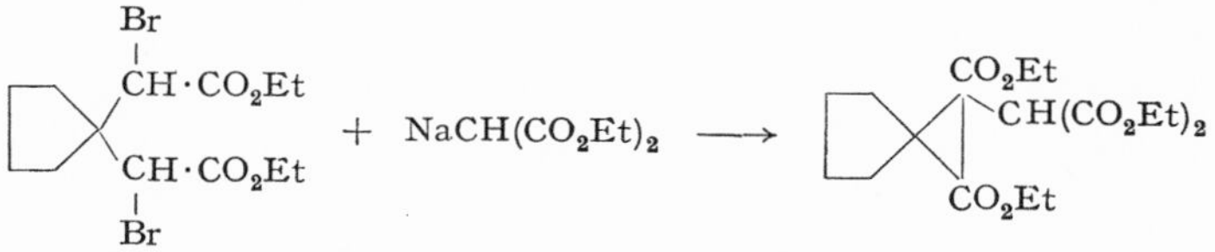

Br, $CH \cdot CO_2Et$, $CH \cdot CO_2Et$, Br + $NaCH(CO_2Et)_2$ ⟶ CO_2Et, $CH(CO_2Et)_2$, CO_2Et

The tricyclic spiranes, **cyclopropanespiro**-trans-**hydrindane-1:2-dicarboxylic acids** (I), cis- m.p. 225°, trans- m.p. 262°, are synthesised as follows (*A. Kandiah*, J. chem. Soc., 1931, 952).

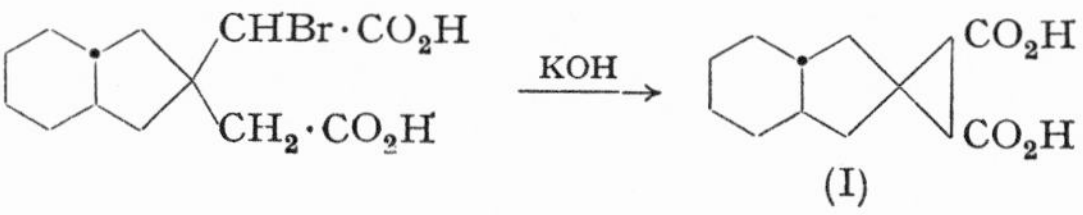

$CHBr \cdot CO_2H$, $CH_2 \cdot CO_2H$ —KOH⟶ CO_2H, CO_2H (I)

(c) Spiro [5:2] octane group

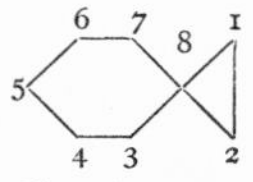

Members of this system are distinguished from all other spiranoid compounds by their great stability and ease of formation. They are resistant to the action of concentrated acid and alkali by which other spiranoid systems are disrupted.

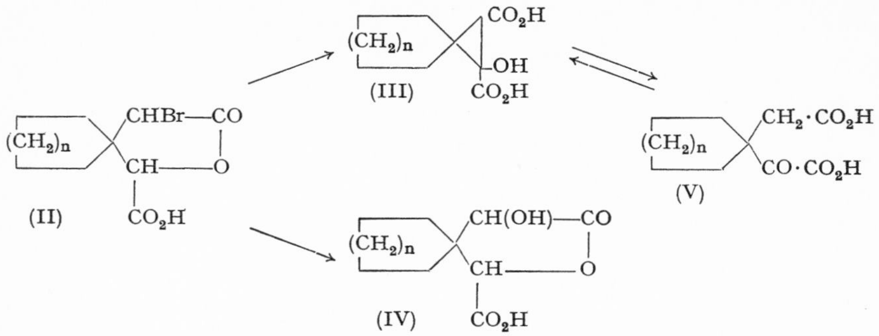

(II) → (III) ⇌ (V); (II) → (IV)

The bromolactone (II) when n = 1 yields with alkali the spiro[5:2]octane (III) (n = 1) almost exclusively, whereas with the corresponding five (n = 0) and seven (n = 2) membered ring compounds the formation of the hydroxy-lactonic acid IV predominates. Again the equilibrium between (III) and the ketoglutaric acid (V) lies very much on the side of the spiro-compound when n = 1 (*C. K. Ingold, J. F. Thorpe et al.*, 1915, **107**, 1080; 1919, **115**, 320; 1923, **123**, 122, 3140).

The parent compound, **spiro[5:2]octane,** b.p. 125·5°/760 mm., f.p. –86·2°, n_D^{20} 1·4476, is prepared by the action of zinc on 1:1-bis(bromomethyl)cyclohexane (*R. W. Shortridge et al.*, J. Amer. chem. Soc., 1948, **70**, 946).

Spiro[5:2]octane-1:2-dicarboxylic acids, cis m.p. 198°, *anhydride* m.p. 102°, *anil* m.p. 119°; trans m.p. 237°, *dianilide* m.p. 292°, are prepared by the action of concentrated potash on cyclohexane-1-acetic ester-1-bromoacetic acid. The corresponding 1-*hydroxy*-compound (as III) m.p. 217°, *dianilide* m.p. 202°, is made as described above (*C. K. Ingold, J. F. Thorpe et al.*, 1915, *loc. cit.*).

5-Methylspiro[5:2]octane-1:2-dicarboxylic acids, cis m.p. 165°, trans m.p. 212°, are made by the Guareschi imide procedure (p. 300). The stability of the spirane system is much reduced by the introduction of the methyl substituent (*R. D. Desai*, J. chem. Soc., 1932, 1047; *S. F. Birch* and *J. F. Thorpe, ibid.*, 1922, **121**, 1821).

trans-**Decalin-β-spirocyclopropane-1:2-dicarboxylic acid** can theoretically exist in four inactive modifications; three of these isomers have been isolated (*K. Rao, ibid.*, 1930, 1162):

trans-acids: m.p. 264°; 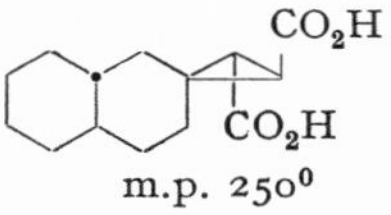 m.p. 250°

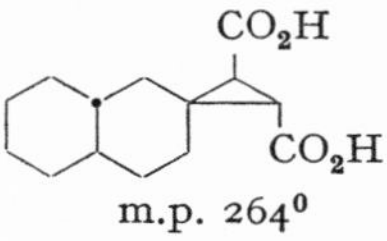

cis-acids: m.p. 186°;  not isolated

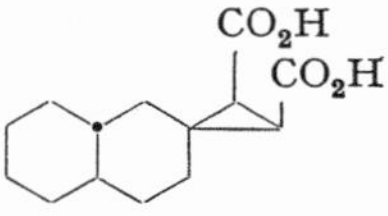

(d) Spiro [6:2] nonane group

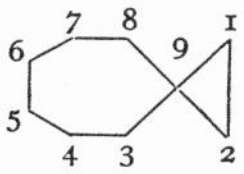

Spiro[6:2]nonane-1:2-dicarboxylic acid, trans m.p. 235°, is obtained by dehydrobromination of cycloheptane-1-acetic-1-bromoacetic ester (*J. W. Baker* and *C. K. Ingold*, J. chem. Soc., 1923, **123**, 122).

(e) Spiro [3:3] heptane group

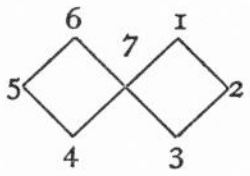

Condensation of pentaerythrityl tetrabromide with sodiomalonic ester gives, after hydrolysis, **spiro[3:3]heptane-2:2:5:5-tetracarboxylic acid** m.p. 219° which is readily decarboxylated to the 2:5-*dicarboxylic acid* m.p. 212°, *dimethyl ester* m.p. 14°, b.p. 141°/11 mm., *diphenyl ester* m.p. 96°. The latter acid has been resolved via its brucine salt (*H. Fecht*, Ber., 1907, **40**, 3883; *H. J. Backer* and *H. B. J. Schurink*, Rec. Trav. chim., 1931, **50**, 921). On bromination it gives the 2:5-*dibromo-2:5-dicarboxylic acid* m.p. 182–183°, *diamide* m.p. 176°, which has also been resolved (*H. J. Backer* and *H. G. Kemper*, Rec. Trav. chim., 1938, **57**, 761).

Bouveault-Blanc reduction of the above diphenyl ester produces 2:5-**di-(hydroxymethyl)spiro[3:3]heptane** b.p. 167°/16 mm. which has been resolved via its *hydrogen phthalate*, m.p. 139° (*H. J. Backer* and *H. G. Kemper*, *loc. cit.*).

The action of methylmagnesium bromide on the methyl ester of the dicarboxylic acid furnishes the tertiary glycol, 2:5-*di(α-hydroxy*iso*propyl)spiro-[3:3]heptane* m.p. 75–76° (*H. J. Backer* and *H. G. Kemper*, Rec. Trav. chim., 1938, **57**, 1249).

(f) Spiro [4:3] octane group

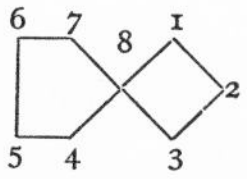

Spiro[4:3]octane-1:1:3:3-tetracarboxylic acid, m.p. 190°, has been prepared by the Guareschi imide method (p. 300) (*P. K. Paul*, J. Indian chem. Soc., 1931, **8**, 717).

(g) Spiro [4:4] nonane group

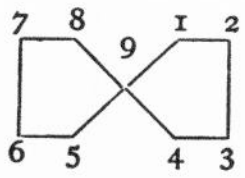

Spiro[4:4]nonan-1-one, b.p. 202–203°/760 mm., n_D^{20} 1·4470 is obtained by the cyclisation of cyclopentane-1-butyric-1-carboxylic acid. On reduction it furnishes the parent hydrocarbon, **spiro[4:4]nonane,** b.p. 156°/748 mm., n_D^{20} 1·4618, d_4^{20} 0·8631 (*N. D. Zelinsky* and *N. V. Elagina*, C.r. Acad. Sci. U.R.S.S., 1945, **49**, 568). Hydrogenation of this hydrocarbon yields cyclopentane homologues and nonanes whilst dehydrogenation gives *o*-methylethylbenzene (*idem, ibid.*, 1946, **52**, 227).

2-*Methylspiro*[4:4]*nonane*-5:7-*dione*, m.p. 101°, is formed by the self-condensation of 1-acetyl-3-methylcyclopentane-1-acetic ester (*J. F. Thorpe et al.*, J. chem. Soc., 1922, **121**, 1496).

Spiro[4:4]*nonan*-3-*one*-1-*carboxylic acid*, m.p. 74°, is obtained from spiro-[4:2]heptane-1:2-dicarboxylic-1-malonic ester (p. 301) by the following procedure (*C. K. Ingold et al.*, *ibid.*, 1923, **123**, 3147):

CO_2Et CO_2Et CO_2Et O — NaOEt → ; CO_2 → CO_2H O ; Na/Hg → CO_2H O

2-*Methylspiro*[4:4]*nonane*-6:7-*dione*-5:8-*dicarboxylic methyl ester*, m.p. 125°, is the condensation product of 3-methylcyclopentane-1:1-diacetic ester and dimethyl oxalate (*R. D. Desai*, *ibid.*, 1932, 1047).

trans-*Hydrindane*-β-*spirocyclopentane*-2:3-*dione* (I) m.p. 111° and its isomer the corresponding 2:4-*dione* (II) m.p. 190° are obtained by the following methods (*A. Kandiah*, J. chem. Soc., 1931, 952):

CO_2Et, CH_2, CH_2, CO_2Et + EtO_2C–EtO_2C → CO_2Et, O, O, CO_2Et → O, O (I)

COCl, $CH_2 \cdot CO_2Et$ — MeZnI → $COCH_3$, $CH_2 \cdot CO_2Et$ — NaOEt → O, O (II)

2:3-6:7-*Dibenzspiro*[4:4]*nonane*-2:6-*diene*-4:5-*dione* m.p. 174°, *oxime* m.p. 215° is a benzenoid spirane prepared by the method outlined on p. 300; as a 1:3-diketone it undergoes reversible decomposition with alkali (*H. Leuchs et al.*, Ber., 1912, **45**, 189; 1913, **46**, 2420).

CH_2 CH_2 C CO CO ⇌ (Alkali / Heat) CH_2 CH CH_2 CO_2H CO

The isomeric 1:4-*dione*, m.p. 150°, is a yellow compound prepared from diketohydrindene and *o*-xylylene dibromide (*H. Fecht*, Ber., 1907, **40**, 3883).

(*h*) *Spiro* [5:4] *decane group*

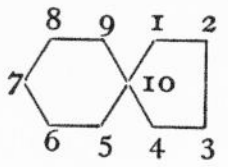

8 9 1 2
7 10
6 5 4 3

As has already been indicated (p. 18) spiranes of this constitution give naphthalene derivatives on dehydrogenation, e.g.

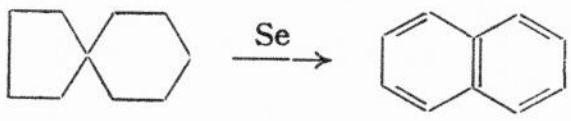

Se →

(*C. S. Marvel* and *L. A. Brooks*, J. Amer. chem. Soc., 1941, **63**, 2630).

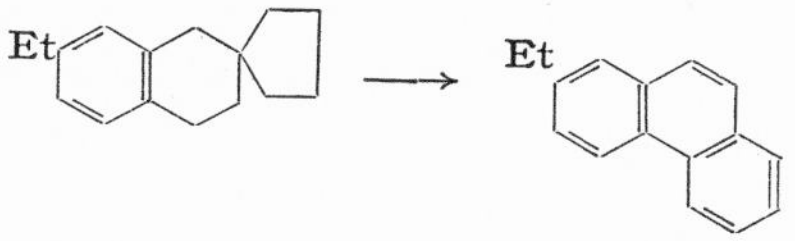

Et → Et

(*S. C. Sengupta*, J. Indian chem. Soc., 1939, **16**, 349. See also *M. T. Bogert et al.*, J. org. Chem., 1941, **6**, 105; J. Amer. chem. Soc., 1942, **64**, 1719; *N. N. Chatterjee*, and *G. N. Barpajari*, J. Indian chem. Soc., 1938, **15**, 639; *R. P. Linstead*, Annual Reports, 1936, **33**, 303; *J. W. Cook* and *C. L. Hewett*, J. chem. Soc., 1934, 365).

The parent hydrocarbon, **spiro**[5:4]**decane**, b.p. 184–186·5°, n_D 1·4744, d_4^{20} 0·8805 is made by the Kishner-Wolff reduction of the 5-ketone (see below); it may also be prepared by the following route:

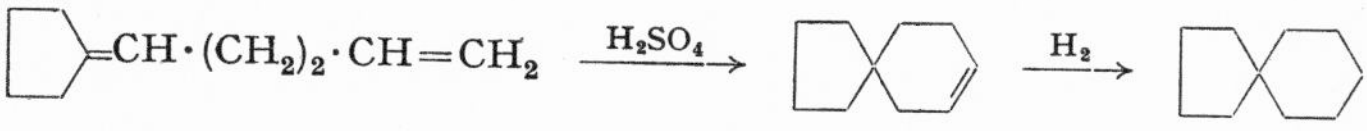

$=CH\cdot(CH_2)_2\cdot CH=CH_2 \xrightarrow{H_2SO_4}$ $\xrightarrow{H_2}$

(*N. D. Zelinsky* and *N. I. Schuikin*, Ber., 1929, **62**, 2180; *C. S. Marvel* and *L. A. Brooks*, *loc. cit.*). The 3-*methyl*-derivative, b.p. 195–197°, n_D^{20} 1·4660, is similarly prepared; on dehydrogenation it furnishes 2-methylnaphthalene (*C. S. Marvel* and *L. A. Brooks*, *loc. cit.*).

Spiro[5:4]**decan-5-one,** b.p. 99–100°/13 mm., n_D^{20} 1·4849, d_4^{20} 0·9890, *benzylidene* compound, m.p. 75°, is obtained by the pinacolic dehydration of dicyclopentyl-1:1′-diol and decalin-9:10-diol (*W. Meiser*, Ber., 1899, **32**, 2055; *W. Hückel*, Ann., 1929, **474**, 121; *G. R. Clemo* and *J. Ormston*, J. chem. Soc., 1932, 1778; *M. Qudrat-I-Khuda* and *A. K. Ray*, J. Indian chem. Soc., 1939, **16**, 525; *N. D. Zelinsky* and *N. V. Elaghina*, C. r. Acad. Sci. U.R.S.S., 1945, **49**, 568) and by the action of nitrous acid on 1:9-diaminodecalin (*P. A. Plattner* and *J. Hulstkamp*, Helv., 1944, **27**, 220). Its constitution is confirmed by its production of cyclopentane-1-butyric-1-carboxylic acid on nitric acid oxidation.

2-*Methylspiro*[5:4]*decane*-6:8-*dione*, m.p. 128°, has been synthesised by the following two methods (*R. D. Desai*, J. Indian chem. Soc., 1933, **10**, 257):

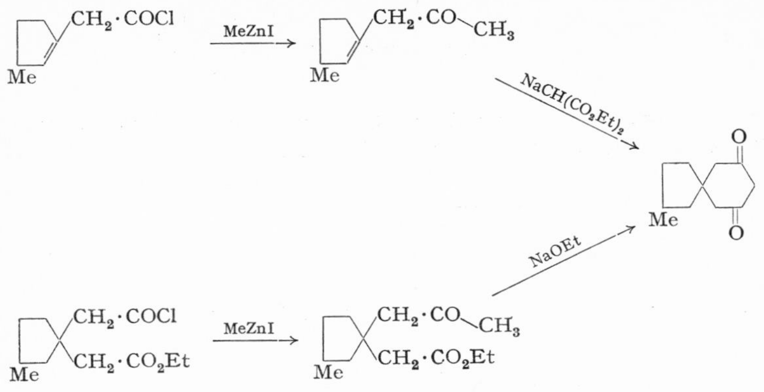

A series of derivatives of this spirane system have been made by the following route (*N. N. Chatterjee* and *G. N. Barpajari, ibid.*, 1938, **15**, 639), illustrated for 6-*methylspiro*[5:4]*decane*-1-*carboxylic acid*, m.p. 65°:

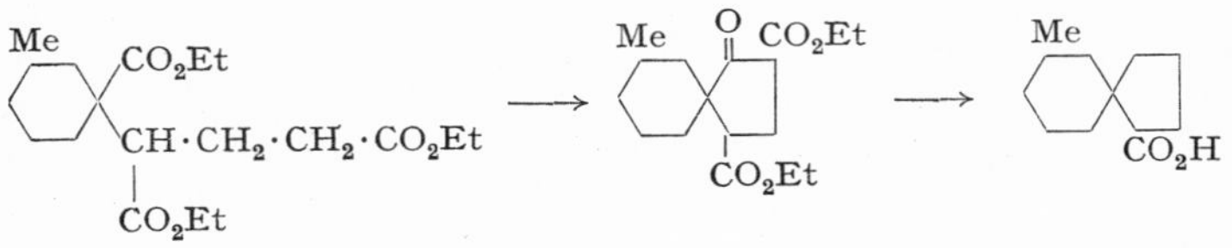

Dehydrogenation of the final acid yields 2-methylnaphthalene.

The interesting dispiranoid diketone (I), b.p. 156°/10 mm., *oxime* m.p. 156–157°, is obtained by the action of sulphuric acid on the dimer of 2-methylene-cyclohexanone; the reaction proceeds as follows (*C. Mannich*, Ber., 1941, **74**, 565):

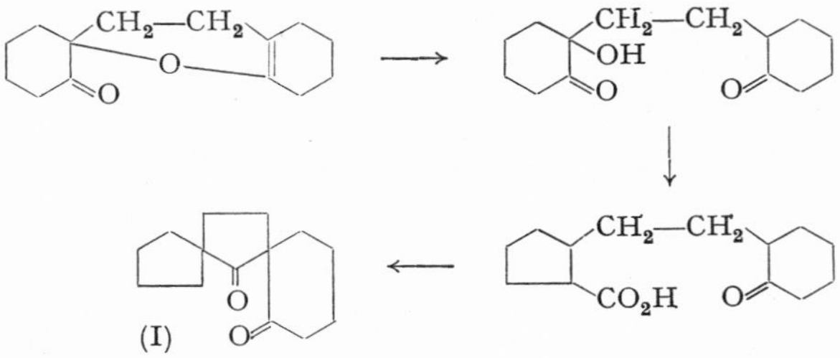

The cyclisation of dienynes as carried out by C. S. Marvel and his collaborators gives products which are probably derivatives of spiro[5:4]decane (for full details see *A. W. Johnson*, "Acetylenic Compounds" Vol. I, p. 167, E. Arnold and Co.; *E. R. H. Jones*, Annual Reports, 1943, **40**, 135).

(i) Spiro[5:5]*undecane group*

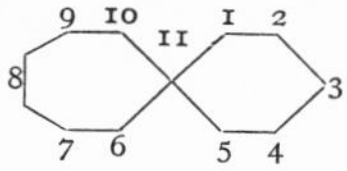

The Michael condensation of cyclohexylideneacetone with diethyl malonate produces 5-*carbethoxyspiro*[5:5]*undecane-2:4-dione, monohydrate*, m.p. 87°, which, on being hydrolysed and decarboxylated, furnishes **spiro**[5:5] **undecane-2:4-dione,** m.p. 170·5° (*W. S. G. P. Norris* and *J. F. Thorpe*, J. chem. Soc., 1921, **119**, 1199). The properties of the dione are exactly similar to those of the analogously constituted dimedone (p. 203) (*idem, ibid.*; *R. D. Desai, ibid.*, 1932, 1079; C.A., 1934, **28**, 6117). Homologous diones of the same type are similarly obtained (*G. A. R. Kon et al.*, J. chem. Soc., 1927, 1536; 1930, 2217).

(j) Spiro[6:5]*dodecane group*

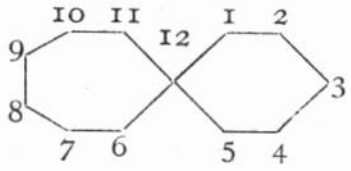

Spiro[6:5]**dodecan-6-one** b.p. 120°/8 mm., *semicarbazone* m.p. 217°, is formed by pinacolic dehydration of dicyclohexyl-1:1′-diol (*M. Qudrat-I-Khuda* and *A. K. Ray*, J. Indian chem. Soc., 1939, **16**, 525).

(k) Spiro[7:6]*tetradecane group*

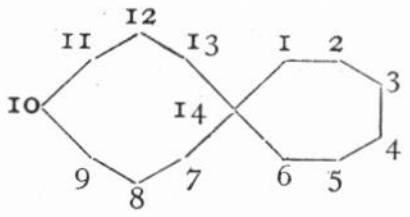

Spiro[7:6]**tetradecan-7-one** m.p. 72°, is produced by pinacolic dehydration of dicycloheptyl-1:1′-diol (*M. Godchot*, Compt. rend., 1928, **186**, 767).

Chapter VIII

Polynuclear Alicyclic Compounds Condensed Cyclic Systems

R. A. RAPHAEL

The condensed cyclic systems comprise structures containing two or more carbocyclic rings fused in such a manner that two adjacent carbon atoms are common to a pair of rings. Such structures are of great importance because of their occurrence in a large number of natural products such as the sesqui-, di- and tri-terpenes and the steroids.

Nomenclature. The bicyclic structures of this type, like those of the bridged ring systems (p. 335) are systematically described by writing the name denoting the number of carbon atoms in the nucleus, prefixing it with "bicyclo" and inserting in square brackets the number of ring members joined to either side of the common carbon atoms (in decreasing order) followed by the cipher o (since there are no bridging carbon atoms in condensed systems). Thus hydrindane (octahydroindene), which is constituted by the fusion of a five-membered ring with a six-membered ring may be designated as bicyclo[4:3:o]nonane.

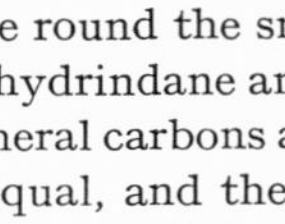

Hydrindane 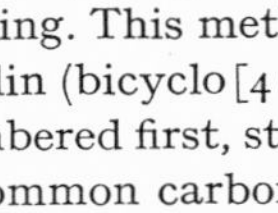   Decalin

Two methods of enumeration are commonly used. The first starts with one of the common carbon atoms, continues round the larger ring to the other common carbon atom and thence round the smaller ring. This method, however, is rarely used for the important hydrindane and decalin (bicyclo[4:4:o]-decane) systems; in these cases the peripheral carbons are numbered first, starting with the smaller ring if the two are unequal, and the two common carbon atoms are numbered last as shown above. The Greek letters α and β are also used as shown. This enumeration arises from the close connection between these systems and their benzenoid analogues. For the sake of consistency this latter method has been adopted throughout this chapter. Double bonds may be indicated in the usual manner or by employing the Greek letter Δ to which are attached numeral superscripts showing the position of the double bond or bonds (for examples see pp. 319, 328).

In the case of polycyclic condensed systems an extension of the nomenclature described above would lead to cumbrous terminology. However, since most of these are obtained by the hydrogenation of aromatic systems they may be conveniently named as derivatives of the latter and numbered in the same way (with extension of the enumeration to the common carbon atoms which in the aromatic series, being incapable of carrying substituents, are not numbered).

The synthetic methods employed for the preparation of condensed ring compounds are very similar to those already detailed for the monocyclic compounds, the processes being applied to compounds having cyclic structures instead of to purely aliphatic systems. As mentioned above many members of the group are obtained by hydrogenation of aromatic compounds with the same carbon skeleton; in many cases this approach constitutes by far the most convenient preparative method.

Stereochemistry of condensed ring systems

The stereochemistry of this group is particularly interesting; the systems bicyclo[4:4:0]decane (decahydronaphthalene, decalin), bicyclo[4:3:0]-nonane (hydrindane) and bicyclo[3:3:0]octane (pentalane) have been well investigated from this aspect and the results will be described in detail. (See *R. P. Linstead*, Annual Reports, 1935, **32**, 305; *W. H. Mills*, Dict. appl. Chem., Supplement 1935, Vol. II, 433; *W. Hückel*, Der Gegenwärtige Stand der Spannungstheorie, 1928.)

(1) *The decalin system* (fusion of two six-membered rings).

It was first pointed out by *E. Mohr* (J. pr. Chem., 1918, [ii], **98**, 321) that if cyclohexane is capable of existing in multiplanar strainless forms as suggested by H. Sachse (p. 3) then it follows that decalin can exist in strainless modifications differing in the type of locking (*cis* or *trans*) at the bridge. It can be demonstrated that eight different structures may be visualised on this basis as shown in the diagram on page 310 (the fourth valency bond is inserted at the bridgeheads to emphasise the type of linkage).

Forms I, Ia and Ib differ only in the boat-chair configurations of the rings and this difference does not involve the *trans*-linking at the bridge. Thus, for the reasons discussed on p. 131, the structures are not discrete and constitute phases of a system best represented by the energetically most favourable constellation I. In similar fashion, II, IIa, IIb, IIc and IId do not constitute isolable isomers of *cis*-decalin. For long this latter has been represented by the familiar Sachse-Mohr formula IIc, but electron diffraction measurements have now indicated that it is more accurately delineated by the L-shaped structure II (*O. Bastiansen* and *O. Hassel*, Nature, 1946, **157**, 765). Confirmation for this view has been provided by *D. H. R. Barton*

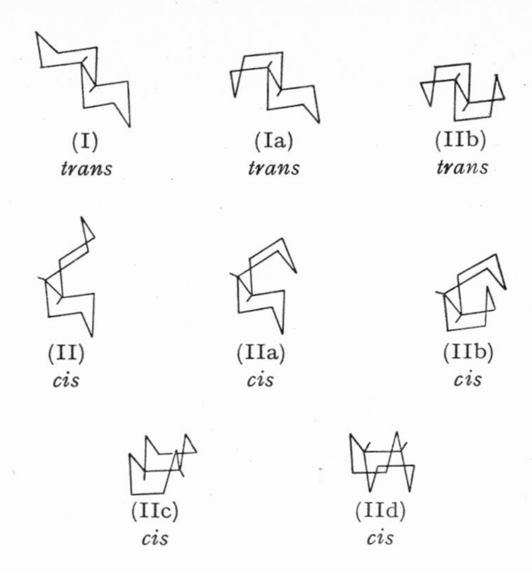

who has shown by calculation that the stabilities of the structures are in the order I > II > IIc (J. chem. Soc., 1948, 340; see also *R. B. Turner,* J. Amer. chem. Soc., 1952, 74, 2118). This order of computed energy differences is borne out by the experimental values of the heats of combustion of *trans*-decalin (1495 kcal./mol.) and *cis*-decalin (1499.9 kcal./mol.). It is to be noted that the classical conceptions of strain do not allow of any energy differences between the above strainless forms; these are due to the interactions between non-bonded atoms (repulsions resulting from interpenetration of electron sheaths) which, of course, would differ in extent for each of the above configurations (*D. H. R. Barton, loc. cit.*).

The fundamental work of *W. Hückel* has verified practically that decalin and its derivatives are in fact capable of existing in *cis*- and *trans*-modifications of the above type (p. 323).

For simplicity of delineation on a plane surface the two decalins may be represented as follows:

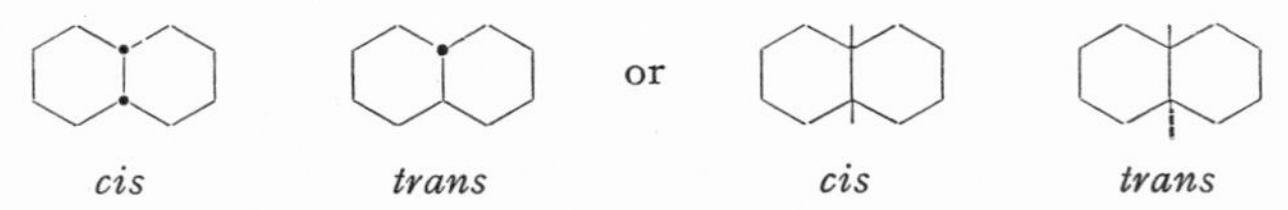

It must be emphasised, however, that these representations are mere ideographs and that the stereochemistry of the system should always be visualised three-dimensionally if misleading conclusions are to be avoided.

(2) *The hydrindane system* (fusion of a six-membered ring with a five-membered ring).

The concepts outlined above may also be applied to the hydrindane system with the production of the following possible structures:

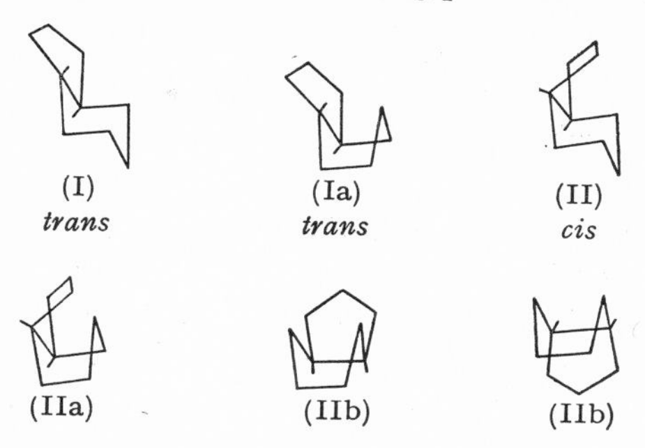

Again only two realisable isomers may be envisaged, one *trans* (I, Ia) and one *cis* (II, IIa, IIb, IIc). These structures have not been investigated in detail in the same manner as their decalin counterparts but from analogy it is probable that the computed stabilities would be in the order I > II > IIb and that II rather than IIb represents the structure of *cis*-hydrindane. This concept provides a ready explanation of the experimental heats of combustion of the hydrindanes, the value for *cis*-hydrindane (1347·5 kcal./mol.) being greater than that for *trans*-hydrindane (1345·7 kcal./mol.). This result is quite inexplicable in terms of classical strain theory which would require structure IIb to possess the greatest stability. Further, structures I and II fit in very well with the modern concept of the puckered five-membered ring (p. 76). The order of the heats of combustion of the β-hydrindanones (*cis*-, 1246·4 kcal./mol.; *trans*-, 1244 kcal./mol.) may be similarly explained. It is noteworthy, however, that equilibration of α-hydrindanone yields an overwhelming preponderance of the *cis*-isomer. This may possibly be due to the fact that the conformation of the *cis*-α-ketone (structure as II) is highly favourable for the occurrence of hydrogen bonding between the carbonyl oxygen and one of the polar hydrogens; this stabilising factor is absent in the *trans*-α-ketone (structure as I).

In this system the carbon atoms of the bridge are both asymmetric but possess identical environments. *trans*-Hydrindane is therefore a *dl*-compound whilst the *cis* isomer is a *meso*-form since two of the latter's phases (IIb and IIc) possess a plane of symmetry.

(3) *The pentalane system* (fusion of two five-membered rings).

As the oscillatory phases of the five-membered ring are more restricted and less well-defined than those of the six-membered ring the *cis*- and *trans*-forms of the pentalane system may be represented by the following three structures only:

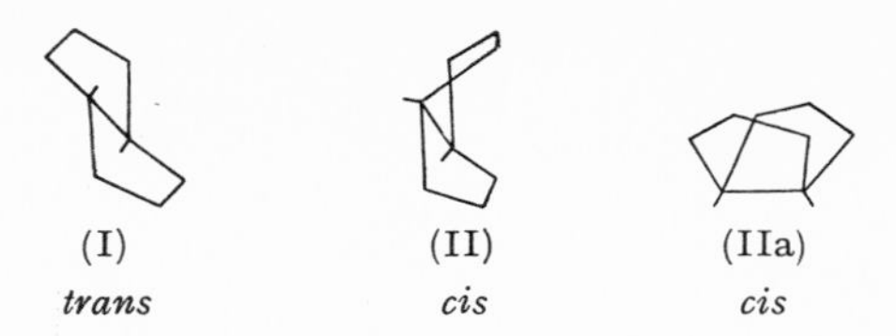

(I) *trans* (II) *cis* (IIa) *cis*

From the point of view of the strain theory IIa should represent a structure more stable than I or II both of which are strained to approximately the same extent. The configuration IIa for *cis*-pentalane is supported by heat of combustion data which indicate that the *cis*-isomer (1094·1 kcal./mol.) is considerably more stable than the *trans*-form (1100·9 kcal./mol.).

It is interesting to compare the stabilities of the above systems between themselves on the basis of their heats of combustion. In order to obtain comparable figures one CH_2 increment must be added to the values for the hydrindanes and two CH_2 increments to the values for the pentalanes; the magnitude of the increment is taken as one-sixth (156 kcal.) of the heat of combustion of the strainless cyclohexane (*R. Spitzer* and *H. F. Huffmann,* J. Amer. chem. Soc., 1947, **69,** 211). Applying this "correction" to the determined heats of combustion of the above hydrocarbons (*W. H. Roth* and *R. Lassé,* Ann., 1925, **441,** 48; *W. Hückel et al.,* Ann., 1935, **518,** 155; 1927, **451,** 132; *J. W. Barrett* and *R. P. Linstead,* J. chem. Soc., 1935, 436; 1936, 611) the following order of stability is obtained (all data expressed as kcal./mol.): *trans*-decalin (1495·2) > *cis*-decalin (1499·9) > *trans*-hydrindane (1501·7) > *cis*-hydrindane (1503·5) > *cis*-pentalane (1509·7) > *trans*-pentalane (1515·8).

In the case of the corresponding *β*-ketones this order has to be rearranged slightly although here the numerical differences are far less: *trans*-hydrindanone (1399·9) > *trans*-decalone (1400·1) > *cis*-hydrindanone (1401) > *cis*-decalone (1402·3) > *cis*-pentalone (1406·1) > *trans*-pentalone (1412·9).

1. Bicyclic ring systems

(*a*) *Bicyclo* [1:1:0] *butane group*

3-Methylbicyclo[1:1:0]**butane-**1:2:4-**tricarboxylic acids** are obtained by the dehydrobromination of 1:3-dibromo-2-methylpropane-1:3-dicarboxylic-2-acetic acid $CH_3\cdot C(CHBr\cdot CO_2H)_2\cdot CH_2\cdot CO_2H$; three isomers are obtained (I, II and III):

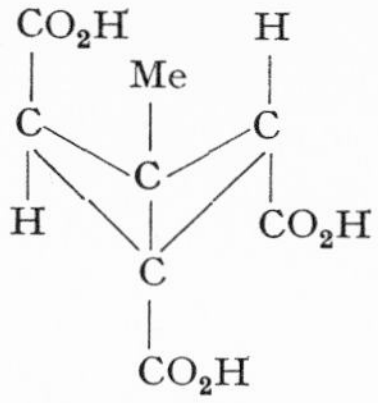

CO₂H H Me C C C H CO₂H C CO₂H

(I) *dl* m.p. 166°

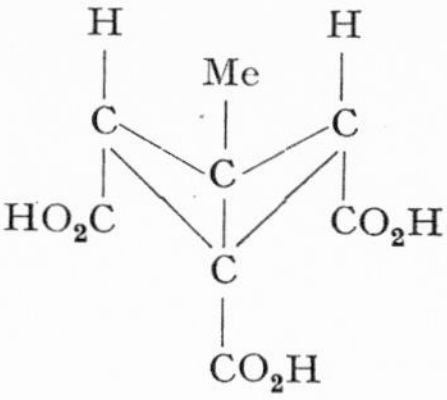

H H Me C C C HO₂C CO₂H C CO₂H

(II) *meso* m.p. 154°

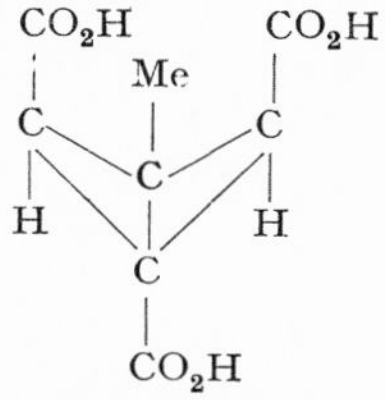

CO₂H CO₂H Me C C C H H C CO₂H

(III) *meso* m.p. 193°

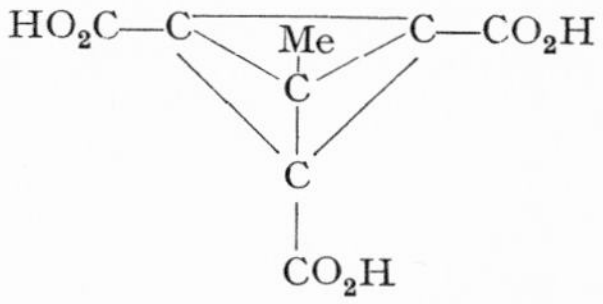

HO₂C—C Me C—CO₂H C C CO₂H

(IV) m.p. 149°

Bromination of (II) or (III) followed by dehydrobromination results in the interesting tetracyclic "cage" compound (IV) (*R. M. Beesley* and *J. F. Thorpe*, J. chem. Soc., 1920, **117**, 591).

(b) *Bicyclo* [2:1:0] *pentane group*

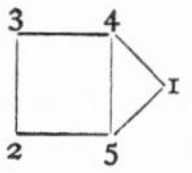

3 4 1 2 5

This ring combination of cyclopropane and cyclobutane seems capable of reacting in a tautomeric monocyclic form.

Whilst the bicyclic structure is borne out by the formation of caronic acid as an oxidation product of certain derivatives of this system (*E. H. Farmer* and *C. K. Ingold*, J. chem. Soc., 1920, 117, 1362) the optical evidence and many of the chemical properties indicate the cyclopentene structure (*N. J. Toivonen*, Chem. Ztbl., 1927, II, 1248; *R. M. Acheson* and *R. Robinson*, J. chem. Soc., 1952, 1127).

The ring system may be obtained by condensing $\alpha\alpha'$-dibromoglutaric esters with malonic ester and by the reaction between cyclopropane-1:2-dicarboxylic esters and cyanoacetic ester (*F. R. Goss* and *C. K. Ingold*, J. chem. Soc., 1928, 1268).

The sodio-salt of the keto-ester (II) is produced by the action of sodium ethoxide on the cyclopropane derivative (I); on hydrolysis 3-*keto*-1:1-*dimethylbicyclo*[2:1:0]*pentane*-2:5-*dicarboxylic acid* (III) m.p. 180° is obtained. On methylation of (I) the cyclopentene derivative (IV) is produced (*W. H. Perkin et al.*, Ber., 1902, **35**, 2126; J. chem. Soc., 1901, **79**, 736; *D. Radulescu*, Ber., 1909, **42**, 2770; *N. J. Toivonen, loc. cit.*).

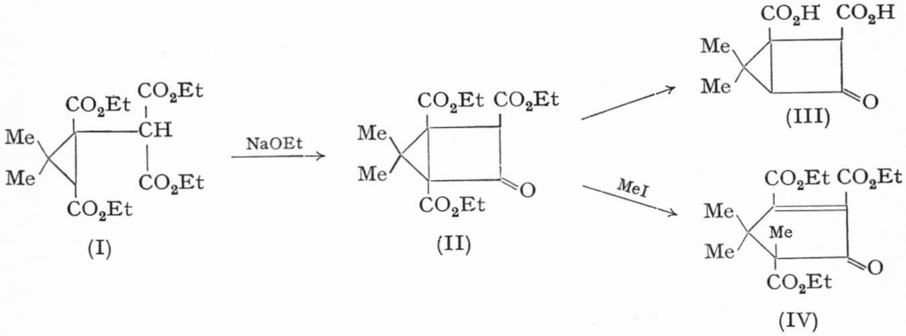

(c) *Bicyclo* [3:1:0] *hexane group*

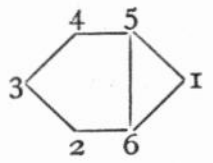

This ring system occurs in several terpenoid compounds (e.g. sabinene, thujyl alcohol, umbellulone, copaene). The bridge linkage is readily broken by both hydrogenation and dehydrogenation with the formation of cyclohexane and benzene derivatives respectively. Oxidation and reduction give cyclopentane and cyclopropane derivatives.

The parent hydrocarbon **bicyclo**[3:1:0]**hexane,** b.p. 80–81°, is formed by the action of zinc on 1-bromo-2-(bromomethyl)cyclopentane and by dehydroiodination of iodomethylcyclopentane (*N. D. Zelinsky et al.*, Bull. Soc. chim. Fr., 1924, [iv], **35**, 484; Ber., 1933, **66**, 1422).

3:3-*Dimethylbicyclo*[3:1:0]*hexane*, b.p. 115°, is formed by the debromination by means of zinc of 1:5-dibromo-3:3-dimethylcyclohexane (*N. D. Zelinsky*, Ber., 1913, **46**, 1466).

(d) *Bicyclo* [4:1:0] *heptane group*

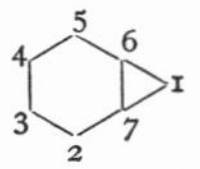

This ring system occurs in the carane group of terpenes; because of this relationship bicyclo[4:1:0]heptane is sometimes called norcarane.

Acids of this system may be synthesised by a general method consisting in interacting diazoacetic ester with benzene and its derivatives (*E. Buchner et al.*, Ber., 1900, **33**, 3453; 1901, **34**, 982; 1903, **36**, 3502; 1904, **37**, 931; Ann., 1908 **358**, 1), e.g.

$$C_6H_6 + CHN_2\cdot CO_2Et \longrightarrow C_6H_6{>}CO_2Et + N_2$$

(I)

Bicyclo[4:1:0]-**hepta**-2:4-**diene**-1-**carboxylic ethyl ester** *(ethyl norcaradiene-carboxylate)* (I), b.p. 108°/13 mm., is made by heating benzene and diazoacetic ester at 140° under pressure. With ammonia it gives the *amide*, m.p. 141°, which is hydrolysed with sulphuric acid to the oily free *acid* (*dibromide*, m.p. 160° dec.; *tetrabromide*, m.p. 235° dec.). The permanganate oxidation of the ester is complex, benzoic, phthalic, terephthalic and cyclopropanetricarboxylic acids being formed. Heating the ester under pressure transforms it into β-cycloheptatrienecarboxylic ester (p. 256) whilst boiling the ester or its amide with alkali gives α-cyclohepta-trienecarboxylic acid (p. 256). Concentrated sulphuric acid converts the amide into phenylacetamide.

The 3-*methyl* homologue, b.p. 122–126°/12 mm., *amide*, m.p. 131°, is similarly prepared from toluene and diazoacetic ester. The amide gives methylcyclohepta-trienecarboxylic acid on hydrolysis with sulphuric acid.

In exactly analogous fashion *m*-xylene yields 3:5-*dimethylbicyclo*[4:1:0]*hepta*-2:4-*diene*-1-*carboxylic ester*, b.p. 125–135°/10 mm., *amide*, m.p. 142°.

Bicyclo[4:1:0]**heptane**-1:7-**dicarboxylic acid,** m.p. 153°, *anhydride*, m.p. 87°, *ethyl ester*, b.p. 160/18 mm. is made by the action of diazoacetic ester on cyclohex-1-ene-1-carboxylic ester.

(e) Bicyclo [5:1:0] octane group

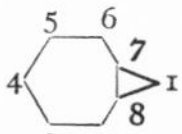

Bicyclo[5:1:0]**octene,** b.p. 137–139°, is formed, together with cyclo-octa-1:5-diene, by the distillation of cyclo-oct-4-enyltrimethylammonium hydroxide (granatanintrimethylammonium hydroxide). The hydrogen bromide adducts are fractionated and the hydrocarbon regenerated with quinoline. Permanganate oxidises it to a hydroxy-ketone, (semicarbazide m.p. 251° dec.) and ozone yields a mono-ozonide. Catalytic hydrogenation yields the saturated **bicyclo**[5:1:0]-**octane,** b.p. 139·5–140.5° (*R. Willstätter et al.*, Ber., 1907, **40**, 957; 1908, **41**, 1485; *C. Harries*, Ber., 1908, **41**, 672).

(f) Bicyclo [2:2:0] hexane group

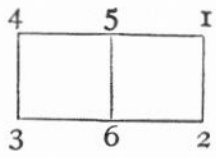

An attempt to prepare the parent hydrocarbon of this series by treating 1:4-dibromocyclohexane with metallic sodium resulted in the formation of a mixture of cyclohexa-1:3-diene, cyclohexene and cyclohexane (*N. D. Zelinsky* and *K. A. Kozeschkov*, Ber., 1927, **60**, 1102; *N. D. Prjanischnikov* and *S. I. Schujkina*, Ber., 1934, **67**, 64).

Vinylacrylic acid, sorbic acid and styrylacrylic acid polymerise with loss of carbon dioxide on heating with baryta. The hydrocarbons so obtained were once regarded as tricyclo-octanes, but later work showed them to be benzene derivatives (*O. Doebner*, Ber., 1907, **40**, 146; Ber., 1902, **35**, 2134; *R. Willstätter* and *H. Veraguth*, Ber., 1905, **38**, 1976; *R. Kuhn* and *A. Deutsch*, Ber., 1932, **65**, 43).

Dodecafluorotricyclo-octane (I), b.p. 80°, m.p. 40°, is obtained by the action of heat on hexafluorobutadiene (*M. Prober* and *W. T. Miller*, J. Amer. chem. Soc., 1949, **71**, 598).

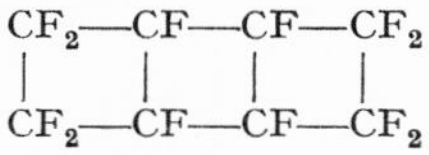

$$\begin{array}{cccccccc} CF_2 & - & CF & - & CF & - & CF_2 \\ | & & | & & | & & | \\ CF_2 & - & CF & - & CF & - & CF_2 \end{array}$$

(I)

(*g*) *Bicyclo* [3:2:0]*heptane group*

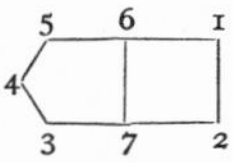

When keten is heated with cyclopentadiene in toluene, **bicyclo**[3:2:0]**hept-3-en-1-one,** b.p. 157·5–159°, *semicarbazone*, m.p. 222°, is obtained, which on hydrogenation yields **bicyclo**[3:2:0]**heptan-1-one,** b.p. 164–165°, *semicarbazone*, m.p. 216°. On oxidation of the latter with nitric acid glutaric acid is produced (*B. T. Brooks* and *G. Wilbert*, *ibid.*, 1941, **63**, 870; *A. T. Blomquist* and *J. Kwiatek*, *ibid.*, 1951, **73**, 2098). Use of dimethylketen in the above condensation gives 2:2-*dimethylbicyclo*[3:2:0]*hept-3-en-1-one*, b.p. 72°/15 mm., *semicarbazone*, m.p. 215° (*T. L. Dawson* and *G. R. Ramage*, J. chem. Soc., 1950, 3523). Diphenylketen furnishes the 2:2-*diphenyl* analogue, m.p. 86–88° (*J. L. Simonsen et al.*, J. chem. Soc., 1937, 1837).

(*h*) *Bicyclo* [4:2:0] *octane group*

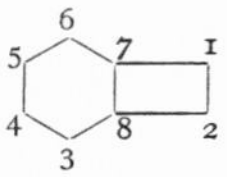

Compounds of this structure are obtained when cyclo-octatetraene (p. 260) is treated with halogens or halogenating agents (*W. Reppe et al.*, Ann., 1948, **560**, 1).

Bicyclo[4:2:0]**octane** (I) has b.p. 136°/760 mm.; 1:2-*dichloro-* (II), b.p. 110°/15 mm., 1:2:3:4:5:6-*hexachloro-* (III), m.p. 127° and 1:2-*dihydroxy*-derivative (IV), m.p. 142°. This glycol (IV) has also been obtained by reduction of *bicyclo*[4:2:0]*octan-1-ol-2-one*, b.p. 67°/0·04 mm., 3:5-*dinitrobenzoate*, m.p.

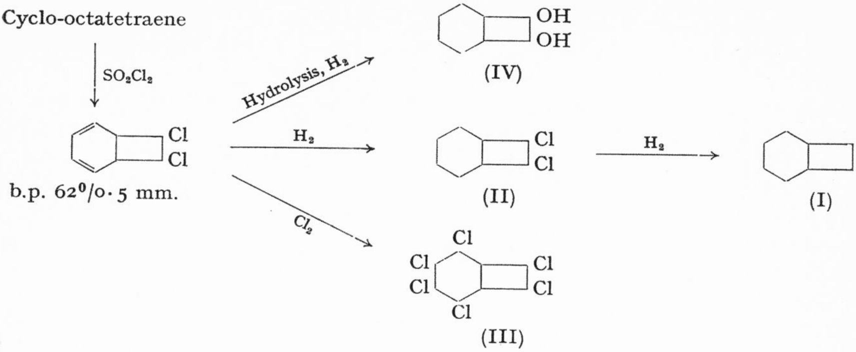

Cyclo-octatetraene

SO_2Cl_2

b.p. 62°/0·5 mm.

Hydrolysis, H_2 → (IV)

H_2 → (II) → H_2 → (I)

Cl_2 → (III)

131–132°, which is produced by the intramolecular acyloin condensation of ethyl *cis*-cyclohexane-1:2-dicarboxylate (*A. C. Cope* and *E. C. Herrick*, J. Amer. chem. Soc., 1950, **72**, 983). Keten condenses with cyclohexa-1:3-diene to give a *bicyclo-*[4:2:0]*octen-1-one*, b.p. 190·5–192°, *semicarbazone*, m.p. 200·5–201° which furnishes (I) on reduction (*A. T. Blomquist* and *J. Kwiatek*, J. Amer. chem. Soc., 1951, **73**, 2098).

(i) *Bicyclo* [3:3:0] *octane (pentalane) group*

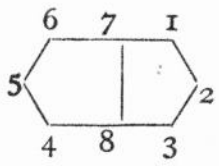

The stereochemistry of this system has already been discussed (pp. 311 ff). No compounds of this structure are known to occur in nature but they may be synthesised by standard procedures.

A series of compounds obtained by degradation of the alkaloid *pseudo*-pelletierine was formerly allotted to this group, but the evidence is equivocal (*R. Willstätter* and *T. Kametaka*, Ber., 1908, **41**, 1485; *G. Schroeter*, Ann., 1922, **426**, 1).

Bicyclo[3:3:0]**octane**, cis-*form*, b.p. 136°/755 mm., n_D^{18} 1·4629, d_4^{18} 0·8719, is obtained by Clemmensen or Kishner-Wolff reduction of bicyclo[3:3:0]octan-1-one (*R. P. Linstead et al.*, J. chem. Soc., 1934, 945, 956; cf. also *F. C. Whitmore et al.*, J. Amer. chem. Soc., 1947, **71**, 751). When heated with aluminium chloride it rearranges to bicyclo[3:2:1]octane (*J. W. Barrett* and *R. P. Linstead*, J. chem. Soc., 1936, 611). The trans-*hydrocarbon*, b.p. 132°/755 mm., m.p. −30°, n_D^{18} 1·4625, d_4^{18} 0·8626 is prepared in similar fashion from *trans*-bicyclo[3:3:0]-octan-2-one (*R. P. Linstead, ibid.*, 1935, 442).

Attempts to dehydrogenate these hydrocarbons to the hitherto unknown non-benzenoid aromatic hydrocarbon pentalene were unsuccessful; the ring system is also stable to hydrogenation (*J. W. Barrett* and *R. P. Linstead, loc. cit.*; *C. T. Blood* and *R. P. Linstead, ibid.*, 1952, 2255). The product obtained by the continued action of aluminium chloride on decalin is probably 1:4-*dimethyl-bicyclo*[3:3:0]*octane* (*idem, ibid.*).

Bicyclo[3:3:0]**octan-1-one,** b.p. 72°/12 mm., *semicarbazone,* m.p. 181°, exists solely in the *cis*-form because the 1-keto-group facilitates the conversion of the strained *trans*-form into the unstrained *cis*-form via the enol. The ketone is obtained when either *cis*- or *trans*-cyclopentane-1-carboxylic-2-propionic acid is heated with a trace of baryta; and also by the Dieckmann condensation of the diethyl esters of those acids (*A. H. Cook* and *R. P. Linstead,* J. chem. Soc., 1934, 946).

cis-**Bicyclo**[3:3:0]**octan-2-one,** b.p. 78°/10 mm., m.p. –28°, *semicarbazone,* m.p. 198°, is obtained by distilling *cis*-cyclopentane-1:2-diacetic acid with baryta at 280° and also by Dieckmann condensation of the diethyl ester of this acid. The configuration of the ketone is confirmed by nitric acid oxidation when *cis*-cyclopentane-1-carboxylic-2-acetic acid is formed. The trans-*form,* b.p. 62°/10 mm., m.p. 18°, *semicarbazone,* m.p. 251°, is produced by heating *trans*-cyclopentane-1:2-diacetic acid with baryta to 340°; the Dieckmann condensation of the diester will not take place because of ring strain. Nitric acid oxidation of this ketone furnishes *trans*-cyclopentane-1-carboxylic-2-acetic acid. The *trans*-diacetic acid can be resolved, thus establishing its configuration; heat treatment of the *l*-acid produces d-trans-*bicyclo*[3:3:0]*octan-2-one,* m.p. 41°, $[\alpha]^{18}$ + 437°. On reduction an optically inactive bicyclo-octane is formed (*R. P. Linstead et al.*, *ibid.*, 1934, 944; 1935, 1069).

7-*Methylbicyclo*[3:3:0]*octan-1-ones* have been obtained by *D. K. Banerjee* and his collaborators (*ibid.*, 1935, 474; J. Indian chem. Soc., 1940, **17,** 423; 1947, **24,** 12).

Bicyclo[3:3:0]**octa-1:4-dione,** m.p. 45°, *dibenzylidene* compound m.p. 240°, has been synthesised by the double Dieckmann cyclisation of tetraethyl hexane-1:3:4:6-tetracarboxylate via the intermediate *bicyclo*[3:3:0]*octa*-1:4-*dione*-2:5-*dicarboxylic ester,* m.p. 57·5°. With amyl formate a 2:5-di(hydroxymethylene) compound is formed, which is oxidised by ozone to butane-1:2:3:4-tetracarboxylic acid (*L. Ruzicka et al.*, Helv., 1934, **17,** 183).

S. Wawzonek has employed this diketone to carry out the following series of reactions (J. Amer. chem. Soc., 1943, **65,** 839):

PhMgBr → (I) → (II) → (III) —H_2→ (IV) —H_2→ (V)

In this way are obtained 1:4-*diphenylbicyclo*[3:3:0]*octane*-1:4-*diol* (I), m.p. 212° (dec.), 1:4-*diphenylbicyclo*[3:3:0]*octa*-1:4-*diene* (II), m.p. 138°, 1:4-*di*-

phenylbicyclo[3:3:0]*octa*-$\Delta^{1:7,4:8}$-*diene* (III), m.p. 190°, 1:4-*diphenylbicyclo*-[3:3:0]*oct*-$\Delta^{7:8}$-*ene* (IV), m.p. 116° and 1:4-*diphenylbicyclo*[3:3:0]*octane* (V), m.p. 100°.

(j) *Bicyclo* [4:3:0] *nonane (hydrindane) group*

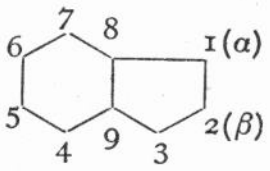

This system is present, fused to another six-membered ring, in the carbon skeleton of compounds of the steroid series, in which it forms rings C and D (Vol. II B). This circumstance has stimulated its study in more recent times. The two main methods of preparation involve the ring closure of relevant cyclohexane acids and the hydrogenation of indene derivatives.

As already indicated (p. 311) it is predictable that this system should exist in *cis* and *trans* modifications. The experimental verification of this concept was provided by the classical investigations of *W. Hückel* and his collaborators (Ann., 1927, **451**, 132; 1935, **518**, 155; Ber., 1941, **74**, 57; *J. W. Barrett* and *R. P. Linstead*, J. chem. Soc., 1935, 1069). They succeeded in isolating two distinct isomers of β-hydrindanone, the configurations of which were established as follows:

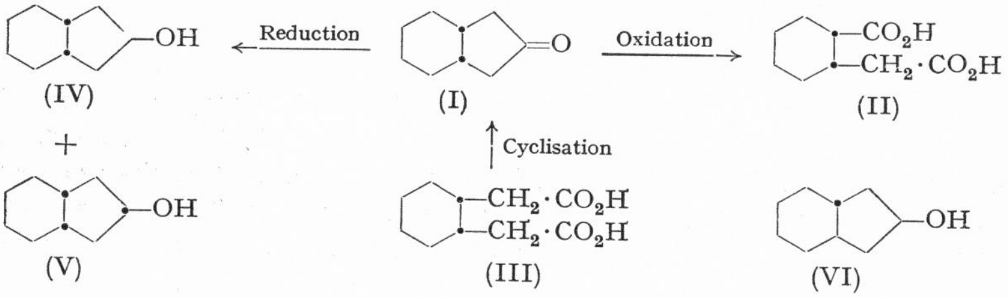

(IV) ← Reduction — (I) — Oxidation → (II) $-CO_2H$, $-CH_2 \cdot CO_2H$

(IV) + (V); (I) ↑ Cyclisation (III) $-CH_2 \cdot CO_2H$, $-CH_2 \cdot CO_2H$; (VI)

Oxidation of the isomer now known as *cis*-β-hydrindanone (I) gave the known *cis*-cyclohexane-1-carboxylic-2-acetic acid (II). This indication of *cis*-linking was confirmed by synthesis of (I) by cyclisation of *meso-cis*-cyclohexane-1:2-diacetic acid (III). The structure of *trans*-β-hydrindanone was similarly established. On this basis the two hydrindanones on reduction should give rise to two *meso-cis*-β-hydrindanols (IV and V) but only one *dl-trans*-β-hydrindanol (VI); these isomers are realised in practice. (It is noteworthy that all mono-β-substituted *cis*-hydrindanes are *meso*-structures whereas the corresponding *trans*-isomers are resolvable).

Catalytic hydrogenation of indene gives a mixture (mainly *cis*) of the two isomeric **hydrindanes** (*N. D. Zelinsky* and *M. B. Turowa-Pollok*, Ber., 1929, **62**, 1658, 2065). The stereochemically pure isomers are obtained by the Clemmensen reduction of the corresponding hydrindan-2-ones; this method gives cis-*hydrindane*, b.p. 166°/760 mm., n_D^{20} 1·4714, dl-trans-*hydrindane*, b.p. 159°/760 mm., n_D^{20} 1·4643, and the l-trans-*isomer*, b.p. 159°/747 mm., $[\alpha]_{5461}^{19}$ −10·8° n_D^{18} 1·4655 (*W. Hückel et al., loc. cit.*, 1927, 1935; Ann., 1938, **533**, 1; *R. P. Linstead et al.*, J. chem. Soc., 1935, 1069; 1938, 666).

The **hydrindanols** are obtained by the catalytic or chemical hydrogenation of the indanones or hydrindanones and by the action of nitrous acid on the hydrindanylamines (*W. Hückel et al., loc. cit.*, 1927, 1938; Ber., 1941, **74**, 57). Their properties are given in Table 1; the *cis*-I series probably has the *cis-cis*-configuration [corresponding to (V) on p. 319] and the *cis*-II series the *cis-trans* configuration [as in (IV) on p. 319].

TABLE 1

α- AND β-HYDRINDANOLS

Alcohol	B.p.⁰ or b.p.⁰/mm.	Hydrogen phthalate m.p.⁰	Hydrogen succinate m.p.⁰	Phenyl-urethane m.p.⁰
cis-α-I	18	127	63	115
cis-α-II	109/13	140	47	100
cis-β-I	5	110	73	103
cis-β-II	10	104	65.5	102
dl-trans-β	23	87	58	114
l-trans-β	12 $[\alpha]_D^{17}$ −12.5⁰		48	131

The primary amines of the series, the **hydrindanylamines,** are procured by reduction of the corresponding oximes (*W. Hückel et al., loc. cit.*, 1935, 1938; Ann., 1937, **533**, 1); cis-α-I, m.p. −2⁰, *benzoyl* deriv., m.p. 180⁰; cis-α-II, *benzoyl* deriv., m.p. 135⁰; cis-β-I, *benzoyl* deriv., m.p. 144⁰; cis-β-II, *benzoyl* deriv., dimorphic forms, m.p.'s 133⁰, 139⁰ and trans-β, b.p. 94⁰/23 mm., *benzoyl* deriv., m.p. 140⁰.

The **hydrindan-2-ones** (β-hydrindones) are obtained by chromic acid oxidation of the corresponding alcohols and by heating the corresponding cyclohexane-1:2-diacetic acids with acetic anhydride (*W. Hückel et al., loc. cit.*, 1935). The cis-*ketone* has m.p. 10⁰, b.p. 225⁰/754 mm., *semicarbazone*, m.p. 215⁰; the dl-trans-*ketone*, m.p. −12⁰, b.p. 217·8/754 mm., *semicarbazone*, m.p. 243⁰ and the d- and l-*enantiomorphs*, m.p. −9.5⁰, b.p. 83⁰/10 mm., $[\alpha]_D^{18.5}$ ± 297·3⁰, *semicarbazone*, m.p. 242⁰.

Hydrindan-1-one (α-hydrindone) obtained by cyclisation of both *cis*- and *trans*-cyclohexane-1-carboxylic-2-propionic acids, appears to be a mixture in which the *cis*-form predominates; interconversion of the two isomers of this structure would be facile via the enol form of the ketone.

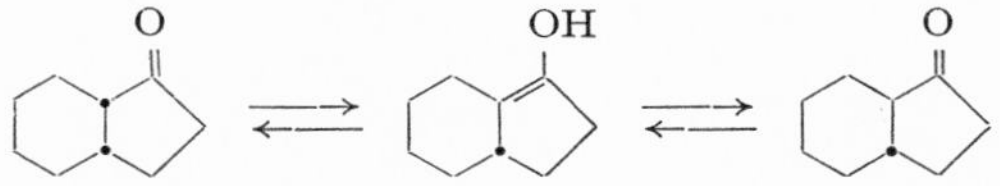

O ⇌ OH ⇌ O

The cis-*oxime* has m.p. 100⁰, trans-*oxime*, m.p. 146⁰.

Many hydrindanones substituted in the cyclohexane ring are known (*W. Hückel* and *E. Goth*, Ber., 1934, **67**, 2104, 2107; *A. H. Cook* and *R. P. Linstead*, J. chem. Soc., 1934, 946; *W. E. Bachmann* and *W. S. Struve*, J. Amer. chem. Soc., 1941, **63**, 2589).

The derivatives of the 8-methylhydrindanones, structures containing an angular methyl group, have been much studied because of the occurrence of the system as the CD rings of the steroids (*inter al.*, *W. E. Bachmann et al.*, J. Amer. chem. Soc., 1941, **63**, 1262; 1943, **65**, 1963; *C. D. Nenitzescu* and *V. Premetzky*, Ber., 1941, **74**, 676; *W. S. Johnson*, J. Amer. chem. Soc., 1944, **66**, 215; *P. Bagchi* and *D. K. Banerjee*, J. Indian chem. Soc., 1946, **23**, 397; 1947, **24**, 12).

Condensation of *cis*- and *trans*-hydrindan-2-one with cyanoacetic ester gives the *imides* of the *hydrindane-2:2-dicyanoacetic acids*, cis, m.p. 262°, trans, m.p. 291°. On hydrolysis these give the *hydrindane-2:2-diacetic acids*, cis, m.p. 188°, *anilic acids*, m.p. 184° and 180°, *anil*, m.p. 140°, trans, m.p. 224°, *anilic acid*, m.p. 203°, *anil*, m.p. 197° (*A. Kandiah*, J. chem. Soc., 1931, 923).

(k) Bicyclo [5:3:0] decane group

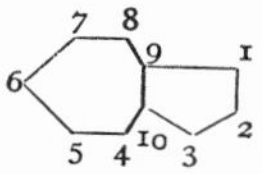

7 8 9 1 6 2 5 4 10 3

Compounds possessing this ring system have received much attention because of their ready dehydrogenation to give derivatives of the non-benzenoid aromatic system azulene. (For review see *N. Campbell*, Annual Reports, 1947, **44**, 162). A number of sesquiterpenoid compounds, including guaiol, partheniol and α- and β-vetivone, belong to the group. The methods employed for their preparation fall into two classes.

(a) The application of the usual ring expansion methods (Chap. 1) to the six-membered ring of hydrindane derivatives furnishes products with the bicyclo-[5:3:0]decane nucleus; e.g. Buchner type:

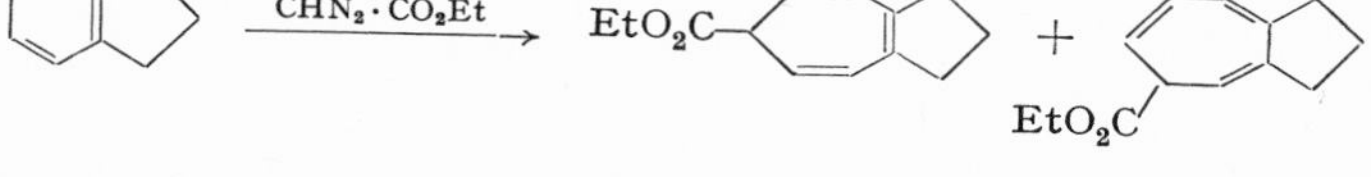

$CHN_2 \cdot CO_2Et$ → EtO_2C– + EtO_2C

(*inter al.*, *P. A. Plattner et al.*, Helv., 1947, **30**, 689, 1320; 1946, **29**, 1604; 1945, **28**, 1636; 1942, **25**, 1077, 590; *T. Wagner-Jauregg et al.*, Ber., 1943, **76**, 694, 1157; 1941, **74**, 1522). Demjanov type:

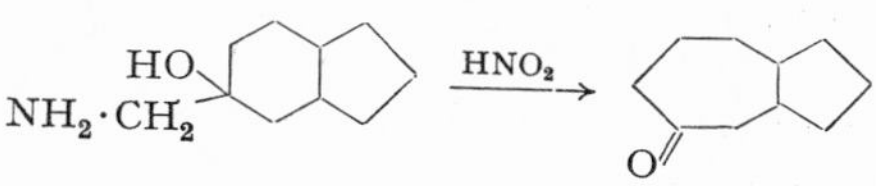

HO, $NH_2 \cdot CH_2$ —HNO_2→ O

(*P. A. Plattner et al.*, Helv., 1947, **30**, 1100; 1945, **28**, 1647; cf. also *H. Arnold*, Ber., 1943, **76**, 777). Diazomethane ring enlargement, e.g.

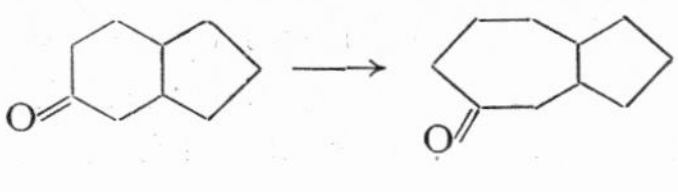

(*P. A. Plattner et al.*, Helv., 1947, **30**, 1091; *R. R. Coats* and *J. W. Cook*, J. chem. Soc., 1942, 559).

The last two methods both lead to **bicyclo[5:3:0]decan-5-one,** cis, b.p. 108°/12 mm., *semicarbazone*, m.p. 203°, trans, b.p. 108°/11 mm., *semicarbazone*, m.p. 151°.

(b) The cyclisation of suitable cyclopentane, and cycloheptane, dicarboxylic acids furnishes ketones of this series. Use of the former type of intermediate is convenient and affords stereochemically pure products, e.g.

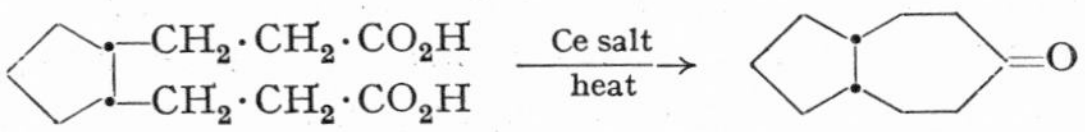

$CH_2 \cdot CH_2 \cdot CO_2H$ / $CH_2 \cdot CH_2 \cdot CO_2H$ —Ce salt, heat→ =O

which method gives **bicyclo[5:3:0]decan-6-one**, b.p. 116°/13 mm., *semicarbazone*, m.p. 183° (*P. A. Plattner* and *H. Studer*, Helv., 1946, **29**, 1432; *F. Sorm*, Coll. Czech. chem. Comm., 1947, **12**, 251); a second method gives **bicyclo[5:3:0]-decan-2-one,** b.p. 112°/11 mm., *semicarbazone*, m.p. 223°, from which is obtained **bicyclo[5:3:0]decane,** b.p. 80°/11 mm., n_D^{21} 1·4734 (*P. A. Plattner et al.*, Helv., 1946, **29**, 730, 740, 1608; Experientia, 1947, **3**, 70).

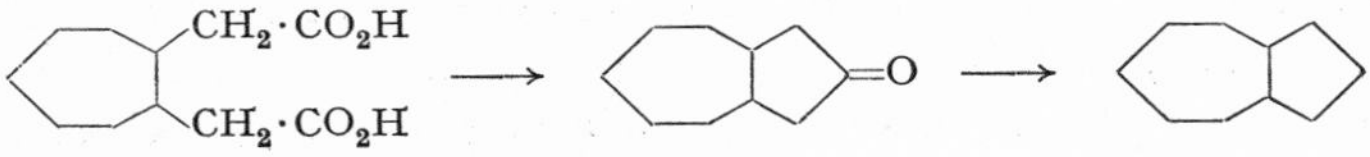

$CH_2 \cdot CO_2H$ / $CH_2 \cdot CO_2H$ → =O →

A special method of producing the bicyclo[5:3:0]decane system is by the intramolecular aldol condensation of cyclodecane-1:6-dione, when **bicyclo[5:3:0]-dec-9-en-4-one,** m.p. 37°, b.p. 123°/12 mm., *oxime*, m.p. 134°, is obtained (*W. Hückel et al.*, Ann., 1929, **474**, 121; Ber., 1933, **66**, 563).

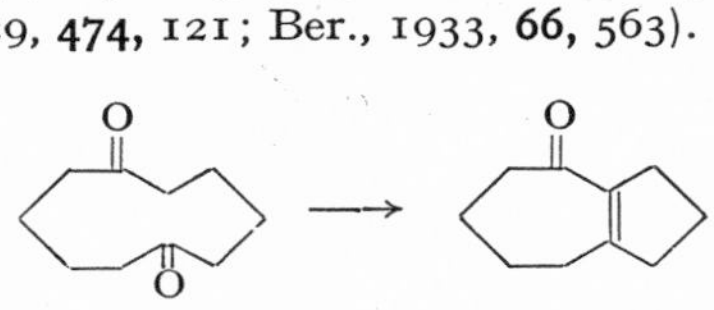

The *meso* position of the double bond is confirmed by the formation, on hydrogenation, of two **bicyclo[5:3:0]decan-4-ones,** cis-*oxime*, m.p. 119°, trans-*oxime*, m.p. 140°. Reduction of the *trans*-oxime gives the corresponding *amine*, b.p. 97°/10 mm., which, on exhaustive methylation, yields *bicyclo*[5:3:0]*dec-4-ene*, b.p. 63·5°/8 mm. This latter hydrocarbon may be oxidised to a dicarboxylic acid which gives hydrindan-1-one on cyclisation by Blanc's method, showing that the carbonyl group in the original ketone must be in the seven-membered ring (*W. Hückel* and *L. Schnitzspahn*, Ann., 1933, **505**, 274).

(*l*) *Bicyclo* [4:4:0] *decane (decalin) group*

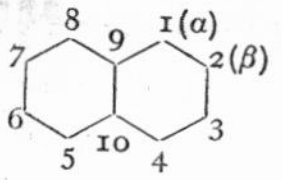

The decalin carbon skeleton is encountered very frequently in natural substances such as sesquiterpenes and allied derivatives e.g. santonin. Synthetically the compounds of this class are readily available by the hydrogenation of naphthalene derivatives and this is the procedure adopted industrially. They may also be procured by ring closure of the relevant cyclohexane acids, by the Diels-Alder diene synthesis, and by the Michael condensation of acetylcyclohexenes with malonic esters. For a review of decalin and its derivatives see *E. H. Rodd*, Dict. appl. Chem., Vol. III, 4th. Edition, p. 433 *et seq*.).

The existence of this system in *cis*- and *trans*-modifications has already been discussed (p. 309). It is found in this series that assignment of configuration may be made employing the Auwers-Skita generalisation that a *cis*-isomer possesses a boiling-point, density, refractive index and viscosity higher than those of the corresponding *trans*-isomer; this guide has proved useful in the investigation of the type of ring-locking in natural compounds (e.g. *L. Ruzicka et al.*, Helv., 1941, **24**, 1171). The absolute determination of configurations in the 2-substituted decalins provided the first verification of the correctness of the Sachse-Mohr hypotheses; the methods employed are indicated in the following scheme (*W. Hückel et al.*, Ann., 1925, **441**, 1; 1927, **451**, 109; 1935, **518**, 155; Ber., 1925, **58**, 1449; 1934, **67**, 1890; 1937, **70**, 2479; 1941, **74**, 57; *J. W. Barrett* and *R. P. Linstead*, J. chem. Soc., 1935, 1069; *G. Cauquil* and *G. Tsatsas*, Compt. rend., 1944, **218**, 463).

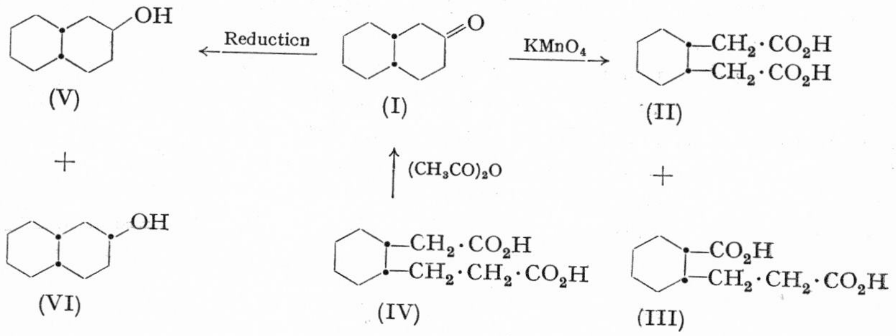

(V) OH ← Reduction — (I) =O — $KMnO_4$ → (II) $-CH_2 \cdot CO_2H$, $-CH_2 \cdot CO_2H$

(V) + (VI) OH; (I) ↑ $(CH_3CO)_2O$ from (IV) $-CH_2 \cdot CO_2H$, $-CH_2 \cdot CH_2 \cdot CO_2H$; (II) + (III) $-CO_2H$, $-CH_2 \cdot CH_2 \cdot CO_2H$

The key compounds in this investigation were the β-decalones, two distinct isomers of which were preparable differing only in the type of ring-locking. The absolute configuration of these two isomers was determined by oxidation methods. By this treatment the isomer now known as *cis*-β-decalone (I) gave *cis*-cyclohexane-1-carboxylic-2-propionic acid (III) and *cis*-cyclohexane-1:2-diacetic acid (II). This latter acid (II) was the important product for purposes of diagnosis; its configuration as the *cis-(meso)*-isomer was indicated by its non-resolvability. This conformation was confirmed synthetically by cyclisation of *cis*-cyclohexane-1-acetic-2-propionic acid (IV). An exactly similar series of reactions established the structure of *trans*-β-decalone. In this case the oxidation product, *trans*-cyclohexane-1:2-diacetic acid, was a *dl*-compound which was resolved.

The above structures demand that each β-decalone give rise to two resolvable β-decalols (V and VI above for the *cis*-series) and two corresponding β-decalyl-amines. A similar number of isomers is required in the α-series. All these predicted isomers are known although absolute configurations with respect to the new asymmetric centre have not yet been rigidly assigned.

(i) Saturated compounds

The **decalins** themselves are prepared by the catalytic hydrogenation of naphthalene; with a platinum catalyst in glacial acetic acid the *cis*-isomer is mainly formed whilst hydrogenation in the gas phase by the Sabatier-Senderens method furnishes chiefly *trans*-decalin. The two isomers can be separated by fractional distillation. They may also be obtained by hydrogenation of the decalones or octalins (*V. N. Ipatiev*, Ber., 1907, **40**, 1287; *R. Willstätter* and *D. Hatt*, Ber., 1912, **45**, 1475; *F. Eisenlohr* and *R. Polenske*, Ber., 1924, **57**, 1639; *N. D. Zelinsky et al.*, Ber., 1929, **62**, 1658; Ann., 1922, **426**, 13; *W. Hückel*, Ann., 1925, **441**, 42). cis-*Decalin* has m.p. −43·25°, b.p. 194·6°, n_D^{20} 1·482, d_4^{20} 0·898; the corresponding data for the trans-*isomer* are m.p. −31·16°, b.p. 185·4°, n_D^{20} 1·4713, d_4^{20} 0·8709 (*W. Hückel*, Ann., 1938, **533**, 25; *W. F. Seyer* and *J. D. Leslie*, J. Amer. chem. Soc., 1942, **62**, 1912).

In the presence of aluminium chloride or bromide *cis*-decalin is isomerised to *trans*-decalin (*N. D. Zelinsky* and *M. B. Turova-Pollak*, Ber., 1925, **58**, 1292; 1929, **62**, 1658; 1932, **65**, 1299).

The photo-oxidation of *trans*-decalin yields the 9-*hydroperoxide*, m.p. 96·5° which may be readily converted to the corresponding alcohol, m.p. 54·7° (*K. I. Ivanov* and *V. K. Savinova*, Brit. chem. Abstr., 1946, AII, 264).

A method much used for the preparation of homologues of decalin carrying a 9-alkyl group consists in the condensation of malonic ester with a 1-acylcyclohex-1-ene and reduction of the diketone thus obtained (*L. Ruzicka et al.*, Helv., 1931, **14**, 1151), e.g.

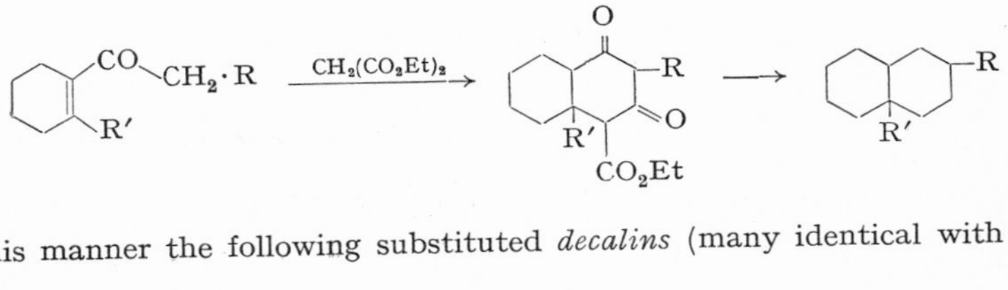

In this manner the following substituted *decalins* (many identical with those derivable from natural compounds) may be obtained: trans-9-*methyl*-, b.p. 70°/12 mm.; cis-4:9-*dimethyl*-, b.p. 85°/12 mm. (obtained also from eudesmol); trans-3-*ethyl*-9-*methyl*-, b.p. 98°/12 mm.; cis-3-*ethyl*-9-*methyl*-, b.p. 102°/12 mm. (obtained also from β-selinene); trans-3-*ethyl*-5:9-*dimethyl*-, b.p. 113°/12 mm.; cis-3-*ethyl*-5:9-*dimethyl*-, b.p. 116°/12 mm. (obtained also by rearrangement of eudesmol).

The *cis*-β-**decalols** may be obtained by the sodium and alcohol reduction of cis-β-decalone and also by the hydrogenation of *ac*-β-tetralol* (1:2:3:4-tetrahydro-2-naphthol) using platinum as catalyst; if nickel be employed the *trans*-β-decalols are produced. A further method for preparing them is by the action of nitrous acid on the corresponding primary amines, the decalylamines (*W. Hückel*, Ann., 1927, **451**, 116; *G. Cauquil* and *G. Tsatsas*, Compt. rend., 1944, **218**, 463).

The α-**decalol** structure has the same number of isomeric possibilities as the β-alcohol and all four modifications are known. The two trans-*α-decalols* are obtained by the catalytic hydrogenation of α-naphthol with nickel. Reduction of either the *ac*- or *ar*-α-tetralol over platinum yields the same cis-*α-decalol*, m.p. 93°; the second cis-*isomer*, m.p. 55°, is obtained indirectly by treating the corresponding amine with nitrous acid (*W. Hückel*, Ann., 1933, **502**, 99. For the correlation between the structures of the decalols and their rates of reaction see *W. Hückel et al.*, Ann., 1937, **533**, 128).

The complete series of decalols is given in Table 2. In the absence of any rigid assignment of the correct stereochemical configuration of the hydroxyl groups the numerals I and II are employed as shown. It is very probable that *cis*-β-decalol-I has the *cis-cis*-configuration (VI; p. 323) and the *cis*-β-decalol-II the *cis-trans*-configuration (V; p. 323) (*W. G. Dauben* and *E. Hoerger*, J. Amer. chem. Soc., 1951, **73**, 1504).

TABLE 2

α- AND β-DECALOLS

Alcohol	M.p.°	Hydrogen phthalate m.p.°	Hydrogen succinate m.p.°	Phenyl-urethane m.p.°
cis-α-I	93	176	66	118
cis-α-II	55	142	54	80
trans-α-I	49	121	107	134
trans-α-II	63	168	85	172
cis-β-I	105	116	81	134
cis-β-II	18	153	59	102
trans-β-I	53	108	64	99
trans-β-II	75	180	81	165

Acetylenic carbinols and glycols derived from the decalones have been prepared (*inter al.*, *C. S. Marvel et al.*, J. Amer. chem. Soc., 1940, **62**, 2659; *V. I. Nikitin*, J. gen. Chem. U.S.S.R., 1945, **15**, 401).

* The prefix *ac* before a tetralin derivative signifies that the substituent is in the alicyclic ring; the prefix *ar* shows it to be in the aromatic ring.

The trans-**decalin**-2:3-**diols,** m.p.'s 141°, 128° and 166°, are obtained by reduction of the corresponding -2:3-*dione,* m.p. 100–101° (*K. Ganapathi,* Ber., 1939, **72,** 1381) or by hydroxylation of *trans*-$\Delta^{2:3}$-octalin. trans-*Decalin*-9:10-*diol,* m.p. 96° is obtained by the action of perbenzoic acid on $\Delta^{9:10}$-octalin followed by hydrolytic fission of the epoxide formed. On dehydration rearrangement occurs to form spiro[5:4]decan-5-one; p. 305) (*W. Hückel et al.,* 1933, **502,** 154; 1929, **474,** 143). cis-*Decalin*-9:10-*diol,* m.p. 89·5°, is produced by the action of osmium tetroxide on $\Delta^{9:10}$-octalin (*R. Criegee,* Ann., 1936, **522,** 75).

The **decalylamines,** the primary amines of this series, are obtained by the reduction of the corresponding ketoximes, and by the action of hydrazoic acid on the corresponding carboxylic acids (*W. Hückel et al.,* Ann., 1927, **451,** 109; Ber., 1937, **70,** 2479; *idem,* 1941, **74,** 57; *W. G. Dauben* and *E. Hoerger,* J. Amer. chem. Soc., 1951, **73,** 1504). They are listed in Table 3; the numeral suffix indicates the steric correlation with the corresponding decalols (Table 2).

TABLE 3

α- AND β-DECALYLAMINES

Amine	M.p.°	Benzoyl deriv. m.p.°	Acetyl deriv. m.p.°
cis-α-I	8	206	181
cis-α-II	— 2	193	141
trans-α-I	—18	112	130
trans-α-II	— 1	195	182
*cis-β-I	ca. 20	128	88
*cis-β-II	15	204	153
trans-β-I	—47	177	130
trans-β-II	15	176	163

cis-β-Decalylamine-II has been resolved via the *d*-camphorsulphonate into the optical enantiomorphs, m.p. 30·5°, $[\alpha]_D^{21}$ +12·42°, *benzoyl* deriv., m.p. 205°. For the interpretation of the Walden inversion of the amines when treated with nitrous acid see *W. Hückel,* Ann., 1937, **533,** 1 and *W. G. Dauben* and *E. Hoerger, loc. cit.*

The 9-*aminodecalins,* cis, m.p. –13°, *benzoyl* deriv., m.p. 147°; trans, m.p. –25°, *benzoyl* deriv., m.p. 148–149°, are obtained by reduction of *cis*- and *trans*-9-nitrodecalins (*W. Hückel et al.,* Ann., 1933, **502,** 114).

cis-9:10-*Diaminodecalin,* m.p. 41°, *diacetyl* deriv., m.p. 242° and trans-9:10-*diaminodecalin,* m.p. 70° are obtained by the reduction of cyclodecane-1:6-dione-dioxime; on treatment with nitrous acid both isomers yield spiro[5:4]decan-5-one (*P. A. Plattner* and *J. Hulstkamp,* Helv., 1944, **27,** 220).

The **decalones** are obtained by the chromic acid oxidation of the corresponding decalols. cis-*α-Decalone,* m.p. 2°, b.p. 126°/20 mm., n_D^{20} 1·49634, *semicarbazone,*

* These are the reverse of Hückel's assignments (see *W. G. Dauben* and *E. Hoerger, loc. cit.*).

m.p. 220–221° (dec.) is very labile and readily passes via an enolic intermediate into trans-*α-decalone*, m.p. 33°, n_D^{23} 1·48372, *semicarbazone*, m.p. 229–230°. On mild oxidation the α-decalones yield the respective geometrical isomer of cyclohexane-1-carboxylic-2-propionic acid but hot permanganate leads to rupture of both rings to give δ-ketosebacic acid (*W. Hückel*, Ann., 1925, **441**, 1). The similar oxidation of the *β-decalones*, cis- m.p. −14°, b.p. 247°/755 mm., n_D^{21}, 1·49180, *semicarbazone*, m.p. 182–183° (dec.), trans- m.p. 6°, b.p. 241°/755 mm. n_D^{19} 1·48088, *semicarbazone*, m.p. 192–193° (dec.) has been discussed on p. 323.

9-**Methyl-α-decalone** has undergone considerable investigation on account of its having the angular methyl group characteristic of steroidal structures (*J. W. Cook* and *C. A. Lawrence*, J. chem. Soc., 1937, 817; *C. K. Chuang et al.*, Ber., 1936, **69**, 1494; *R. P. Linstead et al.*, J. chem. Soc., 1937, 814; 1938, 660; *C. D. Nenitzescu et al.*, Ber., 1940, **73**, 313; *A. A. Plentl* and *M. T. Bogert*, J. org. Chem., 1941, **6**, 669; *W. S. Johnson*, J. Amer. chem. Soc., 1943, **65**, 1317; *J. English* and *G. Cavalieri*, *ibid.*, 1943, **65**, 1085; *W. E. Bachmann* and *N. L. Wendler*, *ibid.*, 1946, **68**, 2580; *W. S. Johnson* and *S. Posvic*, *ibid.*, 1947, **69**, 1361). The most convenient method of preparation is that of the last named authors who employ the following procedure starting from α-decalone:

$Na + H \cdot CO_2Et$ / $CHMe_2I$ → =CHOCHMe$_2$

KNH_2 / MeI

$FeCl_3$ / HCl

9-Methyl-α-decalone

The final product is a mixture of *cis-* and *trans*-forms, easily separable by means of their semicarbazones. cis-9-*Methyl-α-decalone* has b.p. 116°/14 mm., *semicarbazone*, m.p. 226–227°, 2:4-*dinitrophenylhydrazone*, m.p. 165° and the trans-*isomer*, b.p. 119°/14 mm., *semicarbazone*, m.p. 219–220°, 2:4-*dinitrophenylhydrazone*, m.p. 172°. The optical enantiomorphs of the *cis*-ketone have been obtained by indirect means (*A. A. Plentl* and *M. T. Bogert, loc. cit.*).

Oxidation of *trans-β*-decalone by selenium dioxide gives trans-**decalin**-2:3-**dione,** m.p. 99–100°, *bis-semicarbazone*, m.p. 265°, *quinoxaline*, m.p. 177–178° (*K. Ganapathi*, Brit. chem. Abstr., 1938, AII, 286; Ber., 1939, **72**, 1381). *Decalin*-1:5-*dione* (trans, m.p. 165–167°, cis, m.p. 68–72°) has been obtained by oxidation with chromic-acetic acid of the decalindiol obtained by reduction of 1:5-dihydroxynaphthalene (*B. J. F. Hudson* and *R. Robinson*, J. chem. Soc., 1942, 691). *Decalin*-1:4-*dione* (trans, m.p. 122°, cis, m.p. 50°) is obtained by catalytic hydrogenation of the adduct from butadiene and benzoquinone (*K. Alder* and *G. Stein*, Ann., 1933, **501**, 247).

Carboxylic acids. With platinic oxide as catalyst complete hydrogenation of α- and β-naphthoic acids leads respectively to a *decalin-1-carboxylic acid,* m.p. 127°, *amide,* m.p. 198–199° and a *decalin-2-carboxylic acid,* m.p. 72–76°, *amide,* m.p. 145°; the steric configurations of these acids are unknown (*J. Ranedo* and *A. León,* C.A., 1928, **22,** 777). *F. W. Kay* and *N. Stuart* (J. chem. Soc., 1926, 3038) have reported the isolation of four amides (m.p.'s 195–196°, 171–174°, 169–171° and 139–140°) corresponding to the four theoretically possible isomers of decalin-2-carboxylic acid from the reduction product of *ar*-tetrahydro-β-naphthoic acid. Later workers have obtained cis-cis-*decalin-2-carboxylic* acid (I), m.p. 80–81°, *amide,* m.p. 179–180°, by catalytic hydrogenation of β-naphthoic acid; cis-trans-*decalin-2-carboxylic* acid (II), m.p. 92–94°, *amide,* m.p. 186–187° was prepared by the action of carbon dioxide on *cis*-β-decalylmagnesium bromide (*W. G. Dauben* and *E. Hoerger,* J. Amer. chem. Soc., 1951, **73,** 1504).

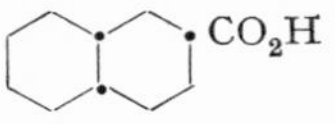

CO_2H CO_2H

(I) 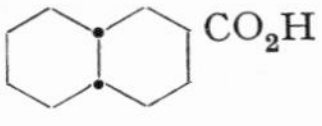 (II)

Decalin-2-carboxylic-2-acetic acids, cis, m.p. 170° (*anhydride,* m.p. 94°), trans, m.p. 150° (*anhydride,* m.p. 91°) are prepared from β-decalone cyanohydrin and sodiocyanoacetic ester (*W. Hückel* and *F. Wiebke,* Ber., 1926, **59,** 2838).

trans-**Decalin-1:1-diacetic acid,** m.p. 169° (*anhydride,* m.p. 94°) is obtained from α-decalone and two molecules of cyanoacetic ester. The **decalin-2:2-diacetic acids,** cis, m.p. 167°, trans, m.p. 175°, are prepared in analogous fashion from the β-decalones (*W. Hückel* and *F. Wiebke, loc. cit.; K. Rao,* J. chem. Soc., 1929, 1954).

Several lactones of the decalin series occur naturally e.g. santonin, artemisin, alantolactone.

(ii) Unsaturated compounds

Octahydronaphthalenes or octalins are obtained by the dehydration of decalols and the deamination of decalylamines. Six isomers are possible, differing in the position of the double bond (four isomers, $\Delta^{1:9}$, $\Delta^{9:10}$, $\Delta^{1:2}$ and $\Delta^{2:3}$) and the type of ring fusion (*cis*- and *trans*-forms of $\Delta^{1:2}$ and $\Delta^{2:3}$). Their heats of combustion are exactly equal but their X-ray diagrams show characteristic differences. Differences in reaction velocity are found for hydrogenation, hydration and the action of perbenzoic acid.

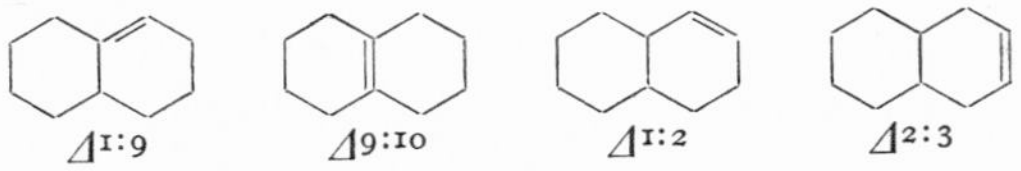

$\Delta^{1:9}$ $\Delta^{9:10}$ $\Delta^{1:2}$ $\Delta^{2:3}$

Octalins

$\Delta^{1:9}$-**Octalin,** b.p. 189·5–193·5°, *nitrosochloride,* colourless, m.p. 127°, *nitrolpiperidide,* m.p. 181°, is most conveniently prepared by the pyrolysis of the xanthate of *trans*-α-decalol, m.p. 63° (for the stereochemistry of this reaction see *D. H. R. Barton,* J. chem. Soc., 1949, 2714). The position of the double bond at the bridge-head implies no increase in energy content as evinced by its normal heat of combustion. The constitution assigned to the hydrocarbon is confirmed by oxidation when first cyclohexan-1-one-2-butyric acid and then octan-4-one-1:8-dicarboxylic acid are formed (*W. Hückel,* Ann., 1933, **502,** 136). For ketones derived from $\Delta^{1:9}$-octalin see *J. Décombe,* Compt. rend., 1941, **213,** 579.

$\Delta^{9:10}$-**Octalin,** m.p. -34^0, b.p. 194–196^0 is obtained by dehydration of the decalols with such acidic reagents as potassium bisulphate and aromatic sulphonic acids; it is also formed by the dehydration of *trans*-2-hydroxydicyclopentyl with zinc chloride and *R. Criegee* and *A. Riebel* (Angew. Chem., 1953, **65,** 136) have obtained it by the dimerisation of cyclopentene. The 9:10 position of the double bond is indicated by the formation of a blue* *nitrosochloride,* m.p. 91^0, and receives confirmation by the formation of cyclodecane-1:6-dione (p. 277) on ozonolysis of the hydrocarbon. Hydroxylation yields the decalln-9:10-diols (see above). The action of selenium dioxide in acetic anhydride furnishes the following products (*W. P. Campbell* and *G. C. Harris,* J. Amer. chem. Soc., 1941, **63,** 2721):

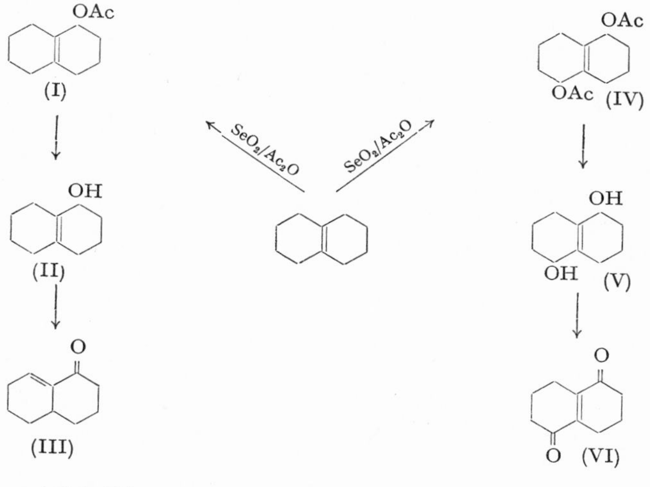

The $\Delta^{9:10}$-α-octalol (II), *acetate* (I), b.p. 125^0/10 mm. furnishes on oxidation $\Delta^{8:9}$-*α-octalone* (III), b.p. 127^0/10 mm., *semicarbazone,* m.p. 243^0; oxidation of $\Delta^{9:10}$-*octalin-1:5-diol* (V), m.p. 196^0, *diacetate* (IV), m.p. 123^0 yields $\Delta^{9:10}$-*octalin-1:5-dione* (VI), m.p. 114^0.

cis-$\Delta^{1:2}$-**Octalin,** *dibromide,* m.p. 61^0, *nitrosochloride,* m.p. 186^0, is the main product of the thermal decomposition of the xanthate of *cis*-α-decalol, m.p. 93^0 (*W. Hückel et al.,* Ann., 1940, **543,** 191; 1933, **502,** 144). It may also be obtained, admixed with the $\Delta^{2:3}$-isomer, by the dehydration of *cis*-β-decalol, m.p. 105^0 (*H. Leroux,* Ann. Chim., 1910, **21,** 458). trans-$\Delta^{1:2}$-*Octalin,* b.p. 185^0, is prepared by the exhaustive methylation of *trans*-α-decalylamine, m.p. -1^0. Its constitution

* The blue colour is characteristic of nitrosochlorides $CR_2(NO)\cdot CR_2Cl$ when neither R is hydrogen.

is verified by the production of *trans*-cyclohexane-1-carboxylic-2-propionic acid on oxidation (*W. Hückel* and *H. Naab*, Ann., 1933, **502**, 150).

trans-$\Delta^{2:3}$-**Octalin,** m.p. –21°, *dibromide,* m.p. 85°, has been prepared in an impure state by the dehydration of *trans-β*-decalol, m.p. 75°. Oxidation yields *trans*-cyclohexane-1:2-diacetic acid (*W. Hückel et al.*, Ann., 1927, **451**, 148; 1933, **502**, 151).

Hexahydronaphthalenes, *hexalins,* occur in nature as representatives of the sesquiterpene class of compounds e.g. cadinene, selinene etc. (Vol. IIB). For synthetic hexalins see *A. Agrestini*, Gazz. chim., 1882, **12**, 495; *C. Graebe* and *P. A. Guye*, Ber., 1863, **16**, 3032; *F. Wreden*, Ann., 1877, **187**, 164; *W. Borsche* and *E. Lange*, Ann., 1923, **434**, 222; *I. Nishimatsu* and *S. Kimura*, Chem. Ztbl., 1928, I, 2369).

The *hexalindione, butadienebenzoquinone adduct* (I), m.p. 58° may be selectively reduced to 1:7-*dihydroxy*-5:6:7:8-*tetrahydronaphthalene* (II), m.p. 185°. With hydrogen bromide it undergoes rearrangement to the 1:4-*dihydroxyhexalin* (III), m.p. 212° (*O. Diels* and *K. Alder*, Ber., 1929, **62**, 2345).

OH (III) ← HBr — O (I) — H_2 → OH (II)

The di- and tetra-hydrogenated naphthalenes in which one ring remains benzenoid are dealt with in Vol. III.

(*m*) *Bicyclo* [5:4:0] *undecane group*

The only non-benzenoid members of this series have been obtained by *P. A. Plattner* (Helv., 1944, **27**, 801) by the following means from benzsuberane (I):

(I) — Pt/H → (II) — Ozone → OH (III) — $ZnCl_2$ → (IV)

These reactions furnish **bicyclo**[5:4:0]**undecane** (II), b.p. 89°/11 mm., *bicyclo*-[5:4:0]*undecan*-10-*ol* (III), b.p. 120°/3 mm., m.p. 30° and *bicyclo*[5:4:0]*undec*-$\Delta^{10:11}$-*ene* (IV), b.p. 91°/12 mm.

(n) Bicyclo [5:5:0] dodecane group

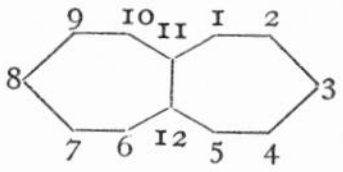

Members of this series have been reported by *G. Büchi* and *O. Jeger* who carried out the following series of reactions (Helv., 1949, **32**, 538):

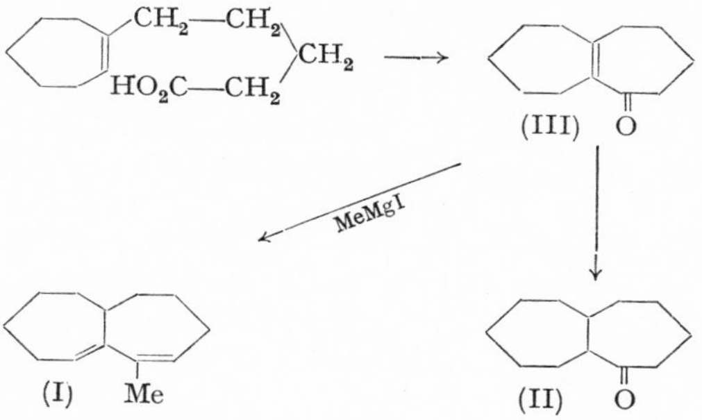

1-Methylbicyclo[5:5:0]-**dodeca**-1:10-**diene** (I) has b.p. 110°/10 mm., n_D^{21} 1·5182. *Bicyclo*[5:5:0]*dodecan*-1-*one* (II) has b.p. 145°/15 mm., *semicarbazone*, m.p. 189°; *bicyclo*[5:5:0]*dodec*-11-*ene*-1-*one*, (III) b.p. 133°/10 mm., *semicarbazone*, m.p. 157°.

Carboxylic acids of this series may be made by the action of diazoacetic ester on benzsuberane derivatives (*D. H. S. Horn* and *W. S. Rapson*, J. chem. Soc., 1949, 2421). Attempts to dehydrogenate these compounds to derivatives of the cyclic conjugated polyene heptalene have not been successful.

2. Highly condensed alicyclic systems

Compounds belonging to these systems are usually obtained by hydrogenation of the corresponding aromatic compounds.

A **per**(**deca-**)**hydroacenaphthene** (I), b.p. 235–236° may be obtained by reduction of acenaphthene with phosphorus and hydriodic acid (*C. Liebermann* and *L. Spiegel*, Ber., 1889, **22**, 781) or with nickel and hydrogen (*V. N. Ipatiev*, Ber., 1909, **412**, 2094). Similarly, fluorene furnishes a **per**(**dodeca-**)**hydrofluorene** (II), b.p. 254–258° (*C. Liebermann* and *L. Spiegel*, *loc. cit.*; *V. N. Ipatiev*, *loc. cit.*; *L. Spiegel*, Ber., 1908, **41**, 885). For perhydrofluorenones see *E. A. Braude* and *J. A. Coles*, J. chem. Soc., 1952, 1430; *R. P. Linstead et al.*, *ibid.*, 1950, 1423.

The stereochemistry of the **per**(**tetradeca-**)**hydrophenanthrenes** is important because of its relevance to the structure of the steroids. Theoretically this structure can exist in six inactive modifications corresponding to those already described for the perhydrodiphenic acids (p. 296). Many products of the complete hydrogenation of phenanthrene and its partially hydrogenated derivatives have been described in the literature (for summary see *R. P. Linstead* and *A. L.

Walpole, J. chem. Soc., 1939, 842) but only one isomer of undoubted stereochemical homogeneity, m.p. 10°, b.p. 141°/18 mm., has been obtained (*idem, ibid.*). This was prepared by Clemmensen reduction of *trans-anti-trans*-9-ketoperhydrophenanthrene and may therefore be represented as (III).

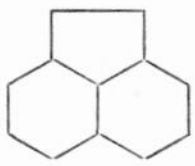

(I) 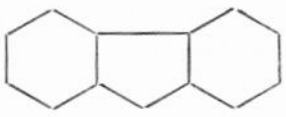 (II) 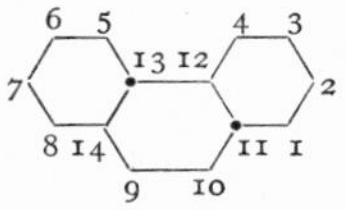 (III)

Corresponding to the above six perhydrophenanthrene isomers there should exist eight inactive perhydro-9-phenanthrones and sixteen inactive perhydro-9-phenanthrols. A number of these isomers have been obtained by hydrogenation of 9-phenanthrol (*C. S. Marvel* and *R. V. White,* J. Amer. chem. Soc., 1940, **62,** 2739; *R. P. Linstead et al.,* J. Amer. chem. Soc., 1942, **64,** 2014), the *as*-hexahydro-9-phenanthrones (*idem, ibid.*; *J. W. Cook et al.,* J. chem. Soc., 1936, 71; 1939, 168) and the perhydro-9-phenanthrones (*R. P. Linstead* and *A. L. Walpole, loc. cit.*). The results may be conveniently summarised in the following manner:

	Perhydro-9-phenanthrones	Perhydro-9-phenanthrols
**cis-syn-cis*	m.p. 44°	→ m.p. 111° → —
trans-syn-cis	m.p. 57°	→ m.p. 89° → m.p. 67°
trans-anti-trans	m.p. 49°	→ m.p. 119° → —

The *trans-anti-trans*-compound has also been obtained by stepwise synthesis (*B. K. Bhattacharyya,* J. Indian chem. Soc., 1945, **22,** 85). The configurations of these perhydrogenated phenanthrene derivatives are confirmed by oxidative fission to the corresponding perhydrodiphenic acids (p. 296).

Complete hydrogenation of 9:10-phenanthraquinone has led to the isolation of three *cis-syn-cis*-glycols, *perhydro*-9:10-*dihydroxyphenanthrenes,* m.p.'s 174°, 174°, and 155°, differing only in the spatial configuration of the hydroxyl groups: a *cis-syn-trans*-glycol m.p. 184° is also produced (*R. P. Linstead* and *P. Levine,* J. Amer. chem. Soc., 1942, **64,** 2022).

Both isomers of the asymmetrical (*as*) hexahydro-9-phenanthrones are known; they are prepared as follows:

* The configuration of the two carbon atoms nearest to the carbonyl group is named first.

$CH_2 \cdot CO_2H$ $\xrightarrow{H_2SO_4}$ O

The properties of the ketones and the alcohols derived therefrom may be summarised thus (*J. W. Cook et al.*, J. chem. Soc., 1936, 71; *R. P. Linstead et al.*, J. Amer. chem. Soc., 1942, **61**, 2014):

	as-Hexahydro-9-phenanthrones	*as*-Octahydro-9-phenanthrols
cis	b.p. 163°/5 mm.	→ m.p. 116° → m.p. 133°
trans	m.p. 96°	→ m.p. 91° → m.p. 101°

as-*Octahydrophenanthrene* itself, b.p. 150°/13 mm., n_D^{25} 1·5528 is made by the partial hydrogenation of phenanthrone with Raney nickel at 130° (*J. R. Durland* and *H. Adkins, ibid.*, 1938, **60**, 1501):

For further derivatives of *as*-octahydrophenanthrene see *R. W. Grewe*, Ber., 1943, **76**, 1072, 1076; *E. C. Horning et al.*, J. Amer. chem. Soc., 1947, **69**, 2929. For symmetrical octahydrophenanthrene derivatives see *inter al.*, *J. R. Durland* and *H. Adkins, ibid.*, 1937, **59**, 135; *C. C. Price et al., ibid.*, 1943, **65**, 2469; *R. P. Linstead et al., ibid.*, 1942, **64**, 2014; *R. T. Arnold* and *R. A. Barnes, ibid.*, 1944, **66**, 960).

From theoretical premises five inactive isomers of **per(tetradeca-)hydroanthracene** would be expected; of these three have been prepared as follows (*J. W. Cook et al.*, J. chem. Soc., 1944, 286; a review of the earlier literature is given):

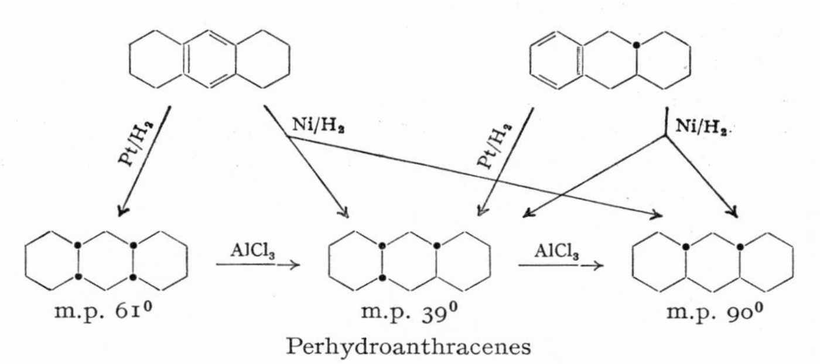

Perhydroanthracenes

The **octahydroanthraquinone,** "bis-butadiene-quinone", obtained by heating benzoquinone with an excess of butadiene, may be converted in stages from the *cis-cis-* to the *trans-trans-*form:

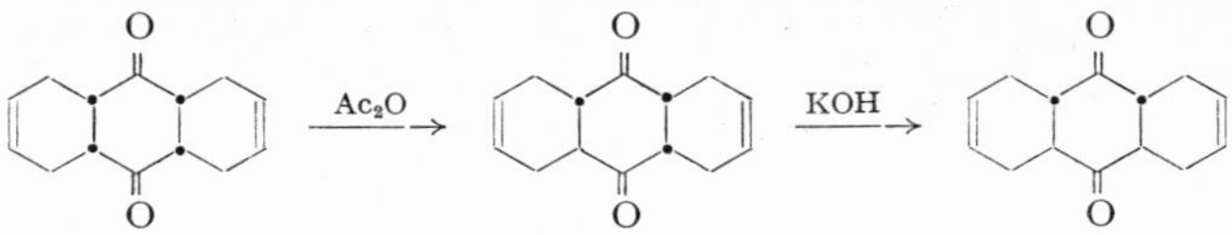

The configurations are confirmed by oxidation to known compounds (*K. Alder* and *G. Stein,* Ann., 1933, **501,** 255).

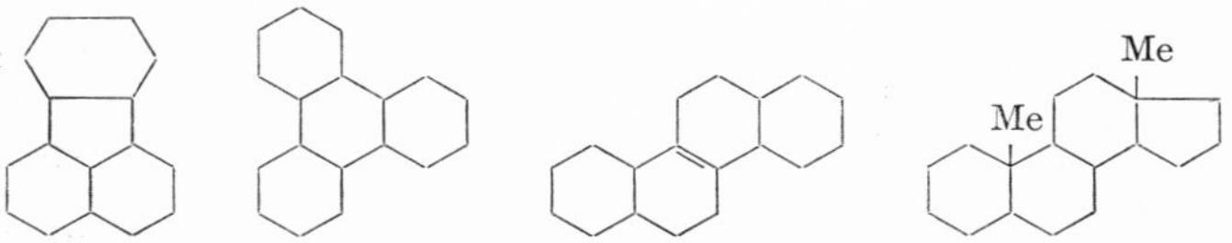

Perhydrofluoranthene (I), b.p. 168–170°/12 mm., is obtained by hydrogenation of fluoranthene (*J. von Braun* and *G. Menz,* Ber., 1930, **63,** 2610).

Perhydrotriphenylene (II), b.p. 175–176°/7 mm. is prepared by condensing 2-hydroxydicyclohexyl with phenol and hydrogenating the resulting dicyclohexylphenol with subsequent ring closure and reduction (*W. Schrauth* and *K. Görig,* Ber., 1923, **56,** 2024).

Hexadecahydrochrysene (III), b.p. 168°/0·5 mm. is the final product of hydrogenation of chrysene (*J. von Braun* and *G. Irmisch,* Ber., 1932, **65,** 883). D-Homoandrostane (Vol. IIB) is a perhydrodimethylchrysene.

The tetracyclic system (IV) represents the basic structure of the steroid classes (Vol. IIB).

Pyrene is very readily hydrogenated over Raney nickel to yield a mixture from which a pure **hexadecahydropyrene,** m.p. 90°, is easily isolated (*J. W. Cook et al.,* J. chem. Soc., 1945, 286).

Perhydropicene, m.p. 175°, is obtained by reduction of picene (*C. Liebermann* and *L. Spiegel,* Ber., 1889, **22,** 779).

Catalytic hydrogenation of coronene yields two stereoisomeric **perhydrocoronenes,** m.p. 370° and 203° (*L. Boente,* C.A., 1947, **41,** 6558).

For the dehydrogenation of such polycyclic systems see *A. V. Grosse et al.,* Ind. Eng. Chem., 1946, **38,** 1041.

Chapter IX

Bridged Ring Systems

R. A. RAPHAEL

Bridged ring compounds have bi- or poly-cyclic structures in which two rings have three or more common carbon atoms. Formula (I) represents a hydrocarbon of this type. It should be noted that this compound may also be represented by (II) or (III); the "bridge" may consist of one, two or three carbon atoms according to the method of delineation adopted. In practice it is usual to write the ideograph containing the least number of carbon atoms in the bridge (i.e. I). It should be realised that the carbon atoms constituting the bridge do not become endowed *per se* with properties different from those of the other carbon atoms; any possible confusion will be avoided if the molecule be represented by its actual three dimensional configuration (IV). Abbreviated ideographs for the structure are shown in (V) and (VI); the former convention will be used in this chapter.

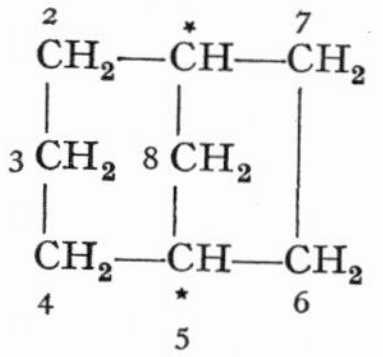

CH_2—$\overset{*}{C}H$—CH_2 (2, 1, 7)
3 CH_2 8 CH_2
CH_2—$\overset{*}{C}H$—CH_2 (4, 5, 6)

(I)

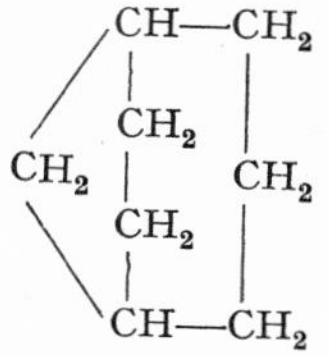

CH—CH_2
CH_2 CH_2 CH_2
CH_2
CH—CH_2

(II)

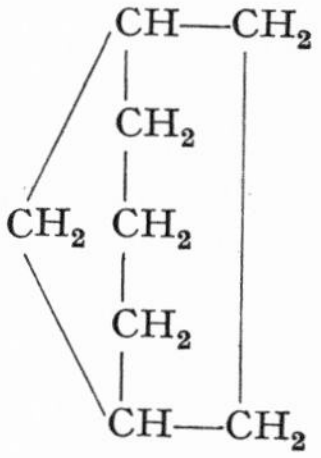

CH—CH_2
CH_2
CH_2 CH_2
CH_2
CH—CH_2

(III)

H_2C CH_2

(V)

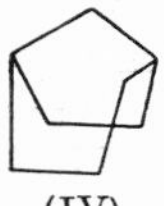

(IV)

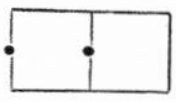

(VI)

Nomenclature. The systematic nomenclature of these systems is analogous to that already described for the fused ring compounds (p. 308); thus (I) may be described as bicyclo[3:2:1]octane. The enumeration begins at one of the bridge-head carbon atoms (*) proceeds via the longest route to the other bridge-head, continues round to the first bridge-head and finishes with the bridge itself. Another nomenclature sometimes employed regards the system as a derivative of the largest ring, the bridge being indicated by "methylene", "ethylene" etc. prefixed by the particle "endo" or "meso"; by this system (I) is termed 1:5-endomethylenecycloheptane or 1:5-mesomethylenecycloheptane. Trivial names derived from the names of structurally analogous terpenes are also used, for example camphane for 1:7:7-trimethylbicyclo[2:2:1]heptane (Vol. II B).

Compounds possessing a bridged ring structure are of wide occurrence in nature. The first recognised as belonging to this class were camphor and pinene and since then many other bicyclic terpenes have been found to be similarly constituted. Such terpenoid compounds are dealt with in separate chapters. In the following pages the synthesis and general properties of bridged ring systems will be considered, followed by a description of some representative types.

Synthesis and properties. The procedures employed for synthesising bridged ring systems fall into three groups.

1. The cyclisation of dicarboxylic acids of the monocyclic series yields bicyclic bridged ring ketones; thus dry distillation of the magnesium salt of cyclohexane-1-carboxylic-4-acetic acid furnishes bicyclo[2:2:2]octan-2-one (*G. Komppa*, Ber., 1935, **68**, 1267).

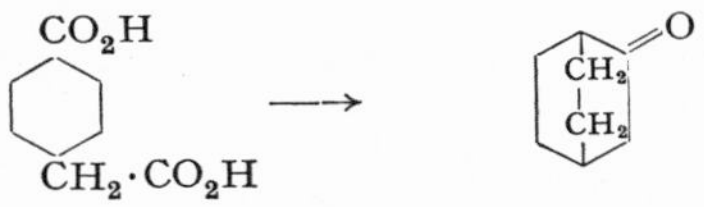

CO_2H

$CH_2 \cdot CO_2H$ ⟶ CH_2 CH_2 =O

An intramolecular Claisen type of condensation may also be used to procure such compounds, e.g.

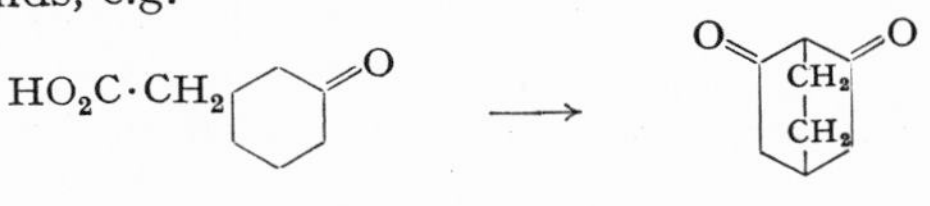

$HO_2C \cdot CH_2$ =O ⟶ O= CH_2 CH_2 =O

(*P. D. Bartlett* and *G. F. Woods*, J. Amer. chem. Soc., 1940, **62**, 2933).

2. Aliphatic dihalides condense with monocyclic compounds containing two active methylene or methine groups to produce bridged ring systems,

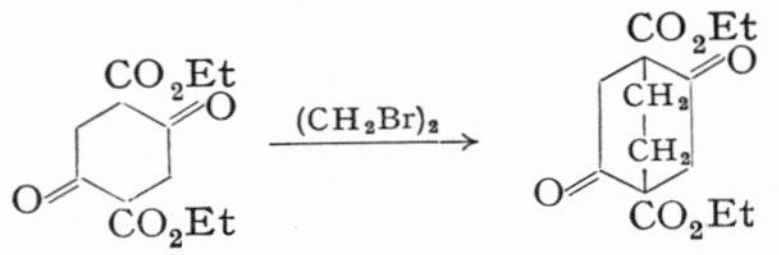

CO_2Et =O O= CO_2Et $\xrightarrow{(CH_2Br)_2}$ CO_2Et =O CH_2 CH_2 O= CO_2Et

(*P. C. Guha*, Ber., 1939, **72**, 1359; *J. D. Roberts et al.*, J. Amer. chem. Soc., 1952, **75**, 637).

3. Application of the Diels-Alder synthesis (p. 127) to the cyclic dienes cyclopenta-1:3-diene and cyclohexa-1:3-diene constitutes the most elegant and flexible method of obtaining a wide range of derivatives of bicyclo-[2:2:1]heptane and bicyclo[2:2:2]octane, e.g.

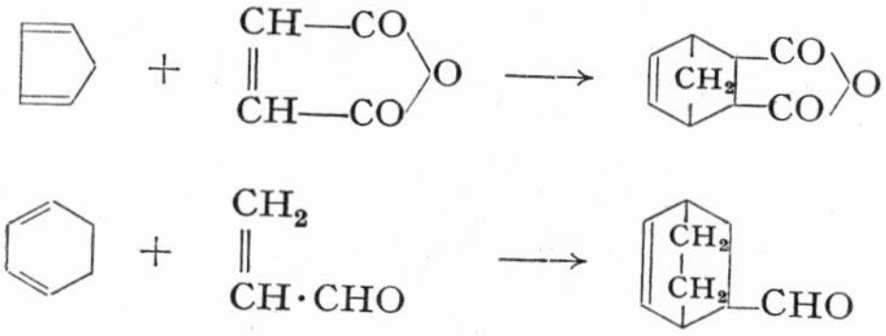

CH—CO
+ ‖ >O ⟶ CH_2 —CO >O
CH—CO —CO

CH_2
+ ‖ ⟶ CH_2 | CH_2 —CHO
CH·CHO

Theoretically the Diels-Alder reaction could give rise to two stereoisomeric products; this may be exemplified for the first reaction above as follows:

(I)

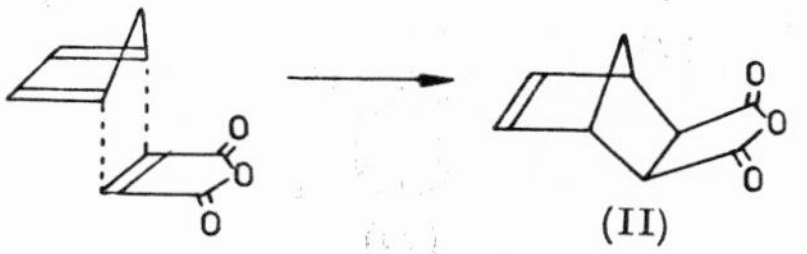

(II)

The two possible configurations are termed "endo" (I) and "exo" (II). In practice it is found that the reaction is stereospecific, the compound of "endo" configuration being exclusively produced at reasonably low temperatures. In explanation of this phenomenon it has been suggested that the two components form a molecular complex prior to reaction and that the steric configuration of the complex would determine that of the adduct. The "endo" form of the complex would be the more stable owing to the greater proximity of the polarisable groups of the two constituents and thus would be favoured at low temperatures (*A. Wassermann et al.*, J. chem. Soc., 1935, 828, 1511; 1942, 618, 623; 1946, 1089, 1090; 1949, 3046; Trans. Faraday Soc., 1939, 35, 841; *R. B. Woodward*, J. Amer. chem. Soc., 1942, 64, 3058; *M. J. S. Dewar*, "Electronic Theory of Organic Chemistry", Oxford University Press, 1949, p. 153).

Computation of the strain involved in the two most important bridged ring systems indicates that the bicyclo[2:2:1]heptane structure (III) is strained whereas the bicyclo[2:2:2]octane system (IV) is strainless, the latter being constituted by three mutually fused boat forms of cyclohexane (*W. Hückel*, Ann., 1927, **455**, 123).

This is borne out by heat of combustion data for corresponding ketones of the two series; if a "strainless" CH_2 increment (157 kcals./mol.; cf. p. 8) be added to the heat of combustion of the ketone derived from (III) a direct comparison may be obtained: (III) ketone 1103·1 kcals./mol.; (IV) ketone 1096·8 kcals./mol. (*K. Alder* and *G. Stein*, Ber., 1934, **67**, 613; *G. Becker* and *W. A. Roth*, Ber., 1934, **67**, 627; *R. P. Linstead*, Annual Reports, 1935, **32**, 315).

This strain in the bicyclo[2:2:1]heptane system is well illustrated by the chemical properties of its unsaturated derivatives such as (VI).

(V) ⇄ cyclopentadiene + $CH \cdot R$ ‖ $CH \cdot R_1$

(VI)

Thus compounds of type (V) readily undergo thermal dissocation as shown (reversed Diels-Alder synthesis) whilst corresponding derivatives of bicyclo-[2:2:2]octane (VI) are stable under the same conditions (*K. Alder* and *H. F. Rickert*, Ann., 1936, **524**, 180). Again substances of type (V) combine readily with azides and diazo compounds to yield dihydrotriazoles and dihydropyrazoles whereas compounds of structure (VI) do not react at all (*L. Wolff*, Ann., 1912, **394**, 68; *K. Alder* and *G. Stein*, Ann., 1930, **484**, 243; 1933, **501**, 1; *O. Diels* and *K. Alder*, Ann., 1931, **490**, 243). A further striking difference is shown by the ability of (V) to act as a dienophile in the Diels-Alder reaction (e.g. the formation of tri-, tetra- and penta-cyclopentadienes) whereas (VI) is incapable of so doing. The special nature of the double bond in (V) is also demonstrated by its particular ease of hydrogenation and by its abnormally high heat of hydrogenation (*K. Alder* and *G. Stein*, Ber., 1934, **67**, 613; *G. B. Kistiakowsky et al.*, J. Amer. chem. Soc., 1935, **57**, 65, 876; 1936, **58**, 137, 146).

It is pertinent to note at this point that in such bridged ring systems the carbon atoms of the bridge-head cannot participate in the formation of an ethylenic linkage. This principle, known as Bredt's rule, is borne out by a great deal of experimental evidence (*J. Bredt*, Ann., 1913, **395**, 26; 1924, **437**, 1; J. pr. Chem., 1918, [ii], **97**, 1; *A. Windaus* and *A. Bohne*, Ann., 1925, **442**, 7; *F. S. Fawcett*, Chem. Reviews, 1950, **47**, 219). It has been found however, that if the ring system be large enough this restriction no longer holds (see p. 275 for a discussion of macrocyclic bridged ring systems of this type).

Those bridged ring systems in which the molecule extends roughly the same amount in the three dimensions of space and thus has a more or less spherical shape are distinguished by an extraordinarily high value for the molecular lowering of the freezing point and are thus useful for molecular weight determinations by the Rast procedure (*J. Pirsch*, Ber., 1932, **65**, 862, 1227, 1839; 1933, **66**, 815, 1694; 1934, **67**, 101, 373). The ratio of the molecular depression value to the molecular weight has been found to be a constant characteristic of each ring system.

(a) *Bicyclo*[3:1:1]*heptane group*

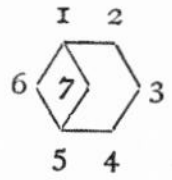

This is the basic structure of the pinane group of terpenes which is discussed in Vol. II B. The filix tannins were once regarded as derivatives of this system.

(b) *Bicyclo*[2:2:1]*heptane group*

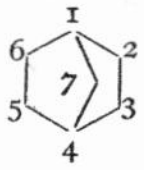

This carbon skeleton occurs in a large group of terpenes called the camphane group after the most important of them, camphor. The properties and interrelationships of these compounds together with the numerous rearrangements associated with their reactions will be described in Vol. II B.

The parent hydrocarbon of the group, **bicyclo**[2:2:1]**heptane,** *norcamphane*, m.p. 86–87°, b.p. 105°, may be obtained by the reduction of the 2-chloro-compound (*G. Komppa*, Naturwiss., 1934, **22**, 171) but is most easily prepared by the hydrogenation of the readily available bicyclo[2:2:1]hept-2-ene (see p. 340). Vapour phase nitration of the hydrocarbon yields the 1-*nitro-compound*, m.p. 63° (*R. T. Bickerstaff* and *H. B. Hass*, J. Amer. chem. Soc., 1946, **68**, 1431) whilst the action of aluminium chloride and *tert*.-butyl chloride furnishes the 2-*chloro-compound*, m.p. −5°, b.p. 62°/20 mm. (*L. Schmerling*, J. Amer. chem. Soc., 1946, **68**, 195).

2-*Methylbicyclo*[2:2:1]*heptane*, b.p. 127°, n_D^{20} 1·4540 may be obtained by

Kishner-Wolff reduction followed by catalytic hydrogenation of the adduct from cyclopentadiene and acrolein (*N. D. Zelinsky et al.*, Ber., 1933, **66**, 1415). It is also produced by the hydrogenation of the corresponding unsaturated hydrocarbons (see below).

2-*Methylenebicyclo*[2:2:1]*heptane*, b.p. 123° is formed by the dehydration of the 2-hydroxymethyl-compound (*O. Diels* and *K. Alder*, Ann., 1929, **470**, 62).

Bicyclo[2:2:1]**hept-2-ene,** *norbornylene*, b.p. 96·1°, m.p. 46°, may be readily obtained by the Diels-Alder condensation of cyclopentadiene with ethylene (*L. M. Joshel* and *L. W. Butz*, J. Amer. chem. Soc., 1941, **63**, 3350; *C. L. Thomas* Ind. Eng. Chem., 1944, **36**, 310). The 5-*methyl* homologue, b.p. 116°/760 mm., n_D^{20} 1·4598 is prepared by a similar process employing propylene in place of ethylene (*G. Calingaert et al.*, Ind. Eng. Chem., 1944, **36**, 1055; cf. *N. D. Zelinsky et al., loc. cit.*).

Alcohols. Hydrolysis and reduction of the Diels-Alder adduct from cyclopentadiene and vinyl acetate yields **bicyclo**[2:2:1]**heptan-2-ol** *(norborneol)*, m.p. 150°, *phenylurethane*, m.p. 160° (*K. Alder* and *H. F. Rickert*, Ann., 1939, **543**, 1).

2-*Hydroxymethylbicyclo*[2:2:1]*heptane*, b.p. 102°/10 mm. is prepared by the reduction of cyclopentadiene-acrolein adduct (*O. Diels* and *K. Alder*, Ann., 1929, **470**, 62).

The natural terpene alcohols of this series, borneol, *iso*borneol and fenchyl alcohol are dealt with in Vol. II B.

Aldehydes. The aldehydes of this series are readily obtainable by means of the Diels-Alder reaction between cyclopentadiene and $\alpha\beta$-unsaturated aldehydes. Thus cyclopentadiene and acrolein yield **bicyclo**[2:2:1]**hept-5-ene-2-aldehyde,** 70–72°/20 mm., *semicarbazone*, m.p. 162°, which is easily hydrogenated to the saturated *aldehyde*, b.p. 75–76°/25 mm., *semicarbazone*, m.p. 142° (*O. Diels* and *K. Alder*, Ann., 1928, **460**, 98; 1929, **470**, 62; 1931, **486**, 202).

In similar fashion crotonaldehyde furnishes two 3-*methylbicyclo*[2:2:1]*hept-5-ene-2-aldehydes*, cis-, b.p. 60–75°/12 mm., *semicarbazone*, m.p. 158° and trans-, b.p. 80°/45 mm., *semicarbazone*, m.p. 181° (*O. Diels* and *K. Alder*, Ann., 1929, **470**, 66).

Ketones. The ketones may be prepared by cyclisation of cyclopentanedicarboxylic acids and also by ozonising the enol acetates of the aldehydes. In this fashion are produced **bicyclo**[2:2:1]**heptan-1-one** *(norcamphor)*, m.p. 92°, *semicarbazone*, m.p. 197° and its 3-*methyl*-homologue, b.p. 68–70°/15 mm., *semicarbazone*, m.p. 185° (*O. Diels* and *K. Alder*, Ann., 1929, **470**, 62; 1931, **486**, 202).

Many ketones of this class are known where the carbonyl group constitutes the bridge (for an exhaustive review see *C. F. H. Allen*, Chem. Reviews, 1945, **37**, 209). Most of these compounds are phenylated derivatives obtained from the Diels-Alder condensation between dienophiles and the readily available polyphenylcyclopentadienones. Their behaviour on pyrolysis is highly characteristic, carbon monoxide being smoothly eliminated with the formation of a cyclohexa-1:3-diene. The reaction provides a convenient route to polyphenylbenzenes, e.g.

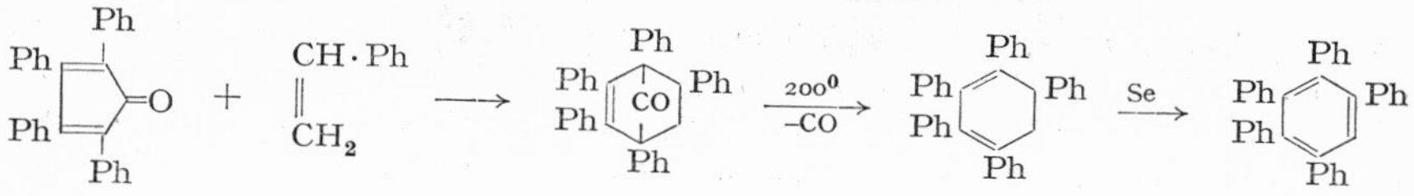

With alkalis the carbonyl bridge is cleaved on one side to form substituted cyclohexanecarboxylic acids (*C. F. H. Allen et al.*, J. Amer. chem. Soc., 1946, **68,** 708); e.g.

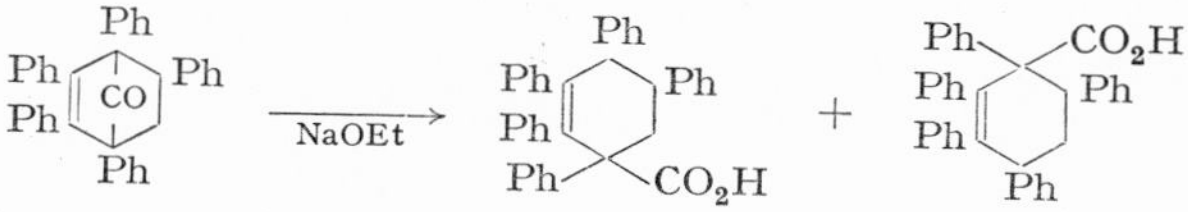

The naturally occurring ketones of this series, camphor and fenchone are discussed in Vol. IIB.

Carboxylic acids. The bicyclo[2:2:1]heptanecarboxylic acids are also prepared by the diene synthesis, starting from cyclopentadiene and $\alpha\beta$-unsaturated carboxylic esters or dicarboxylic anhydrides.

Bicyclo[2:2:1]**hept-5-ene-2-carboxylic acid,** b.p. 132–134°/22 mm., is thus prepared from cyclopentadiene and acrylic acid (*O. Diels* and *K. Alder*, Ann., 1928, **460,** 98).

2-**Methylbicyclo**[2:2:1]**heptane-3-carboxylic acids,** cis-, b.p. 136–137°/13 mm., trans-, m.p. 66° are prepared by oxidation of the corresponding aldehydes (*idem*, Ann., 1929, **470,** 66).

Bicyclo[2:2:1]**heptane-2:3-dicarboxylic acid** (1:4-*endomethylenehexahydro-2:3-phthalic acid*) can exist in three inactive modifications, two of them *cis*-forms, *endo*-(α), m.p. 161°, *anhydride*, m.p. 168°, and *exo*-(β), m.p. 153°, *anhydride* m.p. 79°, which are mutually interconvertible via the *trans*-form, m.p. 194°. The two *cis*-forms are prepared by the selenium dioxide oxidation of *endo*- or *exo*-dihydrodicyclopentadiene (see p. 344); the *cis-endo* compound may also be obtained by hydrogenation of the cyclopentadiene-maleic anhydride adduct (see below)

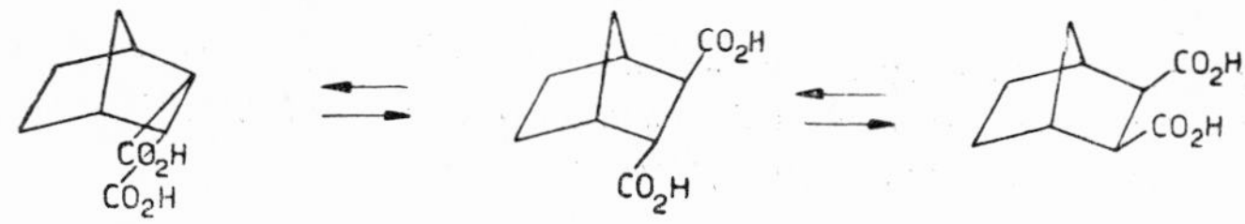

cis-endo-(α) *trans* *cis-exo-*(β)

(*idem*, Ann., 1928, **460,** 113; *K. Alder* and *G. Stein*, Ann., 1933, **504,** 219).

The **bicyclo**[2:2:1]**hept-5-ene-2:3-dicarboxylic acids** exhibit a similar isomerism. The cis-endo-*acid*, m.p. 179°, is obtained by hydrolysis of the endo-*anhydride*, m.p. 164° (prepared from cyclopentadiene and maleic anhydride). The cis-endo-*acid dibromide*, m.p. 188° rearranges on heating to the cis-exo-*acid dibromide*, m.p. 248°, which, on debromination, gives the cis-exo-*acid* itself, m.p. 148°, *anhydride*, m.p. 143°. The *cis-endo*-acid dibromide rearranges also on treatment with hydrogen bromide in glacial acetic acid to give the trans-*acid dibromide*, m.p. 244° (trans-*acid*, m.p. 192°) (*K. Alder et al.*, Ann., 1933, **504**, 244; 1934, **514**, 1; 1936, **524**, 189; *O. Diels* and *K. Alder*, Ann., 1938, **460**, 98; *M. S. Morgan et al.*, J. Amer. chem. Soc., 1944, **66**, 404).

Bicyclo[2:2:1]**hept-2-ene-2:3-dicarboxylic acid** (I), m.p. 212°, *anhydride*, m.p. 99°, may be synthesised by the following two methods:

C—CO_2Me ≡ C—CO_2Me → [CH$_2$] CO_2Me CO_2Me —H_2→ [CH$_2$] CO_2H CO_2H (I)

CBr—CO, CBr—CO >O → [CH$_2$] Br CO_2Me Br CO_2Me —H_2, $-Br_2$→ (I)

(*O. Diels* and *K. Alder*, Ann., 1930, **478**, 137; Ann., 1931, **490**, 236).

Homologues of maleic anhydride react with cyclopentadiene in the same way as the parent compound. Thus citraconic anhydride gives 3-*methylbicyclo*[2:2:1]*hept-5-ene-2:3-dicarboxylic anhydride*, m.p. 138°, pyrocinchonic anhydride yields the 2:3-*dimethyl* homologue, m.p. 155°, and itaconic anhydride furnishes *bicyclo*[2:2:1]*hept-5-ene-2-carboxylic-2-acetic anhydride*, m.p. 54° (*idem*, Ann., 1928, **460**, 98; Ber., 1929, **62**, 554).

Bicyclo[2:2:1]*heptane-2-carboxylic-3-acetic acid*, m.p. 137°, results from the permanganate oxidation of dihydrodicyclopentadiene (*idem*, Ann., 1931, **485**, 223).

The addition of maleic anhydride to fulvenes results in compounds of the general formula

[C=CRR$_1$ bridged ring with —CO—O—CO—]

(*idem*, Ber., 1929, **62**, 2081; *R. B. Woodward* and *H. Baer*, J. Amer. chem. Soc., 1944, **66**, 645).

Bicyclo[2:2:1]**heptane-3:7-dione-1-carboxylic acid,** m.p. 212° *(hydrate)*, *methyl ester*, m.p. 129°, has been synthesised in the following way (*P. C. Guha* and *G. D. Hazra*, J. Indian chem. Soc., 1940, **17**, 107):

CO_2Et, =O, CO_2Et → CO_2Et, CH_2, =O, CO_2Et, CO_2Et → CO_2Et, CO, =O, CO_2Et → CO_2H, CO, =O

The *diethyl ester*, b.p. 110°/1 mm., of *bicyclo*[2:2:1]*heptane-2:5-dione-1:4-dicarboxylic acid* has been obtained in minute yield by condensation of methylene dibromide with succinosuccinic ester (*P. C. Guha*, Ber., 1939, **72**, 1359).

Polymerisation products of cyclopentadiene

A series of more complex derivatives of the bicyclo[2:2:1]heptane structure arise from the polymerisation of cyclopentadiene (for review see *P. J. Wilson* and *J. H. Wells*, Chem. Reviews, 1944, **34**, 1). This hydrocarbon undergoes self-condensation at room temperature in the absence of a catalyst to form a crystalline dimer, **dicyclopentadiene,** m.p. 32° (*G. Kraemer* and *A. Spillker*, Ber., 1896, **29**, 552; *H. Staudinger et al.*, Ber., 1907, **40**, 1145; 1911, **44**, 521; 1926, **59**, 3019; Ann., 1926, **447**, 97, 110; 1928, **467**, 73; Helv., 1924, **7**, 23). The reaction is reversible, cyclopentadiene being readily regenerated on heating the dimer to 160°; the kinetics of the process has been exhaustively studied (*A. Wassermann et al.*, J. chem. Soc., 1935, 829; 1936, 1028; 1939, 362, 870; 1940, 735; 1942, 618, 623; Trans. Faraday Soc., 1939, **35**, 1022, 1052; Nature, 1936, **137**, 496; 1936, **138**, 368; *M. G. Evans*, Trans. Faraday Soc., 1939, **35**, 824, 841; *G. B. Kistiakowsky et al.*, J. Amer., chem. Soc., 1936, **58**, 1060; J. chem. Phys., 1937, **5**, 682; *E. Baur* and *S. Frater*, Helv., 1941, **24**, 768).

(I) (II)

This dimer was for long regarded as possessing the structure (I) but in 1931 *K. Alder* and *G. Stein* conclusively established its constitution as the bicyclo-[2:2:1]heptane derivative (II) (Ann. 1931, **485**, 223; 1932, **496**, 204; 1933, **501**, 247; Angew. Chem., 1934, **47**, 837). This was first indicated by the typical enhanced reactivity of the double bond* (p. 338) which readily formed adducts with phenyl azide and nitrosyl chloride. Hydrogenation rapidly yielded a *dihydro*-derivative (III), m.p. 51° and more slowly a *tetrahydro*-compound, m.p. 77°. Conclusive evidence was furnished by the following two degradations:

(II) $\xrightarrow{H_2}$ (III) $\xrightarrow{KMnO_4}$ $CH_2\cdot CO_2H$, CO_2H $\longrightarrow$ *cis*-Cyclopentane-1:3-dicarboxylic acid

(II) $\xrightarrow{NOCl,\ Hydrolysis,\ H_2}$ ketone $\xrightarrow{HNO_3}$ *cis*-Pentalane-1:3-dicarboxylic acid

It is seen that the above dimerisation constitutes a Diels-Alder diene synthesis; it would therefore be expected that dicyclopentadiene would possess the *endo* configuration (V).

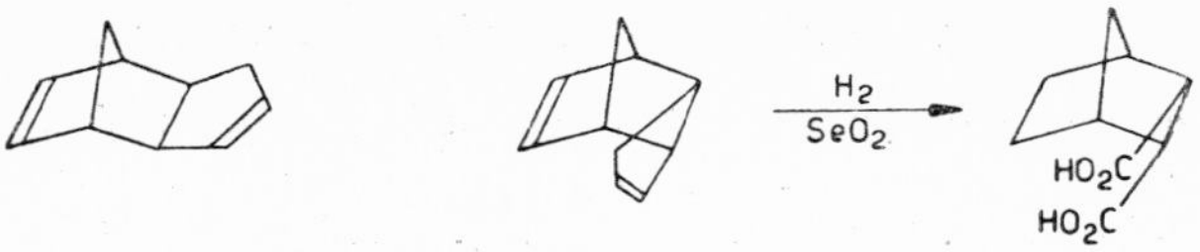

H_2 / SeO_2

HO_2C
HO_2C

(IV) (V) (VI)

This is borne out by the oxidation of dihydrodicyclopentadiene which furnishes the known *endo-cis*-bicyclo[2:2:1]heptane-2:3-dicarboxylic acid (VI) (p. 341) (*K. Alder* and *G. Stein*, Ann., 1933, **504**, 216).

When the dimerisation of cyclopentadiene is carried out at higher temperatures (150°) or if *endo*-dicyclopentadiene be heated (100°) for some time, a liquid dimer can be isolated. This was shown to be *exo*-dicyclopentadiene (IV) since, on partial hydrogenation and oxidation, it furnished *exo-cis*-bicyclo[2:2:1]heptane-2:3-dicarboxylic acid (*idem, ibid.*). It was found later that *endo*-dicyclopentadiene reacts smoothly under acid conditions with proton donors such as water, hydrohalogen acids, alcohols, phenols and carboxylic acids to give products possessing the *exo* configuration (*H. A. Bruson* and *T. W. Riener*, J. Amer. chem. Soc., 1945, **67**, 723, 1178; 1946, **68**, 8; *P. D. Bartlett* and *A. Schneider*, *ibid.*, 1946, **68**, 6; *F. Bergmann* and *H. Japhé*, *ibid.*, 1947, **69**, 1826); i.e.

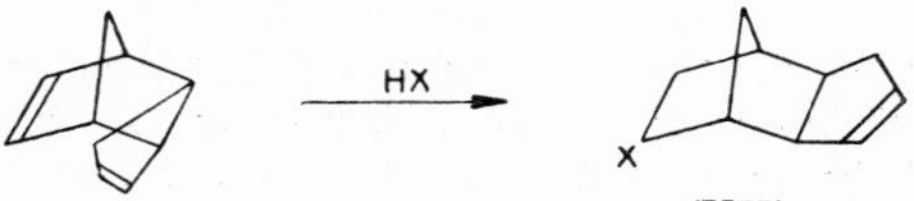

HX

X

(VII)

Dehydrohalogenation of VII (X = Iodine) furnishes pure *exo*-dicyclopentadiene, b.p. 51–53°/12 mm., n_D^{25} 1·5070 (*P. D. Bartlett* and *I. S. Goldstein*, J. Amer. chem. Soc., 1946, **69**, 2553).

The two stereoisomers may be readily distinguished by means of their adducts with phenyl azide and the products derived therefrom (*K. Alder* and *G. Stein*, Ann., 1933, **504**, 216).

N N N CH_2 Ph —H_2→ N N N CH_2 Ph

endo m.p. 128–129°
exo m.p. 123–124°

endo m.p. 129°
exo m.p. 142°

Hydrolysis

PhN CH_2 ←$-H_2O$— HO Ph·NH CH_2

endo m.p. 62°
exo m.p. 68°

endo m.p. 134°
exo m.p. 95°

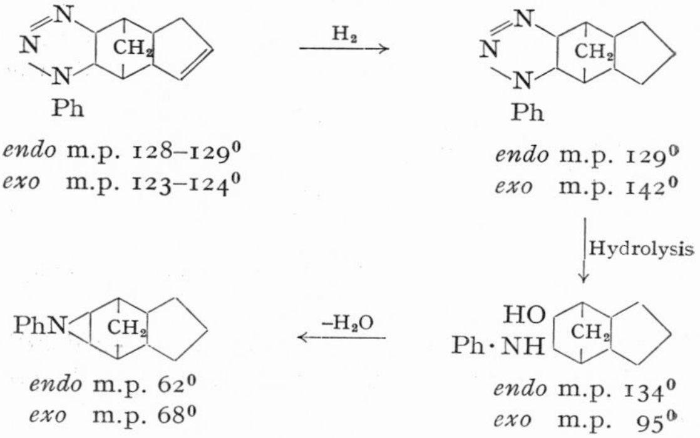

Heat of combustion data indicate that the energy content of the *endo* (α) series is 2–3 kcals./mol. greater than that of the *exo* (β) series (*K. Alder* and *G. Stein*, Ber., 1934, **67**, 613).

The octachloro-derivative of dicyclopentadiene (VIII) known as "chlordane" is a potent insecticide (*D. E. H. Frear*, "Chemistry of Insecticides, Herbicides and Fungicides", Van Nostrand & Co., 1948, p. 83).

(VIII)

As dicyclopentadiene contains the reactive bicyclo[2:2:1]heptene structure (p. 338) it can function as a dienophile and react with a further molecule of cyclopentadiene. This occurs at elevated temperatures with the formation of endo(α)- and exo(β)-**tricyclopentadiene** (IX and X).

IX)

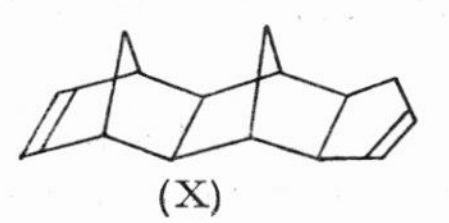

(X)

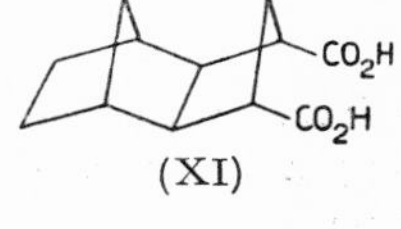

(XI)

(IX)		(X)	
m.p. 68°		b.p. 140°/15 mm.	
phenyl azide adduct	m.p. 200°	*phenyl azide adduct*	m.p. 196°
tetrahydro-deriv.	m.p. 49°	*tetrahydro-deriv.*	m.p. 99°

These structures have been confirmed by oxidation to two series of stereoisomeric degradation products terminating with the common end-product (XI) (*K. Alder* and *G. Stein*, Ann., 1931, **485**, 223; 1932, **496**, 204; 1933, **504**, 216).

Heating dicyclopentadiene at elevated temperatures for long periods results in the formation of *tetra-*, m.p. 207°, *penta-*, m.p. 277° and *hexa-*, m.p. 373° (dec.), *-cyclopentadienes*. These higher polymers are formed with increasing difficulty and do not regenerate cyclopentadiene on heating (*H. Staudinger* and *H. A. Bruson*, Ann., 1926, **447**, 97; *K. Alder* and *G. Stein*, Ann., 1932, **496**, 204; Ber., 1934, **67**, 613).

Certain derivatives of cyclopentadiene dimerise in similar fashion to the parent compound; in this way are formed *dicyclopentadienedicarboxylic acid*, m.p. 209° (dec.) (*J. Thiele*, Ber., 1901, **34**, 69; *K. Alder* and *G. Stein*, Ann., 1932, **496**, 204), *dioximinodicyclopentadiene*, m.p. 186° (dec.) (*J. Thiele*, Ber., 1900, **33**, 669; *K. Alder* and *G. Stein*, *loc. cit.*) and *di-dimethylfulvene*, m.p. 83° (*J. Thiele* and *H. Balhern*, Ann., 1906, **348**, 7; *K. Alder* and *G. Stein*, *loc. cit.*).

Cyclopentadiene-benzoquinone *adduct* (XII) is a yellowish green compound m.p. 78°, *tetrahydro*-deriv. m.p. 57°. On treatment with hydrogen bromide in acetic acid it undergoes enolisation to yield the quinol (XIII). Complete hydrogenation of the adduct furnishes the parent hydrocarbon 1:4-*endomethylenedecalin* (XIV) b.p. 85°/15 mm. (*O. Diels* and *K. Alder*, Ber., 1929, **62**, 2350; Ann.,

1928, **460,** 98; *K. Alder* and *G. Stein,* Ann., 1933, **501,** 247; *W. Albrecht,* Ann., 1906, **348,** 47).

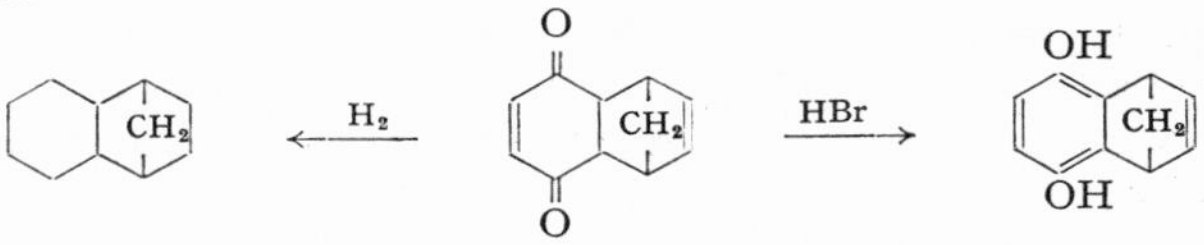

(XIV) ← H_2 — (XII) — HBr → (XIII)

Similarly benzoquinone reacts with two molecules of cyclopentadiene to form an adduct, m.p. 158°, changed by alcoholic KOH into a *stereoisomer* m.p. 184°. On complete reduction it yields the parent hydrocarbon (1:4-5:8-bis-endo-methyleneperhydroanthracene) b.p. 157–159°/16 mm. (*W. Albrecht,* Ann., 1906, **348,** 47; *O. Diels* and *K. Alder,* Ann., 1928, **460,** 98; *K. Alder* and *G. Stein,* Ann., 1933, **501,** 264).

(c) *Bicyclo*[2:2:2]*octane group*

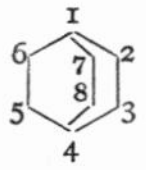

Derivatives of this highly symmetrical system are easily available by employing a cyclohexa-1:3-diene as the diene component in the Diels-Alder reaction.

The parent hydrocarbon, **bicyclo**[2:2:2]**octane,** m.p. 169·5–170·5°, is prepared by Kishner-Wolff reduction of the ketone (*K. Alder* and *G. Stein,* Ann., 1934, **514,** 27), catalytic reduction of the halogen derivatives (*G. Komppa,* Ber., 1935, **68,** 1267; *W. von E. Doering* and *M. Farber,* J. Amer. chem. Soc., 1949, **71,** 1514) and catalytic reduction of *bicyclo*[2:2:2]*oct-2-ene,* m.p. 113–114°, itself obtained by Hofmann degradation of the corresponding saturated amine (*R. Seka* and *O. Tramposch,* Ber., 1942, **75,** 1379; cf. also *G. Calingaert et al.,* Ind. Eng. Chem., 1944, **36,** 1055).

Addition of hydrogen bromide to the unsaturated hydrocarbon yields *2-bromobicyclo*[2:2:2]*octane,* m.p. 64–65·5°; this, on treatment with silver bromide in carbon tetrachloride, undergoes a remarkable rearrangement to furnish *2-bromobicyclo*[3:2:1]*octane* (*W. von E. Doering* and *M. Farber, loc. cit.*).

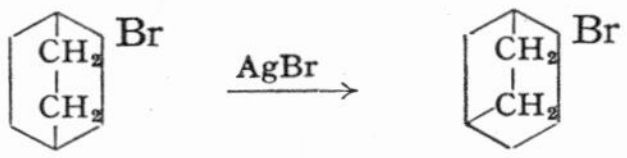

AgBr →

2-**Aminobicyclo**[2:2:2]**octane,** m.p. 138–140° (dec.), *benzoyl* deriv., m.p. 178–179°, may be obtained by reduction of the corresponding ketoxime or Schmidt degradation of the corresponding carboxylic acid (*G. Komppa,* Ber., 1935, **68,** 1267; *R. Seka* and *O. Tramposch, loc. cit.*). The action of nitrous acid yields *bicyclo*[2:2:2:]*octan-2-ol,* m.p. 216–217°.

Cyclohexadiene and acrolein readily condense to yield **bicyclo**[2:2:2]**oct-5-ene-2-aldehyde,** b.p. 84–85°/12 mm., *semicarbazone* m.p. 177°. Catalytic hydrogenation gives the *5-ane-2-aldehyde* m.p. 77°, *semicarbazone* m.p. 192° (*O. Diels* and *K. Alder*, Ann., 1930, **478**, 137).

Bicyclo[2:2:2]**octan-2-one,** m.p. 176°, *oxime* m.p. 118°, *semicarbazone* m.p. 205°, is formed by heating the magnesium salt of cyclohexane-1-carboxylic-4-acetic acid (*G. Komppa, loc. cit.*) and by ozonisation of the enol acetate of the corresponding aldehyde (*O. Diels* and *K. Alder, loc. cit.*).

Bicyclo[2:2:2]**octane-2:5-dione,** m.p. 205–206°, *bis-semicarbazone*, m.p. 244–255°, is obtained by a double Dieckmann cyclisation of the tetramethyl ester of hexane-1:2:5:6-tetracarboxylic acid (*P. C. Guha* and *C. Krishnamurthy*, Ber., 1939, **72**, 1374).

Bicyclo[2:2:2]**octane-2:6-dione** (see p. 336) m.p. 190–191°, *bis-semicarbazone* m.p. 234–236° (dec.), is prepared by the cyclisation of cyclohexan-1-one-3-acetic acid (*P. D. Bartlett* and *G. F. Woods*, J. Amer. chem. Soc., 1940, **62**, 2933).

Bicyclo[2:2:2]*octane-2:6:7-trione*, m.p. 245°, see *W. Theilacker* and *W. Schmid* Ann., 1950, **570**, 15.

Condensation of cyclohexadiene with ethyl acrylate furnishes the *ethyl ester* of *bicyclo*[2:2:2]*oct-5-ene-2-carboxylic acid*, b.p. 98–100°/12 mm., which on hydrogenation and hydrolysis gives **bicyclo**[2:2:2]**octane-2-carboxylic acid** m.p. 84–85° (*R. Seka* and *O. Tramposch*, Ber., 1942, **75**, 1379).

Cyclohexadiene and maleic anhydride furnish *bicyclo*[2:2:2]*oct-5-ene-2:3-dicarboxylic anhydride*, m.p. 147°; on hydrolysis and catalytic hydrogenation this gives the cis-*form*, m.p. 148–152° (dec.), of **bicyclo**[2:2:2]**octane-2:3-dicarboxylic acid,** which on treatment with hydrochloric acid is converted to the trans-*form*, m.p. 234° (*O. Diels* and *K. Alder*, Ann., 1930, **478**, 152; Ber., 1929, **62**, 2087).

Bicyclo[2:2:2]**oct-2-ene-2:3-dicarboxylic anhydride,** m.p. 158°, has been prepared by hydrogenation and debromination of the cyclohexadiene-dibromo-maleic anhydride adduct (m.p. 252°); it may also be obtained from the cyclo-hexadiene-acetylenedicarboxylic ester adduct by hydrolysis, partial hydrogenation and dehydration (*idem*, Ann., 1931, **490**, 236).

More complex anhydrides have been obtained by the condensation of maleic anhydride with coumalin (I) and its derivatives (e.g. coumalic ester, *iso*dehydro-acetic acid). Thus coumalin gives, by the following stages, *bicyclo*[2:2:2]*oct-5-ene-2:3-7:8-tetracarboxylic dianhydride*, (II), m.p. 349°, *tetramethyl ester* m.p. 131° (*idem, ibid.*, 257).

(I) + maleic anhydride → adduct; $-CO_2$ → dihydrophthalic anhydride; Maleic anhydride → (II)

(I)

(II)

Condensation of ethylene dibromide with the disodio-salt of succinosuccinic ester (p. 245) furnishes the *diethyl ester*, m.p. 112°, of **bicyclo[2:2:2]octane-2:5-dione-1:4-dicarboxylic acid** m.p. 286° (*d*, m.p. 271°, $[\alpha]_D^{25}$ +23·85°; *l*, m.p. 271°, $[\alpha]_D^{28.5}$ −23·24°). On partial decarboxylation the free acid gives the corresponding *monocarboxylic acid* m.p. 216–217°. Clemmensen reduction of the diketo-ester produces **bicyclo[2:2:2]octane-1:4-dicarboxylic acid** m.p. 358° (*P. C. Guha et al.*, Ber., 1939, **72**, 1359, 1379; *J. D. Roberts et al.*, J. Amer. chem. Soc., 1953, **75**, 637).

Dicyclohexadiene (III), b.p. 86–87°/3 mm., obtained by the dimerisation of cyclohexadiene, contains the bicyclo[2:2:2]octane ring system. Partial hydrogenation gives the *dihydro*-compound (IV) b.p. 107–108°/16 mm., which has been degraded by the following steps (*K. Alder* and *G. Stein*, Ann., 1932, **496**, 197) to *cis*-cyclohexane-1:4-dicarboxylic acid (V).

CH_2 CH_2 (III) $\xrightarrow{H_2}$ CH_2 CH_2 (IV) $\xrightarrow{KMnO_4}$ CH_2 CH_2 CH_2 CH_2 CO_2H → CH_2 CH_2 O CO CH_2 CH_2 $\xrightarrow{HNO_3}$ CO_2H CO_2H (V)

Complete hydrogenation of the dimer gives the *tetrahydro*-derivative, b.p 101·9°/7·5 mm. (*E. V. Alexeewski*, J. gen. Chem. U.S.S.R., 1939, **9**, 1586), which may be named 1:4-*endo*-ethylenedecalin.

The benzoquinone addition products of the cyclohexadienes are structural and stereochemical analogues of the cyclopentadiene derivatives (p. 345); they may be converted into the corresponding quinols and thence by oxidation to the quinones. These latter compounds undergo a thermal disproportionation to a naphthaquinone and an ethylenic hydrocarbon, the *endo*-ethylene bridge being eliminated. The nature of these two fission fragments throws light on the constitution of the original cyclohexadiene (*O. Diels* and *K. Alder*, Ber., 1929, **62**, 2347).

O O + Me_2CH Me *α*-Phellandrene → O O Me CH_2 $CH\cdot CHMe_2$ —Oxidation→ O O Me CH_2 $CH\cdot CHMe_2$ $\xrightarrow{Heat}$ O O Me + CH_2 ‖ $CH\cdot CHMe_2$

The cyclohexadiene-benzoquinone *adduct*, m.p. 98°, can be reduced to a cis-*tetrahydro*-compound, m.p. 65° which gives *cis*-cyclohexane-1:4-dicarboxylic acid on nitric acid oxidation (*K. Alder* and *G. Stein*, Ann., 1933, **501**, 253). The *adduct* from 2 mols. of cyclohexadiene and 1 mol. of benzoquinone melts at 197° and then undergoes isomeric change and melts at 268° (*O. Diels* and *K. Alder*, Ber., 1929, **62**, 2337; *K. Alder* and *G. Stein*, Ann., 1933, **501**, 288).

For the preparation and properties of bicyclo[2:2:2]octanes substituted at the bridge head see *J. D. Roberts et al., loc. cit.* and *W. von E. Doering*, J. Amer. chem. Soc., 1953, **75**, 1008.

For further details of the numerous diene adducts from cyclohexadiene the relevant reviews should be consulted (see p. 128).

(*d*) *Bicyclo*[3:2:1]*octane group*

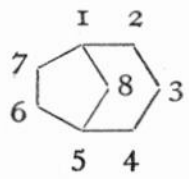

1 2 7 8 3 6 5 4

The parent hydrocarbon, **bicyclo**[3:2:1]**octane,** m.p. 141°, has been obtained by reduction of the bromo-derivative (*W. von E. Doering* and *M. Farber*, J. Amer. chem. Soc., 1949, **71**, 1514; *G. Komppa et al.*, Ann., 1936, **521**, 242), Kishner-Wolff reduction of the ketone (*K. Alder* and *E. Windemuth*, Ber., 1938, **71**, 2404) and by rearrangement of *cis*-bicyclo[3:3:0] octane with aluminium chloride (p. 317) (*J. W. Barrett* and *R. P. Linstead*, J. chem. Soc., 1936, 611).

2-**Bromobicyclo**[3:2:1]**octane,** m.p. 39–41°, is obtained by rearrangement of 2-bromobicyclo[2:2:2]octane (p. 346; *W. von E. Doering* and *M. Farber*, *loc. cit.*). On hydrolysis it yields **bicyclo**[3:2:1]**octan-2-ol,** m.p. 183–184°, *phenylurethane* m.p. 130°, also obtainable by the Demjanov ring enlargement of 2-(amino-methyl)bicyclo[2:2:1]heptane (*K. Alder* and *E. Windemuth*, *loc. cit.*).

CH_2 CH_2NH_2 $\xrightarrow{HNO_2}$ CH_2CH_2 OH

Bicyclo[3:2:1]**octan-6-ol,** m.p. 170°, *phenylurethane* m.p. 133°, is produced by reduction of the corresponding ketone (*G. Komppa et al.*, Ann., 1936, **521**, 242).

Bicyclo[3:2:1]**octan-2-one,** m.p. 129°, *semicarbazone* m.p. 171°, is formed by the oxidation of the corresponding alcohol (*K. Alder* and *E. Windemuth*, *loc. cit.*); oxidation with nitric acid furnishes cyclopentane-1-carboxylic-3-acetic acid.

Heating the alkaline earth salts of cyclohexane-1-carboxylic-2-acetic acid yields **bicyclo**[3:2:1]**octan-6-one,** m.p. 157–158°, *semicarbazone* m.p. 183–183·5° (*G. Komppa et al.*, *loc. cit.*).

2-**Methylbicyclo**[3:2:1]**oct-2-en-4-one,** b.p. 100–105°/9 mm. is formed by the aldol condensation of 1:2-diacetylcyclopentane (santene diketone) (*F. W. Semmler*, Ber., 1907, **40**, 4844; 1908, **41**, 866).

(e) *Bicyclo*[3:3:1]*nonane group*

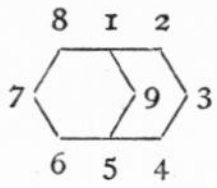

This structure (I) represents a completely strainless arrangement consisting of two chair forms of cyclohexane fused in the 1:3 position.

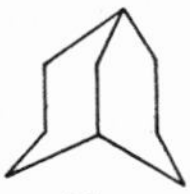

(I)

The main condensation product of methylene-mono- and -bis-malonic methyl esters with sodium ethoxide is *bicyclo*[3:3:1]*nonane*-2:6-*dione*-1:3:5:7-*tetracarboxylic methyl ester* m.p. 163–164°, hydrolysis and decarboxylation of which yields *bicyclo*[3:3:1]*nonane*-2:6-*dione* m.p. 141°; the *bis-semicarbazone*, m.p. 226°, of this ketone on heating with sodium ethoxide furnishes the parent hydrocarbon, **bicyclo**[3:3:1]**nonane,** m.p. 145–146°, b.p. 168·5–170° (*H. Meerwein et al.*, Ann., 1913, **398,** 223; J. pr. Chem., 1922, [ii], **104,** 161).

Another method of synthesising this ring system is by the condensation of cyclohex-2-en-1-ones with ethyl acetoacetate (*P. Rabe,* Ber., 1903, **36,** 225; 1904, **37,** 1671; 1943, **76,** 982), e.g.

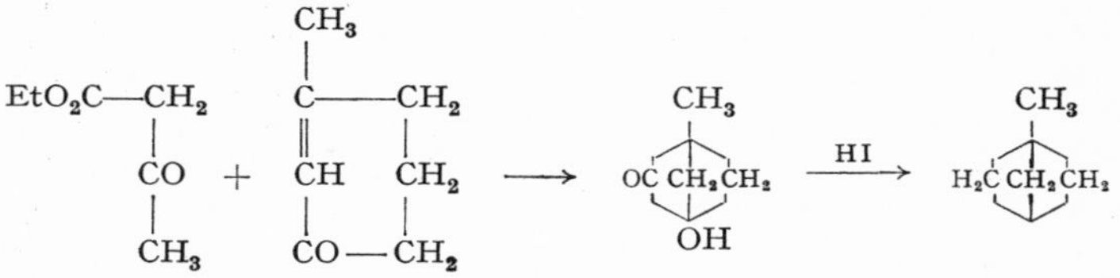

$EtO_2C—CH_2—CO—CH_3$ + $CH_3—C=CH—CO—CH_2—CH_2—CH_2$ (ring) ⟶ CH_3, OC CH_2CH_2, OH $\xrightarrow{HI}$ CH_3, $H_2C\ CH_2CH_2$

1-**Methylbicyclo**[3:3:1]**nonane** thus prepared has b.p. 176–178°, and 9-**methyl**-3-iso**propylbicyclo**[3:3:1]**nonane,** b.p. 232–233°.

(f) *Bicyclo*[3:2:2]*nonanes*

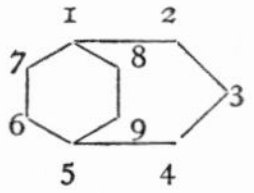

The most readily available compound of this system is the 6:8-*diketo*-1:5-*dicarboxylic acid,* (I) m.p. 238°, the *diethyl ester* of which, m.p. 132°, is obtained by treating the disodio-salt of succinosuccinic ester with trimethylene dibromide; on Clemmensen reduction it gives **bicyclo**[3:2:2]**nonane**-1:5-**dicarboxylic acid** (II), m.p. > 360° (*P. C. Guha,* Ber., 1939, **72,** 1359).

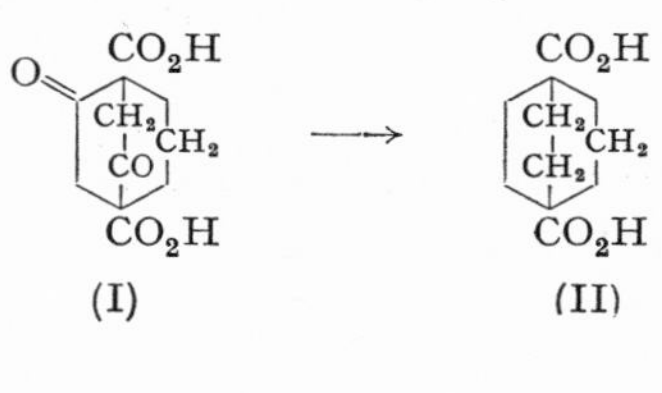

CO_2H, O, CH_2, CH_2, CO, CO_2H ⟶ CO_2H, CH_2, CH_2, CH_2, CO_2H

(I) (II)

(g) Adamantane

In 1933 *S. Landa* and *V. Machacek* isolated from a high boiling petroleum fraction a saturated hydrocarbon, **adamantane,** $C_{10}H_{16}$, with a camphoraceous odour m.p. 268°, *d* 1·07, heat of combustion 1451·7 kcals./mol. (Coll. Czech. chem. Comm., 1933, **5**, 1). The substance is remarkable for its amazing volatility and its chemical inertness, being unaffected by hot nitric acid, chromic acid and potassium permanganate. On the basis of X-ray and crystallographic data the Czech workers assigned to it the configuration (I). It is seen that this structure, consisting as it does of four mutually fused chair forms of cyclohexane with the carbon atoms in a spatial arrangement identical with that of the diamond lattice, provides a ready interpretation of the properties of adamantane.

For convenience adamantane is frequently written as (II) but this planar ideograph conveys no idea of the beautiful compactness and symmetry of the molecule.

The correctness of the assigned structure has been confirmed by the synthesis of adamantane from methyl bicyclo[3:3:1]nonane-2:6-dione-3:7-dicarboxylate (III) in the following manner (*V. Prelog* and *R. Seiwerth*, Ber., 1941, **74**, 1644, 1769; *R. Seiwerth*, Kemijski Vjestnik, 1941–1942, **15/16**, 20).

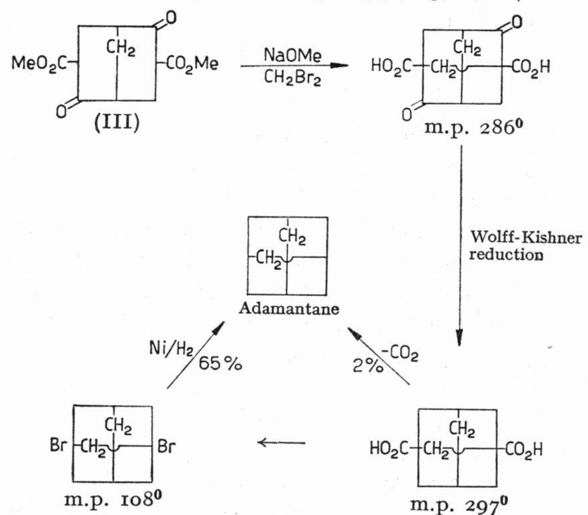

Tricyclene, see Vol. IIB.

Chapter X

The Carotenoid Group *

R. F. HUNTER

The carotenoids constitute an important class of natural fat-soluble pigments (lipochromes) characterised by a long carbon chain containing conjugated double bonds which is responsible for their colour (absorption spectra), sensitivity to oxygen and for the deep blue colour which they give with concentrated sulphuric acid and with a solution of antimony trichloride in chloroform (Carr-Price reaction). In many members of the class the conjugated chain is terminated at one or both ends by a cyclohexene ring, for which reason they are conveniently discussed with alicyclic compounds. The fact that the carbon skeleton shows a polyisoprene structure with appropriate distribution of methyl groups gives the carotenoids a formal relation to terpenes from which they differ in being more unsaturated (see formula of β-carotene, p. 356). With few exceptions members of the class are hydrocarbons of empirical formula $C_{40}H_{56}$ or oxygenated derivatives, alcohols or ketones, of these.

1. Natural occurrence, properties and constitution

Although carotenoids are widely distributed throughout both the vegetable and animal kingdoms, the amounts in which they occur in natural products are very small, as may be illustrated by the best known member of the group, carotene, which is present to the extent of only 0·1 % or less in carrots and typical African palm oils. Whilst their function in plant economy is not very clear, carotene and the dihydroxy-derivative, lutein (formerly called xanthophyll, a name now reserved for the group of hydroxy- and ketone derivatives) are invariably associated with green leaves and grass and there appears to be a connection between carbon dioxide assimilation through chlorophyll and carotenoid concentration. The more highly oxygenated carotenoids, flavoxanthin $C_{40}H_{56}O_3$ and violaxanthin $C_{40}H_{56}O_4$ are responsible for the colour of yellow buttercups and pansies respectively.

* For a full account see "Carotenoids", P. Karrer and E. Jucker, Elsevier Publishing Company, 1950.

Carotenoids are present in small amounts in the blood, the body fat and the tissues of animals in which they arise from ingestion of food. It has been shown that lutein is responsible for the yellow plumage of canaries and that in the absence of this carotenoid in the diet the feathers turn white. In the lower forms of life, carotenoids appear in algae, crustacea and certain purple-coloured bacteria. The very highly oxygenated carotenoid, fucoxanthin, $C_{40}H_{56}O_6$, has been found in certain species of brown algae, in association with β-carotene. The bright red colour which lobsters develop on boiling is associated with the decomposition of a labile chromoprotein which yields a diketodihydroxycarotene, *astaxanthin*, which readily undergoes oxidation to a tetraketone of carotene, astacene $C_{40}H_{56}O_4$, which was first thought to be the original pigment.

The great interest which attaches itself to the carotenoid group from the viewpoint of medicine and nutrition arises, however, from the fact that some ten of the naturally occurring carotenoids are provitamin-A-active, that is to say, they are capable of conversion into vitamin A in the animal body. The physiological activity of vitamin A and the provitamin-A-active carotenoids is characterised by their power to restore growth to animals fed on a diet containing all essentials except vitamin A or provitamin A and by the characteristic degeneration in the structure of the eye known as xerophthalmia which occurs in animals living on a diet seriously deficient in vitamin A. Manifestation of this disease in humans occurred in Denmark during the 1914–1918 war when poorer people ate little butter and margarine was not vitaminised. Defective low intensity of vision (night blindness), decreased resistance to respiratory infections and deterioration of the condition of the genito-urinary tract are amongst the better known symptoms of vitamin A deficiency in humans. The most important biologically active carotenoid and the one on which both humans and animals are mainly dependent for their vitamin A requirements is β-carotene, which at one time constituted the International Standard for biological assay of vitamin A.

The chemistry of the carotenoid group has been elucidated essentially from degradation studies and determination of the number of double bonds and side-chain methyl groups in the substances, supported by syntheses of perhydrobixin and perhydrocrocetin, the fully hydrogenated derivatives of the pigments bixin and crocetin which, although they have the formulae $C_{25}H_{30}O_4$ and $C_{20}H_{24}O_4$ respectively, contain the essential conjugated chain and are usually included in the group. More recently, the major accomplishment of the total syntheses of three of the most important carotenoids, β-carotene, lycopene and α-carotene, has been accomplished by way of acetylene derivatives.

The degradation studies are dependent on the fission of the unsaturated linkages with identification of the smaller fragments (ozonisation) and retention in the larger ones of sufficient of the original structure to assist in the construction of a probable formula, as is illustrated by the case of β-carotene (p. 356). The combination of information of this type with quantitative catalytic hydrogenation, estimation of side-chain methyl groups and other special groups such as hydroxyl (Zerewitinoff), with the insight gained from bixin and crocetin and generalisations obtained from absorption spectroscopical studies has enabled deductions of structure to be made which have received support from isolation of further members from natural sources and from later experimental work both of a degradation and semi-synthetical character.

As might be anticipated, the carotenoids exhibit *cis-trans* isomerism, but with the same special feature of high mobility of interchange observed by *G. S. Hartley* (J. chem. Soc., 1938, 633) for *cis-* and *trans*-azobenzene (cf. *R. F. Hunter et al.*, Biochem. J., 1942, **36**, 697). On account of the large number of double bonds in the extended conjugated system, the number of possible isomers is, of course, very high but actually the majority of isolable isomers readily revert to the more stable all-*trans* configuration favoured by the very much greater majority of the naturally occurring carotenoids.

The chemistry of β-carotene has been more thoroughly investigated than that of any other carotenoid and may be taken as typical of that of the group.

2. Carotenoid hydrocarbons and Vitamin A

(a) The carotenes

β-Carotene. A crystalline pigment to which he gave the name carotene was isolated from carrots by Wackenroder in 1831 but no serious work on the nature of the substance was attempted until Willstätter and his pupils commenced their investigations in 1907. They showed that carotene has the molecular formula $C_{40}H_{56}$ and that it can be isolated from numerous sources other than carrots, such as stinging nettles, berries of the mountain ash, and palm oil. A method of isolation of the crystalline pigment by precipitation from a petroleum-carbon disulphide solution with alcohol was described by *R. Willstätter* and *H. H. Escher* (Z. physiol. Chem., 1910, **64**, 47) which furnished carotene of m.p. 172–174°. Willstätter and his collaborators also isolated a number of other carotenoids, showed that lycopene, the pigment of ripe tomato, was isomeric with carotene, and that lutein had the formula $C_{40}H_{56}O_2$. After a lull of activity in the field for some 14 years, a definite advance was made in 1928 by *L. Zechmeister, L. von Cholnoky* and *V. Vrabely* (Ber., 61, 566) who established the presence of eleven double bonds in carotene by quantitative catalytic hydrogenation and the isolation of a saturated hydrocarbon of the formula $C_{40}H_{78}$. This indicated the presence of two alicyclic rings in the molecule. A similar experiment by *P. Karrer* and *R. Widmer* (Helv., 1928, 11, 751) with lycopene, however, showed the presence of thirteen double bonds and indicated an open-chain structure. Following this, *P. Karrer, A. Helfenstein* and *R. Widmer* (Helv., 1928, 11, 1201) synthesised perhydrolycopene from dihydrophytol and showed this to be identical with the product obtained from lycopene by catalytic hydrogenation. On ozonisation, lycopene gave two molecules of acetone and on oxidation with chromic acid it gave six molecules of acetic acid. On the basis of this, and other evidence, Karrer and his collaborators suggested the formula (I) for lycopene (Helv., 1931, 14, 435).

```
CMe2                                                                                          CMe2
//                                                  :                                            \\
CH  CH·CH:CH·CMe:CH·CH:CH·CMe:CH·CH:CH·CH:CMe·CH:CH·CH:CMe·CH:CH·CH  CH
|   ||                                              :                                  ||   |
CH2 CMe                                                                               CMe CH2
  \/                                                                                     \/
  CH2                         Lycopene (I)                                               CH2
```

As will be seen, this consists essentially of eight isoprene units but, as in the case of squalene, there has been a rearrangement in the middle of the conjugated chain such that the molecule is composed of two equal and symmetrically arranged halves (on either side of the dotted line in (I)).

From oxidation of a benzene solution of carotene (substantially the β-isomer) with cold aqueous potassium permanganate, *Karrer* and *Helfenstein* isolated $\alpha\alpha$-dimethylglutaric acid, $\alpha\alpha$-dimethylsuccinic acid and dimethylmalonic acid (Helv., 1929, 12, 1142). On ozonolysis, *Karrer* and his collaborators obtained geronic acid (*ibid.*, 1930, 13, 1084). These results plainly suggested the presence of at least one β-ionone ring in β-carotene.

```
    CMe2                          CMe2                CMe2
   /    \                        /    \              /    \
CH2     C—      KMnO4         CH2     CO2H   +    CH2     CO2H
|       ||    -------->       |                   |
CH2     CMe                   CH2                 CO2H
   \   /                         \
    CH2                           CO2H
       \
        \   O3                    CMe2
         \                       /    \
          -------->           CH2     CO2H
                              |
                              CH2     COMe
                                 \   /
                                  CH2
```

Chromic acid oxidation of carotene by *R. Kuhn* and *F. L'Orsa* (Z. angew. Chem., 1931, 44, 847) indicated the presence of six methyl groups attached to doubly bonded carbon atoms as in lycopene. A repetition of the ozonolysis experiment with β-carotene free from α-isomer by *P. Karrer* and *R. Morf* (Helv., 1931, 14, 1033) and a similar experiment with β-ionone itself furnished yields of geronic acid indicating the presence of two β-ionone rings in the molecule and Karrer therefore suggested the symmetrical formula (II) for β-carotene, analogous to that of lycopene.

```
  CMe2                                                                                        CMe2
 /    \                                                                                      /    \
CH2   C·CH:CH·CMe:CH·CH:CH·CMe:CH·CH:CH·CH:CMe·CH:CH·CH:CMe·CH:CH·C    CH2
|     ||                                                                                     ||    |
CH2   CMe                                                                                   CMe   CH2
 \    /                                                                                      \    /
  CH2                                                                                         CH2
```

β-Carotene (II)

This structure also provided a satisfactory interpretation of the relation of β-carotene to vitamin A and of the conversion of the former into the latter *in vivo* as shown by *T. Moore's* experiments on rats kept on a vitamin A-free diet (Biochem. J., 1930, 24, 692). It received confirmation from careful degradation experiments subsequently made by *R. Kuhn* and *H. Brockmann* (Ann., 1935, 516, 95). These investigators found that mild oxidation of β-carotene with chromic oxide gave a dihydroxy-β-carotene (III), whose constitution was established by its further oxidation with Criegee reagent (lead tetra-acetate) to semi-β-carotenone (IV).

```
  CMe2                     CMe2              CMe2                  CMe2
 /    \                   /    \            /    \                /    \
CH2   C(OH) —— A —— C    CH2              CH2   CO —— A —— C     CH2
|     |             ||   |                |                 ||    |
CH2   CMe·OH        CMe  CH2              CH2   CO·Me       CMe   CH2
 \    /              \    /                \    /            \    /
  CH2                 CH2                   CH2               CH2
            (III)                                      (IV)
```

(A = –CH:CH·CMe:CH·CH:CH·CMe:CH·CH:CH·CH:CMe·CH:CH·CH:CMe·CH:CH–).

Controlled oxidation of either of these products with chromic acid gave β-carotenone (V), which was also obtained by direct oxidation of β-carotene.

```
  CMe2                  CMe2
 /    \                /    \
CH2   CO —— A —— CO    CH2
|                       |
CH2   CO·Me   Me·OC    CH2
 \    /           \    /
  CH2              CH2
```

β-Carotenone (V)

Final proof of the constitution of β-carotene has been afforded by rational synthesis by *P. Karrer* and *C. H. Eugster* (Helv., 1950, **33**, 1172) from the acetylenic carbinol (VI), the bismagnesium bromide derivative of which with the diketone (VII) furnished the tetrol (VIII) which on partial hydrogenation and subsequent dehydration gave β-carotene, identical with that from natural sources.

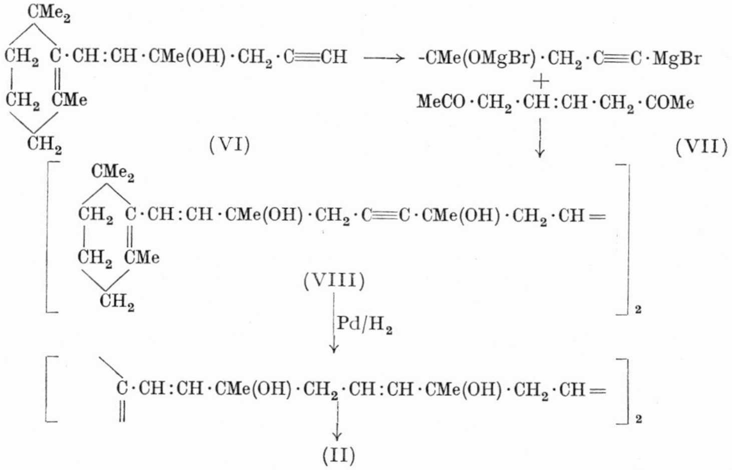

```
 CMe2
 /  \
CH2  C·CH:CH·CMe(OH)·CH2·C≡CH  ——→  -CMe(OMgBr)·CH2·C≡C·MgBr
|    ||                                        +
CH2  CMe                          MeCO·CH2·CH:CH·CH2·COMe
 \  /                                          |
 CH2              (VI)                         ↓                 (VII)
┌  CMe2                                                              ┐
│  /  \                                                              │
│ CH2  C·CH:CH·CMe(OH)·CH2·C≡C·CMe(OH)·CH2·CH=                        │
│ |    ||                                                            │
│ CH2  CMe                                                           │
│  \  /                     (VIII)                                   │
└  CH2                        |                                      ┘2
                              |Pd/H2
                              ↓
┌    \                                                               ┐
│     C·CH:CH·CMe(OH)·CH2·CH:CH·CMe(OH)·CH2·CH=                       │
└     ||                      |                                      ┘2
                              ↓
                             (II)
```

Almost simultaneously, with the appearance of Karrer and Eugster's paper, *H. H. Inhoffen* and his collaborators, who had previously been working on the synthesis of hydrocarbons related to the carotenoids from the C_{14} aldehyde (IX) and acetylene magnesium halide derivatives (Ann., 1948, **561**, 26; 1949, **565**, 45), described an independent synthesis of β-carotene from the former and 1-methoxy-2-hydroxy-2-methylbut-3-yne in accordance with the following scheme:

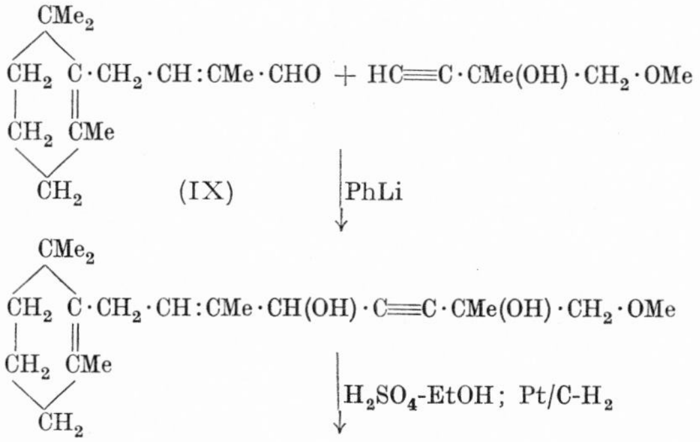

```
 CMe2
 /  \
CH2  C·CH2·CH:CMe·CHO + HC≡C·CMe(OH)·CH2·OMe
|    ||
CH2  CMe
 \  /                       |
 CH2         (IX)           |PhLi
                            ↓
 CMe2
 /  \
CH2  C·CH2·CH:CMe·CH(OH)·C≡C·CMe(OH)·CH2·OMe
|    ||
CH2  CMe                    |
 \  /                       |H2SO4-EtOH; Pt/C-H2
 CH2                        ↓
```

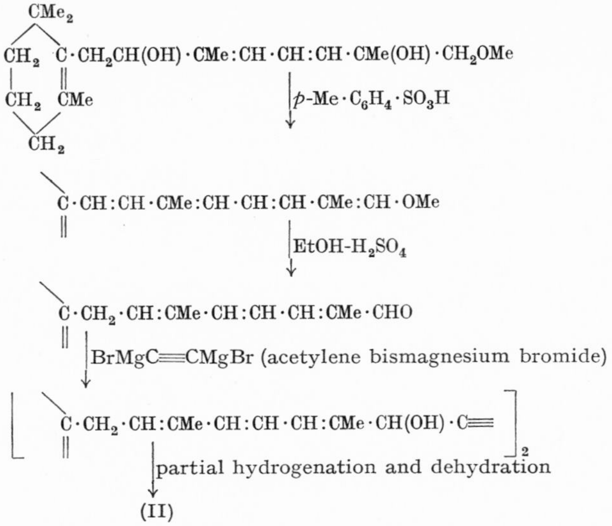

CMe_2

CH_2 $C \cdot CH_2CH(OH) \cdot CMe:CH \cdot CH:CH \cdot CMe(OH) \cdot CH_2OMe$

CH_2 CMe

CH_2

↓ p-$Me \cdot C_6H_4 \cdot SO_3H$

$C \cdot CH:CH \cdot CMe:CH \cdot CH:CH \cdot CMe:CH \cdot OMe$

↓ $EtOH$-H_2SO_4

$C \cdot CH_2 \cdot CH:CMe \cdot CH:CH \cdot CH:CMe \cdot CHO$

↓ $BrMgC{\equiv}CMgBr$ (acetylene bismagnesium bromide)

$[C \cdot CH_2 \cdot CH:CMe \cdot CH:CH \cdot CH:CMe \cdot CH(OH) \cdot C{\equiv}]_2$

↓ partial hydrogenation and dehydration

(II)

H. H. Inhoffen and his collaborators also synthesised β-carotene from the acetylenic carbinol (VI) and the diketone (VII) on lines similar to those of Karrer and Eugster but differing in the order of the intermediate transformations in the following way (Ann., 1950, **569**, 237):

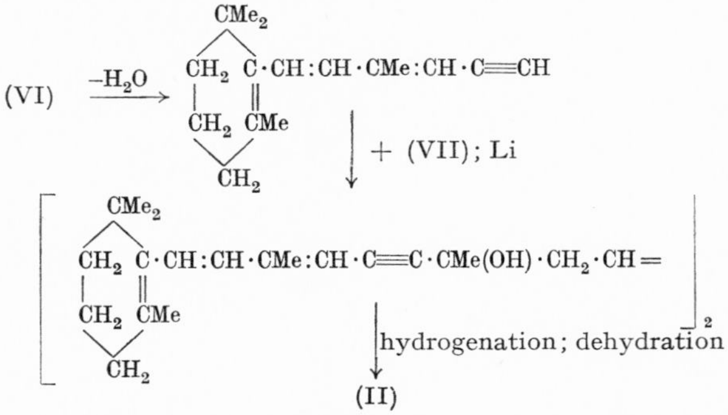

CMe_2

(VI) $\xrightarrow{-H_2O}$ CH_2 $C \cdot CH:CH \cdot CMe:CH \cdot C{\equiv}CH$

CH_2 CMe

CH_2

↓ + (VII); Li

CMe_2

$[CH_2$ $C \cdot CH:CH \cdot CMe:CH \cdot C{\equiv}C \cdot CMe(OH) \cdot CH_2 \cdot CH{=}$

CH_2 CMe

$CH_2]_2$

↓ hydrogenation; dehydration

(II)

Since then, *N. A. Milas* and his collaborators have published still another total synthesis of β-carotene (J. Amer. chem. Soc., 1950, **72**, 4844).

Until 1950, a highly purified sample of β-carotene, issued for many years as a solution in coconut oil and later in refined arachis oil, constituted the International Standard for bio-assay of vitamin A. The first Standard β-carotene was prepared by Karrer and the second by *J. Devine, R. F. Hunter* and *N. E. Williams* (Biochem. J., 1945, **39**, 5). As a result of the International Conference held in London in 1949 under the auspices of the World Health Organisation, however, vitamin A acetate was adopted as the new standard for vitamin A, while the solution of β-carotene in arachis oil was retained as the International Standard for Provitamin A.

Oxidation of β-carotene. Little is known of the reactions which occur during the oxidation of β-carotene in air other than that they lead to ultimate loss of colour and gain in weight and increased solubility. Oxidation in solution in both arachis oil and benzene by oxygen results (*R. F. Hunter* and *R. M. Krakenberger*, J. chem. Soc., 1947, 1) in attack of the double bond of one β-ionone ring and then of the other with the production of mutatochrome (X) (*P. Karrer* and *E. Jucker*, Helv., 1945, 28, 427), aurochrome ($C_{40}H_{56}O_2$ with both β-ionone rings oxidised as in X), epoxide derivatives, semi-β-carotenone (IV) and β-carotenone (V).

```
     CMe2
    /    \
 CH2  C====CH                                                                                     CMe2
  |   |     |                                                                                    /    \
 CH2  CMe  CH·CMe:CH·CH:CH·CMe:CH·CH:CH·CH:CMe·CH:CH·CH:CMe·CH:CH·C    CH2
    \    / \ /                                                                                   ||     |
     CH2  O                                                                                     CMe  CH2
                                                                                                    \    /
                                                                                                     CH2
```

Mutatochrome (X)

Mutatochrome occurs naturally as the pigment previously known as *citroxanthin* which was isolated from orange peel (*Karrer* and *Jucker*, Helv., 1947, 30, 536) and shows 39% of the provitamin-A-activity of β-carotene (*R. F. Hunter et al.*, J. chem. Soc., 1947, 131).

On degradative oxidation with alkaline potassium permanganate, β-carotene furnishes *β-apo-2-carotenal*

```
     CMe2
    /    \
 CH2  C(CH:CH·CMe:CH)2CH:CH·CH:CMe·CH:CH·CH:CMe·CHO
  |   ||
 CH2  CMe
    \    /
     CH2
```

which also shows strong provitamin-A-activity (*P. Karrer* and *U. Solmssen*, Helv., 1937, **20**, 682; *H. von Euler et al.*, *ibid.*, 1938, **21**, 1619).

Physical properties of β-carotene. Crystalline form (a): dark violet hexagonal prisms from benzene-methanol, (b) red, rhombic, almost quadratic plates from petroleum ether; m.p. 181–182° (corr.) (*R. Kuhn* and *E. Lederer*, Ber., 1931, **64**, 1352); 181–182° (uncorr.) (*P. Karrer et al.*, Helv., 1931, **14**, 615); 183° (corr., evacuated capillary, *Kuhn* and *Brockmann*, Ber., 1933, **66**, 408); 187·5° (*Miller*, Chem. Ztbl., 1935, I, 3545). Spectroscopic properties:

Solvent:	*Absorption maxima:*		
Carbon disulphide	520	485	450 mμ
Chloroform	497	466	
Petrol	483·5	452	426
Hexane	477	450	425

The very pure specimen isolated by Hunter and Scott from "Sherbro" palm oil crystallized from acetone in glistening purple red plates, m.p. 184·5° (uncorr.; open melting point tube) and had an $\varepsilon^{1\%}_{1cm}$ value of 2310 at 463 mμ in chloroform. The 20 g. sample of β-carotene prepared by Devine, Hunter and Williams for the new Standard from a carotene concentrate from alfalfa meal had m.p. 183·5° (uncorr., open melting point tube) and had the following spectroscopic characteristics:

Solvent:	*Wave-length of main band* (mμ)	$\varepsilon^{1\%}_{1cm}$
Cyclohexane	456	2480
Chloroform	465	2300
Hexane	453	2530
Benzene	465	2350

α-Carotene. It was discovered fairly early in work on carotene that samples of β-carotene from certain sources contained another form of carotene, designated α-carotene, which also possessed growth-promoting properties but in addition was optically active. This second form, which occurs in carrots, palm oils, and in horse-chestnut leaves, was first prepared by fractional precipitation of the natural mixture of isomers with iodine, when the iodide of β-carotene was first precipitated. It was also obtained by treatment of a petroleum ether solution of the mixture of isomers with fuller's earth, when the β-isomer was preferentially removed. Later, the separation was much more efficiently accomplished by means of chromatographic adsorption on a Tswett column of active alumina or magnesium oxide. The strength of adsorption is determined by the number of conjugated double bonds and the number of hydroxyl groups in a carotenoid, the xanthophylls being adsorbed above the hydrocarbon pigments and in accordance with the number of hydroxyl groups present. The carotene isolated from the lower and lighter coloured zone below the main β-carotene zone when purified by further chromatography and recrystallisation showed high dextrorotation and gave an absorption spectrum in the visible region closely similar to that of β-carotene but with the bands displaced a few mμ towards the region of shorter wave length.

The relation of α- to β-carotene was shown by its ozonisation which gave rise to *iso*geronic acid,

$$Me_2C\begin{cases} CH_2\cdot CH_2\cdot CO_2H \\ CH_2\cdot COMe \end{cases}$$

in addition to geronic acid, indicating that one of the rings is of the α-ionone type. This, together with asymmetry indicated by the optical activity led Karrer to suggest the formula (XI) for α-carotene (*P. Karrer, R. Morf* and *O. Walker*, Helv., 1933, **16**, 975).

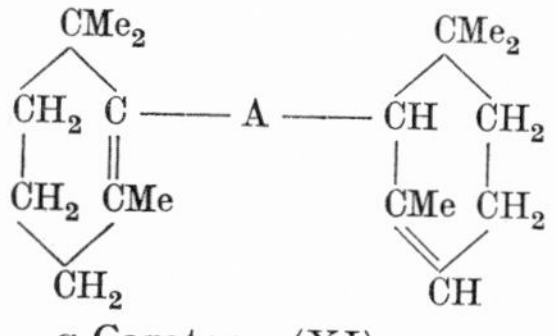

```
    CMe2                  CMe2              CMe2                          CMe2
   /    \                /    \            /    \                        /    \
CH2    C ——— A ——— CH    CH2          CH2    C(OH) ——— A ——— CH    CH2
 |     ||              |     |          |     |                   |     |
CH2    CMe            CMe    CH2       CH2    CMe·OH             CMe    CH2
   \    /                \\   /            \    /                    \\   /
    CH2                   CH                CH2                       CH
α-Carotene (XI)                                       (XII)
```

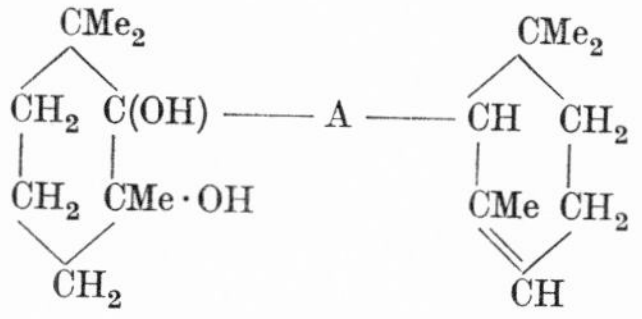

Oxidative degradation experiments provided confirmation of this structure. A biologically inactive *hydroxycarotene* (XII) and a similarly inactive *semi-α-carotenone* believed to be analogous to semi-β-carotenone, in addition to α-carotenone, were isolated in chromic acid oxidation experiments (*P. Karrer, H. von Euler* and *U. Solmssen*, Helv., 1934, **17**, 1169).

Finally, by replacing one of the two molecules of the acetylenic carbinol (VI) in the synthesis of β-carotene by the α-ionone derivative

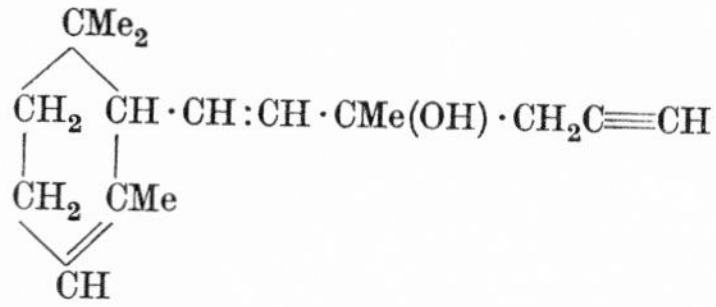

```
    CMe2
   /    \
CH2    CH·CH:CH·CMe(OH)·CH2C≡CH
 |     |
CH2    CMe
   \   //
    CH
```

P. Karrer and *C. H. Eugster* (Helv., 1950, **33**, 1952) have synthesised a racemic specimen of α-carotene.

It will be seen that the formula for α-carotene (XI) differs from that of β-carotene merely in the position of a double bond which lies outside the conjugated system and a hydrogen atom, and that three-carbon prototropy might therefore be expected to occur under sufficiently activating conditions. Attempts to effect the interconversion of both β- to α- and α- to β-carotene by heating with *iso*propyl alcoholic sodium *iso*propoxide by *R. F. Hunter* and *A. D. Scott* proved unsuccessful (Biochem. J., 1944, **38**, 211) but the latter change (α → β) has since been accomplished by *P. Karrer* and *E. Jucker* by heating α-carotene with alcoholic sodium ethoxide and benzene in an evacuated tube at 100–110° for a more prolonged period (Helv., 1947, **30**, 266).

Physical properties of α-carotene. Crystalline form, violet prisms and clusters from benzene-methanol and dark violet prisms or polygons from petroleum ether; m.p. 187–188° (corr.) (*P. Karrer* and *O. Walker*, Helv., 1933, **16**, 642). Spectroscopic properties:

Solvent:	*Absorption maxima:*			
Hexane	475	445	420	395 mμ
Carbon disulphide	509	477		
Petrol	478	447·5		
Chloroform	485	454		

The very pure specimen of α-carotene isolated by Hunter and Scott from "Sherbro" palm oil, crystallized from acetone in glistening red brown crystals, m.p. 187–187·5° (uncorr.; open melting point tube) and showed absorption maxima at 511, 479, and 450 mμ in carbon disulphide, at 489, 458, and 430 mμ in chloroform, and at 489, 458, and 431 mμ in benzene. The $\varepsilon^{1\%}_{1cm}$ value for the maximum at 458 mμ in chloroform was 2430. The antimony trichloride reaction showed a main band at 495 mμ, a weak band at 650 mμ, an inflexion at 527 mμ and a weak inflexion at 605 mμ; $[\alpha]_{5893}$ + 640° (benzene).

γ-Carotene. — A third isomer present in very small amount in carotene from carrots was discovered by *R. Kuhn* and *H. Brockmann* (Ber., 1933, **66**, 407) by chromatographic technique and named γ-carotene. The isolation of this isomer, which is adsorbed just above β-carotene in the Tswett column, provides a striking example of the elegance of chromatographic technique which has contributed so much to developments in the carotenoid field. Starting with 35 g. of commercial carotene, these authors ultimately succeeded in isolating 34 mg. of γ-carotene with which they were able to study its physical, chemical and biological properties. γ-Carotene absorbs 12 molecules of hydrogen in catalytic hydrogenation and ozonolysis yields a molecule of acetone in accordance with an open-chain structure for one end of the molecule. On the basis of this, and the growth-promoting response in rats which was found to be half of that of β-carotene, they suggested the monocyclic formula (XIII) for γ-carotene. In accordance with this, the absorption maxima of γ-carotene in the visible region were found to be intermediate between those of lycopene and β-carotene.

```
  CMe2                     CMe2
 //                       /    \
CH   CH ---- A ---- C      CH2
|    ||             ||     |
CH2  CMe            CMe    CH2
  \  /                \   /
  CH2                  CH2
```

γ-Carotene (XIII)

A reinvestigation of the provitamin-A-activity of γ-carotene by *H. J. Deuel et al.* (Arch. Biochem., 1945, **6**, 157) has shown that all-*trans*-γ-carotene possesses only 26 % of the biological activity of all-*trans*-β-carotene.

The presence of γ-carotene in very small amounts has been observed in most of the special palm oils ("Sherbro", West African Plantation, "Malay",

"Bissao" and "Sese") which have been examined and it was isolated in crystalline condition from a commercial "Sese" palm oil (*R. F. Hunter* and *R. M. Krakenberger*, Biochem. J., 1946, **40,** 492).

γ-Carotene crystallises from a mixture of benzene and methanol in microscopic dark red prisms with a blue lustre, m.p. 176·5° (corr.) (*Kuhn* and *Brockmann, loc. cit.*) (*L. Zechmeister* and *W. Schroeder*, Arch. Biochem., 1942, **1,** 231, report m.p. 178° [corr. in vacuum]). It shows absorption maxima at 533·5, 496, and 463 mμ in carbon disulphide, at 508·5, 475, and 446 mμ in chloroform, and at 494, 462, and 431 mμ in hexane.

*iso***Carotene** *(dehydro-β-carotene).* — The so-called "*iso*carotene", obtained by treatment of the tetraiodide of β-carotene with acetone (*R. Kuhn* and *E. Lederer*, Ber., 1932, **65,** 637) appears from the reinvestigation of *P. Karrer* and *G. Schwab* (Helv., 1940, **23,** 578) to be a dehydro-β-carotene, $C_{40}H_{54}$, in which all twelve double bonds are conjugated. On ozonolysis, it gives neither geronic nor *iso*geronic acid, indicating the absence of β- or α-ionone rings. The formula (XIV) is suggested by *P. Karrer* and *G. Schwab* (*loc. cit.*) which provides an explanation of the formation of the substance from the tetraiodide of β-carotene.

```
 CMe2                                                                                        CMe2
 /  \                                                                                        /  \
CH2  C:CH·CH:CMe·CH:CH·CH:CMe·CH:CH·CH:CH·CMe:CH·CH:CH·CMe:CH·CH:C   CH2
|    |                                                                                       |    |
CH2  CMe                                                                                   CMe  CH2
  \\ //                                                                                     \\  /
   CH                                                                                        CH
```

Dehydro-β-carotene (XIV)

Dehydro-β-carotene crystallises from petroleum ether in glistening violet-blue needles or plates, m.p. 192–193° (corr.) (*P. Karrer et al.*, Helv., 1932, **15,** 1158) and shows absorption maxima at 543, 504, and 472 mμ in carbon disulphide, at 518, 485, and 455 mμ in chloroform, and at 504, 475, and 447 mμ in petroleum ether.

ε_1**-Carotene.** — A carotene containing two α-ionone rings has been synthesised by *P. Karrer* and *C. H. Eugster* (Helv., 1950, **33,** 1172) on lines analogous to their synthesis of β-carotene. This synthetic carotene has m.p. 190° (corr.) and shows absorption maxima at 501 and 470 mμ in carbon disulphide and at 470 and 439 mμ in petroleum ether.

(b) cis-trans-*Isomerism of carotenoids*

The first observations with regard to the C_{40}-carotenoids were made by *A. E. Gillam* and *M. S. El Ridi* (Biochem. J., 1936, **30,** 1735) who reported that when β-carotene was washed from an alumina column with petroleum ether and then readsorbed, it separated into zones showing the absorption spectroscopical characteristics of β- and α-carotene. Elution and readsorption of either zone gave another separation into two zones with spectroscopical characteristics of the original two, the process being reversible. The lower zone containing "*pseudo-α-carotene*" differed, however, from α-carotene since this on similar treatment was found to give a pigment with absorption maxima at still shorter wave length. It was subsequently shown by *L. Zechmeister* and *P. Tuzson* (*ibid.*, 1938, **32**, 1305) that the isomerisation was not due to the action of the adsorbent. The reversible changes, which were also observed with other carotenoids, are spontaneous and occur with much greater rapidity at higher temperatures. The changes are plainly *cis-trans* rearrangements, and when the number of double bonds in a polyene molecule is considered, it is obvious that there are many spatial possibilities. Not all the double bonds in the extended conjugated chain are, however, necessarily available for a spatial rearrangement and they can be divided into "stereochemically effective" and "stereochemically ineffective" double bonds, the latter being hindered in assuming the *cis*-configuration. In a C_{40}-carotenoid, only one double bond in each isoprene unit is able to assume the *cis* configuration and, according to *L. Pauling*, these are those double bonds which carry methyl side chains and the central double bond of the conjugated system. On this basis, *L. Zechmeister* (Chem. Reviews, 1944, **34**, 267) has calculated that there are 20 possible stereoisomers of β-carotene and 32 possible stereoisomers of α-carotene. In γ-carotene and lycopene the number is greater (64 and 72 respectively). Fortunately, it can be reliably stated that the overwhelming majority of the carotenoids present in vegetable tissues have the all-*trans* configuration. *cis*-Isomers, such as prolycopene and pro-γ-carotene have, however, been isolated from vegetable tissue by *Zechmeister* and his collaborators (J. Amer. chem. Soc., 1942, **64**, 1075, 1173; J. biol. Chem., 1942, **144**, 315). The usual methods of isomerisation of carotenoids consist in heating in solution in the absence of light or catalysts, isomerisation by melting crystals, iodine catalysis at room temperature, and acid catalysis. A number of different stereoisomeric carotenoids have been obtained by Zechmeister and his collaborators, many of which are so highly labile as to be only recognisable by chromatography and spectroscopic characteristics in solution. Thus, *L. Zechmeister* and *A. Polgár* obtained some nine or ten stereoisomers of β-carotene, but on addition of iodine all of these yielded a preponderant quantity of β-carotene and minor stereoisomers (J. Amer. chem. Soc., 1942, **64**, 1856). One of these, however, *neo-β-carotene U*, which is adsorbed chromatographically rather more strongly than β-carotene, was obtained crystalline. This isomer is considered to have only one *cis* double bond, while the pseudo-α-carotene of Gillam and El Ridi may contain two *cis* double bonds. These two stereoisomers have the following properties:

	Pseudo-α-carotene		*Neo-β-carotene U*	
Melting point	166°		122–123° (corr., block)	
Absorption maxima				
Carbon disulphide	507	477 mμ	512·5	478·5 mμ
Chloroform	486	456	493·5	461
Petroleum ether	477	446	481	450
Ethanol	478	447	482	450·5

The change from *trans* to *cis* configuration is accompanied by a shift of absorption maxima towards the region of shorter wave length in accordance with

R. S. Mulliken's conclusion, from wave mechanical considerations, that the most elongated isomers should have the highest wave length bands.

Another important feature of the *trans-cis* isomerisation of carotenoids is the appearance of a new but minor maximum in the ultra-violet region between 320 and 380 mμ, termed the "*cis* peak" (*Zechmeister* and *Polgár*, *ibid.*, 1943, **65**, 1522). This has a definite position in the extinction curve and the difference between its wave length and that of the longest wave-length maximum of the all-*trans* form is practically constant (about 142 mμ in hexane).

Synthetic higher homologues of the carotenes, see p. 390.

(c) Vitamin A

Vitamin A *(axerophthol)*. — Although vitamin A itself is not a carotenoid, it is of such importance in relation to the biological activity of the members of the group that it is desirable to deal with the more essential features of its chemistry in the present account.

The name vitamin A is given both to vitamin A alcohol, which is sometimes termed *axerophthol,* and to a number of fatty acid esters of this which occur in the unsaponifiable matter of the liver of fish and animals. The alcohol and its esters are characterised spectroscopically by a well defined absorption band in the ultra-violet at 328 mμ and by an intense maximum at 620 mμ in the blue colour produced with antimony trichloride in chloroform (Carr-Price reaction).

Although vitamin A was not isolated as a pure crystalline substance until more than ten years later, its constitution as the polyene alcohol (XV) was suggested by *P. Karrer* in 1931 (Helv., 1931, 14, 1431) on the basis of ozonisation experiments on vitamin A concentrates which furnished geronic acid and T. Moore's experiments on the conversion of carotene into vitamin A *in vivo*.

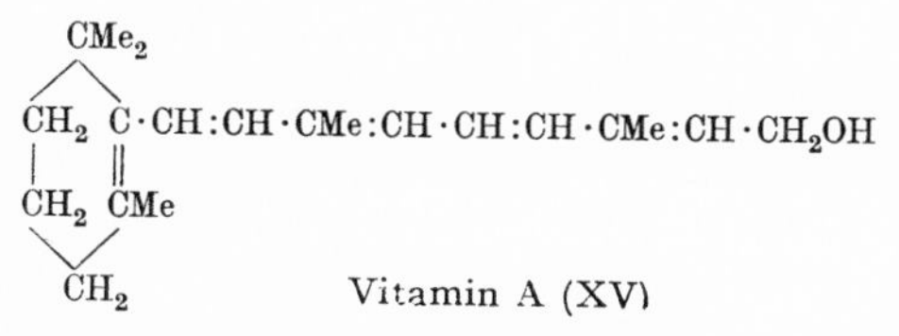

Vitamin A (XV)

Confirmation of this was afforded by the synthesis of perhydrovitamin A from β-ionone which proved identical with the product obtained by catalytic hydrogenation of the natural vitamin (*P. Karrer et al.*, Helv., 1933, 16, 625).

Synthesis of vitamin A and related compounds

In 1937 *R. Kuhn* and *C. J. O. R. Morris* (Ber., **70**, 853) described a rational synthesis of vitamin A alcohol from ethyl β-ionylideneacetate (XVI) obtained from β-ionone by Reformatsky reaction with ethyl bromoacetate. This was converted into its *o*-toluidide (XVII) which gave the chloro-imide (XVIII) on treatment with phosphorus pentachloride in ether, reduced by the chromous chloride method of *von Braun* (Ber., 1934, **67**, 269, 1735) to the *o*-tolil of the "key substance" β-ionylidene-acetaldehyde, from which the latter (XX) was obtained by hydrolysis with oxalic acid. On condensation with β-methylcrotonaldehyde in the presence of piperidine acetate, this furnished vitamin A aldehyde (XXI) which was then reduced to the alcohol (XV) with aluminium *iso*propoxide by the Pondorff method.

$$\text{(ring: }CMe_2, CH_2, CH_2, CH_2, CMe\text{)}\ C\cdot CH{:}CH\cdot CMe{:}CH\cdot CO_2Et \longrightarrow C\cdot CH{:}CH\cdot CMe{:}CH\cdot CO\cdot NH\cdot C_6H_4Me$$

(XVI) (XVII)

$$\longrightarrow C\cdot CH{:}CH\cdot CMe{:}CH\cdot CCl{:}N\cdot C_6H_4Me \xrightarrow{CrCl_2} C\cdot CH{:}CH\cdot CMe{:}CH\cdot CH{:}N\cdot C_6H_4Me$$

(XVIII) (XIX)

$$\longrightarrow C\cdot CH{:}CH\cdot CMe{:}CH\cdot CHO \longrightarrow \text{(ring: }CMe_2, CH_2, CH_2, CH_2, CMe\text{)}\ C\cdot CH{:}CH\cdot CMe{:}CH\cdot CH{:}CH\cdot CMe{:}CH\cdot CHO \longrightarrow (XV)$$

(XX) (XXI)
Vitamin A aldehyde

The material so obtained, although biologically active, was very impure and showed a maximum at 606 mμ instead of at 620 mμ in the antimony trichloride reaction. The vitamin A content calculated on the basis of the "blue value", which would certainly be an overestimate, was only 7·5 %. Considerable doubt was cast on the validity of this work by the later experiments of *P. Karrer* and *A. Ruegger* (Helv., 1940, **23**, 384) which showed that the condensation of β-ionylideneacetaldehyde with β-methyl-crotonaldehyde gives rise to a mixture of polyenes the chief of which gives a blue colour with antimony trichloride showing an absorption maximum at 602 mμ, and by unsuccessful attempts to repeat the synthesis both in Russia (*M. V. Krauze* and *M. Ya. Slobodin,* J. gen. Chem. U.S.S.R., 1940, **10**, 907) and London (*I. M. Heilbron et al.*, J. chem. Soc., 1942, 727). The original claim of Kuhn and Morris has since, however, been substantiated by *J. F. Arens* and *D. A. van Dorp* (Rec. Trav. chim., 1948, **67**, 973) who obtained an aldehyde agreeing in description with the ionylideneacetaldehyde of the former authors by Grignard reaction of β-ionone with ethoxyacetylene to give an acetylenic ether (XXII), partial hydrogenation of this to the ethylenic ether (XXIII) and rearrangement of the last to the unsaturated aldehyde by treatment with dilute acid. On condensation with β-methylcrotonaldehyde this gave a product which on fractional crystallisation of the semicarbazone furnished vitamin A aldehyde semicarbazone.

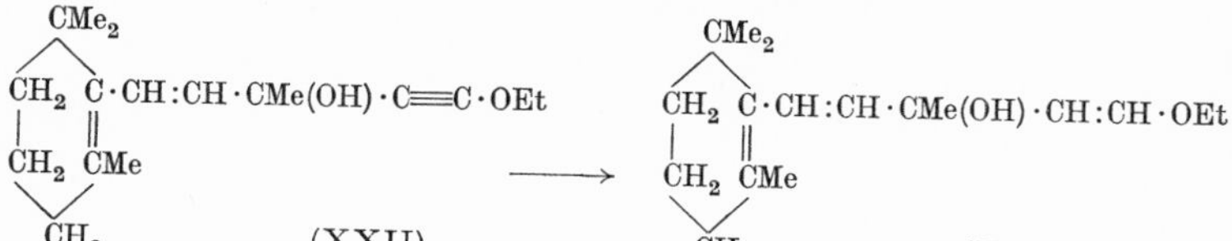

```
     CMe2
    /    \
CH2       C·CH:CH·CMe(OH)·C≡C·OEt
 |        ||
CH2       CMe
    \    /
     CH2                      (XXII)

          ⟶

     CMe2
    /    \
CH2       C·CH:CH·CMe(OH)·CH:CH·OEt
 |        ||
CH2       CMe
    \    /
     CH2                      (XXIII)
```

While searching for new routes to the synthesis of vitamin A, the attention of Sir Ian Heilbron and his collaborators was attracted to a paper by *S. Ishikawa* and *T. Matsuura* (Chem. Ztbl., 1937, 3452) in which was described the preparation of a C_{14} aldehyde from β-ionone and ethyl chloroacetate to which the formula (XXIV) was assigned.

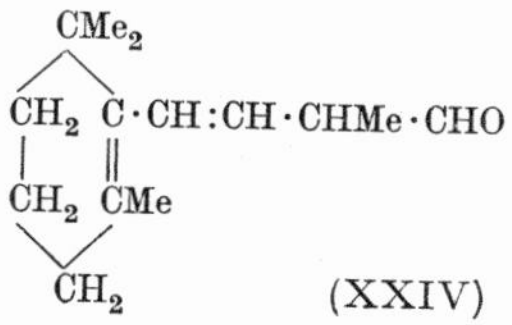

```
     CMe2
    /    \
CH2       C·CH:CH·CHMe·CHO
 |        ||
CH2       CMe
    \    /
     CH2                      (XXIV)
```

Re-examination of the reaction showed that the aldehyde actually has the the constitution (IX) (p. 357) and combination with a ketone Me·CO·CH_2·CH_2OR by way of a molecule of acetylene might be expected to lead to a structure convertible into vitamin A. Pressure of other work during the war prevented the complete realisation of this by *Heilbron et al.*, and the first rational synthesis on these lines was accomplished by *O. Isler* and his collaborators in the Hoffmann-La Roche laboratories in Switzerland. In 1946, these authors described the synthesis of vitamin A methyl ether (XXVII) from the aldehyde (IX) by condensation with 1-methoxy-3-methylpent-2-en-4-yne, catalytic semi-hydrogenation of the resulting acetylenic carbinol (XXV) and conversion of the product (XXVI) into *vitamin A methyl ether* by rearrangement and simultaneous dehydration by treatment with acetic anhydride in the presence of potassium acetate (*O. Isler et al.*, Experientia, 1946, **2**, 31).

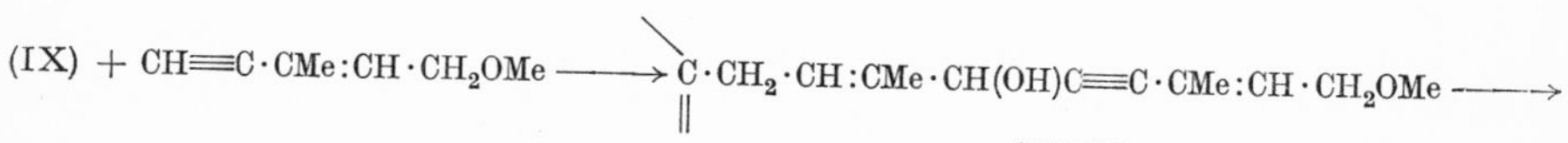

```
                                  \
(IX) + CH≡C·CMe:CH·CH2OMe  ⟶      C·CH2·CH:CMe·CH(OH)C≡C·CMe:CH·CH2OMe  ⟶
                                  ||
                                                (XXV)
```

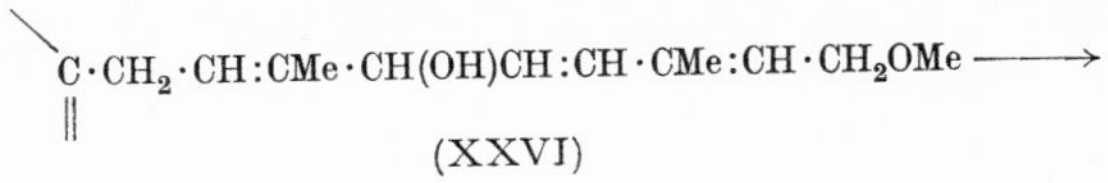

$$\diagdown C\cdot CH_2\cdot CH{:}CMe\cdot CH(OH)CH{:}CH\cdot CMe{:}CH\cdot CH_2OMe \longrightarrow$$

(XXVI)

$$CMe_2 \text{ ring: } CH_2, CH_2, CH_2, C\cdot CH{:}CH\cdot CMe{:}CH\cdot CH{:}CH\cdot CMe{:}CH\cdot CH_2OMe, \; \| \; CMe$$

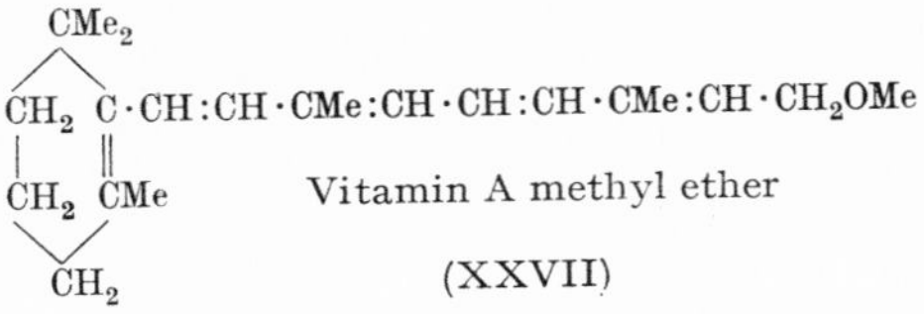

Vitamin A methyl ether

(XXVII)

The ether, which was first obtained as a yellow oil showing an absorption maximum at 325–328 mμ and was reported to possess biological activity "at least as great as that of β-carotene", was later obtained crystalline (Helv., 1949, **32**, 489).

In the following year, *Isler* and his collaborators (Helv., 1947, **30**, 1911) described the actual synthesis of crystalline vitamin A from the aldehyde (IX) by condensation with the di-Grignard complex of 3-methylpentenynol (XXVIII), semi-hydrogenation of the resulting acetylenic carbinol (XXIX), and acetylation of the resulting glycol, followed by rearrangement and simultaneous dehydration of the product (XXX) by heating with toluene in the presence of a trace of iodine, when *vitamin A acetate* was obtained. The vitamin A alcohol obtained by hydrolysis of this was purified by way of the anthraquinone-2-carboxylate, from which the crystalline alcohol was obtained by regeneration.

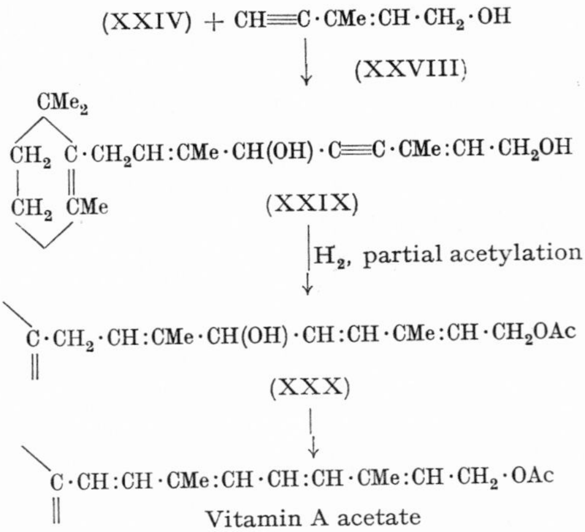

$$(XXIV) + CH{\equiv}C\cdot CMe{:}CH\cdot CH_2\cdot OH$$

$\downarrow$ (XXVIII)

$$CMe_2 \text{ ring: } CH_2, CH_2, C\cdot CH_2CH{:}CMe\cdot CH(OH)\cdot C{\equiv}C\cdot CMe{:}CH\cdot CH_2OH, \; \| \; CMe$$

(XXIX)

$\downarrow$ H_2, partial acetylation

$$\diagdown C\cdot CH_2\cdot CH{:}CMe\cdot CH(OH)\cdot CH{:}CH\cdot CMe{:}CH\cdot CH_2OAc$$

(XXX)

$\downarrow$

$$\diagdown C\cdot CH{:}CH\cdot CMe{:}CH\cdot CH{:}CH\cdot CMe{:}CH\cdot CH_2\cdot OAc$$

Vitamin A acetate

Almost simultaneously with the publication of Isler's synthesis of vitamin A methyl ether, *J. F. Arens* and *D. A. van Dorp* (Rec. Trav. chim., 1946, **65**,

338) announced the synthesis of *vitamin A acid* (XXXIV) by a route contemporaneously explored by both *Sir Ian Heilbron* and his collaborators (J. chem. Soc., 1946, 866) and by *P. Karrer* and his co-workers (Helv., 1946, **29**, 704). The C_{17} acid (XXXI) obtained by condensation of β-ionone with methyl γ-bromocrotonate by the Reformatsky method was converted by treatment with lithium methyl into the C_{18} ketone (XXXII), which was then in turn condensed with ethyl bromoacetate to give the hydroxy-ester (XXXIII), which on dehydration and saponification furnished vitamin A acid (XXXIV).

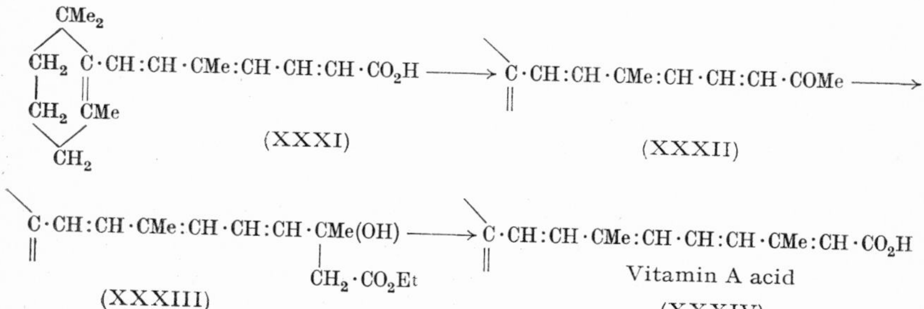
CMe₂
CH₂ C·CH:CH·CMe:CH·CH:CH·CO₂H
CH₂ CMe
CH₂
C·CH:CH·CMe:CH·CH:CH·COMe
C·CH:CH·CMe:CH·CH:CH·CMe(OH)
CH₂·CO₂Et
C·CH:CH·CMe:CH·CH:CH·CMe:CH·CO₂H
Vitamin A acid

(XXXI) (XXXII) (XXXIII) (XXXIV)

The acid when dissolved in vegetable oil had only about one thirteenth of the biological activity of vitamin A, but the sodium salt when buffered to pH 10 was found to have activity comparable with that of the ordinary vitamin.

Vitamin A alcohol was later prepared from the C_{18} ketone (XXXII) by *Arens* and *Van Dorp* (Nature, 1947, **160**, 189) by condensation with ethoxyacetylene to give the acetylenic carbinol (XXXV), which on semi-hydrogenation gave an enol ether (XXXVI) which was converted into vitamin A aldehyde by anionotropic rearrangement under the influence of dilute hydrochloric acid.

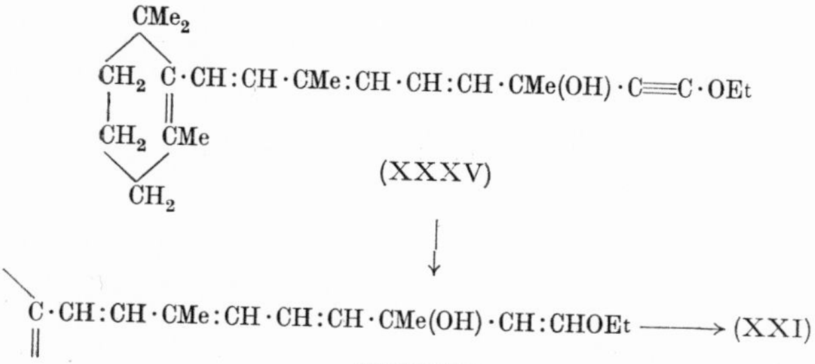
CMe₂
CH₂ C·CH:CH·CMe:CH·CH:CH·CMe(OH)·C≡C·OEt
CH₂ CMe
CH₂
C·CH:CH·CMe:CH·CH:CH·CMe(OH)·CH:CHOEt
(XXI)

(XXXV) (XXXVI)

Reduction by the Pondorff method of the vitamin A aldehyde thus obtained furnished an oil having about 35 % of the biological activity of the crystalline vitamin.

An easier route to vitamin A from the C_{18} ketone was later provided by reduction of esters of vitamin A acid with lithium aluminium hydride which gave a 95% yield of vitamin A alcohol (*O. Schwarzkopf et al.*, Helv., 1949, 32, 443).

All these syntheses commenced with β-ionone, which has certain disadvantages as a starting material, and a novel departure from this route, commencing with the ethynylcyclohexenes, has been pursued by *Heilbron* and his co-workers (J. chem. Soc., 1949, 287) for the synthesis of substances of similar structure to vitamin A, a modification of which has now provided a synthesis of vitamin A from 2-methylcyclohexanone (*J. Attenburrow et al.*, J. chem. Soc., 1952, 1094).

Condensation of ethynylcyclohexene (XXXVII) with crotonylideneacetone (XXXVIII) by the Grignard method gave the tertiary alcohol, (XXXIX) which on shaking with acids underwent anionotropic change yielding the fully conjugated carbinol (XL). On Oppenauer oxidation this gave the ketone (XLI), which on Reformatsky condensation with ethyl bromoacetate, dehydration and saponification gave the acetylenic vitamin A acid analogue (XLII) which was isolated in two forms, the sodium salt of one of which showed weak biological activity of the order of 0·1 % of that of vitamin A.

$$\text{(XXXVII)} \; C_6H_9\cdot C{\equiv}CH + Me\cdot CO[CH{:}CH]_2Me \;\text{(XXXVIII)} \longrightarrow C\cdot C{\equiv}C\cdot Me(OH)\cdot CH{:}CH\cdot CH{:}CHMe \;\text{(XXXIX)} \longrightarrow$$

$$C\cdot C{\equiv}C\cdot CMe{:}CH\cdot CH{:}CHMe(OH) \;\text{(XL)} \longrightarrow C\cdot C{\equiv}C\cdot CMe{:}CH\cdot CH{:}CH\cdot COMe \;\text{(XLI)}$$

$$\longrightarrow C_6H_9\cdot C{\equiv}C\cdot CMe{:}CH\cdot CH{:}CH\cdot CMe{:}CH\cdot CO_2H \;\text{(XLII)}$$

(Ring in XXXVII and XLII: CH_2–CH_2–CH_2–CH_2–$CH{=}C$ cyclohexene.)

Following this, the corresponding analogue of vitamin A alcohol was synthesised by condensation of ethynylcyclohexene with vinylcrotonylideneacetone (XLIII) and conversion of the resulting carbinol (XLIV) into the required polyene alcohol (XLV) by anionotropic rearrangement with dilute acid (*G. W. Cheeseman, Sir Ian Heilbron, E. R. H. Jones* and *B. C. L. Weedon*, J. chem. Soc., 1949, 3120).

(XXXVII) + Me·CO·CH:CH·CMe:CH·CH:CH_2 (XLIII) ⟶

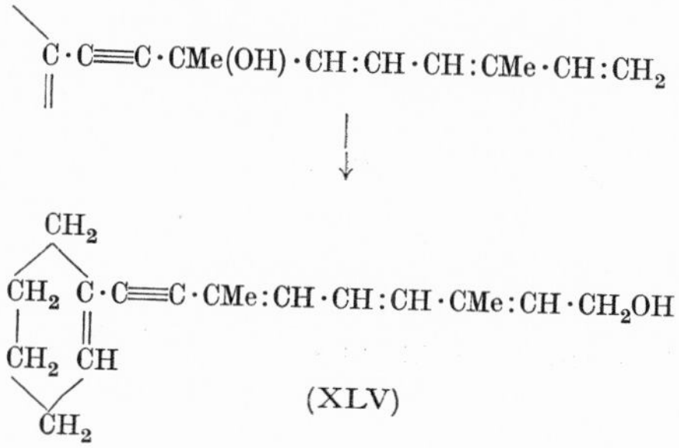

(XLIV)

(XLV)

The alcohol (XLV) also showed biological activity of the order of about 0·1 % of that of vitamin A.

A similar procedure with 2:2:6-trimethylethynylcyclohexene would be expected to furnish an acetylene derivative (XLVI) whose partial hydrogenation would provide a synthesis of vitamin A.

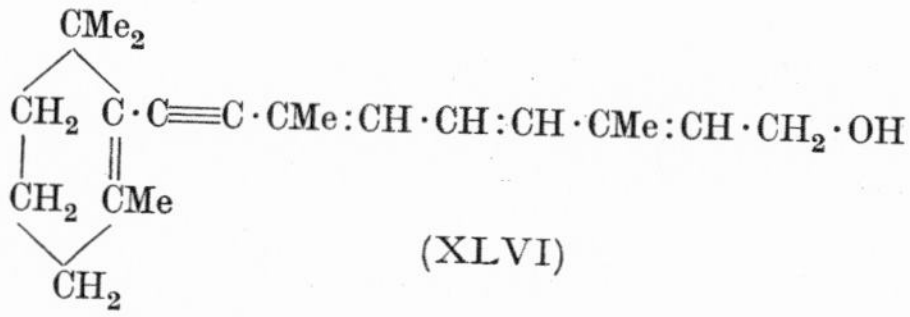

(XLVI)

The synthesis of the dehydrovitamin (XLVI) was accomplished on these lines by J. Attenburrow and his co-workers but considerable difficulty was encountered in attempts to convert this into vitamin A by selective semi-hydrogenation of the triple bond. The synthesis of vitamin A from 2:2:6-trimethylcyclohexanone was, however, accomplished by a modification of the original route. 1-Ethynyl-2:2:6-trimethylcyclohexanol (XLVII), obtained from the trimethylcyclohexanone and sodium acetylide, was condensed with vinylcrotonylideneacetone and the product (XLVIII) converted by rearrangement into the C_{20} glycol (IL). On treatment with lithium aluminium hydride, the triple bond in the latter underwent selective semi-hydrogenation yielding the diol (L), which on partial acetylation and dehydration with *p*-toluenesulphonic acid in toluene furnished vitamin A acetate.

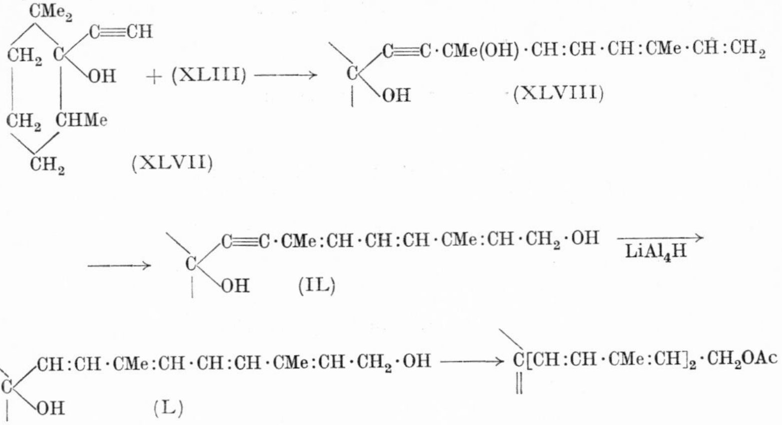

$$CMe_2 \ / \ \backslash \ CH_2 \ C(C{\equiv}CH)(OH) \ | \ | \ CH_2 \ CHMe \ \backslash / \ CH_2 \quad (XLVII) \quad + (XLIII) \longrightarrow \ \gt C(OH) \cdot C{\equiv}C \cdot CMe(OH) \cdot CH{:}CH \cdot CH{:}CMe \cdot CH{:}CH_2 \quad (XLVIII)$$

$$\longrightarrow \ \gt C(OH) \cdot C{\equiv}C \cdot CMe{:}CH \cdot CH{:}CH \cdot CMe{:}CH \cdot CH_2 \cdot OH \quad (IL) \xrightarrow{LiAl_4H}$$

$$\gt C(OH) \cdot CH{:}CH \cdot CMe{:}CH \cdot CH{:}CH \cdot CMe{:}CH \cdot CH_2 \cdot OH \quad (L) \longrightarrow \ \gt C{=}C[CH{:}CH \cdot CMe{:}CH]_2 \cdot CH_2OAc$$

Physical properties of vitamin A. — The specimen of crystalline vitamin A alcohol obtained by *J. G. Baxter* and *C. D. Robeson* (J. Amer. chem. Soc., 1942, **64**, 2411) and assumed to possess the all-*trans* configuration crystallised in yellow prisms, m.p. 63–64° and had an $\varepsilon^{1\%}_{1cm}$ value of 1750 at 325 mμ.

Neovitamin A. — A biologically active isomer of ordinary vitamin A which occurs in amount up to 35 % of the total vitamin A content in fish liver oils and is separated from the latter by "molecular" distillation, was isolated by *C. D. Robeson* and *J. G. Baxter* (*ibid.*, 1947, **69**, 136) in the form of needles, m.p. 58–60°. This isomer, which has its ultra-violet maximum slightly displaced towards the region of longer wave length (λ_{max} at 328 mμ with $\varepsilon^{1\%}_{1cm}$ 1645) is regarded as having a *cis*-configuration (probably 5-mono-*cis*).

Anhydrovitamin A (*"cyclised" vitamin A*). A most usefully characteristic reaction of vitamin A is its facile conversion under the action of alcoholic hydrochloric acid into an anhydro derivative showing narrow absorption bands at 392, 370, and 351 mμ in the ultra-violet with retention of maximum at 620 mμ in the antimony trichloride reaction, which was first thought to be a cyclised derivative (*I. M. Heilbron et al.*, Biochem. J., 1932, **26**, 1194). The absence of the hydroxyl group required by the cyclised formula originally suggested by Heilbron and his collaborators was shown by Zerewitinoff determination on concentrates of the substance obtained by chromatography (*E. M. Shantz et al.*, J. Amer. chem. Soc., 1943, **65**, 901; *E. G. E. Hawkins* and *R. F. Hunter*, Biochem. J., 1944, **38**, 34) and quantitative catalytic hydrogenation of a crystalline specimen gave figures corresponding with the presence of 5.9 and 5.8 double bonds (*R. F. Hunter*, unpublished results). The most probable of the three formulae suggested by Shantz *et al.*, for anhydrovitamin A is the methylene structure (LI), the formation of which by dehydration from vitamin A alcohol involves movement of the whole conjugated system (cf. *P. Meunier et al.*, Compt. rend., 1943, **216**, 907).

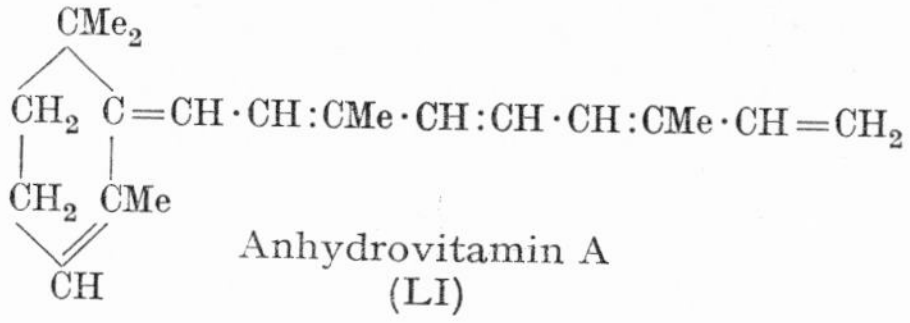

$$
\begin{array}{l}
\quad CMe_2 \\
\diagup \quad \diagdown \\
CH_2 \;\; C{=}CH\cdot CH{:}CMe\cdot CH{:}CH\cdot CH{:}CMe\cdot CH{=}CH_2 \\
| \qquad | \\
CH_2 \;\; CMe \\
\diagdown \quad /\!\!/ \\
\quad CH
\end{array}
$$

Anhydrovitamin A
(LI)

The purest specimen of anhydrovitamin A obtained by Hawkins and Hunter crystallised in orange prisms, m.p. 77–78°, $\varepsilon^{1\%}_{1cm}$ 3760 at 372 mμ.

Vitamin A_2. It was early observed that certain vitamin A concentrates showed an absorption band at 693 mμ in addition to the usual maximum at 620 mμ in the antimony trichloride reaction, and in 1937 *E. Lederer* and *V. A. Rozanova* (Biokhimiya, 1937, 6, 293) in examining the liver oils of Russian fresh water fish observed instances in which the main band was at 693 mμ with a subsidiary maximum at 620 mμ. The ultra-violet absorption spectrum of this second form of vitamin A, designated vitamin A_2, which is characterised by a maximum at 350 mμ, suggested that it had a structure similar to the ordinary vitamin but possessing an additional conjugated double bond. On this basis, together with ozonisation experiments on vitamin concentrates from halibut liver oil and fresh water liver oil which gave practically the same quantities of geronic acid, and a biological test which indicated that vitamin A_2 possessed growth-promoting activity in rats, *A. E. Gillam, I. M. Heilbron et al.* (Biochem. J., 1938, **32**, 450) suggested it was a homologue of vitamin A having the formula (LII).

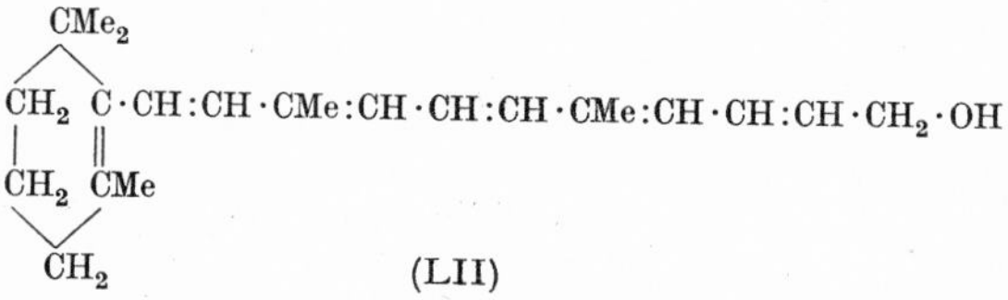

$$
\begin{array}{l}
\quad CMe_2 \\
\diagup \quad \diagdown \\
CH_2 \;\; C\cdot CH{:}CH\cdot CMe{:}CH\cdot CH{:}CH\cdot CMe{:}CH\cdot CH{:}CH\cdot CH_2\cdot OH \\
| \qquad \| \\
CH_2 \;\; CMe \\
\diagdown \quad \diagup \\
\quad CH_2
\end{array}
$$

(LII)

A. L. Gray and *J. D. Cawley* (J. biol. Chem., 1940, **134**, 397) on the basis of experiments on the "molecular" distillation of mixtures of vitamin A and vitamin A_2 came to the conclusion, however, that the vitamin A_2 molecule contains the same number of carbon atoms as vitamin A. About this time, *N. D. Embree* (*ibid.*, 1940, **132**, 619) also observed that vitamin A_2 like vitamin A gave, on treatment with alcoholic hydrochloric acid, an anhydro derivative which showed ultra-violet absorption maxima identical with those of anhydrovitamin A while retaining the absorption maximum at 693 mμ in the antimony trichloride reaction. Following this, *P. Karrer et al.* (Helv., 1941, **24**, 161E) drew attention to the smaller shift in ultra-violet absorption maximum than might be anticipated for the presence of an additional conjugated double bond in the vitamin A structure and suggested the open-chain formula (LIII) for vitamin A_2. Additional evidence against the original formula (LII) was provided by the formation during the oxidation of β-carotene by hydrogen peroxide of a higher homologue of vitamin A aldehyde, presumably β-apo-5-carotenal (*R. F. Hunter* and *N. E. Williams*, J. chem. Soc., 1945, 554), which gave an alcohol furnishing an anhydro derivative with ultra-violet absorption maxima very close to those of the derivative of axerophthylidene*iso*propyl alcohol (*E. G. E. Hawkins* and *R. F. Hunter*, Biochem. J., 1944, **38**, 34).

```
   CMe2
  //
CH   CH·CH:CH·CMe:CH·CH:CH·CMe:CH·CH2OH
|    ||
CH2  CMe
  \  /
   CH2                (LIII)
```

R. A. Morton (Nature, 1947, **159**, 744) suggested that vitamin A_2 aldehyde (retinene$_2$) is identical with the C_{20} aldehyde obtained by oxidation of vitamin A alcohol with aluminium *tert.*-butoxide in the presence of diethyl ketone (*A. Haworth, I. M. Heilbron et al.*, J. chem. Soc. 1939, **128**; *E. G. A. Hawkins* and *R. F. Hunter, loc. cit.*) for which the formula (LIV) containing an additional conjugated double bond in the β-ionone ring was suggested.

```
    CMe2
   /    \
CH2   C·CH:CH·CMe:CH·CH:CH·CMe:CH·CHO
|     ||
CH    CMe
  \\  /
   CH               (LIV)
```

In 1950, *P. Karrer* and *P. Sneider* (Helv., 1950, **33**, 38) abandoned the open-chain formula (LIII) and submitted evidence that vitamin A_2 has the formula $C_{20}H_{28}O$. Finally, *E. R. H. Jones* and his collaborators announced a total synthesis of vitamin A_2 which established its structure as the dehydrovitamin (LVI) (Chem. and Ind., 1951, **70**, 49; J. chem. Soc., 1952, 2657).

```
    CMe2                                  CMe2
   /    \                                /    \
CH2   C[CH:CH·CMe:CH]2CO2H            CH2   C[CH:CH·CMe:CH]2CH2OH
|     ||                              |     ||
CH    CMe                             CH    CMe
  \\  /                                 \\  /        Vitamin A2
   CH          (LV)                      CH            (LVI)
```

Treatment of the methyl ester of vitamin A acid with N-bromosuccinimide gave a 3-bromo-derivative readily debrominated by N-phenylmorpholine to the methyl ester of vitamin A_2 acid (LV) which on saponification, methylation by diazomethane and reduction of the pure methyl ester by lithium aluminium hydride gave vitamin A_2 (LVI).

(d) Conversion of carotenes into vitamin A and the effect of stereochemical configuration on biological activity

Although the conversion of β-carotene into vitamin A which occurs *in vivo* is represented in most standard works as a hydrolytic fission of the central double bond with production of two molecules of vitamin A alcohol according to the equation

$$C_{40}H_{56} + 2\,H_2O = 2\,C_{20}H_{29}\cdot OH$$

this picture seems quite erroneous. Apart from the fact that one is unable to recall any example of hydrolytic fission of this type in organic chemical literature, numerous *ad hoc* experiments on the hydrolysis of colloidal solutions of β-carotene with water, aqueous organic solvents in the presence of mild alkali and various emulsifying agents such as lecithin, sodium cholate, and polyglycerol esters, under pressure, have failed to furnish any evidence of the formation of vitamin A alcohol (Devine and Hunter, unpublished results). From the work of *R. A. Morton* and his collaborators on rhodopsin (Nature, 1948, **161**, 424), it appears much more probable that the biological conversion occurs by way of oxidative fission of β-carotene to vitamin A aldehyde (XXI) and subsequent reduction of the latter to vitamin A alcohol (XV), analogous to the chemical conversion first accomplished by Hunter and Williams. Very small yields (ca. 1 %) of vitamin A aldehyde were obtained by oxidative fission of β-carotene by hydrogen peroxide in glacial acetic acid under carefully controlled conditions and the aldehyde was reduced to vitamin A alcohol by the Pondorff method with aluminium *iso*propoxide (*R. F. Hunter* and *N. E. Williams*, J. chem. Soc., 1945, 554).

```
              CMe2
             /    \
            CH2   C·CH:CH·CMe:CH·CH:CH·CMe:CH·CHO  ——→  C[CH:CH·CMe:CH]2·CH2·OH
(II) ——→    |     ||                                    ||
            CH2   CMe
             \    /
              CH2
                          (XXI)                                 (XV)
```

A biological test of a solution in arachis oil of the vitamin A thus obtained showed growth-promoting activity in rats (ten litter-mate growth comparisons) of the order indicated by spectroscopic assay. Much more satisfactory chemical conversion has been reported by *N. L. Wendler et al.*, (J. Amer. chem. Soc., 1950, **72**, 234) who claim a 22 % yield of vitamin A from β-carotene by using hydrogen peroxide-osmium tetroxide and subsequent reduction of the vitamin A aldehyde with lithium aluminium hydride.

It had been generally assumed that the liver was the site of the conversion of carotene into vitamin A in the animal body. The storage of vitamin A in this organ and the fact that there is a decrease in vitamin A formation in the body when it is poisoned or damaged lent support to this view. Experiments carried out by Morton and his associates at Liverpool University indicated, however, that conversion occurs in the intestinal wall and it has furthermore been shown by *R. F. Kraus* and *H. B. Pierse* (Arch. Biochem., 1948, **19,** 145) that carotene can be converted into vitamin A in rats in which the liver has been isolated by a ligature on the portal vein. It therefore appears probable that the intestinal wall is the main site of conversion in mammals.

R. Kuhn and *H. Brockmann* (Ber., 1931, **64,** 1859) first reported similar growth responses for α- and β-carotenes in rats but later found that 2.5 γ of β-carotene produced the same growth effect as 5 γ of α-carotene and concluded that the α-isomer possesses only half the biological activity of β-carotene (Klin. Wochschr. 1933, **12,** 972). A careful biological assay of the very pure specimens of α- and β-carotene which were isolated by Hunter and Scott from "Sherbro" palm oil, using a large number of animals, has since provided striking confirmation of the 1:2-ratio for the potencies of α- and β-carotene (*H. Wilkinson,* Biochem. J., 1941, **35,** 824). This and the similar "half activity" of other carotenoids containing a single unsubstituted β-ionone ring is in agreement with the view that conversion of provitamin A active carotenoids to vitamin A occurs by fission of the central double bond of the conjugated system and is consistent with the fact that it is the β-ionone ring which is preferentially attacked in the oxidation of α-carotene.

As might be anticipated, stereochemical configuration plays an important role in the biological activity of the carotenoids. The most active carotenoid is ordinary crystalline β-carotene, which possesses the all-*trans* configuration. Change of this to the 3-mono-*cis* isomer, neo-β-carotene U, however, causes a fall to 38 % of the growth promoting activity in rats (*H. J. Deuel et al.,* Arch. Biochem., 1944, **5,** 107) and change from the all-*trans* configuration of ordinary α-carotene to the *cis* isomer, neo-α-carotene U results in a loss of more than two thirds of the biological activity (*Deuel et al., ibid.,* 1945, **6,** 157).

(e) Biogenesis of the carotenoids

It was early suggested by *P. Karrer* and his collaborators (Helv., 1930, **13,** 1084) that the formation of lycopene in fruits might be pictured as a benzoin condensation of two molecules of the aldehyde corresponding to phytol, followed by dehydrogenation of the intermediate complex:

```
CHMe2                                                     CHMe2
 /                                                            \
CH2 CH[CH:CH·CMe:CH]2CH:CH[CH:CMe·CH:CH]2CH  CH2
 |   ||                                                   ||    |
CH2 CMe                                                 CMe CH2
  \ /                                                       \ /
  CH2                       (LVII)                         CH2
```

Support is given to this by the fact that carotenoids are mostly found in the green parts of plants where they are always associated with chlorophyll and furthermore, the formation of the carotenoid appears to follow the gradual disappearance of chlorophyll.

It was later suggested by Hunter and Scott that lycopene, β-carotene, and γ-carotene might be formed simultaneously from an intermediate complex such as (LVII) and that the appearance of γ-carotene in palm oil would correspond to the simultaneous operation of both dehydrogenation processes which might account for the small amount of this isomer present. The formation of α-carotene was pictured as an asymmetric isomerisation of β-carotene by way of a three-carbon prototropic change of the type analogous to the racemization of azomethine derivatives observed by *C. K. Ingold* and his collaborators (J. chem. Soc., 1935, 1778). On the basis of this, the proportion of α- to β-carotene might be expected to vary with the degree of ripeness of the fruit. In an investigation in which samples of oil prepared from specially selected bunches of unripe and ripe palm fruit from a West African plantation were examined, it was found, however, that while the proportion of α- to β-carotene varied from tree to tree, the proportion of isomers obtained from unripe and ripe fruit from the same tree remained constant (*R. F. Hunter* and *A. D. Scott*, Biochem. J., 1944, **38**, 211).

The most significant contribution to the problem of biogenesis of the carotenoids is the isolation by *L. Zechmeister* and *A. Sandoval* of the colourless carotenoid *phytofluene* which occurs in vegetable tissues in association with carotenoid pigments (Arch. Biochem., 1945, **8**, 425). This substance, which is adsorbed on the chromatogram just below α-carotene, shows a greenish grey fluorescence in ultra-violet light and is characterised by an ultra-violet absorption spectrum with sharp maxima (331, 348, and 367 mμ in hexane) closely similar to that of "*iso*anhydrovitamin A" (330, 349, and 370 mμ) (*N. D. Embree* and *A. M. Shantz*, J. Amer. chem. Soc., 1943, **65**, 906). From the investigation of purified samples obtained by Zechmeister and Sandoval from commercial tomato paste, it appears reasonably certain that phytofluene is a polyene, $C_{40}H_{64}$, containing seven double bonds, of which five are conjugated (*ibid.*, 1946, **68**, 197).

The occurrence of phytofluene with carotenoids in various plants suggests that it is an intermediate product in the biogenesis of the latter. This would imply the formation, in the first instance, of a short unstabilised conjugated chain, followed by further dehydrogenation leading to the carotenoid pigment. The observation that oxygen is necessary during carotenoid formation in the final stages of ripening of tomatoes and red peppers agrees with such a picture. That this, if correct, is not the only mechanism of carotenoid biogenesis is indicated by the absence of phytofluene in spinach and grass, which have a high chlorophyll content. There is the possibility (as has already been pointed out by Zechmeister and Sandoval) that phytofluene and the carotenoid pigments are derived from a common precursor.

The occurrence of phytofluene in association with β- and γ-carotene has been observed in the yeast *Rhodotorula rubra* (*J. Bonner et al.*, Arch. Biochem., 1946, **10**, 113) and its presence in small amounts has also been observed in the yolks of fresh eggs (*A. Sandoval et al.*, *ibid.*, 1946, **11**, 373).

(*f*) *Lycopenes*

Lycopene. The red colouring matter of the tomato was first isolated as a dark red crystalline pigment from *Tamus communis* L. by *Hartsen* in 1873 (Compt.

rend., **76**, 385). Two years later, *Millardet* (Bull. Soc. Sci. Nancy, 1875, **1**, 21) obtained an impure form of lycopene from tomatoes and twenty eight years later *C. A. Schunck* (Proc. roy. Soc., 1903, **72**, 165) showed that the pigment has an absorption spectrum different from that of carotene. Following this *R. Willstätter* and *H. H. Escher* (*loc. cit.*) showed that lycopene has the formula $C_{40}H_{56}$ and is isomeric with carotene. This carotenoid is also present in various fruits (Karrer and Jucker, *op. cit.*, p. 113), and in different varieties of palm oil (*R. F. Hunter* and *A. D. Scott, loc. cit.*; *R. F. Hunter et al.*, Biochem. J., 1944, **38**, 209; *R. F. Hunter* and *R. M. Krakenberger, loc. cit.*) but its contribution to the colour of the latter is relatively small.

The investigations which established the constitution of lycopene have already been dealt with in the section on β-carotene. Confirmation of the accepted formula (I, p. 355) has since been afforded by the rational synthesis by *P. Karrer, C. H. Eugster* and *E. Tobler* (Helv., 1950, **33**, 1349) from the open-chain acetylene derivative (LVIII).

CMe_2
//
$CH \quad CH \cdot CH{:}CH \cdot CMe(OH) \cdot CH_2 \cdot C{\equiv}CH$
| ||
$CH_2 \quad CMe$
\ /
CH_2 (LVIII)

Lycopene, which is considered to have the all-*trans* configuration, crystallises from carbon disulphide and ethanol in long red needles and from petroleum ether in hair-like needles and occasionally, in dark red violet prisms. In contrast to the carotenes, the crystals of lycopene show little metallic lustre. The melting point is reported by *P. Karrer* and *R. Widmer* (Helv., 1928, **11**, 751) as 173° (uncorr.) and as 175° (corr.) by *L. Zechmeister* and *P. Tuzson* (Ber., 1930, **63**, 2881). Spectroscopic properties:

Solvent:	*Absorption maxima:*		
Carbon disulphide	548	507·5	477 mμ
Chloroform	517	480	453
Benzene	522	487	455
Petroleum ether	506	475·5	447

On heating in solution, or on treatment with iodine, lycopene affords a number of labile stereoisomers which have been spectroscopically characterised by *L. Zechmeister et al.* (J. Amer. chem. Soc., 1943, **65**, 1940). *Neolycopene A*, the isomer which is present in substantial quantities in the equilibrium mixture and is mainly responsible for the *cis* peak effect, appears to be 6-*cis*-lycopene. "Neolycopene" has been observed in small amounts in the unsaponifiable matter of several varieties of palm oil but probably arises from the saponification process, or in the preparation of the oil fro them palm fruit.

Prolycopene, which was first isolated from the tangerine tomato (*A. L. Le Rosen* and *L. Zechmeister*, J. Amer. chem. Soc., 1942, **64**, 1075) has been found in several other plants, including *Pyrocantha angustifolia* (*L. Zechmeister* and *W. A.*

Schroeder, J. biol. Chem., 1942, **144**, 315) and *Evonymus fortunei* (*L. Zechmeister* and *R. B. Escue*, *ibid.*, p. 321). This naturally occurring stereoisomer of lycopene shows a difference in absorption maxima in the visible region of 36 to 47 mμ from the all-*trans* pigment and probably contains six *cis* double bonds. It crystallises from petroleum ether or ethanol in plates, m.p. 111° and shows absorption maxima at 500·5 and 469·5 mμ in carbon disulphide, at 485 and 455·5 mμ in benzene, and at 470 and 443·5 mμ in petroleum ether.

Amongst the well defined oxidation products of lycopene, mention may be made of *apo-2-lycopenal* (formerly called *lycopenal*), m.p. 147°,

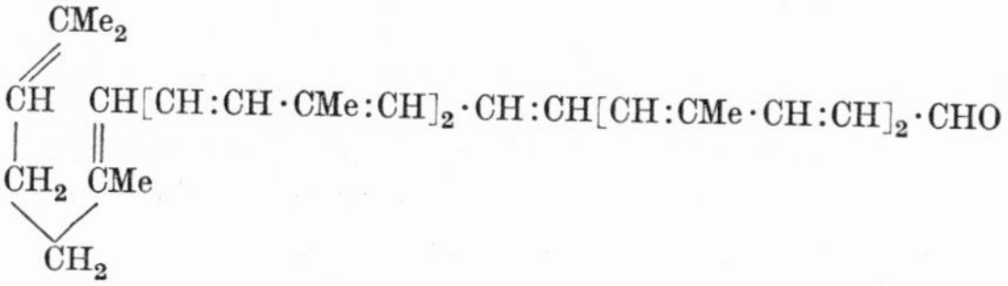

$$\begin{array}{l} CMe_2 \\ /\!\!/ \\ CH\quad CH[CH{:}CH\cdot CMe{:}CH]_2\cdot CH{:}CH[CH{:}CMe\cdot CH{:}CH]_2\cdot CHO \\ |\qquad \| \\ CH_2\ CMe \\ \diagdown\ \diagup \\ CH_2 \end{array}$$

obtained by chromic acid oxidation of lycopene (*R. Kuhn* and *C. Grundmann*, Ber., 1932, **65**, 900); *apo-3-lycopenal*, m.p. 138°,

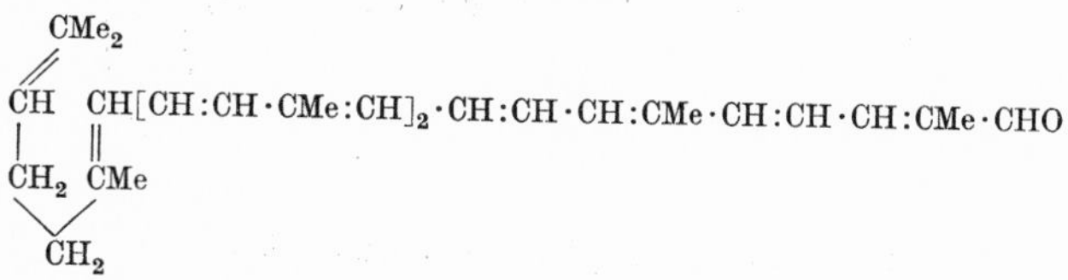

$$\begin{array}{l} CMe_2 \\ /\!\!/ \\ CH\quad CH[CH{:}CH\cdot CMe{:}CH]_2\cdot CH{:}CH\cdot CH{:}CMe\cdot CH{:}CH\cdot CH{:}CMe\cdot CHO \\ |\qquad \| \\ CH_2\ CMe \\ \diagdown\ \diagup \\ CH_2 \end{array}$$

obtained by mild oxidation of lycopene with potassium permanganate (*P. Karrer* and *W. Jaffé*, Helv., 1939, **22**, 69); and *bixindialdehyde*, m.p. 220° (corr.),

$$OHC\cdot[CH{:}CH\cdot CMe{:}CH]_2\cdot CH{:}CH[CH{:}CMe\cdot CH{:}CH_2]_2\cdot CHO$$

which is obtained by oxidation of both lycopene and lycopenal with chromic acid (*Kuhn* and *Grundmann*, Ber., 1932, **65**, 1882; *P. Karrer* and *W. Jaffé*, *loc. cit.*).

Lycopenal, apo-3-lycopenal, and bixindialdehyde show the following absorption maxima in carbon disulphide and in petrol:

	Carbon disulphide			*Petrol*		
Lycopenal	569	528·5	493·5 mμ	525·5	490·5	455·5 mμ
Apo-3-lycopenal	545	508	ca. 478	502	473	
Bixindialdehyde	539·5	502	467·5	502	468	437·5

3. Carotenoids containing hydroxyl groups; xanthophylls

The name "xanthophyll" was first given to the yellow pigment of autumn leaves by Berzelius more than a century ago. The crystalline "xanthophyll" isolated by *Willstätter* and *Mieg* in 1907 from green leaves (Ann., 355, 1) was, however, a mixture of components, the principal of which was the pigment lutein found in egg yolk (*R. Kuhn, A. Winterstein* and *E. Lederer*, Z. physiol. Chem., 1931, **197**, 141).

Lutein. With the exception of carotene, with which it is found, together with chlorophyll, in the green parts of all plants, this is the most abundant carotenoid in nature. It also occurs frequently in the form of its esters, such as helenien, the dipalmitate, in red and yellow blossoms. The presence of lutein in small amounts has also been observed in a palm oil from a West African plantation and in the oil obtained from the *Abepa* variety of palm fruit of the Sese district of the Gold Coast (*R. F. Hunter* and *R. M. Krakenberger*, Biochem. J., 1946, **40**, 492).

The constitution of lutein as the dihydroxy-α-carotene (LIX) was largely established by the researches of *P. Karrer* and his collaborators (Helv., 1930, **13**, 268, 1084; 1941, **14**, 614, 843, and later).

```
          CMe2                                                              CMe2
         /    \                                                            /    \
       CH2   C(CH:CH·CMe:CH)2·CH:CH(CH:CMe·CH:CH)2CH   CH2
        |     ||                                                         |      |
  HO·CH     CMe                                                   CMe  CH·OH
         \    /                                                            \\    /
          CH2                       Lutein (LIX)                             CH
```

The presence of the two hydroxyl groups was established by Zerewitinoff determination and the number of side-chain methyl groups by chromic acid and permanganate oxidations.

As might be anticipated lutein, having the same chromophoric system as α-carotene, shows an identical absorption spectrum in the visible region and is optically active. It differs from α-carotene, however, in giving a maximum at 620 mμ in the antimony trichloride reaction. The introduction of hydroxyl into the β-ionone ring results in complete loss of provitamin A activity.

Further confirmation of the structure (LIX) for lutein was afforded by the isolation of *α-citraurin*

```
          CMe2
         /    \
       CH2    C·CH:CH·CMe:CH·CH:CH·CMe:CH·CH:CH·CH:CMe·CH:CH·CH:CMe·CHO
        |     |
  HO·CH     CMe
         \   //
          CH
```

by *P. Karrer et al.* (Helv., 1938, **21**, 445) from careful oxidation of the former with potassium permanganate.

Lutein has m.p. 193° (corr.); $[\alpha]^{20}_{Cd}$ + 145° (ethyl acetate), and + 160° (chloroform). Spectroscopic properties:

Solvent:	*Absorption maxima:*		
Carbon disulphide	508	475	445 mμ
Chloroform	487	456	428
Ethanol	476	446·5	420
Petrol	477·5	447·5	420

Zeaxanthin. The corresponding dihydroxy derivative of β-carotene, the constitution (LX) of which was established by Karrer and his collaborators on lines similar to the investigations on lutein, occurs in leaves and fruits but is most readily isolated from maize (*P. Karrer et al.*, Helv., 1930, **13**, 268; *R. Kuhn et al.*, Ber., 1930, **63**, 1489).

```
          CMe2                                                          CMe2
         /    \                                                        /    \
       CH2   C(CH:CH·CMe:CH)2CH:CH(CH:CMe·CH:CH)2C    CH2
        |       ||                                                      ||      |
HO·CH   CMe                                                     CMe  CH·OH
         \    /                                                         \    /
          CH2                Zeaxanthin (LX)                      CH2
```

Zeaxanthin occurs also in the form of its *dipalmitic ester, physalien,* in *Physalis alkekengi* and *Physalis franchetti* (*R. Kuhn* and *W. Wiegand,* Helv., 1929, **12**, 499) and in numerous other plants (*P. Karrer* and *H. Wehrli,* Helv., 1930, **13**, 1104; *A. Winterstein* and *U. Ehrenberg,* Z. physiol. Chem., 1932, **207**, 26).

Further confirmation of the constitution of zeaxanthin was afforded by its partial oxidative degradation by potassium permanganate to *β-citraurin*

```
          CMe2
         /    \
       CH2   C(CH:CH·CMe:CH)2·CH:CH·CH:CMe·CH:CH·CH:CMe·CHO
        |       ||
HO·CH   CMe
         \    /
          CH2
```

a carotenoid originally isolated from orange peel by *L. Zechmeister* and *P. Tuzson* (Ber., 1936, **69**, 1878; 1937, **70**, 1966) whose close relationship to β-apo-2-carotenal was established by *Karrer* and *Solmssen* (Helv., 1937, **20**, 682).

Like lutein, zeaxanthin is devoid of provitamin-A-activity.

The following physical properties are reported for zeaxanthin: m.p. 205° (uncorr.) and 215·5° (corr.). Spectroscopic properties:

Solvent:	*Absorption maxima:*		
Carbon disulphide	517	482	450 mμ
Chloroform	495	462	429
Ethanol	483	451	423·5
Petrol	483·5	451·5	423

Lutein and zeaxanthin are thermolabile in solution and give complex chromatograms ("Leaf Xanthophylls", Carnegie Institute of Washington Publication No. 490, 1938). The isomerisation of these carotenoids formed the subject of subsequent study by *Zechmeister* and his collaborators (Ber., 1939, **72**, 1340, and later), who found that whilst the *neo*-isomers showed displacement of absorption maxima towards the region of shorter wave length, they were, in contrast to hydrocarbon carotenoids, adsorbed on the chromatogram above the parent pigments. The two main isomers of lutein, neolutein A and neolutein B, have almost identical visual spectra (501 and 468 mμ and at 502 and 470 mμ in carbon disulphide) and the former is regarded as probably having the 6- or 5-mono-*cis* configuration. Neolutein has been observed in small amount in the unsaponifiable matter of a number of palm oils. Zeaxanthin gives rise to two main isomers, neozeaxanthin A and neozeaxanthin B, having identical spectra in the visual region (abs. maxima at 508 and 475·5 mμ in carbon disulphide), which are distinghuished by having different *cis* peaks. The former is thought to be 6-mono-*cis*-zeaxanthin and the latter, the 5-mono-*cis*-isomeride.

Flavoxanthin, the yellow pigment of the buttercup and the dandelion, $C_{40}H_{56}O_3$, which was first thought to contain three hydroxyl groups (*Kuhn* and *Brockmann*, Z. physiol. Chem., 1932, **213**, 192) has been shown to be the furanoid derivative of lutein (LXI) by its partial synthesis from the diacetate of lutein by way of the epoxide obtained from this and monoperphthalic acid and subsequent treatment with very dilute hydrochloric acid (*P. Karrer* and *E. Jucker*, Helv., 1945, **28**, 300).

```
        CMe2
       /    \
    CH2  C=====CH                                                          CMe2
     |    |     |                                                         /    \
HO·CH    C     CH·CMe:CH·CH:CH·CMe:CH·CH:CH[CH:CMe·CH:CH]2CH   CH2
     \   / | \  /                                                      |      |
      CH2  |  O                                                      CMe  CH·OH
          Me                                                           \    /
                                                                         CH
```

Flavoxanthin (LXI)

Flavoxanthin crystallises from methanol in lustrous golden yellow prisms, m.p. 184° (corr. evacuated capillary). It is optically active, $[\alpha]_D^{20}$ + 190° (benzene), and shows the following absorption maxima: 479 and 499 mμ in carbon disulphide, 459 and 430 mμ in chloroform, and 448 and 421 mμ in ethanol.

Violaxanthin, the pigment of yellow panzies, $C_{40}H_{56}O_4$. first isolated by *Kuhn* and *Winterstein* (Ber., 1931, **64**, 326) and later investigated by *Karrer et al.* (Helv., 1931, **14**, 1044; 1933, **16**, 977; 1936, **19**, 1024; 1944, **27**, 1684) has been shown to be the diepoxide of zeaxanthin (LXII).

```
        CMe2                                                      CMe2
       /    \                                                    /    \
    CH2    C[CH:CH·CMe:CH]2CH:CH[CH:CMe·CH:CH]2C      CH2
     |     |\                                          /|       |
     |     | O                                        O |       |
     |     |/                                          \|       |
HO·CH    CMe                                          CMe   CH·OH
      \  /                                                \    /
       CH2                                                  CH2
```

Violaxanthin (LXII)

Violaxanthin crystallises from methanol in yellow-orange prisms, m.p. 200°

and shows the following absorption maxima: 501, 470, and 440 mμ in carbon disulphide, 482, 451·5 and 424 mμ in chloroform, and 471·5, 442·5 and 417·5 mμ in ethanol.

Lycophyll, which was isolated from the berries of *Solanum dulcamara* by *Zechmeister* and *von Cholnoky* (Ber., 1936, **69,** 422) is probably the dihydroxy-lycopene analogue (LXIII) of lutein and zeaxanthin.

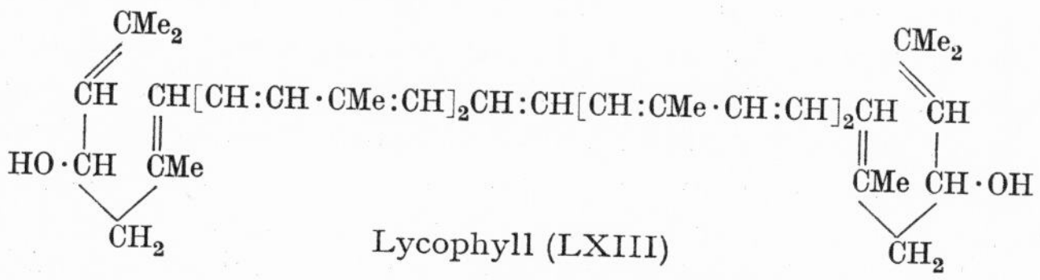

```
        CMe2                                                              CMe2
       //                                                                    \\
      CH  CH[CH:CH·CMe:CH]2CH:CH[CH:CMe·CH:CH]2CH  CH
      |   ||                                                         ||   |
HO·CH  CMe                                                     CMe CH·OH
     \   /                                                          \   /
      CH2                Lycophyll (LXIII)                          CH2
```

It crystallises from benzene-methanol in violet leaflets, m.p. 179° (corr.); ab-absorption maxima, 546, 506, and 472 mμ in carbon disulphide, 521, 487, and 456 mμ in benzene, and 505, 474, and 444 mμ in ethanol.

Cryptoxanthin. This monohydroxycarotene, isolated from berries of the Physalis species by *R. Kuhn* and *C. Grundmann* (Ber., 1933, **66,** 1746) and also occurring in yellow maize, egg yolk, and peaches, is of particular interest on account of its provitamin-A-activity. The generally accepted constitution (LXIV) was deduced by Kuhn and Grundmann from the uptake of 11 mols of hydrogen by the pigment on hydrogenation, the presence of the single hydroxyl group indicated by Zerewitinoff determination, and the identity of the absorption spectrum with that of β-carotene.

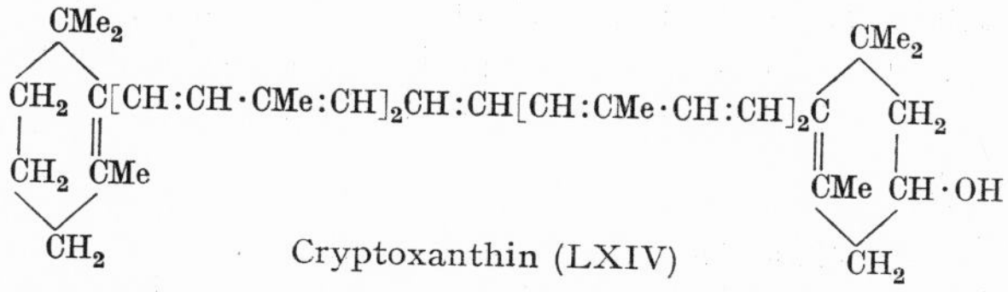

```
   CMe2                                                              CMe2
  /    \                                                            /    \
CH2  C[CH:CH·CMe:CH]2CH:CH[CH:CMe·CH:CH]2C    CH2
 |    ||                                                      ||     |
CH2  CMe                                                     CMe  CH·OH
  \  /                                                          \  /
  CH2            Cryptoxanthin (LXIV)                           CH2
```

Kuhn and Grundmann observed that cryptoxanthin showed growth-promoting activity in rats in doses of 5 to 10 γ in contrast to β-carotene which was effective in doses of 2·5 γ. More precise evidence with regard to the biological activity of cryptoxanthin has since been obtained by *H. I. Deuel et al.* (Arch. Biochem., 1946, **10,** 491) who reported that the provitamin A activity of all-*trans*-cryptoxanthin is 60% of that of all-*trans*-β-carotene. Cryptoxanthin has m.p. 169° (corr., evacuated capillary). Spectroscopic properties:

Solvent:	*Absorption maxima:*		
Carbon disulphide	519	483	452 mμ
Chloroform	497	463	433
Ethanol	486	452	424
Petrol	485·5	452	424

Ordinary crystalline cryptoxanthin, which is considered to have the all-*trans* configuration, undergoes the usual *trans-cis* isomerisations on heating in benzene solution under reflux (*Zechmeister* and *Tuzson*, Biochem. J., 1938, **32,** 1305; Ber., 1939, **72,** 1340), on fusion of the crystals and on iodine catalysis at room temperature. Three isomers, neocryptoxanthin U, neocryptoxanthin A, and neocryptoxanthin B have been separated by chromatography, the last of which is considered to be 6-mono-*cis*-cryptoxanthin (*L. Zechmeister* and *R. M. Lemmon*, J. Amer. chem. Soc., 1944, **66,** 317).

Rubixanthin, the carotenoid which occurs in different species of roses but which is not widely distributed in nature, was first isolated by *R. Kuhn* and *C. Grundmann* who showed that it was isomeric with cryptoxanthin (Ber., 1934, **67,** 339, 1133). From its uptake of 12 mols of hydrogen on catalytic hydrogenation, the formation of approximately 1 mol. of acetone on ozonisation, the presence of a hydroxyl group as indicated by Zerewitinoff determination, and the identity of the absorption spectrum with that of γ-carotene, these authors assigned the constitution (LXV) to the pigment.

```
       CMe2                                                    CMe2
      /    \                                                      \\
   CH2    C[CH:CH·CMe:CH]2CH:CH[CH:CMe·CH:CH]2CH   CH
    |     ||                                        ||    |
 HO·CH    CMe                                       CMe  CH2
      \   /                                            \  /
       CH2          Rubixanthin (LXV)                   CH2
```

In accordance with this, rubixanthin shows no provitamin A activity.

Lycoxanthin. This hydroxycarotenoid which was isolated in small amount from *Solanum dulcamara* in company with lycophyll by *L. Zechmeister* and *L. von Cholnoky* (*loc. cit.*) has an absorption spectrum almost identical with that of lycopene and probably has the constitution (LXVI).

```
     CMe2                                                    CMe2
    //                                                          \\
  CH    CH[CH:CH·CMe:CH]2CH:CH[CH:CMe·CH:CH]2CH   CH
   |    ||                                         ||    |
  CH2   CMe                                        CMe  CH·OH
     \  /                                             \  /
      CH2          Lycoxanthin (LXVI)                  CH2
```

4. Carotenoids containing ketonic groups

Rhodoxanthin. This diketonic carotenoid was first observed in the reddish brown leaves of *Potamogeton natans* by *N. A. Monteverde* in 1893, later found by *M. Tswett* in a number of conifers (Compt. rend., 1911, **152,** 788), and subsequently isolated in a crystalline state by *N. A. Monteverde* and *V. N. Lubimenko* (Bull. Acad. Sci. Petrograd, 1913, **7,** 1105). *R. Kuhn* and *N. Brockmann* (Ber., 1933, **66,** 828), who isolated rhodoxanthin from yew trees, assigned the constitution (LXVII) to the carotenoid on the basis of its behaviour on catalytic hydrogenation (rapid uptake of 12 mols. of hydrogen, followed by slower uptake of a further 2 mols.), the formation of a dioxime, and its absorption spectrum.

```
   CMe2                                                                                              CMe2
  /    \                                                                                            /    \
CH2  C:CH·CH:CMe·CH:CH·CH:CMe·CH:CH·CH:CH·CMe:CH·CH:CH·CMe:CH·CH:C                                    CH2
 |    |                                                                                          |     |
CO   CMe                                                                                        CMe   CO
  \  //                                                                                           \\  /
   CH                                                                                               CH
```

Rhodoxanthin (LXVII)

Confirmation of this was later afforded by *Karrer* and *Solmssen's* conversion of rhodoxanthin into zeaxanthin by way fo its dihydro derivative (Helv., 1935, **18**, 477).

Rhodoxanthin crystallises from benzene-methanol in dark violet needles, m.p. 219⁰ (corr., evacuated capillary) and shows the following absorption maxima: 564, 525 and 491 mμ in carbon disulphide; 546, 510, and 482 mμ in chloroform; 524, 489, and 458 mμ in petrol or hexane.

Myxoxanthin. An epiphasic carotenoid, $C_{40}H_{56}O$, was found by *I. M. Heilbron, B. Lythgoe* and *R. F. Phipers* (Nature, 1935, 136, 989) in the algae *Rivularia nitida* and later in *Oscillatoria rubescens* (*Heilbron* and *Lythgoe*, J. chem. Soc., 1936, 1376) which showed provitamin-A-activity and for which the constitution (LXVIII) was suggested.

```
   CMe2                                                           CHMe2
  /    \                                                               \
CH2  C[CH:CH·CMe:CH]2CH:CH[CH:CMe·CH:CH]2CH                             CH
 |    ||                                    ||                          ||
CH2  CMe                                   CMe                          CH
  \  /                                        \                        /
   CH2                                                   CO
```

(LXVIII)

This formula is, however, open to objection on spectroscopic grounds (*T. W. Goodwin* and *M. M. Taha*, Biochem. J., 1950, **47**, 244) and it seems likely that this carotenoid is identical both with the pigment echinenone isolated by *E. Lederer* (Compt. rend., 1935, **201**, 300) from the sea urchin *Paracentrotus lividus*, and with aphanin (p. 389).

Astacene. This interesting carotenoid was first isolated by *R. Kuhn* and *E. Lederer* (Ber., 1933, **66**, 438) from lobster shell and its constitution as the tetra-keto-β-carotene (LXIX) was established by *P. Karrer et al.* (Helv. 1934, **17**, 412, 745; 1935, **18**, 98; 1936, **19**, 479).

```
   CMe2                                                   CMe2
  /    \                                                 /    \
CH2  C[CH:CH·CMe:CH]2CH:CH[CH:CMe·CH:CH]2C                     CH2
 |    ||                                   ||                   |
CO   CMe                                  CMe                  CO
  \  /                                       \                /
   CO                                                 CO
```

Astacene (LXIX)

Two of the keto groups differ from the others in that astacene forms a dioxime containing four active hydrogen atoms, two of which arise from enolisation of the 3 and 3′-keto groups. On catalytic hydrogenation, astacene shows an uptake corresponding to the presence of 13 double bonds, two being due to enolisation. It has been shown by *R. Kuhn* and *N. A. Sörensen* (Z. angew. Chem., 1938, **51**, 465; Ber., 1938, **71**, 1879) that astacene is not itself the pigment of the shells but is formed by atmospheric oxidation of the natural pigment, **astaxanthin** (LXX) during saponification of the chromoproteid.

```
        CMe2                                                         CMe2
       /    \                                                       /    \
    CH2      C[CH:CH·CMe:CH]2CH:CH[CH:CMe·CH:CH]2C              CH2
     |       ||                                   ||              |
HO·CH        CMe                                  CMe         CH·OH
       \    /                                        \        /
        CO                                              CO
```

Astaxanthin (LXX)

In the absence of air, astaxanthin forms a deep blue salt in potassium hydroxide solution, but under aerobic conditions it absorbs 2 mols. of oxygen in alkaline solution and is converted into astacene.

Astacene crystallises from aqueous pyridine in violet needles having a metallic lustre, m.p. 240–243° (corr., in vacuum) and shows a broad absorption band at about 500 mμ in pyridine.

Capsanthin. The relationship of the pigments present in paprika to carotenoids was recognised as long ago as 1869 by *J. L. Thudichum* and received spectroscopic confirmation from a number of early investigators. In 1927, *L. Zechmeister* and *L. von Cholnoky* (Ann., **454**, 54) isolated capsanthin from *Capsicum annuum* and the constitution of this carotenoid (LXXI) was established by their work (Ann., 1934, **509**, 269; 1935, **516**, 30) and that of *P. Karrer et al.* (Helv., 1931, **14**, 614; 1936, **19**, 474).

```
        CMe2                                                         CMe2
       /    \                                                       /    \
    CH2      C[CH:CH·CMe:CH]2CH:CH[CH:CMe·CH:CH]2CO             CH2
     |       ||                                                      |
HO·CH        CMe                                   Me·CH2        CH·OH
       \    /                                             \      /
        CH2                                                 CH2
```

Capsanthin (LXXI)

Interesting confirmation of this was later afforded by the synthesis of a polyene alcohol (formula as LXXI without a hydroxyl group in the β-ionone ring) from β-apo-2-carotenal (p. 359) and pinacolone having the same chromophoric system as capsanthin (*P. Karrer* and *E. Jucker*, Helv., 1944, **27**, 1588).

Capsanthin has m.p. 176° (uncorr.); $[\alpha]_{Cd}$ +36° (chloroform); absorption maxima at 542 and 503 mμ in carbon disulphide, at 505 and 475 mμ in petrol, and at 520 and 486 mμ in benzene.

Capsorubin, a pigment isolated by *Zechmeister* and *von Cholnoky* during chromatographic purification of capsanthin obtained from *Capsicum annuum* (Ann., 1934, **509**, 269) probably has the constitution (LXXII).

```
     CMe2                                                        CMe2
    /    \                                                      /    \
 CH2    CO[CH:CH·CMe:CH]2CH:CH[CH:CMe·CH:CH]2CO              CH2
  |                                                           |
HO·CH   CH2Me                                        Me·CH2  CH·OH
    \   /                                                 \  /
     CH2               Capsorubin (LXXII)                  CH2
```

5. Carotenoid carboxylic acids

Whilst the carotenoid carboxylic acids do not fall within the definition of "hydrocarbons of the formula $C_{40}H_{56}$ or oxygenated derivatives of these", this small group possesses considerable interest in relation to the elucidation of the constitution of the former and is therefore included in this account.

Bixin, the pigment of *Bixa orellana,* was first described by Boussingault in 1825 and isolated in a crystalline condition by Etti in 1878. Whilst its empirical formula, $C_{25}H_{30}O_4$, was established by *A. Heiduschka* and *A. Panzer* in 1917 (Ber., **50,** 546, 1525), no fundamental advance was made with regard to determination of the constitution of the substance until the investigations of Kuhn and his collaborators more than ten years later (Helv. 1928, **11,** 427; 1929, **12,** 64; Ber., 1931, **64,** 1732; 1932, **65,** 646, 1873). On the basis of degradative oxidation experiments with potassium permanganate and chromic acid, which indicated the presence of four side-chain methyl groups, and the constitution of the ozonization products of bixin, Kuhn and Winterstein suggested the structure (LXXIII) for the pigment which received subsequent confirmation from the investigations of *Karrer* and his collaborators and the synthesis of perhydronorbixin (Helv. 1932, **15,** 1218, 1399).

$MeO_2C·CH:CH·CMe:CH·CH:CH·CMe:CH·CH:CH·CH:CMe·CH:CH·CH:CMe·CH:CH·CO_2H$

(LXXIII)

The isolation of a stereoisomer of bixin was first reported by *J. Herzig* and *F. Faltis* (Ann., 1923, **431,** 40) who obtained a higher melting form which they termed β-bixin. It was suggested by Karrer and his collaborators that the isomerism might be of the *cis-trans* type (Helv., 1929, **12,** 741) and this was supported by conversion of normal labile bixin into β-bixin by treatment with iodine. From the spectroscopical evidence obtained by *L. Zechmeister* and *R. B. Escue* (J. Amer. chem. Soc., 1944, **66,** 322) from a study of the isomerisation of the methylbixins it appears probable that the isomerism is associated with the second double bond from the free carboxyl group.

Labile (natural) bixin crystallises from acetic acid in deep violet prisms, m.p. 198° (rapid heating), and shows absorption maxima at 523·5, 489, and 457 mμ in carbon disulphide; stable (*trans*) bixin crystallises in flakes, m.p. 216–217° (uncorr., with decomp.) and shows absorption maxima at 526, 491, and 457 mμ in carbon disulphide.

Crocetin, whose *digentiobiose ester, crocin,* constitutes the colouring matter of saffron, is of particular interest in that the elucidation of its constitution, like that of bixin, played an important part in the development of ideas with regard to the principles governing the structure of the carotenoids.

The investigations of *P. Karrer* and *H. Salomon* (Helv., 1928, **11**, 513) and of *R. Kuhn* and *F. L'Orsa* (Ber., 1931, **64**, 1732) established the presence of seven double bonds and of four side chain methyl groups in the molecule and confirmation of the symmetrical structure (LXXIV) suggested by Karrer was provided both by degradation of perhydrocrocetin to 6:11-dimethylhexadecane-2:15-dione and by the total synthesis of the former (*P. Karrer et al.*, 1933, **16**, 297).

$$HO_2C\cdot CMe:CH\cdot CH:CH\cdot CMe:CH\cdot CH:CH\cdot CH:CMe\cdot CH:CH:CMe\cdot CO_2H$$

Crocetin (LXXIV)

Stereoisomers of the *dimethyl ester* of crocetin were first isolated by *R. Kuhn* and *A. Winterstein* (Ber., 1933, **66**, 209; 1934, **67**, 344) who observed that the more easily fusible isomer (m.p. 141°), presumed to have the *cis* configuration, was converted into the higher melting isomer (m.p. 222°) on illumination.

Stable crocetin separates from acetic anhydride in brick red crystals, m.p. 285° and shows absorption maxima at 482, 453, and 426 mμ in carbon disulphide.

Azafrin, the pigment of the roots of the South American plant *Escobedia scabrifolia,* which is used in Paraguay for colouring fats, has been shown by *R. Kuhn* and his collaborators (Ber., 1933, **66**, 883; 1934, **67**, 885) to have the constitution (LXXV).

```
       CMe2
      /    \
   CH2    C(OH)[CH:CH·CH·CMe:CH]2CH:CH·CH:CMe·CH:CH·CO2H
    |      |
   CH2    CMe(OH)
      \    /
       CH2
```

Azafrin (LXXV)

It crystallises from benzene in orange red needles, m.p. 212–214° (corr.) and shows absorption maxima at 458 and 428 mμ in chloroform and in pyridine.

6. Carotenoids of partly known constitution

Amongst the carotenoids of partly established constitution, mention may be made of *rhodoviolascin,* the pigment present in certain purple bacteria, *aphanin* which occurs in the blue alga *Aphanizomenon flos-aquae* and shows provitamin A activity, and *fucoxanthin,* which has been observed in a number of species of brown algae and diatoms.

Rhodoviolascin, $C_{42}H_{60}O_2$, the pigment found in rhodovibrio-bacteria and thiocystis-bacteria (*P. Karrer* and *U. Solmssen,* Helv., 1935, **18**, 25, 1306; 1936,

19, 3, 1019, and later) probably has the constitution (LXXVI) (*P. Karrer* and *H. Koenig*, Helv., 1940, **23**, 460).

```
        CHMe2                                                  CHMe2
       /                                                            \
    CH2  CH[CH:CH·CMe:CH]2CH:CH[CH:CMe·CH:CH]2CH   CH2
    |    ||                                         ||    |
MeO·C    CMe                                      CMe  C·OMe
      \\ /                                           \ //
        CH                  (LXXVI)                   CH
```

It crystallises from benzene in glistening deep red crystals, m.p. 218° and shows absorption maxima at 573·5, 534 and 496 mμ in carbon disulphide and at 548, 511, and 482 mμ in benzene.

Aphanin, $C_{40}H_{54}O$, which was isolated from the blue alga *Aphanizomenon flos-aquae* by *J. Tischer* (Z. physiol. Chem., 1938, **251**, 109; 1939, **260**, 257) is a ketonic derivative showing provitamin-A-activity about half of that of β-carotene; the constitution (LXXVI) has been suggested.

```
      CMe2                                                  CMe2
     /    \                                               /    \
  CH2    C[CH:CH·CMe:CH]2CH:CH[CH:CMe·CH:CH]2C       CH2
   |     ||                                      ||     |
  CH2    CMe                                    CMe    CO
     \  /                                          \  /
      CH2                 (LXXVI)                   CH2
```

It crystallises from benzene-methanol in large blue-black leaflets, m.p. 176° (corr.) and shows broad absorption bands with approximate centres at 534 and 494 mμ in carbon disulphide and at 505 and 472 mμ in benzene.

Fucoxanthin, which was separated from the other pigments of brown algae by chromatography by Tswett in 1906, was first obtained in the crystalline state by *R. Willstätter* and *H. J. Page* (Ann., 1914, **404**, 237). *P. Karrer* and his collaborators (Helv., 1931, **14**, 623) obtained analytical results in agreement with the formula $C_{40}H_{56}O_6$ for fucoxanthin, whilst *I. M. Heilbron* and *R. F. Phipers* (Biochem. J., 1935, **29**, 1364) tentatively assigned the formula $C_{40}H_{60}O_6$ to the carotenoid and suggested the constitution (LXXVII) which is not, however, wholly in agreement with the properties of the compound.

```
       CMe2                                                      CMe2
      /    \                                                   /    \
   CH2    CO[CH:CH·CMe:CH]2CH:CH[CH:CMe·CH:CH]2CO          CH2
    |                                                            |
HO·CH    CHMe·OH                                    HO·CHMe   CH·OH
      \  /                                                \  /
       CH2         Fucoxanthin (LXXVII) (?)                CH2
```

Fucoxanthin melts at 166–168° (uncorr.) and shows absorption maxima at 510 and 477 mμ in carbon disulphide and at 492 and 457 mμ in chloroform.

7. Synthetic higher homologues of the carotenes

P. Karrer and *C. H. Eugster* have extended their syntheses of β-carotene and lycopene to the synthesis of higher homologues of β-carotene containing fifteen conjugated double bonds (Helv., 1951, 34, 28) and of ε_1-carotene containing thirteen conjugated double bonds (*ibid.*, p. 823).

Decapreno-β-carotene, $C_{50}H_{68}$, was synthesised by condensation of the C_{18} ketone (XXXII) with bromomethylacetylene and zinc to give the carbinol (LXXVIII), whose Grignard derivative on condensation with 4-octene-2:7-dione furnished the tetraol (LXXIX). This, on partial reduction of the two acetylenic triple bonds with Pd-$BaSO_4$ in acetic acid and subsequent treatment with *p*-toluenesulphonic acid gave a mixture of pigments from which *trans*-decapreno-β-carotene (LXXX) was isolated in pure form.

```
      CMe2
     /    \
    |      ||
   CH2    C·CH:CH·CMe:CH·CH:CH·CMe(OH)·CH2·C≡CH
    |      ||
   CH2    CMe
     \    /
      CH2                    (LXXVIII)
                                 |
                                 ↓
[ \                                                              ]
   C·CH:CH·CMe:CH·CH:CH·CMe(OH)·CH2·C≡C·CMe(OH)·CH2·CH=
   ||                                                            ]2
                              (LXXIX)
                                 |
                                 ↓
[     CMe2                                                        ]
     /    \
   CH2    C·CH:CH·CMe:CH·CH:CH·CMe:CH·CH:CH·CMe:CH·CH=
    |      ||
   CH2    CMe
     \    /
      CH2                     (LXXX)                              ]2
```

Decapreno-β-carotene crystallises from benzene-petroleum ether in black violet spear-like crystals, which in reflected light appear almost black, m.p. 192° (corr., *in vacuo*) and show absorption maxima at 582, 542, and 515 mμ in carbon disulphide and at 544, 509, 479, and 405 mμ in cyclohexane.

Decapreno-ε_1-carotene (formula LXXX with α-ionone rings in place of β-ionone rings) was synthesised by Karrer and Eugster on lines similar to decapreno-β-carotene. The intermediate products, which were oils, were not isolated in pure form but the synthetic homologue of ε_1-carotene was obtained in black-red microscopic prisms which had m.p. 216–217° (corr.) and showed absorption maxima at 575·5, 535, and 496 mμ in carbon disulphide and at 542, 504, and 474 mμ in cyclohexane.

Chapter XI

Open-chain and Cyclic Polymers derived from Olefinic Compounds; Rubber and Rubber-like Compounds, Natural and Synthetic, and their Derivatives

R. G. R. BACON

Introduction

The molecules of the naturally occurring terpenes, which are discussed in Vol. IIB have polyisoprene structures, their carbon skeletons being formally derived by the self-addition of two, three, or more units of the conjugated diolefine isoprene (Vol. I, p. 269). The relationship of isoprene to the terpenes is a formal one in the sense that the compounds and reactions responsible for the biogenesis of terpenes have not been established. On the other hand, self-addition processes which are termed *polymerisations*, are easily effected with isoprene and other diolefines in the laboratory, and the resulting open-chain or cyclic *polymers* include substances of terpenic types.

The present chapter is largely concerned with the chemistry of rubber, which is another naturally occurring polyisoprene. It resembles certain terpenes, such as myrcene (Vol. I, p. 271) and geraniol (Vol. IIB) in having an open-chain structure, but it differs from all terpenes in having a very high molecular weight. Since it has not been proved to originate from isoprene in nature, its classification as an isoprene polymer is, as in the case of the terpenes, a formal one (cf. p. 426).

The naturally occurring polyisoprenes of gutta percha and balata are included here alongside rubber (p. 427). Also included (pp. 428 ff) is an account of the artificial, high molecular-weight polymers, superficially alike in possessing rubber-like elasticity, which are usually collectively termed *synthetic elastomers*. In commerce they are closely linked with natural rubber, and the two types provide raw materials for the rubber manufacturing industry. The chief synthetic elastomers are chemically related to natural rubber, being derived mainly from conjugated diolefines.

A tendency to polymerise is a characteristic of most classes of compounds containing one or more olefinic bonds; synthetic elastomers are only one of the many types of polymer which may result. A general review of the polymerisation products of olefinic compounds is therefore given in the earlier sections of this chapter. Among the types included there are the terpene-like polymers of diolefines and the important group of high molecular-weight vinyl polymers which have industrial applications as *plastics* and *synthetic fibres*.

1. Polymerisation products of olefinic compounds

(a) General features of the polymerisation of olefinic compounds

Additive polymerisation is summarised in the expression $nM \rightarrow (M)_n$, where M represents a molecule of the polymerisable olefinic *monomer*, n is the *degree of* polymerisation (sometimes abbreviated to D.P.), and $(M)_n$ represents the polymeric product. If the latter is relatively low in molecular weight it may be called a *dimer, trimer, tetramer*, etc., n being 2, 3, 4, etc. The term *high molecular-weight polymer* (or high polymer) is conventionally used for products in which n is greater than about 100. Typical products of this type, including those which have practical importance as elastomers, plastics and fibres, may have n in the range 100–10,000. Polymers of an intermediate size, where n may be of the order of 10–100, have much less practical value and have been relatively little investigated.

Some olefinic compounds polymerise spontaneously at ordinary temperatures, but usually the process has to be stimulated. This may be done by physical means, e.g. by the application of heat, ultra-violet irradiation, high pressure, or X-rays. Commonly a chemical catalyst is used, typical *initiators* being peroxy-compounds, reactive inorganic halides and alkali metals. Certain other types of substances, e.g. phenols and amines, termed *inhibitors*, may retard polymerisation. Ease of polymerisation depends upon the technique employed and upon the structure of the monomer. These two factors also affect the size and structure of the resulting polymer.

Among mono-olefines, polymerisation occurs particularly readily with substances containing unsymmetrically substituted double bonds, as in *vinyl* compounds, $CH_2{:}CHX$, and *vinylidene* compounds, $CH_2{:}CXY$. If X and Y are substituents with a marked polar character, such as Cl and CN, then polymerisation is usually extremely easy. Several types of polymeric product may be formed from mono-olefinic compounds. (i) Unsaturated open-chain dimers, trimers, etc. are often produced. In certain cases, fission products from a different type of molecule may add terminally during the polymerisation, giving short saturated open-chain polymers, a process which has come to be known as *telomerisation*. Then if X is an aryl group the formation of an unsaturated linear dimer may be succeeded by cyclisation between the chain and the aromatic nucleus. (ii) Some mono-olefinic compounds form cyclic dimers, usually containing a cyclobutane ring; the formation of cyclic trimers is very rare. (iii). The common mode of polymerisation of the most reactive mono-olefinic compounds is their conversion into saturated linear polymers of high molecular weight. Vinyl and vinylidene plastics belong to this last group.

Among olefinic compounds with two or more double bonds, conjugated diolefines, containing the structure ·C:C·C:C·, have by far the greatest importance in polymerisation chemistry. Like mono-olefines, they produce various types of polymer. (i) Unsaturated open-chain dimers, trimers, etc. may be formed, and in practically all cases this is a reaction involving telomerisation. Such polymers are structurally related to the open-chain terpenes. (ii) Various kinds of cyclic dimer may be formed, the commonest type being cyclohexene derivatives, which are structurally related to cyclic terpenes. Cyclic trimers, tetramers, etc. are easily formed also. (iii) Many conjugated diolefines are readily converted into unsaturated polymers of high molecular weight, which are essentially linear in structure, but which also exhibit varying amounts of branching and cross-linking between carbon chains. This group of polymers is the main source of synthetic elastomers.

The variety of polymeric products obtainable from olefinic compounds may be extended by the process of *copolymerisation* (also called *interpolymerisation*), whereby monomer molecules of two or more species may be caused to combine in the same polymeric chains, giving *copolymers (interpolymers)*; these have great practical importance. Further variations may be obtained by subjecting natural or synthetic high molecular-weight polymers to chemical treatment, e.g. to addition or substitution reactions; this is particularly important for natural rubber. High molecular-weight polymers may also be subjected to degradation, and if this gives rise to monomer molecules, or to related dimers, trimers, etc. the process is called *depolymerisation*.

During the nineteenth century, whilst rubber was being chemically examined and coming into use in manufacture, the conversion of certain olefinic compounds into polymers was sporadically reported, but the main developments in olefinic polymer chemistry have occurred since about 1920. These advances have been accompanied by extensive and varied industrial applications. Many of the chief scientific discoveries of the period have been made in industrial laboratories. Inevitably the literature is especially voluminous for substance, such as 1:3-butadiene (Vol. I, p. 269) and styrene (Vol. III), and their polymers, which have the greatest industrial importance. Much of this literature deals with polymers in their physico-chemical and technological aspects. For these aspects, the reader is referred to general works cited within this chapter and in the supplementary bibliography at the end (p. 436).

(b) Low molecular-weight polymers from mono-olefinic compounds

Reviews of the pre-1939 literature have been given by *E. H. Farmer* (in "The Science of Petroleum", Dunstan, Nash, Brooks, and Tizard, Oxford, 1938; Trans. Faraday Soc., 1939, **35**, 1034), by *E. Bergmann* (*ibid.*, 1939, **35**, 1025), and by *W. J. Sparks et al.*, (*ibid.*, 1939, **35**, 1040).

(i) Open-chain polymers without terminal addenda

Ethylene, propene, *n*-butene, and other unbranched olefinic hydrocarbons are relatively difficult to polymerise, but in the vapour-phase at high temperatures they yield dimers and other low polymers. The reaction is often complex and may involve rearrangements in the carbon skeleton (cf. Vol. I, p. 257), but the simplest mode of polymerisation observed is an addition of molecules with shift of hydrogen (*W. J. Sparks et al., loc. cit.*). Thus, at about 500°, ethylene gives mainly *n*-butene (*A. E. Dunstan et al.*, J. Soc. chem. Ind., 1931, **50**, 313T; *ibid.*, 1932, **51**, 131T), whilst in a high-frequency electric discharge it gives good yields of 1-butene and 1-hexene (*G. Mignonac* and *R. V. de Saint-Aunay*, Compt. rend., 1929, **189**, 106):

$$CH_2{:}CH_2 + CH_2{:}CH_2 \longrightarrow CH_2{:}CH{\cdot}CH_2{\cdot}CH_3$$

$$CH_2{:}CH_2 + CH_2{:}CH{\cdot}CH_2{\cdot}CH_3 \longrightarrow CH_2{:}CH{\cdot}CH_2{\cdot}CH_2{\cdot}CH_2{\cdot}CH_3.$$

The presence of substituent methyl groups on double-bonded carbon facilitates polymerisation, which is initiated by warm, fairly concentrated sulphuric acid, or, even at low temperatures, by catalysts of the Friedel-Crafts type, such as aluminium chloride and boron trifluoride. Dimers may result when branched-chain olefines are prepared by acid-promoted dehydration of alcohols. *F. C. Whitmore* interpreted the initiation of polymerisation by acids as involving transient formation of a carbonium ion, such as $CH_3{\cdot}\overset{+}{C}Me_2$ (from $CH_2{:}CMe_2$), arising by addition of a proton at the double bond (Ind. Eng. Chem., 1934, **26**, 94; J. Amer. chem. Soc., 1932, **54**, 3274). The ion can then give a dimer molecule by reaction with a second olefine molecule, followed by loss of proton, and, before completion of these processes, can undergo skeletal rearrangement (cf. Vol. I, p. 179, and, for discussion of the Whitmore mechanism, *G. W. Wheland*, "Advanced Organic Chemistry", 2nd. Edition, New York, 1949, Chap. 12). Friedel-Crafts catalysts are likewise believed to function by an ionic mechanism (cf. p. 406).

*iso*Butene is converted by sulphuric acid into a *di*iso*butene* fraction, b.p. 101–103°, and a *tri*iso*butene* fraction, b.p. 177–179°, observed by *A. Butlerow* (Ann., 1877, **189**, 46; Ber., 1879, **12**, 1482). The former consists of 2:4:4-*trimethyl-1-pentene* and 2:4:4-*trimethyl-2-pentene* (*R. J. McCubbin* and *H. Adkins*, J. Amer. chem. Soc., 1930, **52**, 2547), together with traces of other hydrocarbons (*P. Pomerantz*, J. Res. nat. Bur. Stand., 1952, **48**, 76):

$$2\,CMe_2{:}CH_2 \longrightarrow CMe_2{:}CH{\cdot}CMe_2{\cdot}CH_3 \text{ and } CH_2{:}CMe{\cdot}CH_2{\cdot}CMe_2{\cdot}CH_3.$$

It is hydrogenated to *iso*octane (*G. Edgar*, Ind. Eng. Chem., 1927, **19**, 145; cf. Vol. I, p. 248). Tri*iso*butene contains 2:2:4:6:6-*pentamethyl-3-heptene*, $CH_3 \cdot CMe_2 \cdot CH_2 \cdot CMe : CH \cdot CMe_2 \cdot CH_3$, and several other isomers (*R. J. McCubbin*, J. Amer. chem. Soc., 1931, **53**, 356; *F. C. Whitmore et al., ibid.*, 1941, **63**, 2035).

Tetramethylethylene (2:3-dimethyl-2-butene; Vol. I, p. 258), treated with boron trifluoride at -10^0, dimerises with rearrangement, mainly by the process:

$$2\,CMe_2{:}CMe_2 \longrightarrow CHMe_2{\cdot}CHMe{\cdot}CH{:}CMe{\cdot}CMe_3$$

(*H. Brunner* and *E. H. Farmer*, J. chem. Soc., 1937, 1039). Three additional dimers arise from catalysis by sulphuric acid at 0^0 (*F. C. Whitmore* and *P. L. Meunier*, J. Amer. chem. Soc., 1941, **63**, 2197).

The best known low molecular-weight polymers of aryl-substituted olefines are likewise dimers, consisting of substituted butenes, which, however, readily pass into indane compounds; these are described in section (*iii*). Open-chain trimers and other low molecular-weight polymers have also been isolated. Thus styrene (phenylethylene) gives the following series of open-chain polymers when treated with stannic chloride in conjunction with hydrogen chloride (*G. Williams* and *H. Thomas*, J. chem. Soc., 1948, 1867):

$$n\,CHPh{:}CH_2 \longrightarrow CHPh{:}CH{\cdot}(CHPh{\cdot}CH_2)_{n-1}\,H \;(n = 2\text{–}5).$$

Low molecular-weight styrene polymers of slightly different structure may result from the thermal depolymerisation of high molecular-weight polystyrene (*H. Staudinger* and *A. Steinhofer*, Ann., 1935, **517**, 35).

Formation of open-chain dimers is not common when the olefinic bond carries substituents other than hydrocarbon radicals. The following exceptional cases are known. Trichloroethylene (Vol. I, p. 281) at 200^0 gives a linear dimer, considered to be an equilibrium mixture of $CHCl_2{\cdot}CCl_2{\cdot}CH{:}CCl_2$, $CHCl_2{\cdot}CCl{:}CH{\cdot}CCl_3$ and $CHCl{:}CCl{\cdot}CHCl{\cdot}CCl_3$ (*A. L. Henne* and *R. P. Ruh*, J. Amer. chem. Soc., 1947, **69**, 279). Acrylic esters (Vol. I, p. 631) and crotonic esters (Vol. I, p. 633) are dimerised by sodium ethoxide:

$$2\,CHR{:}CH{\cdot}CO_2R' \longrightarrow CHR{:}C(CO_2R'){\cdot}CHR{\cdot}CH_2{\cdot}CO_2R'$$

(R = H or Me; R′ = Me or Et) (*H. von Pechmann*, Ber., 1900, **33**, 3323; *H. von Pechmann* and *O. Röhm*, *ibid.*, 1901, **34**, 427).

Alicyclic mono-olefines can give various polymers, including, as in the case of open-chain olefines, dimers formed by hydrogen-transfer reactions. Thus, cyclopentene, at 200^0 over phosphorus pentoxide, gives *1-cyclopentylcyclopentene*, b.p. 187–$193^0/740$ mm., d_{18}^{18} 0·901, n_D^{18} 1·490 (*R. Truffault* and *J. Dumontet*, Compt. rend., 1950, **231**, 1068). Cyclohexene, boiled with phosphorus pentoxide, similarly gives *1-cyclohexylcyclohexene*, b.p. 238–$239^0/760$ mm., d^{20} 0·904, n_D^{20} 1·493 (*R. Truffault*, *ibid.*, 1935, **200**, 406) and, treated with hydrogen fluoride, gives the same dimer, together with fractions ranging from trimers to heptamers (*S. M. McElvain* and *J. W. Langston*, J. Amer. chem. Soc., 1944, **66**, 1759). Indene (Vol. III) is converted by acids or Friedel-Crafts catalysts into *1-1′-indanylindene*, m.p. 53^0 (*H. Stobbe* and *E. Färber*, Ber., 1924, **57**, 1838; *E. Bergmann* and *H. Taubadel*, *ibid.*, 1932, **65**, 463) and it readily yields resinous polymers of higher molecular weight.

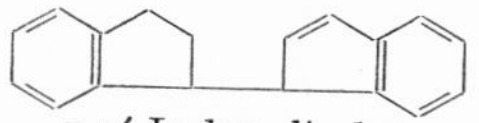

1-1′-Indanylindene

(ii) Open-chain polymers with terminal addenda (telomers)

Mono-olefinic compounds, in the presence of peroxidic catalysts, normally give high molecular-weight linear polymers (p. 405), but when a large proportion of a second substance, of suitable reactivity, is also present, some monomers yield short, saturated chain molecules (telomers) terminated by fission products of the second substance:

$$n\,CH_2{:}CHX + AB \longrightarrow A\cdot(CH_2\cdot CHX)_n\cdot B \quad (n = \text{e.g. } 1\text{–}10).$$

This type of reaction seems first to have been reported by *J. W. Breitenbach et al.* (Öst. Chem.-Ztg., 1938, **41**, 182; Z. physik. Chem., 1940, **A 187**, 175), for the polymerisation of styrene in carbon tetrachloride. Later examples, described by *R. M. Joyce et al.* (J. Amer. chem. Soc., 1948, **70**, 2529; 1950, **72**, 2213), are the peroxide-initiated polymerisation of ethylene in the presence of chloroform, carbon tetrachloride, or methylene dihalides, which yield mixtures of telomers, such as $H\cdot(CH_2\cdot CH_2)_n\cdot CCl_3$ and $Cl\cdot(CH_2\cdot CH_2)_n\cdot CCl_3$ ($n = 1$–5). Similarly, under the influence of ultra-violet light, trifluoro-iodomethane reacts with ethylene, giving $CF_3\cdot(CH_2\cdot CH_2)_n\cdot I$ ($n = 1$–3), or with tetrafluoroethylene (Vol. I, p. 282), giving $CF_3\cdot(CF_2\cdot CF_2)_n\cdot I$ ($n = 1$–10) (*R. N. Haszeldine*, J. chem. Soc., 1949, 2856).

A different type of telomerisation is shown by some aryl-substituted olefines, which, like conjugated diolefines (p. 399) may dimerise with terminal addition of alkali metal (*W. Schlenk* and *E. Bergmann*, Ann., 1928, **463**, 3; *K. Ziegler et al.*, *ibid.*, 1929, **473**, 36), e.g.:

$$2\,CPh_2{:}CH_2 + 2\,Na \longrightarrow Na\cdot CPh_2\cdot CH_2\cdot CH_2\cdot CPh_2\cdot Na.$$

Another formally similar reaction, though again different in mechanism, is the alkali-catalysed polymerisation of acrolein (Vol. I, p. 502) or α-methylacrolein, to give saturated chains with water as a terminal addendum (*E. E. Gilbert* and *J. J. Donleavy*, J. Amer. chem. Soc., 1938, **60**, 1737):

$$5\,CH_2{:}CH\cdot CHO + H_2O \longrightarrow HO\cdot[CH_2\cdot CH(CHO)]_5\cdot H$$

$$n\,CH_2{:}CMe\cdot CHO + H_2O \longrightarrow HO\cdot[CH_2\cdot CMe(CHO)]_n\cdot H \quad (n = 3\text{–}5)$$

(iii) Dimerisation accompanied by cyclisation between carbon chains and aromatic rings

It is well established that aryl-substituted olefines, under the influence of acids or Friedel-Crafts halides, dimerise to give a mixture of a butene derivative and an indane derivative, the latter arising from the cyclisation of the former. Thus, styrene, with sulphuric acid, stannic chloride, etc. gives 1:3-*diphenyl-1-butene*, b.p. 167°/9 mm., d_4^{20} 1·002, n_D^{20} 1·5930, and 1-*methyl-3-phenylindane*, b.p. 155°/8 mm., d_4^{20} 1·027, n_D^{20} 1·5805 (*J. Risi* and *D. Gauvin*, Canad. J. Res., 1936, **B 14**, 255; *P. E. Spoerri* and *M. J. Rosen*, J. Amer. chem. Soc., 1950, **72**, 4918):

$$2\ C_6H_5\text{—}CH{:}CH_2 \longrightarrow C_6H_5\text{—}CH\cdot CH_3(CH{:}CHPh) \longrightarrow \text{indane: } CH\cdot CH_3,\ CH_2,\ CHPh$$

Similarly, α-methylstyrene (2-phenyl-1-propene) gives 4-*methyl*-2:4-*diphenyl*-2-*pentene*, b.p. 166–167°/15 mm., and 1:1:3-*trimethyl*-3-*phenylindane*, m.p. 51–52° (*E. Bergmann et al.*, Ber., 1931, **64**, 1493). 1:1-Diphenylethylene similarly gives 1:1:3:3-*tetraphenyl*-1-*butene*, m.p. 113°, and 3-*methyl*-1:1:3-*triphenylindane*, m.p. 143° (*E. Bergmann* and *H. Weiss*, Ann., 1930, **480**, 49; *C. S. Schoepfle* and *J. D. Ryan*, J. Amer. chem. Soc., 1930, **52**, 4021).

Analogous behaviour is shown by propenyl-substituted benzenoid compounds, R·CH:CHMe (R = C_6H_5 etc.), which polymerise much more readily than the isomeric allyl-substituted compounds, R·CH_2·CH:CH_2 (*H. Staudinger* and *E. Dreher*, Ann., 1935, **517**, 73). Polymerisation occurs especially easily in propenylbenzenes in which the ring is activated, e.g. by methoxyl- or amino-substituents. Several such methoxy-compounds (ethers of propenylphenols) are well known as plant constituents (see Vol. III) and their dimerisation has been extensively investigated; for a general review of the process and its mechanism see *A. Müller*, J. org. Chem., 1952, **17**, 1077. Thus, anethole (*p*-methoxypropenylbenzene) yields the olefinic dimer, iso*anethole*, in a solid (? *trans*-) form, m.p. 40–40·5°, and a liquid (? *cis*-) form, b.p. 174°/0·05 mm., n_D^{20} 1·5764, together with the isomeric indane derivative, *metanethole*, m.p. 134° (*W. Baker et al.*, J. chem. Soc., 1940, 1094; *ibid.*, 1948, 1984; *A. Müller* and *A. Richl*, Ber., 1943, **76**, 1119):

$$2\ MeO\text{—}C_6H_4\text{—}CH{:}CHMe \longrightarrow MeO\text{—}C_6H_4\text{—}CHEt\text{—}CMe{=}CH\text{—}C_6H_4\text{—}OMe \longrightarrow \text{indane: } MeO,\ CHEt,\ CHMe,\ CH\text{—}C_6H_4\text{—}OMe$$

*iso*Safrole (3:4-methylenedioxy-1-propenylbenzene) likewise gives two dimers (*M. Pailer et al.*, Monatsh., 1947, **72**, 45; *ibid.*, 1948, **79**, 620). Other members of the group give only the indane type of dimer. Thus, *iso*eugenol (4-hydroxy-3-methoxy-1-propenylbenzene) gives only the indane derivative, *diiso*e*ugenol*, m.p. 179–180° (*A. Müller* and *A. Horváth*, Ber., 1943, **76**, 855; *N. J. Cartwright* and *R. D. Haworth*, J. chem. Soc., 1947, 948).

In the case of α-phenylacrylonitrile a different type of cyclisation occurs during dimerisation; this monomer changes spontaneously into a tetrahydronaphthalene derivative (*H. A. Newey* and *J. G. Erickson*, J. Amer. chem. Soc., 1950, **72**, 5645):

$$2\ C_6H_5\text{—}C(CN){:}CH_2 \longrightarrow \text{tetrahydronaphthalene: } C(H)(CN),\ CH_2,\ CH_2,\ C(Ph)(CN)$$

(iv) Polymerisation involving alicyclic ring formation

In a limited number of cases olefinic compounds are known to dimerise to cyclobutane derivatives. This is a property of some fluorine-substituted olefines. Thus, at 200°, chlorotrifluoroethylene undergoes "head-to-head, tail-to-tail" addition, giving 3:4-*dichloro*-1:1:2:2:3:4-*hexafluorocyclobutane*, f.p. –24°, b.p. 59·87°, d_4^{20} 1·6441, n_D^{20} 1·3340:

$$2\,CClF{:}CF_2 \longrightarrow \begin{array}{l} CClF\text{—}CF_2 \\ | \qquad\quad | \\ CClF\text{—}CF_2 \end{array}$$

and 1:1-dichloro-2:2-difluoroethylene similarly gives 1:1:2:2-*tetrachloro*-3:3:4:4-*tetrafluorocyclobutane*, m.p. 84·8°, b.p. 131·6°/762 mm. (*A. L. Henne* and *R. P. Ruh*, J. Amer. chem. Soc., 1947, **69**, 279). Tetrafluoroethylene, by thermal polymerisation, similarly gives *octafluorocyclobutane*, m.p. –48°, b.p. –5° (*J. Harmon*, U.S.P. 2,404,374), also obtained by depolymerisation when polytetrafluoroethylene is pyrolysed (*A. F. Benning et al.*, U.S.P. 2,394,581; *F. E. Lewis* and *N. A. Naylor*, J. Amer. chem. Soc., 1947, **69**, 1968). A similar dimerisation occurs, to a small extent, with acrylonitrile (this Vol., p. 54).

Examples involving phenyl substituents have been known for much longer. The photodimer, m.p. 164–165°, of stilbene (1:2-diphenylethylene, Vol. III) is believed to be 1:2:3:4-*tetraphenylcyclobutane* (*G. Ciamician* and *P. Silber*, Ber., 1902, **35**, 4129; *M. Pailer* and *A. Müller*, Monatsh., 1948, **79**, 615). An extensively investigated case is cinnamic acid, the *cis*- and *trans*-forms of which dimerise in ultra-violet light to give truxinic and truxillic acids (p. 60), which give cinnamic acid, by depolymerisation, on distillation.

Methyl and ethyl methylenemalonate, $CH_2{:}C(CO_2R)_2$, are difficult to prepare because of polymerisation (Vol. I, p. 987; cf. *G. B. Bachman* and *H. A. Tanner*, J. org. Chem., 1939, **4**, 493). The ethyl ester gives an amorphous "meta"-polymer and a "para"-polymer, m.p. 154–156°, the latter being apparently the cyclobutane dimer, *tetraethyl cyclobutane*-1:1:3:3-*tetracarboxylate*; it is depolymerised by heat.

Rings with more than four members do not commonly result from the polymerisation of olefinic compounds. One exceptional case is the conversion of *iso*butene, at about 400°, into 1:1:3-*trimethylcyclopentane*, b.p. 105°, d_4^{20} 0·7480, n_D^{20} 1·4108, presumably by cyclisation of di*iso*butene (*J. B. McKinley et al.*, J. Amer. chem. Soc., 1945, **67**, 1455). Another case, which may be a unique instance of formation of a cyclic vinyl trimer, is the conversion of mesityl vinyl ketone, by the action of potassium carbonate in hot methanol, into 1:3:5-*trimesitoylcyclohexane*, m.p. 150–151° (*R. C. Fuson* and *C. H. McKeever*, *ibid.*, 1940, **62**, 2088):

$$3\,CH_2{:}CH{\cdot}COR \longrightarrow \begin{array}{c} CH_2 \\ ROC{\cdot}CH \quad CH{\cdot}COR \\ | \qquad\quad | \\ CH_2 \quad CH_2 \\ CH{\cdot}COR \end{array}$$

$$(R = 2{:}4{:}6\text{-}C_6H_2Me_3{\cdot})$$

(c) Low molecular-weight polymers of diolefinic compounds

(i) Open-chain polymers without terminal addenda

Dimerisation with hydrogen transfer, such as occurs fairly readily with many mono-olefines, could conceivably convert a conjugated diene into a triene. If such reactions occur, the products are highly reactive and consequently difficult to isolate before they undergo further change. The conversion of isoprene, by an active clay, into mixed polymers, including a small amount of an open-chain monoterpenic dimer, $C_{10}H_{16}$, with three double bonds, hydrogenated to give mixed dimethyloctanes, was recorded by *T. Wagner-Jauregg* and *T. Lennartz* (Ber., 1943, **76**, 1161).

(ii) Open-chain polymers with terminal addenda (telomers)

Several types of telomerisation reaction have been established for conjugated diolefines.

Hydrogen addition. In presence of potassium and ethanol, isoprene is dimerised, with terminal addition of hydrogen, to give a mixture of 2:6-, 2:7- and 3:6-*dimethyl*-2:6-*octadienes*, b.p. 163–167° (*T. Midgley, Jr.* and *A. L. Henne*, J. Amer. chem. Soc., 1929, **51**, 1294):

$$2\,CH_2{:}CMe{\cdot}CH{:}CH_2 \longrightarrow \begin{cases} CH_3{\cdot}CMe{:}CH{\cdot}CH_2{\cdot}CH_2{\cdot}CMe{:}CH{\cdot}CH_3 \\ CH_3{\cdot}CMe{:}CH{\cdot}CH_2{\cdot}CH_2{\cdot}CH{:}CMe{\cdot}CH_3 \\ CH_3{\cdot}CH{:}CMe{\cdot}CH_2{\cdot}CH_2{\cdot}CMe{:}CH{\cdot}CH_3 \end{cases}$$

Additions of alkali-metals and organo-alkali compounds. These reactions have been extensively studied for 1:3-butadiene, isoprene, and other conjugated diolefines, by *K. Ziegler et al.* (Ber., 1928, **61**, 253, and later papers). Organo-alkali compounds (Vol. I, p. 428) in ether cause linear polymerisation, and at the same time add terminally, giving a mixture of low molecular-weight polymers:

$$n\,CH_2{:}CH{\cdot}CH{:}CH_2 + MR \longrightarrow M{\cdot}(CH_2{\cdot}CH{:}CH{\cdot}CH_2)_n{\cdot}R$$
$$(M = Li,\ Na,\ K;\ R = C_4H_9,\ CH_2Ph,\ CPhMe_2,\ etc.;\ n = 1\text{–}10)$$

Alkali metals may act similarly (*K. Ziegler et al.*, Ann., 1935, **511**, 64):

$$n\,CH_2{:}CH{\cdot}CH{:}CH_2 + 2\,M \longrightarrow M{\cdot}(CH_2{\cdot}CH{:}CH{\cdot}CH_2)_n{\cdot}M$$
$$(M = Li,\ Na;\ n = 1\text{–}5).$$

The union of the diene units may occur by 1:2-, as well as by 1:4-addition, giving branched chains:

$$\ldots\ldots CH_2{\cdot}CH{:}CH{\cdot}CH_2{\cdot}CH_2{\cdot}\underset{\displaystyle CH{:}CH_2}{CH}{\cdot}CH_2{\cdot}CH{:}CH{\cdot}CH_2\ldots\ldots$$

These investigations are important in connection with the use of alkali-metals, in catalytic quantities, as initiators in the production of synthetic elastomers (p. 430).

Acetic acid addition. In acetic acid solution, with sulphuric acid as catalyst, isoprene is converted into α-terpineol and 1:4- and 1:8-cineol, all three of which are cyclic terpenes, and it is converted, at the same time, by the following process (n = 2) into the acetate of geraniol (Vol. II B), an open-chain monoterpene alcohol (*T. Wagner-Jauregg*, Ann., 1932, **496**, 52):

$$n\,CH_2{:}CMe\cdot CH{:}CH_2 + CH_3\cdot CO_2H \longrightarrow H\cdot(CH_2\cdot CMe{:}CH\cdot CH_2)_n\cdot O\cdot CO\cdot CH_3$$

Production, by the same process, of the acetates of the sesquiterpene alcohol farnesol (n = 3) and of the diterpene alcohol protophytol (n = 4) has been claimed by *T. Lennartz* (Ber., 1943, **76**, 831). Analogous products (n = 1, 2, 3) have been isolated from the telomerisation of 1:3-butadiene in acetic or propionic acids, with perchloric acid as catalyst (*E. L. Jenner* and *R. S. Schreiber*, J. Amer. chem. Soc., 1951, **73**, 4348).

Addition of alkoxide groups. In the presence of alkoxy-radicals, generated, e.g., from a mixture of a ferrous salt and *tert.*-butyl hydroperoxide, 1:3-butadiene undergoes telomerisation, giving mainly 1:8-*di*-tert.-*butoxy*-2:6-*octadiene*, b.p. 65–70°/0·05 mm., n_D^{20} 1·4485 (*M. S. Kharasch et al.*, J. org. Chem., 1951, **16**, 1556):

$$2\,CH_2{:}CH\cdot CH{:}CH_2 + 2\cdot OBu^t \longrightarrow Bu^tO\cdot(CH_2\cdot CH{:}CH\cdot CH_2)_2\cdot OBu^t$$

(iii) Cyclobutane type dimers

Unlike mono-olefinic compounds, conjugated diolefines do not, in general, give cyclobutane type dimers with any ease. An exception is 1:3-butadiene, the crude dimer of which, obtained by heating at 150° in an autoclave, contains a small amount of trans-1:2-*divinylcyclobutane*, b.p. 112–113°, d_{20}^{20} 0·7831, n_D^{20} 1·4451 (*H. W. B. Reed*, J. chem. Soc., 1951, 685):

$$2\,CH_2{:}CH\cdot CH{:}CH_2 \longrightarrow \begin{array}{l} CH_2\!-\!CH\cdot CH{:}CH_2 \\ |\qquad\;\; | \\ CH_2\!-\!CH\cdot CH{:}CH_2 \end{array}$$

(iv) Cyclopentene type dimers

This type of cyclic dimer is also rare. The dimer, b.p. 210–212°/12 mm., of 1-phenyl-1:3-butadiene, is deduced, from its oxidation products, to be 3-*benzyl*-4-*styryl*-1-*cyclopentene* (*E. Bergmann*, J. chem. Soc., 1935, 1359):

$$2\,CHPh{:}CH\cdot CH{:}CH_2 \longrightarrow \begin{array}{c} CHPh{:}CH\cdot CH\!-\!CH\cdot CH_2Ph \\ |\qquad | \\ CH_2\quad CH \\ \diagdown\!\!\diagup\!\!\!\diagup \\ CH \end{array}$$

(v) Cyclohexene type dimers

This is the common type of cyclic dimer, resulting from thermal treatment, or sometimes from acid treatment, of a conjugated diolefine. In cases where *cis*- and *trans*-isomers of the monomer have been isolated, only the *trans*-form readily dimerises; examples are 1:3-pentadiene (piperylene; Vol. I, p. 269) (*R. L. Frank et al.*, J. Amer. chem. Soc., 1947, **69**, 2313), 1-phenyl-1:3-butadiene (*O. Grummitt* and *F. J. Christoph*, *ibid.*, 1951, **73**, 3479), and 1-cyano-1:3-butadiene (*H. R. Snyder* and *G. I. Poos*, *ibid.*, 1949, **71**, 1395).

It was pointed out in Vol. I (p. 268) that this mode of dimerisation resembles the Diels-Alder reaction. The dimer of 1:3-butadiene is *4-vinyl-1-cyclohexene* (*O. Aschan*, Ber., 1924, **57**, 1959, gives b.p. 125·8–126·5°, d_4^{20} 0·8319, n_D^{20} 1·4624); see *S. V. Lebedev* (J. Soc. phys.-chem. Russe, 1910, **42**, 949, and later papers) for this dimerisation and many other diene dimerisations:

$$2\ CH_2{:}CH{\cdot}CH{:}CH_2 \longrightarrow C_6H_9{-}CH{:}CH_2$$

A dimer of the cyclohexene type has only one structural isomer when formed from a symmetrically substituted butadiene. Thus, analogously with 1:3-butadiene, 2:3-dimethyl-1:3-butadiene (Vol. I, p. 269) gives only 1:2:4-trimethyl-4-*iso*-propenyl-1-cyclohexene on thermal treatment. The literature is reviewed for this dimer by *E. H. Farmer* and *R. C. Pitkethly* (J. chem. Soc., 1938, 11), who obtained it by sulphuric acid catalysis of polymerisation in acetic acid solution and also prepared it (b.p. 206·5–207·5°, d_4^{16} 0·8626, n_D^{16} 1·4823), by an independent synthesis.

If an unsymmetrical, α-substituted butadiene, $CHR{:}CH{\cdot}CH{:}CH_2$, dimerises similarly, four structural isomers can theoretically result:

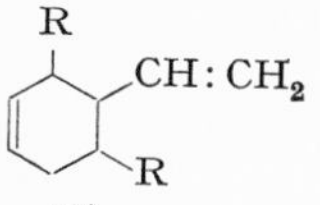

R, CH:CH$_2$, R (I) — R, R, CH:CH$_2$ (II) — R, CH:CHR (III) — R, CH:CHR (IV)

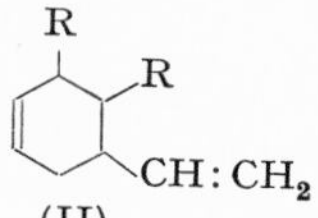

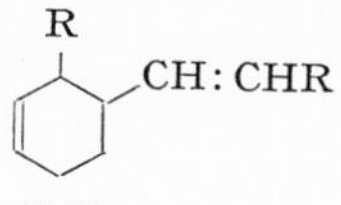

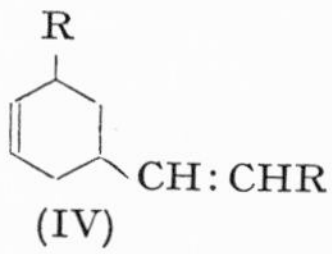

1:3-Butadiene-1-carboxylic acid (Vol. I, p. 645) gives a dimer of type III (R = CO_2H), modified by addition between the ring-carboxyl group and the side-chain double bond to give a *lactone*, m.p. 147° (*K. Alder* and *W. Vogt*, Ann., 1950, **570**, 190). 1-Cyano-1:3-butadiene (α-cyanoprene) polymerises on storage, giving a *dimer*, m.p. 53–54°, also of type III (R = CN) (*J. L. Charlish* and *W. H. Davies*, J. chem. Soc., 1950, 1385).

Similarly, an unsymmetrical, β-substituted butadiene, $CH_2{:}CR{\cdot}CH{:}CH_2$, can theoretically yield four structural isomers:

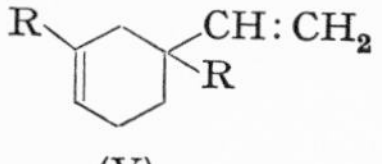

R, CH:CH$_2$, R (V) — R, CH:CH$_2$, R (VI) — R, CR:CH$_2$ (VII) — R, CR:CH$_2$ (VIII)

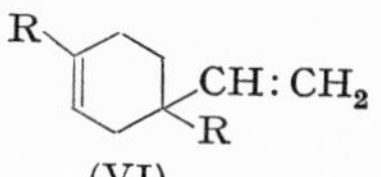

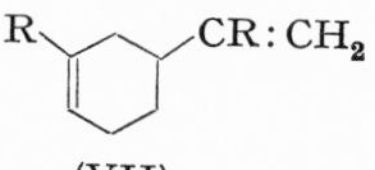

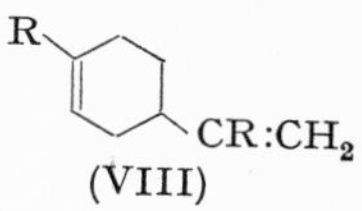

Thermal polymerisation of isoprene, which has been extensively investigated, gives dimers of structures VIII (R = Me) and VII (R = Me). The former dimer is dipentene (1-methyl-4-*iso*propenyl-1-cyclohexene), the optically inactive form of the naturally occurring terpene limonene (Vol. IIB); it may also be obtained by the thermal depolymerisation of natural rubber (p. 417). Recorded physical data vary considerably; *F. Richter* and *W. Wolff* give b.p. 178·0°/760 mm., n_D^{18} 1·4727 (Ber., 1930, **63**, 1721); *J. W. Brühl* gives d_4^{21} 0·8402 (J. chem. Soc., 1907, 115). The other dimer, b.p. 173–175°/750 mm., d_4^{20} 0·8457, n_D^{20} 1·4735, was termed *diprene* (2-methyl-4-*iso*propenyl-1-cyclohexene) by *T. Wagner-Jauregg* (Ann., 1931, **488**, 176; Ber., 1943, **76**, 1161), who prepared it and identified it with the products of earlier workers. 2-Phenyl-1:3-butadiene at 160° forms a dimer, m.p. 60°, of structure VI (R = C_6H_5), dehydrogenated to *p*-terphenyl (*K. Alder* and *J. Haydn*, Ann., 1950, **570**, 201). 2-Chloro-1:3-butadiene (chloroprene, Vol. I, p. 282) forms a liquid "β-polymer" on storage or heating in solution (*W. H. Carothers et al.*, J. Amer. chem. Soc., 1931, **53**, 4203; 1933, **55**, 789). This contains a dimer of structure VIII (R = Cl), b.p. 53°/0·9 mm., d_4^{25} 1·1653, n_D^{25} 1·5135, and a 1-chloro-4-vinylcyclohexadiene, formed by loss of hydrogen chloride from a dimer of structure VI (R = Cl) (*A. L. Klebanskii* and *M. M. Denisova*, J. gen. Chem. U.S.S.R., 1947, **17**, 703; *A. C. Cope* and *W. R. Schmitz*, J. Amer. chem. Soc., 1950, **72**, 3056). 2-Cyano-1:3-butadiene readily changes on storage into a dimer of structure VI (R = CN) (*C. S. Marvel* and *N. O. Brace*, *ibid.*, 1949, **71**, 37).

The best investigated unsymmetrical disubstituted butadiene is sorbic acid (1:3-pentadiene-1-carboxylic acid, Vol. I, p. 645), which at 190–230° gives a mixture of polymers, containing, apparently, all four of the theoretically possible dimeric structural isomers (*E. H. Farmer* and *C. R. Morrison-Jones*, J. chem. Soc., 1940, 1339; *D. H. Wheeler*, J. Amer. chem. Soc., 1948, **70**, 3467).

(vi) Cyclo-octadiene-type dimers

A high-boiling fraction observed by Carothers in the "β-polymer" of chloroprene (see above), and later shown to be a dichlorocyclo-octadiene (*L. G. T. Brown et al.*, J. chem. Soc., 1944, 101), was finally identified as 1:6-*dichlorocyclo-octa-1:5-diene*, f.p. 13·8°, b.p. 64°/0·25 mm., d_4^{25} 1·2167, n_D^{25} 1·5339, formed by "head-to-head, tail-to-tail" dimerisation (*A. C. Cope* and *W. R. Schmitz*, *loc. cit*):

$$2\ CH_2{:}CCl{\cdot}CH{:}CH_2 \longrightarrow$$ (1,6-dichlorocyclo-octa-1,5-diene ring: Cl, Cl)

This can be used as an intermediate in the synthesis of cyclo-octatetraene (p. 260) (*A. C. Cope* and *W. J. Bailey*, J. Amer. chem. Soc., 1948, **70**, 2305). 2:3-Dichloro-1:3-butadiene forms an analogous dimer, m.p. 98–99° (*R. E. Foster* and *R. S. Schreiber*, *ibid.*, 1948, **70**, 2303).

Similarly, a higher-boiling compound which accompanies vinylcyclohexene in the thermal dimerisation of 1:3-butadiene (*S. V. Lebedev* and *S. Sergjenko*, J. gen. Chem. U.S.S.R., 1935, **5**, 1829) was identified as cyclo-octa-1:5-diene (Chap. VI, p. 259), m.p. −70·1°, b.p. 150·8°/755 mm, d_4^{20} 0·8811, n_D^{20} 1·4918 (*K. Ziegler* and *H. Wilms*, Ann., 1950, **567**, 1). It was assigned a *cis-cis*-"boat"-

configuration and was thus differentiated from the highly unstable stereoisomeric *trans-trans*-compound of *R. Willstätter* and *H. Veraguth* (Ber., 1905, **38**, 1975; 1907, **40**, 957).

(vii) Bicyclic dimers

The most fully investigated case of this kind was reported by *Farmer* and *Pitkethly* in their study (*loc. cit.*) of 2:3-dimethyl-1:3-butadiene, which yielded, as a minor product in the dimer fraction, a camphor-like, volatile, solid dimer, m.p. 66°, shown to have, probably, the annexed structure (cf. *idem*, J. chem. Soc., 1938, 287; *E. H. Farmer* and *J. F. Martin, ibid.*, 1940, 1169).

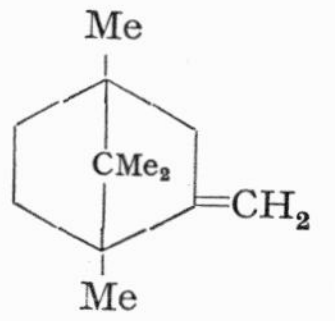

Me

CMe$_2$ =CH$_2$

Me

The dimers and higher polymers of cyclopentadiene (p. 82) and cyclohexadiene (p. 149) are polycyclic compounds.

(viii) Cyclic trimers, tetramers, etc.

When diolefinic compounds are converted into cyclic dimers, varying amounts of more complex polymers are usually also present, and these can often be separated as higher-boiling fractions. Few investigations of their structure have been made. A mixture of polymers, obtained from 2:3-dimethyl-1:3-butadiene (*Farmer* and *Martin, loc. cit.*), was separated, by means of a molecular still, into fractions ranging from trimers to hexamers. One of the trimers was shown to have the annexed probable fused-ring structure.

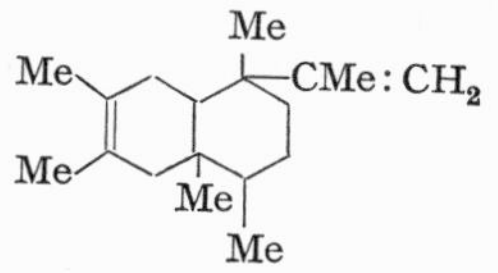

Me
Me CMe:CH$_2$
Me
Me
Me

There is also evidence for the formation of cyclic trimers, without fused rings, by reaction of a further monomer molecule with the extracyclic olefinic bond of a dimer molecule. Thus, the dimer of 1:3-butadiene can add monomer to give *di-(cyclohex-3-enyl)*, b.p. 230–232° (*K. Alder* and *H. F. Rickert*, Ber., 1938, **71**, 373):

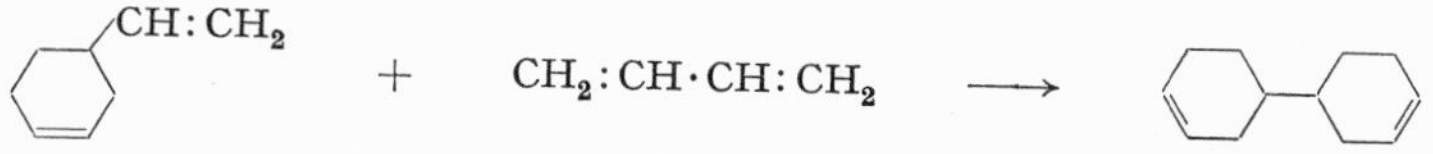

CH:CH$_2$ + CH$_2$:CH·CH:CH$_2$ ⟶

(ix) Allene polymers

Allene hydrocarbons (Vol. I, p. 266) undergo thermal polymerisation, giving products which range from volatile, reactive, liquid dimers to viscous and solid polymers of high molecular weight. They have been little investigated since they were assigned cyclobutane structures by *S. V. Lebedev* (J. Soc. phys.-chem. Russe, 1911, **43**, 820; 1913, **45**, 1249, 1357). Dimerisation appears to occur by the process:

$$2\,CH_2{:}C{:}CH_2 \longrightarrow \begin{array}{l} CH_2\text{—}C{:}CH_2 \\ \;|\qquad\;\;| \\ CH_2\text{—}C{:}CH_2 \end{array}$$

but the double bonds of the dimer readily participate in further reactions.

(x) *Polymers of non-conjugated dienes*

The simplest diene of this class is 1:4-pentadiene (Vol. I, p. 269). As is usual with non-conjugated dienes, it does not easily polymerise, but at 250–290° it forms a mixture of polymers, including a dimer, b.p. 176°, which is principally 1-*allyl*-2-*methylcyclohex*-3-*ene*, perhaps formed after partial conversion of the monomer into its conjugated isomer (*A. Ahmad* and *E. H. Farmer*, J. chem. Soc., 1940, 1176):

$$CH_2{:}CH{\cdot}CH_2{\cdot}CH{:}CH_2 \;+\; CH_2{:}CH{\cdot}CH{:}CH{\cdot}CH_3 \longrightarrow \text{(cyclohexene ring)}\begin{array}{l} /CH_2{\cdot}CH{:}CH_2 \\ \text{—Me} \end{array}$$

(d) *Polymers of trienes and higher polyenes*

The multiplication of conjugated olefinic bonds in a carbon chain, as in the carotenoids (Chap. X) and in the synthetic polyene hydrocarbons $Me{\cdot}(CH{:}CH)_n{\cdot}Me$ ($n = 3, 4, 6$), prepared by *R. Kuhn* and *C. Grundmann* (Ber., 1938, **71**, 442) leads to an increase in ease of polymerisation, though terminal aryl groups, as in the series $Ph{\cdot}(CH{:}CH)_n{\cdot}Ph$ (*R. Kuhn* and *A. Winterstein*, Helv., 1928, **11**, 87), have a stabilising effect. Little is known concerning the structure of polymers of the higher polyenes. The simplest monomer of the series, 1:3:5-hexatriene (Vol. I, p. 271), is very readily transformed into a mixture of polymers, in which the dimeric fraction, b.p. 50–55°/3 mm., contains 1-1′-*butadienyl*-2-*vinylcyclohex*-3-*ene* (*M. S. Kharasch* and *E. Sternfeld*, J. Amer. chem. Soc., 1939, **61**, 2320):

$$2\,CH_2{:}CH{\cdot}CH{:}CH{\cdot}CH{:}CH_2 \longrightarrow \text{(cyclohexene ring)}\begin{array}{l} \text{—}CH{:}CH_2 \\ \backslash CH{:}CH{\cdot}CH{:}CH_2 \end{array}$$

(e) *High molecular-weight polymers from mono-olefinic compounds; vinyl and vinylidene plastics*

For the extensive literature in this field, see e.g. *Carleton Ellis*, "Chemistry of Synthetic Resins", New York, 1935; *R. S. Morrell* and *H. M. Langton*, "Synthetic Resins and Allied Plastics", Oxford, 1951; *C. E. Schildknecht*, "Vinyl and Related Polymers", New York, 1952; *R. G. R. Bacon*, Dict. appl. Chem., Vol. 10, London, 1950.

Typical polymers of this class (see under appropriate monomers in Vol. I) have molecular weights in the range 10,000–500,000, and, from chemical and physical evidence, are believed to consist predominantly of long carbon chains in which the monomer units are joined "head-to-tail":

$$n\,CH_2{:}CHX \longrightarrow \ldots\ldots CH_2{\cdot}CHX{\cdot}CH_2{\cdot}CHX{\cdot}CH_2{\cdot}CHX\ldots\ldots$$

$$n\,CH_2{:}CXY \longrightarrow \ldots\ldots CH_2{\cdot}CXY{\cdot}CH_2{\cdot}CXY{\cdot}CH_2{\cdot}CXY\ldots\ldots$$

At the ends of the chains may be found, for example, groups derived from catalyst or solvent, and olefinic or saturated groups formed by disproportionation reactions (Vol. I, pp. 206, 214). The linearity of these polymers may be broken by a minor degree of chain-branching.

The polymers are heterogeneous in that they comprise mixtures of chains of varying length. The molecular weights determined from them (e.g. by osmotic pressure or viscosity measurements) are therefore average values. Molecules of different sizes may be laboriously separated into more or less homogeneous fractions (cf. p. 413), and, by examining these separately, a molecular-weight distribution curve may be constructed. The same considerations apply to copolymerisation products, which have the additional complication that variation in the sequence of monomer units in the polymer chain is probable. Copolymerisation (cf. pp. 393, 430) is widely practised with pairs of vinyl compounds. The compounds used in copolymer-pairs do not necessarily polymerise easily when treated separately. There is now a good deal of co-ordinating theory concerning the ability or non-ability of monomers to participate in copolymer-formation (*T. Alfrey, J. J. Bohrer* and *H. Mark*, "Copolymerisation", New York, 1952).

Most linear polymers soften and gradually melt when heated; i.e. they are *thermoplastic*. They usually dissolve in suitably chosen solvents. Non-linear polymers may behave differently. These are formed from monomers such as *p*-divinylbenzene, $CH_2{:}CH{\cdot}C_6H_4{\cdot}CH{:}CH_2$, or diallyl esters, $CH_2{:}CH{\cdot}CH_2{\cdot}O{\cdot}CO{\cdot}R{\cdot}CO{\cdot}O{\cdot}CH_2{\cdot}CH{:}CH_2$, containing two olefinic bonds, each of which may become incorporated in a separate polymer chain. By varying the choice of monomer composition between (i) a pure divinyl compound, (ii) mixtures, taken for copolymerisation, of the divinyl and a monovinyl compound, and (iii) the pure monovinyl compound, then a series of polymers may be formed in which the molecular structure is, respectively, (i) a network, (ii) aggregates of chains with a varying number of cross-links (cf. rubber vulcanisation, p. 423), and (iii) unattached chains. With increasing cross-linking, the fusibility and solubility of the polymer decline and its molecular weight becomes increasingly large and ill-defined.

The physical and chemical properties, and hence the practical applications, of vinyl and vinylidene polymers, $-(CH_2{\cdot}CHX)_n-$ and $-(CH_2{\cdot}CXY)_n-$, are largely determined by the nature of the substituent groups, X and Y. These differences are briefly summarised below for the more important representatives of the group. Most of these polymers are made with the aid of peroxidic catalysts (e.g. hydrogen peroxide, persulphates, benzoyl peroxide), which are believed to function by a free-radical mechanism (Vol. I, p. 203). Such polymerisations may be carried out (i) on undiluted monomer (*mass* or *bulk* polymerisation), (ii) in a solvent (*solution* polymerisation), (iii) with the monomer very finely dispersed in an aqueous medium (*emulsion* polymerisation), or (iv) with the monomer coarsely dispersed in an aqueous medium (*granular* or *pearl* polymerisation). A modified process, applied to ethylene and some other rather stable olefines, involves polymerisation at about 200°, with very high pressures (500–1000 atmospheres), in the presence of a trace of oxygen. A different method of initiating polymerisation involves use of catalysts of the Friedel-Crafts type, e.g. in a diluent at −100°. This is believed to proceed by an ionic mechanism (for discussions, see J. chem. Soc., 1947, 252, and Nature, 1952, **169**, 828; *P. H. Plesch*, "Cationic Polymerisation", London, 1952). Among the polymers listed below, this technique is used for poly*iso*butene and polyvinyl ethers.

Polyethylene (**polythene**), $-(CH_2{\cdot}CH_2)_n-$, is a fairly inert material, of wax-like appearance, easily moulded or formed into films, and possessing excellent insulating properties. **Polyisobutene,** $-(CH_2{\cdot}CMe_2)_n-$, is further discussed (pp. 429, 435) in connection with synthetic elestomers. **Polystyrene,** $-(CH_2{\cdot}CHPh)_n-$, is a tough, transparent resin, easily moulded, and possessing good optical and insulating properties. Styrene and its polymers are probably the most extensively investigated of all the vinyl compounds (see *R. H. Boundy* and *R. F. Boyer*, editors, "Styrene. Its Polymers, Copolymers, and Derivatives", New York, 1952). **Polyvinyl chloride,** $-(CH_2{\cdot}CHCl)_n-$, is a white powder, which, when heated with suitable liquids, such as phthalic and phosphoric esters (plasticisers) gives rubbery gels, which have important uses as films, coatings, and moulded products. Some related vinyl chloride/vinyl acetate copolymers, as well as chlorinated derivatives of polyvinyl chloride, have fibre-forming properties. Polymers of vinyl chloride (and vinylidene chloride) tend to darken on exposure to heat and light unless suitable chemicals (e.g. lead salts) are incorporated as stabilisers. **Polyvinylidene chloride** $-(CH_2{\cdot}CCl_2)_n-$, and related copolymers are also white powders, convertible into fibres. **Polytetrafluoroethylene,** $-(CF_2{\cdot}CF_2)_n-$, is a tough, white solid, very high melting, and extremely inert towards corrosive chemicals.

Polyvinyl ethers, $-[CH_2{\cdot}CH(OR)]_n-$ (R = Me, Et, Bu, etc.) are very sticky materials, readily soluble in many organic solvents. **Polyvinyl acetate,** $-[CH_2{\cdot}CH(O{\cdot}CO{\cdot}CH_3)]_n-$, the commonest of the vinyl ester polymers, is a resin, readily soluble in many organic solvents, and possessing good adhesive properties. On hydrolysis it yields **polyvinyl alcohol,** $-[CH_2{\cdot}CH(OH)]_n-$, a white solid, which gives viscous, starch-like, aqueous solutions, and which, on reaction with aldehydes, gives acetals; the best known are *polyvinyl formal, acetal,* and *butyral.* **Polyacrylic esters,** $-[CH_2{\cdot}CH(CO_2R)]_n-$ (R = Me, Et, etc.) are soft, rather sticky resins. Among polymethacrylic esters, **polymethyl methacrylate,** $-[CH_2{\cdot}CMe(CO_2Me)]_n-$ is important as a tough, glass-like resin, easily moulded, and possessing excellent optical properties. Polymethacrylic esters of the higher alcohols are resins which are increasingly soft as the size of the alkyl group is increased. Hydrolysis of the preceding two groups of polymeric esters gives, respectively, **polyacrylic acid,** $-[CH_2{\cdot}CH(CO_2H)]_n-$, and **polymethacrylic**

acid, $-[CH_2 \cdot CMe(CO_2H)]-_n$, which are also obtainable by hydrolysis of the corresponding polymeric nitriles, or by polymerisation of the respective monomeric acids. The polymeric acids forms viscous aqueous solutions and give polymeric salts with alkalis.

Polyacrylonitrile, $-[CH_2 \cdot CH(CN)]_n-$, is a white powder, which decomposes before its high softening point is reached, and which dissolves only in a few relatively uncommon solvents, such as dimethylformamide. This polymer and some related copolymers have important fibre-forming properties. N-Vinyl polymers include *poly-(N-vinylpyrrolidone)*, a water-soluble material, which has been used as a blood-plasma substitute, and *poly-(N-vinylcarbazole)*.

2. Natural high molecular-weight isoprene polymers

(a) Natural rubber and its derivatives

(i) Nature, occurrence and isolation of natural rubber

Natural rubber, a product of vegetable metabolism, is mainly composed of high molecular-weight olefinic hydrocarbon. Its composition may be represented by the molecular formula $(C_5H_8)_n$, where n is large but variable, and is typically 5000 or more. The C_5H_8 units, which are united linearly to form long-chain molecules, have the structure $-CH_2 \cdot C(CH_3):CH \cdot CH_2-$. At each double bond the carbon atoms of the chain possess a *cis*-configuration.

Natural rubber is handled rarely, if ever, as a homogeneous material. In nature the rubber hydrocarbon is accompanied by varying amounts of many other substances, and some of these are normally retained during the isolation of rubber. The hydrocarbon chains vary in length and quite readily undergo structural changes by fission, cross-linking and cyclisation. They are readily attacked by oxygen, and by many other substances, and they may contain a small amount of combined oxygen, even when the rubber has been freshly isolated. In commercial use, rubber usually becomes additionally heterogeneous by being mixed (compounded) with other materials and by being chemically modified by reaction with sulphur (vulcanisation).

A bibliography issued in 1942 (*A. I. Moyle*, Texas Agric. exp. Sta. Circular 99) listed 1791 species of plants which had been reported to contain rubber. *J. von Wiesner* ("Die Rohstoffe des Pflanzenreiches", Leipzig, 1927) gave 490 species which produce rubber in significant quantities. It is not found in monocotyledons, gymnosperms, or lower plants; in dicotyledons it tends to occur more commonly in particular families, e.g. the *Moraceae*, *Euphorbiaceae*, and *Compositae* (*J. Bonner*, "Plant Biochemistry", New York, 1950; *J. Bonner* and *A. W. Galston*, Bot. Rev., 1947, **13**, 543). The most important rubber-bearing trees and plants are found wild, or are cultivated, in tropical zones of Asia, South America, and Africa. The raw rubber of commerce is derived almost entirely, to the extent of more than one million tons per annum, from the *Hevea brasiliensis* plantations of Malaya, Indonesia and other territories of South-East Asia. Among others, the following rubber-bearing plants have been experimentally cultivated in temperate or sub-tropical parts of the U.S.A.: *Parthenium argentatum* (the guayule shrub), *Cryptostegia grandiflora* (a vine), and species of *Solidago* (golden-rod) (*H. L. Trumbull*, Ind. Eng. Chem., 1942, **34**, 1328; *E. P. Jones*, *ibid.*, 1948, **40**, 864). Since about 1930 the cultivation of rubber-bearing plants related to the dandelion (*Taraxacum kok saghyz* and allied species) has been developed in the U.S.S.R.

The early European explorers of South America found that native inhabitants made use of wild rubber. About 1736 Charles de la Condamine brought samples to Europe from a Peruvian expedition and François Fresneau described rubber-bearing trees of Guiana. The French "caoutchouc" and German "Kautschuk" are derived from a South American term meaning "weeping tree", a reference to the exudation of latex from a cut tree. Rubber was known to Joseph Priestley (ca. 1770) who called it "India-rubber" from its erasing properties. It was first analysed by *Michael Faraday* (Quart. J. Sci., 1826, **21**, 19). During the 19th century rubber was utilised industrially in coating and moulding processes; sulphur vulcanisation (discovered 1839) and other manufacturing processes were developed. Rubber vastly increased in economic importance with the development of motor transport at the beginning of the 20th century.

Until about 1910 commercial raw rubber came mainly from wild trees of the Amazon valley. The most important of these was *Hevea brasiliensis*, a member of the *Euphorbiaceae*, a tree which may attain some 30 metres in height. In 1876 Henry Wickham brought 70,000 of its seeds from the Amazon to Kew Gardens, and plants obtained from these were used to found the rubber plantations of Ceylon and ultimately of Malaya and the East Indies.

Rubber hydrocarbon is present in *H. brasiliensis* and other plants as a dispersion in an aqueous serum. The dispersion has a milky appearance and is called a *latex*. In *H. brasiliensis* it occurs in a system of communicating latex vessels in the cambium of the trunk and is released by *tapping*, i.e., cutting through the bark. Tapping is begun about 5 years after a tree is planted and yields 2–7 lb. of rubber per tree annually. In guayule, rubber is not found in special vessels but is distributed through the pith and cortex cells of stem and root, forming sometimes 20 % of the dry weight of the plant. In *Solidago* it is not present as a latex but as solid particles in leaf cells.

Hevea latex may be directly utilised in industry after it has been stabilised and concentrated, but most of it is first converted into solid rubber by the process of coagulation (see below). This is carried out by adding very dilute acetic or formic acid to the latex. The resulting junket-like mass, or coagulum, is converted into dry rubber, usually in the form of *pale crepe* or *smoked sheet*. For pale crepe, the coagulum is squeezed, washed, and disintegrated on a corrugated roller mill and is air-dried; for smoked sheet, slabs of coagulum are squeezed on smooth-rolled mills, and dried at 40–50° in an atmosphere of wood smoke.

As a preliminary to making *vulcanised rubber*, the form which is usually needed for technical purposes, dry rubber is softened by a process of hot milling *(mastication)*, giving *masticated rubber*, in which the rubber molecules have undergone some degradation. For *vulcanisation* the masticated rubber is mixed (compounded) with sulphur, an organic accelerator (vulcanisation catalyst), zinc oxide, antioxidant and fillers, and the mixture subjected to heat and pressure. Chemical aspects of vulcanisation are discussed on p. 423.

By far the largest consumption of vulcanised rubber is in the manufacture of tyres. Other important applications are the manufacture of tubing, belting, electric cables, flooring, coated textiles and cellular (sponge) compositions.

(ii) Composition and properties of rubber latex

The latex of *H. brasiliensis* (see e.g. *H. P. Stevens* and *W. H. Stevens*, "Rubber Latex", London, 1936) is a mobile, white (or slightly discoloured) fluid. Its composition is affected by the season, conditions of tapping, etc., the rubber content varying approximately over the range 20–60 %, with an average of about 40 %.

It is a colloidal dispersion of particles of rubber hydrocarbon in an aqueous medium, which also contains non-rubber components, both water-soluble and water-insoluble. The rubber particles are globular or pear-shaped and exhibit Brownian movement. Their diameter varies from about 2 microns downwards, a substantial proportion being of submicroscopic dimensions (*E. E. Langeland*. Ind. Eng. Chem. Anal. Ed., 1936, **8**, 174; *F. L. Lucas*, Ind. Eng. Chem., 1938, **30**, 146; *ibid.*, 1942, **34**, 1371; *M. van den Tempel*, Trans. Instn. Rubb. Ind., 1951, **27**, 290). The specific gravity of rubber hydrocarbon is about 0·92 and that of 40 % latex is about 0·97. When latex is allowed to stand, the rubber particles tend to rise to the surface, forming a cream, which can be redispersed by shaking. The non-rubber constituents readily undergo bacterial decomposition, with accompanying coagulation of the rubber particles. This is commonly prevented by adding ammonia to the latex; other stabilisers include caustic alkalis, formalin, and sodium pentachlorophenate.

For use in industry, latex is usually concentrated to a rubber content of 60–70 %. The chief methods used are: partial evaporation of water, under reduced pressure, in the presence of stabilising agent; or centrifuging, when a layer enriched in rubber separates above a serum layer which is practically free of rubber; or treatment of latex with creaming agents, which have the same effect as a centrifuge. Creaming agents (see e.g. *H. C. Baker*, Trans. Instn. Rubb. Ind., 1937, **13**, 70; *W. S. Davey* and *K. C. Sekar*, *ibid.*, 1947, **23**, 77; *G. E. van Gils* and *G. M. Kraay*, Adv. Colloid Sci., 1942, I, 247) are water-soluble colloids, such as vegetable gums, alginates, cellulose derivatives and alkali-metal salts of polyacrylic acid; they appear to cause some aggregation of the rubber particles, but the mechanism of their action is not completely elucidated.

The composition of a typical (non-concentrated) *H. brasiliensis* latex is as follows (figures are averages from various compilations):

	per cent by weight
Rubber hydrocarbon	40
Proteins and amino-acids	2
Lipids and fatty acids	1
Sterols	0·5
Quebrachitol	1
Carbohydrates	0·5
Inorganic salts	0·5

The inorganic ions include Na^+, K^+, Mg^{++}, Ca^{++}, $PO_4^{\equiv}$, $CO_3^{=}$, and $SO_4^{=}$.

The proteins are largely present as an adsorbed layer on the surface of the rubber particles and are probably an important factor in promoting the stability of the dispersion (*C. Bondy* and *H. Freundlich*, C.r. Lab. Carlsberg, 1938, **22**, 89; *A. R. Kemp* and *W. G. Straitiff*, J. phys. Chem., 1940, **44**, 788). Proteins have been separated by several workers and in some cases their amino-acid constituents have been reported (*W. N. C. Belgrave*, Malay. agric. J., 1925, **13**, 154, 367; *R. O. Bishop*, *ibid.*, 1927, **15**, 27; *R. F. A. Altman*, Arch. Rubbercultuur, 1939, **23**, 239; *T. Midgley et al.*, J. Amer. chem. Soc., 1937, **59**, 2501; *G. R. Tristram*, Biochem. J., 1940, **34**, 301; *ibid.*, 1941, **35**, 413; *C. P. Roe* and *R. H. Ewart*, J. Amer. chem. Soc., 1942, **64**, 2628). *G. S. Whitby* and *H. Greenberg* (Biochem. J., 1941, **35**, 640) identified several free α-amino-acids in the serum of Hevea latex. *R. F. A. Altman* (Ind. Eng. Chem., 1948, **40**, 241), in an examination of nitrogenous latex constituents which have the property of accelerating sulphur vulcanisation, reported the presence of choline and ethanolamine, derived respectively from lecithins and cephalins. Latex also contains various enzymes (see, e.g., *L. N. S. De Haan-Homans*, Ind. Eng. Chem., 1951, **43**, 403). Enzyme action is probably involved in the spontaneous coagulation of unstabilised latex.

The lipid constituents include a small amount of phospholipid (*E. Rhodes* and *R. O. Bishop*, Quart. J. Rubb. Res. Inst. Malaya, 1930, **2**, 125) and stearic, oleic and linoleic acids (*G. S. Whitby et al.*, J. chem. Soc., 1926, **129**, 1448). Like the proteins, this acid fraction appears to be largely adsorbed on the surface of the rubber particles (*H. C. Baker*, Trans. Instn. Rubb. Ind., 1940, **16**, 165).

Unidentified sterol constituents of rubber were reported by *G. S. Whitby et al.* *(loc. cit.)* and by *H. A. Bruson et al.* (Ind. Eng. Chem., 1927, **19**, 1187). The latter workers also reported the presence of a ketone, $C_{15}H_{24}O$, a hydrocarbon, $C_{15}H_{24}$, and *n*-octadecyl alcohol. When similar work was carried out by *I. M. Heilbron, E. R. H. Jones et al.* (J. chem. Soc., 1941, 344) they obtained a sterol mixture containing β-sitosterol and a dehydrostigmastanol, together with eicosyl alcohol.

Various reducing sugars have been reported in Hevea latex, but its main water-soluble constituent is *quebrachitol*, $C_7H_{14}O_6$, a colourless, crystalline solid, m.p. 192–193°, $[\alpha]_D^{20}$ −81·2° in 5% aqueous solution; see p. 168). Quebrachitol was first reported in Hevea latex serum by *A. W. K. de Jong* (Rec. Trav. chim., 1906, **25**, 48) and may be isolated from this source in about 0·4% yield

(*E. Rhodes* and *J. L. Wiltshire*, J. Rubb. Res. Inst. Malaya, 1932, **3**, 160; *J. van Alphen*, Ind. Eng. Chem., 1951, **43**, 141).

The rubber particles in Hevea latex are negatively charged and can be deposited on an anode. The coagulation of latex (see above) involves the coalescence of the dispersed particles into large aggregates and occurs when external conditions affect the charged surface layer of the particles. Coagulation may be brought about by addition of acids, salts of polyvalent metals, ethyl alcohol, or certain enzymes, such as papain. It is also promoted by heating, and readily occurs as the result of mechanical action (e.g. stirring in contact with coarse powders or rough surfaces). By treating latex with a large excess of acid the charge on the particles may be reversed and a stable, positively charged dispersion results.

"Whole latex rubber", obtained by the evaporation of latex, contains all the original serum constituents. On the other hand, ordinary raw rubber, obtained by coagulation, contains very little water-soluble material, but has perhaps 7% of non-rubber constituents which include proteins, fatty acids and sterols. Part of this may be removed by acetone extraction, a process which is used in the routine analysis of raw rubber. The extracted "resin", which may amount to about 3% of the weight of dry rubber, is a mixture which includes the fatty acids and sterols of the latex (*G. S. Whitby et al., loc. cit.*). Some of the "resin" constituents are natural antioxidants (*H. A. Bruson et al., loc. cit.*).

Provided that suitable precautions are taken to maintain a stable dispersion, rubber can be subjected in latex form to some of the chemical reactions which are more commonly carried out in solution (see below; for a review see *G. Salomon et al.*, Ind. Eng. Chem., 1951, **43**, 315).

(iii) Rubber solutions

Most chemical reactions of rubber are studied in solution in organic solvents. Alternatively, in suitable cases, reaction may be performed on latex or solid rubber.

Occasionally, rubber latex is transferred in its entirety into an organic solvent. A toluene-pyridine mixture has been used for this purpose by *W. J. van Essen* (Rec. Trav. chim., 1950, **69**, 753), whilst *G. F. Bloomfield* (J. Rubb. Res. Inst. Malaya, 1951, **13**, Communication 271) employed benzene-treatment, followed by removal of the water originally in the serum. Normally, crepe or smoked sheet is employed for preparing solutions. If these are first degraded by mastication, dissolution occurs more easily, but on the other hand vulcanised rubbers, which have a cross-linked structure, swell in solvents but do not dissolve.

Aromatic hydrocarbons (benzene, toluene, xylene) are probably the most useful of the common solvents. Lightly masticated crepe, shaken with benzene, gradually swells and slowly passes into a homogeneous, slightly turbid, pale brown solution, of typical colloidal character; at a concentration of about 5% it is very viscous and sticky. Other useful solvents are chlorinated hydrocarbons (carbon tetrachloride, chloroform, chlorobenzene, etc.), aliphatic and alicyclic hydrocarbons, carbon disulphide and ether. Highly polar compounds, such as the lower alcohols and ketones, are usually non-solvents, and, if added in excess to rubber solutions, cause precipitation. On the other hand, a mixture of a limited amount of a polar liquid, with e.g. benzene, may be an excellent solvent. Rubber is insoluble in water, but it can absorb water to the extent of about 25 % of its weight, largely on account of water-soluble contaminants present in it.

The swelling of rubber in organic liquids, and the viscosity and other characteristics of its solutions, have been extensively studied (see *G. Gee*, Annual Reports, 1942, **39**, 7; Adv. Colloid Sci., 1946, II, 145; Quart. Reviews, 1947, **1**, 265).

(iv) Rubber hydrocarbon: purification, heterogeneity, structure and molecular size

Rubber hydrocarbon is believed to be predominantly a linear polyisoprene with the isoprene units joined "head-to-tail" in a regular 1:4-pattern:

$$\ldots.CH_2{\cdot}C(CH_3){:}CH{\cdot}CH_2{\cdot}CH_2{\cdot}C(CH_3){:}CH{\cdot}CH_2\ldots.$$

This is supported by the following evidence, which will appear in subsequent sections: chemical analysis; results of pyrolysis; conversion of isoprene into synthetic polymers which show some resemblance to natural rubber; reaction with hydrogen, and some other additive reagents for olefines, ultimately to the extent of approximately 1 molecule per isoprene unit; results of ozonolysis; physical measurements, particularly infra-red absorption spectra and X-ray crystallographic data.

The ozonolysis experiments of C. D. Harries, from 1904 onwards (see under "Oxidation") have provided the most important chemical evidence for this structure, but originally *Harries* considered the isoprene units to be linked by 1:4-bonds into dimeric 1:5-dimethylcyclo-octa-1:5-diene structures, which were further united, in an uncertain manner, to form rubber hydrocarbon molecules (Ber., 1905, **38**, 1195). Later he considered the rubber molecule to consist of numerous isoprene units linked 1:4 in a very large ring (Ann., 1914, **406**, 173); this suggestion had previously been made by *S. S. Pickles* (J. chem. Soc., 1910, **97**, 1085). The concept that rubber is a macromolecular substance, that hundreds or thousands of isoprene units may be involved in the structure of a single chain (not necessarily a large ring), is due primarily to *H. Staudinger* (Ber., 1920, **53**, 1073 and later papers; "Die Hochmolekularen Organischen Verbindungen", Berlin, 1932). Subsequently, and particularly in its more physical aspects, the development of rubber chemistry has been very closely interwoven with that of other branches of high-polymer chemistry.

Other workers have considered the following problems: the extent to which the molecules differ among themselves in size and structural detail; whether small amounts of combined oxygen and nitrogen are present; what groups terminate the chains, or whether the chains are really huge rings; and whether branching, cyclisation, or cross-linking interrupts the linearity of the chains.

Because of its commercial importances *H. brasiliensis* rubber has been used in nearly all structural studies. Data relating to rubbers from other sources are scanty, but their general trend is to indicate that these rubbers are likewise linear polyisoprenes, comparable in molecular weight with Hevea rubber. Some wild African rubbers which have been examined showed similarities to Hevea rubber in analysis, molecular weight, certain physical properties and X-ray crystallographic data, though some samples had a very high content of non-rubber constituents and differed in oxygen-sensitivity and in the characteristics of derived vulcanisates (*G. R. Tristram, G. Gee, L. R. G. Treloar* and *G. A. Jeffrey*, Trans. Instn. Rubb. Ind., 1943, **18**, 253; *G. Martin, ibid.*, 1943, **19**, 38). The rubbers of *Cryptostegia grandiflora* (*H. L. Trumbull*, Ind. Eng. Chem., 1942, **34**, 1328) and of *Asclepias syriaca* (*E. B. Paul et al.*, Canad. J. Res., 1943, **B 21**, 219) also resemble Hevea rubber in X-ray crystallographic characteristics. The hydrocarbon of gutta-percha and related materials (see p. 427) is also a linear high molecular-weight polyisoprene, but is a geometrical isomer of rubber.

Isolation of pure rubber hydrocarbon from crude Hevea rubber has two aspects: removal of oxygen- and nitrogen-containing materials, and fractionation of the hydrocarbon itself into components of different molecular weight. After acetone extraction, rubber is still contaminated with protein, which is difficult to remove. *R. Pummerer et al.* (Ber., 1927, **60**, 2148, 2152; *ibid.*, 1928, **61**, 1583; Kautschuk, 1929, **5**, 129) employed alkaline hydrolysis of the protein, but failed to eliminate nitrogen completely. By a similar process *A. D. Cummings* and *L. B. Sebrell* (Ind. Eng. Chem., 1929, **21**, 553) reduced the nitrogen content below 0·01 %, whilst *H. C. Baker* (Trans. Instn. Rubb. Ind., 1940, **16**, 165) found a non-removable residue of 0·03 %, which he suggested might be chemically combined. *W. H. Smith et al.* (J. Res. nat. Bur. Stand., 1933, **10**, 479) claimed complete removal of protein by enzymic hydrolysis.

Purification may be carried further by fractionation with a solvent, or, more usually, with a solvent mixture (e.g. benzene and ethyl alcohol, light petroleum and acetone). One method used is fractional precipitation, carried out by progressive addition of a non-solvent to a rubber solution, or, preferably, by a series of operations in each of which a solution of rubber in hot mixed solvents yields, on cooling, an insoluble fraction, enriched in the highest molecular-weight components (*R. Pummerer* and *A. Koch*, Ann., 1924, **438**, 295; *T. Midgley et al.*, J. Amer. chem. Soc., 1931, **53**, 2733; *ibid.*, 1932, **54**, 3343). A second method is fractional solution, carried out by allowing rubber to diffuse into solvent, or into mixed solvents of varying composition (*A. R. Kemp* and *H. Peters*, J. phys. Chem., 1939, **43**, 1063; *G. F. Bloomfield* and *E. H. Farmer*, Trans. Instn. Rubb. Ind., 1940, **16**, 69).

Carbon and hydrogen values, reported by various workers for purified samples of rubber hydrocarbon, are exceedingly close to the values required for $(C_5H_8)_n$. The determination of n, i.e. molecular-weight measurement, is usually based on the osmotic or viscosity properties of rubber solutions. The techniques and mathematical relationships involved are common to the study of all types of linear macromolecules (for reviews see *G. Gee*, Annual Reports, 1942, **39**, 7; *P. Johnson, ibid.*, 1946, **43**, 30). The molecular weights thus obtained will be averages unless the rubber fractions used are homogeneous. It may be doubted, however, whether absolutely homogeneous rubber samples have yet been obtained.

The earlier molecular-weight determinations of various rubber samples gave values from below 10,000 to above 100,000 (see e.g. *H. Staudinger* and *H. F. Bondy*, Ann., 1931, **488**, 127), but more recent work with purified, non-degraded fractions has given values of the order of 300,000 (*G. F. Bloomfield* and *E. H. Farmer*, Trans. Instn. Rubb. Ind., 1940, **16**, 69; *H. Staudinger* and *K. Fischer*, J. pr. Chem., 1941, **157**, 19; *K. H. Meyer et al.*, Helv., 1940, **23**, 430; 1941, **24**, 217; *G. Gee*, Trans. Faraday Soc., 1940, **36**, 1163, 1171; 1942, **38**, 108; *W. J. van Essen*, Rec. Trav. chim., 1950, **69**, 753). In general, nitrogen-containing fractions are found to have high molecular weights and oxidised materials low molecular weights.

According to present views the heterogeneity of rubber is best represented by a molecular-weight distribution curve, but formerly a distinction was made between two supposedly distinct types, termed sol-rubber and gel-rubber (also alpha- and beta-rubber), the former being ether-soluble and the latter ether-insoluble (see e.g. *E. A. Hauser*, Ind. Eng. Chem., 1929, **21**, 249). This distinction has been correlated with the supposed existence of a fluid phase beneath the external layers of rubber latex particles (*H. Freundlich* and *E. A. Hauser*, Kolloid-Z., 1925, **36**, Suppl., 24). This is not a clear-cut differentiation and the use of other solvents gives different results (*G. S. Whitby*, J. phys. Chem., 1932, **36**, 198). Some workers have regarded gel-rubber as being sol-rubber which is cross-linked by oxidation (*H. Staudinger* and *H. F. Bondy*, Ann., 1931, **488**, 153; *A. R. Kemp* and *H. Peters*, J. phys. Chem., 1939, **43**, 923).

In considering the possible presence of combined oxygen in rubber, it is necessary to distinguish between oxygen present in the rubber molecules within the Hevea tree and oxygen which may have entered the molecules by atmospheric oxidation after the tapping process. Rubber samples containing combined oxygen have been isolated by the fractionation of crepe in the absence of air (*T. Midgley et al.*, J. Amer. chem. Soc., 1935, **57**, 2318; *G. F. Bloomfield* and *E. H. Farmer*, Trans. Instn. Rubb. Ind., 1940, **14**, 69). By fractionating Hevea rubber in Malaya, *K. C. Roberts* (J. chem. Soc., 1938, 215, 219) claimed to have isolated "caoutchol", $C_{80}H_{130}(OH)_2$, an elastic component comprising 2–5% of the rubber. The existence of this substance was not substantiated (*G. M. Kraay* and *R. F. A. Altman*, Arch. Rubbercultuur, 1938, **22**, 231; *K. C. Roberts*, J. chem. Soc., 1942, 223) but the presence of combined oxygen in fresh Hevea rubber was not disproved.

A re-examination of freshly tapped Hevea latex in absence of air (*G. F. Bloomfield*, J. Rubb. Res. Inst. Malaya, 1951, **13**, Communications 271, 272, 273) revealed small fractions, in the molecular-weight range 50,000 to less than 30,000, containing 0·5–1% of combined oxygen. The same investigations showed much higher molecular weights (about 60% of the material being in the range 1,300,000 to 3,000,000) than have been recorded for rubber after reaching European or American laboratories. Also, a large proportion of the freshly-tapped rubber was of the "gel" type, insoluble in light petroleum, and was regarded as "micro-gel" (rubber chains cross-linked within the confines of individual rubber latex globules present in the tree), in the sense of the term employed by *W. O. Baker* (Ind. Eng. Chem., 1949, **41**, 511). Bloomfield suggested that the combined oxygen may be present as hydroxyl or carboxyl groups, which may terminate the polyisoprene chains.

(v) Physical properties of rubber

The practical importance of rubber is due largely to its physical properties, which have been very extensively studied (see e.g. *C. C. Davis* and *J. J. Blake*, Editors, "The Chemistry and Technology of Rubber", New York, 1937, and general references given p. 436; for solvent effects see above). In general, physical properties are considerably affected by processing operations, such as mastication and vulcanisation. Numerous types of mechanical and electrical tests (particularly of vulcanised rubber) are used for the evaluation and routine control of industrial products.

The most characteristic property of rubber, its *elasticity*, i.e., reversible long range extensibility, is interpreted by a kinetic theory, which has been developed mathematically by several authors, notably *W. Kuhn* (Kolloid-Z., 1934, **68**, 2; 1936, **76**, 258), *E. Guth* and *H. Mark* (Monatsh., 1934, **65**, 93), and *E. Guth* and *H. M. James* (Ind. Eng. Chem., 1941, **33**, 624 and later papers) (for reviews see *H. Mark*, Chem. Reviews, 1939, **25**, 121; *K. H. Meyer*, *ibid.*, 1939, **25**, 137; *P. J. Flory*, *ibid.*, 1944, **35**, 51; *E. Guth*, *H. M. James* and *H. Mark*, Adv. Colloid Sci., 1946, II, 253; *L. R. G. Treloar*, "Physics of Rubber Elasticity", Oxford, 1949). Unstretched rubber is envisaged as a mass of intertwined, highly coiled long-chain molecules; on deformation, followed by removal of stress, the system rapidly reverts to a coiled condition. Degraded rubber, such as results from mastication, is characterised not only by plasticity (deformation under load) but also by "permanent set" (i.e. some retention of deformation) on removal of stress, but vulcanised rubber, in which the coiled molecules are lightly cross-linked, to form a net-work, is a less mobile system and shows a high degree of recovery from stress (i.e. is resilient). Depending upon their composition, typical compounded and vulcanised rubbers show elongations of 300–700% under breaking loads of 70–250 kg./sq.cm.

Unstretched rubber gives an amorphous X-ray diffraction pattern, but if rubber is stretched (below about 60°), or if it is cooled, regions of the material (possibly 80–90% of the whole in favourable cases) undergo orientation, and a crystalline X-ray diffraction pattern is obtained. This was first examined, for stretched rubber, by *J. R. Katz* (Chem. Ztg., 1925, **49**, 353). Later work (see *K. H. Meyer*, "High Polymers", New York, 1942, Vol. IV, 122; *C. W. Bunn*, Adv. Colloid Sci., 1946, II, 95; *idem*, Proc. roy. Soc., 1942, **A, 180**, 40, 67, 82) indicates a crystalline structure in which slightly coiled chains, of *cis* configuration, are accommodated in monoclinic unit cells, of dimensions $12 \cdot 5 \times 8 \cdot 1$ (axis) $\times\ 8 \cdot 9$ Å., containing four isoprene units. Crystallisation of rubber by cooling (see *L. A. Wood*, Adv. Colloid Sci., 1946, II, 57) occurs between -45° (being particularly fast at -25^0) and $+15^0$; melting may extend to considerably higher temperatures. Crystallisation results in increased toughness, increased density, changes in mechanical properties, and optical double refraction effects, and is accompanied by thermal changes. At -73^0 rubber exhibits a *second-order solid transition effect,* changing from a tough but elastic to a brittle solid. At the transition temperature the physical properties show a change in slope when plotted as a function of temperature (*R. F. Boyer* and *R. S. Spencer, ibid.*, 1946, II, 1).

The infra-red absorption spectrum of rubber shows bands which are in accordance with the postulated structure (*R. B. Barnes et al.*, Ind. Eng. Chem. Anal. Ed., 1944, **16**, 9; *H. W. Thompson* and *P. Torkington,* Trans. Faraday Soc., 1941, **41**, 246).

(vi) Chemical properties of rubber

(1) Thermal decomposition and cyclisation.

In air, rubber undergoes gradual softening, at temperatures, depending upon its molecular weight, in the region of 100–150^0; in a vacuum these temperatures are higher. Softening occurs during the mastication of crepe or smoked sheet, which is carried out, with heating, on a roller mill or in an internal mixer. This is not simply a physical change, since masticated rubber, unlike crepe, is plastic at room temperature, dissolves much more easily than crepe in organic solvents, and possesses a lower molecular weight. *F. H. Cotton* (Trans. Instn. Rubb. Ind., 1931, **6**, 487) demonstrated the necessity for air in mastication, indicating that in this process chain-shortening occurs through oxidation. It is possible that fission of carbon chains also occurs because of the powerful frictional forces employed in mastication.

Above about 250^0 rubber undergoes a chemical change, other than oxidation, which results in a reduction in its unsaturation (*H. L. Fisher* and *A. E. Gray,* Ind. Eng. Chem., 1926, **18**, 414; *H. Staudinger* and *E. Geiger,* Helv., 1926, **9**, 549); at 250–350^0 at least half of the unsaturation is lost. This change is attributed to intramolecular cyclisation of the rubber chains. Cyclorubbers have the same molecular formula as rubber itself, $(C_5H_8)_n$.

Cyclorubbers are obtained not only by heating rubber, but also, more conveniently, by treating it with various chemical reagents. These include concentrated sulphuric acid (*F. Kirchhof,* Kolloid-Z., 1920, **27**, 311; 1922, **30**, 176; Chem. Ztg., 1923, **47**, 513; *H. L. Fisher,* Ind. Eng. Chem., 1927, **19**, 1325), sulphonic acids or sulphonyl chlorides (*H. L. Fisher, loc. cit.*), and reactive inorganic halides, such as stannic chloride and titanium tetrachloride, these last-named reagents yielding complexes, which are decomposed to cyclorubber by alcohol (*H. A. Bruson et al.,* Ind. Eng. Chem., 1927, **19**, 1033). The sulphuric acid method can be applied to stabilised latex (*G. J. van Veersen,* J. Polymer Sci., 1951, **6**, 29; *M. Gordon,* Ind. Eng. Chem., 1951, **43**, 386). Cyclisation has been interpreted by carbonium-ion mechanisms (*M. Gordon, loc. cit.*), such as:

$$\begin{array}{c}\diagup CH_2 \diagdown \\ CH \\ \| \\ \diagup CMe \quad \diagup \\ CH_2 \quad CH_2 \\ | \qquad | \\ CH_2 \quad CMe \\ \diagdown CH \diagup\!\!\diagup \end{array} \xrightarrow{+H^+} \begin{array}{c}\diagup CH_2 \diagdown \\ CH_2 \\ | \\ \diagup CMe^+ \quad \diagup \\ CH_2 \quad CH_2 \\ | \qquad | \\ CH_2 \quad CMe \\ \diagdown CH \diagup\!\!\diagup \end{array} \xrightarrow{-H^+} \begin{array}{c}\diagup CH_2 \diagdown \\ CH_2 \\ | \\ \diagup CMe \diagdown \diagup \\ CH_2 \quad CH \\ | \qquad | \\ CH_2 \quad CMe \\ \diagdown CH \diagup\!\!\diagup \end{array}$$

A third method of preparing cyclorubbers is to treat solutions of rubber hydrohalides (see below) with zinc dust (*H. Staudinger* and *W. Widmer*, Helv., 1926, **9**, 529, 549). Staudinger represented this process as:

$$\text{—}CH_2\text{—}\overset{\overset{\displaystyle CH_3}{|}}{C}Cl\,(CH_2\text{—}CH_2\text{—}CH_2)\overset{CH_3}{C}Cl\text{—}CH_2\text{—}CH_2\text{—} \xrightarrow{-2HCl} \text{—}CH_2\text{—}\overset{\overset{\displaystyle CH_3}{|}}{C}\!\!<\!\!\begin{array}{l}CH_2\text{—}\\ CH_2\text{—}CH_2\text{—}CH=\end{array}\!\!C\text{—}CH_2\text{—}CH_2\text{—}$$

Cyclorubbers are non-elastic, resinous, and give an amorphous X-ray diffraction pattern. They vary in appearance, hardness, softening point, solubility and molecular weight, and may superficially resemble such materials as balata, shellac, and ebonite. They have been used industrially (Thermoprene, Plioform, etc.; see *H. R. Thies* and *A. M. Clifford*, Ind. Eng. Chem., 1934, **26**, 123).

Above about 300° rubber is transformed not only into cyclorubbers but also into numerous volatile depolymerisation products. These include isoprene, first obtained in this way by *C. G. Williams* (Proc. roy. Soc., 1860, **10**, 516) and later isolated in yields of 10% (pyrolysis at 700°) (*T. Midgley* and *A. L. Henne*, J. Amer. chem. Soc., 1929, **51**, 1215), 16·7% (*H. L. Bassett* and *H. G. Williams*, J. chem. Soc., 1932, 2324), and 58% (at 750°/10 mm.) (*B. B. S. T. Boonstra and G. J. van Amerongen*, Ind. Eng. Chem., 1949, **41**, 161). Dipentene, $C_{10}H_{16}$, is also formed in 20–25% yield. Higher boiling oils, probably terpenic, $C_{15}H_{24}$, $C_{25}H_{40}$, etc. have also been reported (*G. Bouchardat*, Bull. Soc. chim. Fr., 1875, **24**, 108; *C. Harries*, Ber., 1902, **35**, 3256; *H. Staudinger et al.*, Helv., 1922, **5**, 785; 1926, **9**, 549). Small amounts of trimethylethylene, a reduction product of isoprene, have been recorded by *W. Ipatiew* and *N. Wittorf* (J. pr. Chem., 1897, [ii], **55**, 1) and by *T. Midgley* and *A. L. Henne* (*loc. cit.*); the latter workers also obtained low yields of other olefines and of aromatic hydrocarbons.

(2) *Addition reactions of rubber.*

Most reagents which attack simple olefines will also attack rubber. Owing to the polymeric nature of rubber, an additive reagent can give rise to a series of derivatives, differing in the proportion of chemically modified isoprene units per molecule. Reactions are usually effected in solution and generally occur more sluggishly than with analogous simple olefines, particularly if full modification is desired. As in the case of other olefines, addition is often complicated by substitution, cross-linking and fission, but in the cases next to be considered it is the additive mode of reaction which is of main chemical interest.

Hydrogenation. **Hydrorubber,** $(C_5H_{10})_n$, is produced by catalytic hydrogenation:

$$[\cdot CH_2\cdot C(CH_3):CH\cdot CH_2\cdot]_n + n\ H_2 \longrightarrow [\cdot CH_2\cdot CH(CH_3)\cdot CH_2\cdot CH_2\cdot]_n$$

It is difficult to effect complete saturation on account of the size and coiled configuration of the rubber molecules. *R. Pummerer et al.* (Ber., 1922, **55**, 3458; Ann., 1924, **438**, 295) operated for long periods at moderate temperatures, using platinum catalyst and very dilute purified rubber solutions. *H. Staudinger* and *J. Fritschi* (Helv., 1922, **5**, 785) worked in the absence of solvent, with large amounts of platinum catalyst, at about 280° and 100 atmospheres. *E. H. Farmer* pointed out (Endeavour, 1944, **3**, 72; Adv. Colloid Sci., 1946, II, 302) that Staudinger's product was partly cyclised, was degraded, and was possibly branched. Farmer avoided these reactions by using a supported nickel catalyst at 170–195° and 15–20 at. and obtained hydrorubber (molecular weight 150,000) as an elastic solid, resistant to oxidation.

Reaction with hydrogen halides, hypochlorous acid, etc. Rubber forms derivatives with all the hydrogen halides, though only the *hydrochloride* has been extensively studied or has practical importance. It was first prepared by *W. O. Weber* (Ber., 1900, **33**, 779) and is considered to be formed in accordance with the equation:

$$[\cdot CH_2\cdot C(CH_3):CH\cdot CH_2\cdot]_n + n\ HCl \longrightarrow [\cdot CH_2\cdot CCl\ (CH_3)\cdot CH_2\cdot CH_2\cdot]_n$$

The existence of tertiary chlorine atoms (in accordance with Markownikow's rule; see Vol. I, p. 254) is supported by observations on their rate of reaction with organic bases (*G. Salomon* and *C. Koningsberger*, Rec. Trav. chim., 1950, **69**, 711). Rubber hydrochloride is readily formed by passing gaseous hydrogen chloride into solutions of rubber and isolating the product by precipitation or steam-blowing. On a commercial scale, reaction between solid rubber and gaseous or liquefied hydrogen chloride may also be employed. Reaction may be carried out between hydrochloric acid and suitably stabilised latex, giving a product containing 98–99% of the theoretical amount of chlorine (*G. J. van Veersen*, Proc. 2nd. Rubber Tech. Conf., London, 1948, 87).

Rubber hydrochloride is a white, non-elastic solid, which can be converted into thermoplastic films (e.g. Pliofilm) which have low moisture permeability and are used for wrapping; plasticisers are incorporated, as well as stabilising agents, which counteract a tendency of the material to lose hydrogen chloride. It gives a crystalline X-ray diffraction pattern (*S. D. Gehman et al.*, Proc. Rubber Tech. Conf., 1938, 961), which has been interpreted in detail by *C. W. Bunn* and *E. V. Garner* (J. chem. Soc., 1942, 654). Cyclorubbers (see p. 416), obtained from rubber hydrochloride by elimination of hydrogen chloride, were studied by C. Harries and later by H. Staudinger. *H. Staudinger* and *W. Widmer* (Helv., 1924, **7**, 842) converted rubber hydrochloride into *homologues of hydrorubber* by the action of zinc alkyls; e.g.

$$[\cdot CH_2\cdot CCl(CH_3)\cdot CH_2\cdot CH_2\cdot]_n + \tfrac{n}{2}\,Zn(CH_3)_2 \longrightarrow [\cdot CH_2\cdot C(CH_3)_2\cdot CH_2\cdot CH_2\cdot]_n + \tfrac{n}{2}\,ZnCl_2$$

Hypochlorous acid reacts with rubber, either in organic solvents or as latex (*G. F. Bloomfield* and *E. H. Farmer*, J. Soc. chem. Ind., 1934, **53**, 43T, 47T). The products, white or yellow powders, appear to be formed by the process:

$$[\cdot CH_2\cdot C(CH_3):CH\cdot CH_2\cdot]_n + nHOCl \longrightarrow [\cdot CH_2\cdot CCl(CH_3)\cdot CH(OH)\cdot CH_2\cdot]_n$$
$$\text{or } [\cdot CH_2\cdot C(CH_3)\ (OH)\cdot CHCl\cdot CH_2\cdot]_n$$

with chlorination as an accompanying reaction.

Reaction is claimed to occur between rubber and chloromethyl alkyl ethers (Vol. I, p. 484) (*E. I. du Pont de Nemours and Co.*, U.S.P. 2,053,271, 1934).

Reaction with sulphur compounds (see also vulcanisation). Thiocyanogen reacts additively with rubber, the reaction being represented, by analogy with simpler olefines, as:

$$[\cdot CH_2\cdot C(CH_3):CH\cdot CH_2\cdot]_n + n(SCN)_2 \longrightarrow [\cdot CH_2\cdot C(CH_3)(SCN)\cdot CH(SCN)\cdot CH_2\cdot]_n$$

This reagent, as well as iodine chloride, was used by *R. Pummerer* and *H. Stärk* (Ber., 1931, **64**, 825) to determine the unsaturation of rubber. Reaction proceeds readily in solution at room temperature and is accompanied by gelling. Fully thiocyanogenated rubber is resinous; lightly thiocyanogenated rubber is resilient and solvent-resistant (*I.C.I. Ltd.*, B.P. 525,973, 1940).

The partial modification of rubber by thiocyanic acid, HSCN, a very sluggish reaction, is promoted by ultra-violet light (*R. F. Naylor*, J. chem. Soc., 1945, 247).

Thioglycollic acid, $SH\cdot CH_2\cdot CO_2H$, was reported by *B. Holmberg* (Ber., 1932, **65**, 1349) to react very slowly with crepe rubber, but neither this compound nor other mercaptans were found to combine with rubber, under any conditions, when examined by *J. I. Cunneen* (J. chem. Soc., 1947, 36). On the other hand *Cunneen* found (*ibid.*, 1947, 134) that rubber combines fairly readily, in irradiated solutions, with thioacetic acid (Vol. I, p. 594). Thus prepared, *thiolacetyl rubber* (50% modified) is a white, elastic solid, containing (by analogy with simple methyl-substituted olefines) the group $\cdot CH_2\cdot CH(CH_3)\cdot CH(S\cdot CO\cdot CH_3)\cdot CH_2\cdot$. It is hydrolysed by sodium ethoxide to *rubber thiol*, a fibrous, white solid, containing the group $\cdot CH_2\cdot CH(CH_3)\cdot CH(SH)\cdot CH_2\cdot$. Similarly, monochloro-, dichloro-, or trichloro-thioacetic acids give *monochloro-*, *dichloro-*, or *trichloro-thiolacetyl rubbers*, in which the presence of chlorine leads to solvent resistance and to greater hardness.

Sheet rubber combines with compressed sulphur dioxide (*B. F. Goodrich Co.*, U.S.P. 1,925,879, 1930), giving a tough product of undetermined structure.

Reaction with nitrogen compounds (see also vulcanisation). Solid rubber or rubber solutions react with nitric oxide, nitrogen trioxide, and nitrogen tetroxide, giving complex mixtures of derivatives of ill-defined composition. Addition seems to be complicated by oxidation, since the products possess a higher O:N ratio than the oxide employed. The products are white or yellow powders, soluble in organic solvents and sometimes in alkali, and are often considerably lower in molecular weight then the original rubber. See *G. F. Bloomfield* and *G. A. Jeffrey* (J. chem. Soc., 1944, 120) for the nitric oxide and *F. Emden* (Ber., 1925, **58**, 2522), for the nitrogen tetroxide reaction.

The reaction of rubber with nitrosobenzene and other aromatic nitroso-compounds, giving the so-called *rubber-nitrones*, is likewise complex (*G. Bruni* and *E. Geiger*, Atti Accad. Lincei, 1927, [vi], **5**, 823; *R. Pummerer* and *W. Gündel*, Ber., 1928, **61**, 1591). It has been interpreted as involving the abstraction of hydrogen (creating a new double bond), as well as addition of the nitroso-compound.

The reaction of tetranitromethane with rubber appears to be an uncomplicated addition process, introducing NO_2 and $C(NO_2)_3$ groups, but the uptake is restricted to a mol. of $C(NO_2)_4$ per 4 to 6 isoprene units (*R. Pummerer* and *H. Pahl*, Ber., 1927, **60**, 2152).

Concentrated nitric acid attacks rubber, giving derivatives of ill-defined composition.

(3) *Reaction of rubber with chlorine and other halogens.*

All the halogens react with rubber. In the case of chlorine at least, substitution is as important as addition.

Reaction of chlorine with rubber, known since 1801, is usually carried out in solution (preferably in carbon tetrachloride) and occurs with great facility, even in the dark at -80^0. The existence of substitutive, as well as additive reaction, noted by *J. H. Gladstone* and *W. Hibbert* (J. chem. Soc., 1888, **53**, 679) was studied in detail by *J. McGavack* (Ind. Eng. Chem., 1923, **15**, 961) and by *G. F. Bloomfield* (J. chem. Soc., 1943, 289). McGavack considered the final product to be $C_{10}H_{13}Cl_7$, but Bloomfield distinguished three reaction-phases, with $C_{10}H_{11}Cl_7$ as the final product:

substitution:	$C_{10}H_{16} + 2Cl_2 \longrightarrow C_{10}H_{14}Cl_2 + 2HCl$,
addition and substitution:	$C_{10}H_{14}Cl_2 + 2Cl_2 \longrightarrow C_{10}H_{13}Cl_5 + HCl$,
further substitution:	$C_{10}H_{13}Cl_5 + 2Cl_2 \longrightarrow C_{10}H_{11}Cl_7 + 2\,HCl$.

Lack of unsaturation in the final product was accounted for by cyclisation (cf. *Hj. Staudinger* and *H. Staudinger*, J. pr. Chem., 1943, **162**, 148) and some chain-degradation was also noted. By carrying out chlorination with phenyliodo-dichloride, or with sulphuryl chloride in the presence of benzoyl peroxide, substitution is suppressed and *rubber dichloride* $(C_5H_8Cl_2)_n$ (molecular weight ca. 120,000) obtained as a white, fibrous solid, which undergoes substitutive reaction with gaseous chlorine (*G. P. Bloomfield*, J. chem. Soc., 1944, 114).

Chlorinated rubber (e.g. Alloprene), which is used industrially as a surface-coating material (with incorporation of stabilisers to counteract a tendency to lose chlorine), is prepared by chlorination of highly masticated rubber in carbon tetrachloride and contains about 65% chlorine (see *J. P. Baxter* and *J. G. Moore*, J. Soc. chem. Ind., 1938, **57**, 327). Chlorinated rubber of at least 60% chlorine content can be prepared from chlorine and stabilised latex (*G. Salomon et al.*, Ind. Eng. Chem., 1951, **43**, 315).

Reactions of bromine with rubber may likewise, under some conditions, involve substitution as well as addition. A *rubber dibromide* $(C_5H_8Br_2)_n$, was described by

Gladstone and *Hibbert (loc. cit.)* and by *C. O. Weber* (Ber., 1900, **33**, 779). *G. F. Bloomfield (loc. cit.)* found that bromination was exclusively additive in chloroform below 0^0 and could be used for determination of double bonds in rubber; with N-bromosuccinimide, bromination was substitutive and was accompanied by cyclisation.

Iodine chloride reacts additively with rubber and this reaction can also be used for analysis (*A. R. Kemp* and *G. S. Mueller*, Ind. Eng. Chem. Anal. Ed., 1934, **6**, 52). The reaction of rubber with iodine is complicated (*W. O. Weber, loc. cit.; F. W. Hinrichsen* and *R. Kempf*, Ber., 1913, **46**, 1287). A *monofluororubber* is obtained by substitutive reaction of rubber with *p*-tolyliododifluoride (*C. F. H. Allen et al.*, J. Amer. chem. Soc., 1937, **59**, 1827).

Rubber halides have been used in reactions with phenol, aniline and other compounds, to prepare further derivatives of rubber.

(4) *Oxidation of rubber.*

By ozone. Ozone causes perishing of rubber, due to oxidative attack on the double bonds. As noted above, the study of this ozonolysis reaction, investigated by *C. Harries* (Ber., 1909, **42**, 446, and later papers), was instrumental in establishing the position of the double bonds in the rubber molecule. An ozonide $(C_5H_8O_3)_n$ is first formed, and on hydrolysis this yields mainly laevulic aldehyde (Vol. I, p. 719) and laevulic acid, or their decomposition products, as is required by a structure containing isoprene units with 1:4-linkages:

$$\ldots CH_2\cdot C(CH_3):CH\cdot CH_2\cdot CH_2\cdot C(CH_3):CH\cdot CH_2\ldots \longrightarrow CHO\cdot CH_2\cdot CH_2\cdot CO\cdot CH_3$$

R. Pummerer et al. (Ber., 1931, **64**, 804, 809; 1936, **69**, 170) showed that about 90 % of the rubber structure could be thus accounted for.

By oxygen (autoxidation). When kept, particularly under warm conditions or in sunlight, rubber readily undergoes deterioration, with decrease in molecular weight, giving sticky or resinous products (for reviews see *C. C. Davis* and *J. T. Blake*, Editors, "Chemistry and Technology of Rubber", New York, 1937). This change is associated with atmospheric oxidation, a process which is autocatalytic and is usually referred to as autoxidation. For the commercial testing of rubber, it may be accelerated by heating in an air oven, or under pressure with oxygen, or by exposure in air to ultra-violet radiation.

Autoxidation is involved in mastication (see p. 409). It is strongly catalysed by the addition of small amounts of copper or manganese salts, which in any case, are trace constituents of Hevea latex (ca. 0·0003–0·0005 %). Paint driers, such as cobalt linoleate, are also powerful autoxidation catalysts, either with rubber solutions, when resinous oxidation products, e.g. of approximate composition $(C_{10}H_{16}O_3)_n$ can be isolated (*G. F. Bloomfield* and *E. H. Farmer*, J. Soc. chem. Ind., 1935, **54**, 125T), or on a hot mill with masticated rubber, which is degraded to a sticky material termed *Rubbone* (*H. P. Stevens* and *F. J. Popham*, *ibid.*, 1938, **57**, 128T). The effect of certain "peptising agents", including some mercaptans and hydrazine derivatives, which greatly reduce the viscosity of rubber on a mill or in solution, may also be due to catalysis of autoxidation.

On the other hand, autoxidation is inhibited by many phenols, amines and other compounds *(antioxidants)*, which are regularly incorporated for this purpose in vulcanised rubber.

The course of autoxidation has been explored by *E. H. Farmer et al.* (for reviews see Trans. Faraday Soc., 1942, **38**, 340, 348; J. Soc. chem. Ind., 1947, **66**, 86), and also, particularly in its kinetic aspects, by *L. Bateman, J. L. Bolland et al.* (see Quart. Reviews, 1949, **3**, 1; Trans. Instn. Rubb. Ind., 1950, **26**, 246); for earlier work by C. Dufraisse see *Davis* and *Blake (op. cit.)*. It is interpreted as a chain reaction, initiated and maintained by free radicals (cf. Vol. I, pp. 214, 326). Hydroperoxides, formed on carbon atoms adjacent to the double bond, were shown to be primary oxidation products both of rubber and of analogous olefines of low molecular weight, e.g.

$$\cdot CH_2\cdot C(CH_3):CH\cdot CH_2\cdot \longrightarrow \cdot CH(OOH)\cdot C(CH_3):CH\cdot CH_2\cdot$$

(*Farmer et al.*, J. chem. Soc., 1942, 121, 139; 1943, 119, 122, 125, 356). For polyisoprenes, including rubber, the formation of more complex cyclic primary products, containing groupings such as the following, was later demonstrated:

$$\cdot CH_2\cdot C(CH_3):CH\cdot CH\begin{matrix} CH_2\text{—}C(CH_3)\cdot OOH \\ \\ O\text{——}O \end{matrix}CH\cdot CH_2\cdot$$

(*Bolland et al., ibid.*, 1949, 492; Trans. Faraday Soc., 1949, **45**, 93). Little is yet known about the mechanism of the chain-scission which is one of the most obvious consequences of autoxidation.

By other oxidising agents. Reaction of rubber with aqueous potassium permanganate was found by *J. M. Robertson* and *J. A. Mair* (J. Soc. chem. Ind., 1927, **46**, 41T) to result in its degradation to formic, acetic, oxalic, and laevulic acids, complex acidic resins and complex oxygenated neutral products. The same authors *(loc. cit.)* also used chromyl chloride.

Hydrogen peroxide in acetic acid (i.e. peracetic acid) reacts with solid rubber or rubber solutions (*J. A. Mair* and *J. Todd*, J. chem. Soc., 1932, 386; *G. F. Bloomfield* and *E. H. Farmer*, J. Soc. chem. Ind., 1934, **53**, 121T) or with stabilised latex (*G. Salomon et al.*, Ind. Eng. Chem., 1951, **43**, 315), to give white powders, soluble in many types of solvent. The reaction appears to involve glycol formation:

$$\cdot CH_2\cdot C(CH_3):CH\cdot CH_2\cdot \longrightarrow \cdot CH_2\cdot C(CH_3)(OH)\cdot CH(OH)\cdot CH_2\cdot$$

Typically, about 80% of the isoprene units are thus affected; some of the hydroxyl groups are present in acetylated form, and chain degradation occurs. Perbenzoic acid reacts with rubber, presumably forming epoxide groups at the double bonds (*R. Pummerer* and *P. A. Burkard*, Ber., 1022, **55**, 3458). The action of benzoyl peroxide is discussed under vulcanisation (below).

(5) *Vulcanisation of rubber.*

By reaction with small quantities of vulcanising agents the physical properties of rubber are modified in a manner which is advantageous for its practical applications. Vulcanisation is usually effected above room temperature, after incorporating the appropriate substances in masticated rubber on a mill, or by adding them, as aqueous dispersions, to rubber latex. Vulcanisation may also be studied in rubber solutions. Sulphur far exceeds all other vulcanising agents in practical importance. Its introduction into rubber manufacture is chiefly associated with Charles Goodyear (1839); sulphur vulcanisation of latex was discovered by *P. Schidrowitz* (B.P. 193,451, 1921; 208,235, 1922). Irrespective of the agent employed, vulcanisation is now generally believed to occur through the formation of intermolecular or intramolecular cross-linking groups. This could result from a reaction in which direct union between carbon atoms of chains occurs, or from a reaction in which an atom, or group of atoms, from a vulcanising agent provides the link or "bridge". Very few such links are needed, per molecule, to produce a profound change in the shape of the molecular system and hence in the elastic behaviour of the material and in its response to solvents. For reviews of vulcanisation studies and theories see *Davis* and *Blake (op. cit.)*.

Sulphur vulcanisation. Technologists have found empirically that rubber gives vulcanisates with optimum physical properties by heating it, mixed with about 3 % of sulphur, 5 % of zinc oxide, and 0·5–1·0 % of an accelerator, e.g. for 30 minutes at 140°. The accelerator may be drawn from several classes of compounds, among which the following are important (listed in approximate order of increasing efficiency, the most vigorous being employed at relatively low temperatures): aldehyde-amine condensation products, e.g. acetaldehyde-aniline; guanidines, e.g. diphenylguanidine, $NH:C(NHC_6H_5)_2$; thiazole derivatives, e.g. 2-mercaptobenzthiazole,

$$C_6H_4\langle{}^{S}_{N}\rangle C\cdot SH;$$

dithiocarbonic acid derivatives, including tetramethylthiuram disulphide, $NMe_2\cdot CS\cdot S\cdot S\cdot CS\cdot NMe_2$, dithiocarbamates, e.g. zinc diethyldithiocarbamate, $Zn(S\cdot CS\cdot NEt_2)_2$ and xanthates, e.g. zinc *iso*propyl xanthate, $Zn(S\cdot CS\cdot O\cdot CHMe_2)_2$.

Vulcanisation is an extremely complicated process and the chemical reactions involved in it are imperfectly understood. Various mechanisms, often involving free radicals, have been proposed. Knowledge of the reactions of sulphur with simple mono-, di- and poly-olefines, and with rubber, has recently been extended by *E. H. Farmer et al.* (*E. H. Farmer*, Trans. Faraday Soc., 1942, 38, 356; Adv.

Colloid Sci., II, 1946, 299; J. Soc. chem. Ind., 1947, **66,** 86; *E. H. Farmer* and *F. W. Shipley*, J. Polymer Sci., 1946, **1,** 293; J. chem. Soc., 1947, 1519; *R. F. Naylor*, J. Polymer Sci., 1946, **1,** 305; J. chem. Soc., 1947, 1532; *G. F. Bloomfield*, J. Polymer Sci., 1946, **1,** 312; J. chem. Soc., 1947, 1546, 1547; J. Soc. chem. Ind., 1945, **64,** 274; *ibid.*, 1948, **67,** 14; *ibid.*, 1949, **68,** 66) and the following conclusions may be drawn (see also *R. T. Armstrong et al.*, Ind. Eng. Chem., 1944, **36,** 628). In general, reaction of sulphur with rubber does not change the carbon/hydrogen ratio, but there is a loss of unsaturation, roughly equivalent to one double bond for one (or more) sulphur atom incorporated. As with oxygen in autoxidation processes, sulphur appears to attack carbon atoms adjacent to the double bond, and some intermolecular sulphide or polysulphide links, such as the following, may be formed:

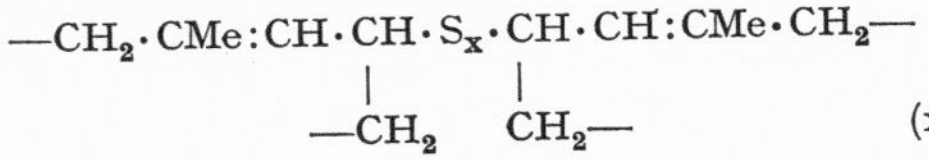

```
—CH₂·CMe:CH·CH·Sₓ·CH·CH:CMe·CH₂—
            |       |
         —CH₂     CH₂—              (x = 1–6).
```

Hydrogen sulphide, a product of such reactions, has been shown to combine with double bonds of rubber, under vulcanisation conditions *(Naylor, loc. cit.)*, and it also functions as a catalyst for the reaction with sulphur. A further process, which has great importance, probably predominating over intermolecular linking, is the intramolecular formation of cyclic sulphides, sometimes with double-bond shift. In this way reduced thiopyran rings may be formed, as shown below:

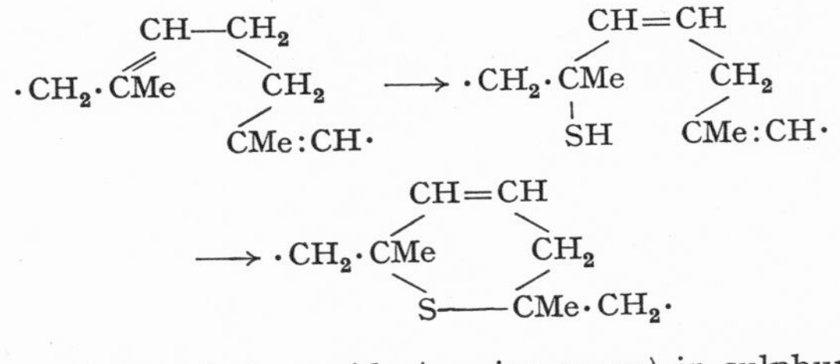

```
        CH—CH₂                          CH=CH
       //     \                        /     \
·CH₂·CMe       CH₂    ——→  ·CH₂·CMe         CH₂
              /                  |          /
       CMe:CH·                   SH    CMe:CH·

                CH=CH
               /     \
  ——→  ·CH₂·CMe       CH₂
               \     /
                S——CMe·CH₂·
```

The catalytic activity of zinc oxide (or zinc soaps) in sulphur vulcanisation may be associated with the formation and decomposition of zinc mercaptide groups on the rubber chains or in the accelerator molecules (*E. H. Farmer, loc. cit.*, 1946; *B. C. Barton*, Ind. Eng. Chem., 1950, **42,** 671; for a comparison with other metal oxides see *F. H. Cotton* and *J. Westhead*, Trans. Instn. Rubb. Ind., 1937, **13,** 230). The various accelerators (or their metallic derivatives) may function by undergoing fission into free radicals, which may then participate in the cross-linking processes; the precise mechanisms have not yet been elucidated.

The presence of sulphide links in vulcanised rubber is revealed by the action of methyl iodide, giving trimethylsulphonium iodide (*M. L. Selker* and *A. R. Kemp*, Ind. Eng. Chem., 1944, **36,** 16, 20), possibly by the process:

$$:CH\cdot\dot{C}H\cdot S\cdot\dot{C}H\cdot CH: \xrightarrow{3MeI} :CH\cdot\dot{C}H\cdot SMeI\cdot\dot{C}H\cdot CH: \longrightarrow 2:CH\cdot\dot{C}HI + SMe_3I.$$

The presence of polysulphide bridges is shown by the removal of a very small amount of sulphur by sodium sulphite. Infra-red spectra also provide information concerning groups present in vulcanised rubber molecules (*N. Sheppard* and *G. B. B. M. Sutherland*, Trans. Faraday Soc., 1945, **41**, 261; J. chem. Soc., 1947, 1540).

When rubber is heated with excess of sulphur (30–50% of the weight of the rubber is employed commercially) *hard rubber* or *ebonite* is obtained (reviewed by *A. R. Kemp* in *Davis* and *Blake, op. cit.*). This is a saturated, tough, non-elastic material, resistant to oxygen, solvents, and chemical reagents. It gradually softens on heating, begins to evolve hydrogen sulphide above about 100°, and on pyrolysis gives products including alkyl-substituted thiophens, a result which has been attributed to the presence in it of cyclic sulphide structures (*T. Midgley et al.*, J. Amer. chem. Soc., 1932, **54**, 2953; 1934, **56**, 1326).

Vulcanising agents other than sulphur. Theoretically, any bifunctional additive reagent may cause vulcanisation by reacting with two double bonds, intermolecularly or intramolecularly, thus forming cross-links or rings. Many vulcanising agents do not possess obvious additive properties and may function by forming free radicals; generalised theories of their action have been put forward, especially by *E. H. Farmer* (see references under sulphur vulcanisation; also *E. H. Farmer* and *S. E. Michael*, J. chem. Soc., 1942, 513). Earlier work on vulcanising agents other than sulphur is reviewed by *I. I. Ostromislensky* (who discovered vulcanisation by nitro-compounds and peroxides) in *Davis* and *Blake* (*op. cit.*); see also *H. L. Fisher* (Ind. Eng. Chem., 1939, **31**, 1381).

Sulphur monochloride, S_2Cl_2, known since 1846 as a "cold-curing agent" for rubber, probably functions additively (*K. H. Meyer* and *H. Mark*, Ber., 1928, **61**, 1939):

$$2\begin{matrix}\dot{C}Me\\ \vdots\\ CH\\ \cdot\end{matrix} + S_2Cl_2 \longrightarrow \begin{matrix}\dot{C}MeCl & & \dot{C}MeCl\\ \cdot & & \cdot\\ CH & -S- & CH\\ \cdot & & \cdot\end{matrix} + S$$

Hydrogen sulphide and sulphur dioxide, mixed together in the presence of rubber, cause vulcanisation in the cold (*S. J. Peachey* and *A. Skipsey*, J. Soc. chem. Ind., 1921, **40**, 5T). This has been ascribed to intermediate formation of an active form of sulphur.

Selenium vulcanises rubber in the presence of accelerators, but functions best when sulphur is also present.

Thiuram disulphides, such as the tetramethyl compound, not only function as vigorous accelerators of sulphur vulcanisation (see above), but are themselves vulcanising agents when used alone. Chemical aspects of their action have been studied by *D. Craig et al.* (J. Polymer Sci., 1950, **5**, 709; 1951, **6**, 1, 7, 13).

Aromatic nitro-compounds, especially 1:3-dinitrobenzene and 1:3:5-trinitrobenzene, have been known as vulcanizing agents since 1915.

Some quinones, such as chloranil, and their derivatives such as quinone oximes, are vulcanising agents (*H. L. Fisher, loc. cit.*).

Benzoyl peroxide and other peroxides have been known as vulcanising agents since 1915. Benzoyl peroxide is believed to attack carbon atoms adjacent to the double bond, acting both as an oxidising agent and as a cross-linking agent (*E. H. Farmer* and *S. E. Michael, loc. cit.*).

Many diazoamino-compounds, such as diazoaminobenzene, $C_6H_5 \cdot N:N \cdot NH \cdot C_6H_5$, are vigorous vulcanising agents (*T. G. Levi*, Gomma, 1937, **1**, 4).

Grignard reagents cause cross-linking of lightly oxidised rubber molecules in ether solution, but the effect is reversible, since gelling disappears on treating the product with water (*T. Midgley et al.*, J. Amer. chem. Soc., 1934, **56**, 1156).

Photogelling is a term applied to the formation of gels from rubber solutions, particularly in chlorinated hydrocarbon solvents, when exposed to sunlight or a mercury-vapour lamp. Oxygen must be absent. Substances such as chloranil, benzaldehyde, and other carbonyl compounds act as sensitisers. The product is equivalent to a lightly vulcanised rubber and appears to be cross-linked. Photogelling has been described by *H. P. Stevens* (Adv. Colloid Sci., 1946, II, 363; cf. *E. H. Farmer*, *ibid.*, 319).

(6) *Reaction of rubber with unsaturated and resin-forming substances.*

Some vinyl-compounds (e.g. acrylonitrile, acrylic esters) if allowed to polymerise in emulsion, with per-compounds as catalysts, in the presence of rubber latex, are reported to form chains which are linked to the rubber molecule, thereby modifying its properties (*E. I. du Pont de Nemours and Co.*, U.S.P. 2,422,550, 1947; *P. Compagnon* and *J. Le Bras*, Compt. rend., 1941, **212**, 616). Maleic anhydride and maleic esters react with rubber under suitable conditions (*R. G. R. Bacon* and *E. H. Farmer*, Proc. Rubber Tech. Conf., London, 1938, 256; *E. H. Farmer*, J. Soc. chem. Ind., 1947, **66**, 86).

Rubber also reacts with the reaction products of phenols and formaldehyde, such as saligenin and the more complex polynuclear "novolaks" (*E. H. Farmer*, Endeavour, 1944, **3**, 72; *J. I. Cunneen et al.*, J. chem. Soc., 1943, 472). Linkages with the rubber molecule are believed to occur through chroman rings.

(vii) The biogenesis of rubber

Rubber tends to be regarded as a metabolism by-product which is not utilised by the plant. In *H. brasiliensis* it appears to be formed at the expense of carbohydrates. Indirect evidence that rubber and terpenes have a common, unknown, precursor was supplied by *S. G. Wildman et al.* (Arch. Biochem., 1946, **10**, 141) from breeding experiments with two *Cryptostegia* species which are respectively sources of rubber and of the triterpene alcohol lupeol. There appears to be no evidence that isoprene itself is a precursor of rubber in plants, though the view that it may be has been encouraged by the observation (see p. 432) that "redox" systems (which possess some analogies with enzyme systems) are powerful catalysts for diene polymerisations in the laboratory.

The possibility that carbonyl compounds act an precursors, through aldol-type condensations (Vol. I, p. 466), has also been suggested (e.g. *A. A. Prokofiev*, Bull. Acad. Sci. U.R.S.S., Sér. biol., 1939, 908). Evidence supporting this has been provided by *J. Bonner et al.* (Arch. Biochem., 1949, **21,** 109; 1950, **26,** 178; 1951, **31,** 234), who showed that rubber production in guayule was substantially increased by supplying the aqueous nutrient medium with acetate, acetone, or β-methylcrotonic acid (Vol. I, p. 636), but was not affected by other substances. Further, by using, as substrate, acetate labelled with ^{14}C in the carboxyl group, the assimilated labelled carbon was found to be present in proteins (over 50 %, largely as leucine residues), in resins which probably included higher terpenes (11–27 %), and in the rubber (about 1 %). The following (partial) scheme for *in vivo* synthesis of rubber was suggested:

$$2\,CH_3\cdot CO_2H \longrightarrow CH_3\cdot CO\cdot CH_2\cdot CO_2H \longrightarrow CH_3\cdot CO\cdot CH_3 + CO_2$$

$$CH_3\cdot CO\cdot CH_3 + CH_3\cdot CO_2H \longrightarrow CH_3\cdot C(CH_3):CH\cdot CO_2H$$

$$CH_3\cdot C(CH_3):CH\cdot CO_2H \longrightarrow [?] \longrightarrow [\cdot CH_2\cdot C(CH_3):CH\cdot CH_2\cdot]_n.$$

(b) *Polyisoprenes of gutta-percha, balata, etc.*

Gutta-percha is a tough, horny, non-rubbery, but thermoplastic material, obtained from a latex which exudes on cutting through the bark of certain trees of the *Sapotaceae* family; these are found wild, or are cultivated, in Malaya and Indonesia. **Balata** is a similar product, obtained from a tree, also belonging to the *Sapotaceae,* which grows in Guiana, Venezuela, and neighbouring areas of South America. *J. N. Dean* has reviewed these materials in *Davis* and *Blake (op. cit.).*

Both gutta-percha and balata contain a linear polyisoprene, $(C_5H_8)_n$, in which the isoprene units are geometrical isomers of those in rubber, their double bonds having a *trans* configuration. This hydrocarbon is accompanied by very large quantities of resin, which contains triterpenes, aliphatic and aromatic carboxylic acids, and other components. After cleansing, the polyisoprene-resin mixture is used commercially, particularly for the insulation of submarine cables. To obtain hydrocarbon free from resin, it may be precipitated with acetone from a solution of the mixture in benzene.

Mean molecular-weight values for gutta- and balata-polyisoprene have been calculated to be about 100,000 (*G. Gee,* Adv. Colloid Sci., 1946, II, 173). As might be expected for a *trans*-compound, the hydrocarbon crystallises more readily than the stereoisomeric *cis*-polyisoprene of rubber. It differs from rubber in its X-ray diagram and infra-red absorption spectrum, A crystalline α-form of gutta, m.p. about 65°, is the form found in nature, and is also obtained by slowly cooling the amorphous hydrocarbon. A crystalline β-form, m.p. about 56°, results from rapid cooling of the amorphous hydrocarbon. The α- and β-forms, with repeat distances in the crystal of 8·8 and 4·7 Å. respectively, differ in single-bond configurations; their crystal structures have been studied by *C. W. Bunn* (*ibid.,* p. 106; Proc. roy. Soc., 1942, A, **180,** 40) and others. Ordinary gutta-hydrocarbon has a density of about 0·95. When heated it becomes sufficiently plastic for moulding purposes at about 100°. It is soluble in similar solvents to those which dissolve rubber hydrocarbon.

Gutta-percha is similar in most chemical properties to natural rubber. It is in general readily oxidised, though very resistant to ozone, and undergoes sulphur vulcanisation. Unsaturation values for the hydrocarbon show one double bond per isoprene unit. It gives a hydrogenated product similar to that obtained from natural rubber (*H. Staudinger*, Kautschuk, 1925, **1**, 9), adds hydrogen chloride, nitrosobenzene, etc., in a similar fashion, and shows identical behaviour to natural rubber when chlorinated (*G. Kraus* and *W. B. Reynolds*, J. Amer. chem. Soc., 1950, **72**, 5621). Gutta-percha is unattacked by hydrofluoric acid and has therefore been the usual material for making containers for this acid.

High molecular-weight polyisoprenes occur in several other vegetable gums, including *chicle* (a gum from *Sapota achras*, a Central American tree), the hydrocarbon of which is a mixture of *cis*- and *trans*-polyisoprene according to *W. Schlesinger* and *H. M. Leeper* (Ind. Eng. Chem., 1951, **43**, 398).

3. Synthetic elastomers

(a) History of "synthetic rubber"

Contributory evidence for the structure of natural rubber (p. 412) was provided by the fact that isoprene changes spontaneously, or under the action of catalysts, into a product which may superficially resemble rubber (*G. Bouchardat*, Compt. rend., 1879, **89**, 1117; *W. A. Tilden*, J. chem. Soc., 1884, **45**, 410, and later workers). Such observations, together with a growing industrial demand for natural rubber, led to attempts to produce a synthetic rubber. None of the early synthetic products proved to be comparable in quality with natural rubber. The chief technical advance of the pre-1914 period was the discovery that sodium is a useful catalyst for isoprene polymerisation (*F. E. Matthews* and *E. H. Strange*, B.P. 24,790, 1910; *F. Bayer and Co.*, B.P. 1125, 1911; *C. Harries*, Ann., 1911, 383, 157). Most later workers ceased attempts to synthesise polyisoprene, identical with natural rubber, but examined every available conjugated diene in a search for rubber-like polymerisation products.

During the war of 1914–1918 a synthetic elastomer, "methyl rubber", derived from 2:3-dimethyl-1:3-butadiene, was manufactured to the extent of about 2,500 tons in Germany and used with limited success as a rubber substitute. After 1926, technical developments made in the laboratories of the I.G. Farbenindustrie led eventually to the industrial production of successful synthetic elastomers. The chief developments were: the adoption of 1:3-butadiene as the main polymerisable monomer; the production of polybutadiene, either by sodium catalysis (Buna 85, etc.), or, preferably, by polymerisation in aqueous cmulsions, and the introduction of butadiene-copolymers. An emulsion copolymer from a: 1-mixture (by weight) of butadiene and styrene was manufactured as a general-purpose rubber substitute (Buna S; see *I.G. Farbenind.*, B.P. 339,255, 1929), whilst an emulsion copolymer from butadiene and minor amounts of acrylonitrile was manufactured as a solvent-resistant rubber (Buna N; see *I.G. Farbenind.*, B.P. 360,821, 1930. Chemical and technological aspects of German work, particularly for the war period, 1939–1945, are given in B.I.O.S. and F.I.A.T. reports (summarised by *T. R. Dawson*, B.I.O.S. Overall Report No. 7, London, 1948); see also an account by *E. Konrad* and *W. Becker* in F.I.A.T. Review of German Science, 1939–1946, Preparative Organic Chemistry, Part III, edited by *K. Ziegler*, Wiesbaden, 1948. The earlier history of "synthetic rubber" was comprehensively reviewed by *G. S. Whitby* and *M. Katz* (Ind. Eng. Chem., 1933, **25**, 1204, 1338).

In the United States a polymer of 2-chloro-1:3-butadiene (chloroprene) was developed as a synthetic elastomer in the laboratories of Messrs. du Pont de Nemours and Co. It was first manufactured, in 1932, as a mass-polymer (cf. p. 406) called Duprene, and later, from 1935 onwards, was manufactured by emulsion processes, giving Neoprene E, G, W, etc. (cf. p. 434). There were contemporary developments in the U.S.S.R., where polybutadiene made by sodium-catalysis (SKA, SKB) and polychloroprene (Sovprene) were manufactured. Elsewhere, rubbery properties were observed in the saturated high molecular-weight polymers preparable from *iso*butene (cf. pp. 406, 435), with the aid of Friedel-Crafts catalysts at very low temperatures. These were manufactured as Vistanex (Standard Oil Co., U.S.A.) and Oppanol (I.G. Farbenind., Germany). Later, a vulcanisable modification of this type of polymer, incorporating minor amounts of a diene as an interpolymer component, was produced as Butyl rubber (U.S.A., 1943 onwards).

In consequence of the Japanese occupation of the plantation regions of Malaya and Indonesia during the war of 1939–1945, a very large "synthetic rubber" industry came into existence in the United States. This produced mainly butadiene/styrene elastomer, by an emulsion process (GR-S), with smaller amounts of butadiene/acrylonitrile elastomer (Hycar; also made in emulsion), Butyl and Neoprene. After the war this manufacture was continued in the United States on a somewhat reduced scale. Manufacture is also carried out in Germany and in Canada. An important development has been the establishment in America of low-temperature emulsion polymerisation processes with "redox" catalysts (p. 432), giving the so-called "cold rubber", which is claimed to be superior to the older types.

World production of synthetic elastomers amounted to 44,000 tons (mainly in Germany) in 1940, attained over 800,000 tons (mainly in the United States) in 1944, and was over 500,000 tons in 1950. By comparison, world production of plantation rubber rose from zero in 1900 (wild rubber production being then about 50,000 tons), to over 300,000 tons in 1920, and to 1,400,000 tons in 1940; the 1950 production was 1,800,000 tons.

(b) Techniques used in preparing elastomers from dienes

Diene polymerisation techniques and the structure and properties of the products have been extensively explored. For references to pre-1939 work see

R. E. Burk, H. E. Thompson, A. J. Weith and *I. Williams*, "Polymerisation", New York, 1937; *H. Mark* and *R. Raff*, "High Polymeric Reactions", New York, 1941. The rate of polymerisation and the properties of the elastomers are determined both by the nature of the monomer (or monomer mixture), and by the preparative technique employed.

(i) Relationship of monomer structure to rubber-like properties in the derived polymer

Many polymerisation products have been described in the chemical literature as "rubbery", but the term has no precise significance. Proper comparison of a synthetic product with natural rubber can be achieved only after it has been compounded, vulcanised, and evaluated in a large number of physical tests.

Certain generalisations may be made (cf. *W. H. Carothers*, Ind. Eng. Chem., 1934, **26**, 30). If the 1:3-butadiene chain, ·C:C·C:C·, is regarded as the fundamental feature of "rubber"-producing monomers, then substituent methyl groups or halogen atoms are not disadvantageous, but large alkyl groups, or aryl groups, or more than one group of any kind (especially more than two) generally act unfavourably, the diene often polymerising slowly, or giving products which are too hard or too soft. From an industrial point of view, 1:3-butadiene is by far the most important of all dienes, followed in importance by chloroprene. Isoprene and other 2-alkyl-1:3-butadienes (*C. S. Marvel et al.*, J. Polymer Sci., 1949, **4**, 583), and piperylene, may also produce satisfactory elastomers. As pointed out above, it has been found easier to make good elastomers by copolymerising 1:3-butadiene with a minor amount of a second unsaturated component than by polymerising 1:3-butadiene alone. Ease of copolymerisation and properties of the copolymers were described by *H. W. Starkweather et al.* (Ind. Eng. Chem., 1947, **39**, 210), who gave data for copolymers of 1:3-butadiene with over two hundred second components. Styrene (for general purposes) and acrylonitrile (for oil resistance) remain by far the most important second components from an industrial point of view. Methyl methacrylate and methyl vinyl ketone have also given satisfactory elastomers with 1:3-butadiene.

(ii) Alkali metals as polymerisation catalysts

Polymerisation occurs at moderate temperatures on treating liquid dienes with a small amount of finely divided sodium or other alkali metal. Although, as described above, the use of this technique in industry declined in favour of emulsion methods, it has continued to be explored for the preparation of butadiene/styrene copolymers (*C. S. Marvel et al.*, J. Polymer Sci., 1946, **1**, 275; *W. A. Schulze et al.*, Ind. Eng. Chem., 1949, **41**, 414). The function of the alkali metal, which forms intermediate products with the diene, was investigated by *K. Ziegler et al.* (see p. 399; see also Chem. Ztg., 1938, **62**, 125). A variation in this technique (*J. D. D'Ianni et al.*, Ind. Eng. Chem., 1950, **42**, 95) is to use an "Alfin" catalyst, i.e. a mixture of a sodium alkoxide with a sodium alkyl (e.g. sodium *iso*propoxide and sodium allyl); these were developed by *A. A. Morton et al.* (*ibid.*, 1950, **42**, 1488; J. Amer. chem. Soc., 1946, **68**, 93, and later papers).

(iii) Polymerisation in emulsion

This technique is also widely used in the polymerisation of vinyl compounds (p. 406). In a typical diene polymerisation it is carried out in a system with a composition such as the following (parts are by weight); monomer or monomer mixture 100; distilled water 180; soap (emulsifying agent) 5; potassium persulphate (catalyst) 0·3; and dodecyl mercaptan (modifier) 0·5. During several hours at 40–50°, a butadiene/styrene monomer emulsion thus becomes converted into a polymer dispersion, which resembles natural rubber latex in appearance and may similarly be coagulated by addition of electrolytes (after addition of, e.g., phenyl-2-naphthylamine as antioxidant).

The soap stabilises both the emulsion of finely dispersed monomer droplets and the polymer particles which replace them. Also, soap micelles are believed to have special importance in providing loci for initiation of polymersisation (*W. D. Harkins*, J. chem. Phys., 1945, **13**, 381). As in vinyl polymerisations (Vol. I, p. 206) the catalyst is believed to provide a source of free radicals, which initiate polymerisation:

$$R^{\cdot}\text{ (radical from catalyst)} + M\text{(monomer molecule)} \longrightarrow R - M^{\cdot}\text{ (initiation)}$$

$$R{-}M^{\cdot} + M \longrightarrow R{-}[M]_2^{\cdot}$$

$$R{-}[M]_{n-1}^{\cdot} + M \longrightarrow R{-}[M]_n^{\cdot} \qquad \text{(propagation)}$$

$$R{-}[M]^{\cdot}_n + R{-}[M]^{\cdot}_m \longrightarrow R{-}[M]_{m+n}{-}R \qquad \text{(termination)}$$

($^{\cdot}$ here signifies an unpaired electron).

The mercaptan (or other type of modifier) is believed to control the size of the polymer molecules by acting as a chain-terminating agent (the above scheme includes an alternative mode of termination). When it terminates a chain the mercaptan is believed to provide a new source of free radicals:

$$R - [M]^{\cdot}_n + ASH\text{ (Alkyl mercaptan)} \longrightarrow R - [M]_n - H\text{ (polymer)} + {}^{\cdot}SA\text{ (radical)}$$

(see, e.g., *I. M. Kolthoff* and *W. E. Harris*, J. Polymer Sci., 1947, **2**, 41, 49, 72, 82). Polymerisations, by emulsion or other methods, were first described for chloroprene by *W. H. Carothers* (J. Amer. chem. Soc., 1931, **53**, 4203; see also "Collected Papers of W. H. Carothers on High Polymeric Substances", New York, 1940). Modifiers, such as sulphur and mercaptans, have subsequently been employed in the emulsion polymerisation of chloroprene and it has been shown, using radioactive sulphur, that they become incorporated in the polymer (*W. E. Mochel* and *J. H. Petersen*, J. Amer. chem. Soc., 1949, **71**, 1427).

The efficiency of conventional peroxidic catalysts (persulphates, hydrogen peroxide, benzoyl peroxide; cf. Vol. I, p. 268) is very greatly increased by using them in conjunction with certain reducing agents. Free radicals generated in the oxidation-reduction process are believed to initiate polymerisation. Such "*redox*" or "*reduction-activation*" polymerisation systems were investigated in Germany (*W. Kern*, in F.I.A.T. Review of German Science, *loc. cit.*; *idem*, Makromol. Chem., 1947, **1**, 199, 209, 229, 249; 1948, **2**, 48, 63; 1951, **5**, 216; Angew. Chem., 1949, **61**, 471); in the United States (*W. L. Semon*, Chem. Eng. News, 1946, **24**, 2900; *W. B. Reynolds*, J. chem. Educ., 1950, **27**, 494); and in Britain (*R. G. R. Bacon*, Trans. Faraday Soc., 1946, **42**, 140).

The later development of "redox" polymerisation processes for butadiene/styrene emulsion copolymerisation in the United States has enabled "cold rubber" to be prepared in a few hours at 5°. The systems developed are varied and often involve a large number of components. In place of the persulphate used in the earlier manufacture of GR-S, a three-component catalyst system is typically employed, comprising a peroxide (e.g., cumene hydroperoxide), a reducing agent (e.g., a sugar or an amine), and ferrous pyrophosphate (see Symposium on low-temperature rubber, Ind. Eng. Chem., 1949, **41**, 1553–1621; *G. S. Whitby et al.*, *ibid.*, 1950, **42**, 445; *V. C. Neklutin et al.*, *ibid.*, 1951, **43**, 1246; *C. S. Marvel et al.*, J. Polymer Sci., 1948, **3**, 128, 433; *I. M. Kolthoff et al.*, *ibid.*, 1949, **4**, 377; 1950, **5**, 391).

(iv) Friedel-Crafts polymerisation catalysts

In the manufacture of elastomers this technique is important only for "Butyl" rubber (pp. 429, 435). Typical conditions comprise polymerisation of *iso*butene, mixed with a few per-cent of butadiene or isoprene, in a diluent at about −100°, with a little boron trifluoride (or similar reactive halide) as catalyst (*R. M. Thomas et al.*, J. Amer. chem. Soc., 1940, **62**, 276; Ind. Eng. Chem., 1940, **32**, 1283). Such low-temperature polymerisations are extremely rapid and are believed to proceed by an ionic mechanism.

(c) Structure of synthetic elastomers from dienes

The structure of polymers from any particular monomer or monomer-mixture is variable. It depends upon the polymerisation technique, upon the catalyst, modifier, and other ingredients employed in the polymerisation, upon the temperature used, and upon the percentage conversion of monomer into polymer. The generalisation may, however, be made that all synthetic polymers and copolymers from diene hydrocarbons differ from natural polyisoprenes in the non-uniform character of the linkages between monomer units in the chain. Thus, a characteristic section of butadiene/styrene copolymer might be:

$$\mathrm{m\,CH_2{:}CH{\cdot}CH{:}CH_2 + n\,CH_2{:}CH{\cdot}C_6H_5 \longrightarrow}$$

$$\mathrm{\vdots CH_2{\cdot}CH{:}CH{\cdot}CH_2 \vdots CH_2{\cdot}CH(C_6H_5) \vdots CH_2{\cdot}CH{:}CH{\cdot}CH_2 \vdots CH_2{\cdot}\underset{\underset{CH_2}{\overset{\cdot\cdot}{\dot{C}H}}}{CH} \vdots CH_2{\cdot}CH{:}CH{\cdot}CH_2 \vdots}$$

(1:4) (1:4) (1:2) (1:4)

This shows a styrene unit incorporated among butadiene units, some of which are linked by 1:4-bonds (as in natural polyisoprenes), but others by 1:2-bonds (cf. p. 399). The effect of 1:2-bonds is to create vinyl side-chains, and, since such unsaturated groups may become incorporated in other chains during polymerisation, the resulting polymer may possess highly branched or cross-linked molecules, rather than linear molecules. If the diene is unsymmetrical, as in the case of isoprene, a 1:2-linkage differs from a 3:4-linkage; i.e. the side-chains could be $\cdot CH{:}CH_2$ or $\cdot CMe{:}CH_2$. The possibility that the residual (2:3-) double bonds in the chain may be *cis* or *trans* provides a further variable. Elastomer structures have been investigated by the following methods.

(i) Physical methods

Infra-red absorption spectra have been used to show the presence of 1:2- and 1:4-linkages and to distinguish between *cis*- and *trans*-bonds (*H. W. Thompson* and *P. Torkington*, Trans. Faraday Soc., 1945, **41**, 246; *R. B. Barnes et al.*, Ind. Eng. Chem. Anal. Ed., 1943, **15**, 83; 1944, **16**, 9; *E. J. Hart* and *A. W. Meyer*, J. Amer. chem. Soc., 1949, **71**, 1980; *L. E. Nielsen et al.*, Ind. Eng. Chem., 1951, **43**, 341). Lack of crystallinity prevents the application of X-ray diffraction methods to butadiene polymers (cf. Neoprene and Butyl below).

(ii) Ozonolysis

As with natural rubber, degradation by ozone reveals the position of double bonds in the polymer (*R. Hill et al.*, Trans. Faraday Soc., 1939, **35**, 1067, 1073; *E. N. Alekseeva* and *R. M. Belitzkaya*, J. gen. Chem. U.S.S.R., 1941, **11**, 353, 358; *C. S. Marvel et al.*, J. Amer. chem. Soc., 1950, **72**, 3887; J. org. Chem., 1951, **16**, 838). In general, the recovery of oxidation products is not as high as can be attained with natural rubber.

(iii) Oxidation by permanganate

According to *Konrad* and *Becker (loc. cit.)* this method of degradation has advantages over ozonolysis (cf. *F. J. Naples* and *J. D. D'Ianni*, Ind. Eng. Chem., 1951, **43**, 471).

(iv) Perbenzoic acid titration

This method depends upon the fact that double bonds in the main chain of the polymer react more readily than those in the vinyl side-chains when treated with perbenzoic acid, $C_6H_5{\cdot}CO{\cdot}O{\cdot}OH$, to form epoxides (*Konrad* and *Becker, loc. cit.*, F.I.A.T. Report 618; *I. M. Kolthoff et al.*, J. Polymer Sci, 1947, **2**, 206, 220;

J. D. D'Ianni, Ind. Eng. Chem., 1948, **40**, 253; *A. Saffer* and *B. L. Johnson*, *ibid.*, 1948, **40**, 538). Kolthoff's figures for side-chain bonds vary from 20% or less (in emulsion polymers) to 60% or more (sodium-catalysed polymers).

(d) Properties of individual types of elastomers derived from dienes

(i) Polymers and copolymers of 1:3-butadiene and its homologues

The most important product of this type, butadiene/styrene emulsion copolymer, is very roughly comparable with natural rubber in molecular size, in the kind of solvents which affect it, in reactions due to ethylenic unsaturation, in its capacity to undergo oxidation by air and oxidising agents, in its vulcanisation characteristics, and in the tensile properties of its vulcanisates. Its heterogeneous, branched structure is reflected in its high content of "gel" material, which has high molecular weight and limited swelling capacity in organic solvents, and in its toughness and the difficulty of working it on a hot mill. The latter property has led, in industrial use, to its plasticisation by hot-air treatment or by incorporation of softeners. The properties of the polymer may be widely modified by varying the styrene content.

Chemical modification appears to proceed more readily with synthetic polyisoprenes (in which there has been revived interest in the U.S.A.) than with butadiene/styrene interpolymers. The former have been converted into cyclised products (with stannic chloride), chlorinated derivatives, and hydrochloride (*J. D. D'Ianni et al.*, Ind. Eng. Chem., 1946, **38**, 1171; *G. Kraus* and *W. B.. Reynolds*, J. Amer. chem. Soc., 1950, **72**, 5621).

(ii) Polychloroprene (Neoprene)

Chloroprene polymerises very readily, to give elastic polymers which have a density of about 1·23 and afford a crystalline X-ray diagram on stretching (*W. H. Carothers et al., loc. cit.*), or on cooling. *C. W. Bunn* showed the crystal structure to be analogous to that of *β*-gutta-percha, with *trans*-bonds in the chain (Proc. roy. Soc., 1942, A, **180**, 40). **Neoprene** is generally considered to contain predominantly 1:4-linkages, i.e.

$$—CH_2·CCl{:}CH·CH_2·CH_2·CCl{:}CH·CH_2—$$

Typical Neoprene GN contains polymer of varying molecular weight up to about 1,000,000, but species with a molecular weight af about 100,000 predominate (*W. E. Mochel et al.*, J. Amer. chem. Soc., 1948, **70**, 2185). It swells less strongly than natural rubber in organic solvents, and is more resistant to oxidation and to attack by chemical reagents in general. It can be masticated like natural rubber but differs in the method of vulcanisation, which, for most Neoprene types, is effected, without sulphur, by metallic oxides, particularly those of zinc and magnesium (*H. W. Starkweather* and *H. W. Walker*, Ind. Eng. Chem., 1937, **29**, 872; *L. R. Mayo, ibid.*, 1950, **42**, 696; *D. B. Forman et al., ibid.*, 1950, **42**, 686).

(iii) Butyl rubbers (cf. p. 429)

These are highly extensible elastomers in which the diene units, incorporated in the poly*iso*butene chain in quantity equivalent to only 1–3% of the unsaturation of natural rubber, permit vulcanisation of the product with sulphur and active accelerators (*R. M. Thomas et al., ibid.*, 1940, **32**, 1283; *J. P. Haworth* and *F. P. Baldwin, ibid.*, 1942, **34**, 1301). Butyl rubber may contain structures such as:

$$—CH_2\cdot CMe_2\cdot CH_2\cdot CMe_2\cdot CH_2\cdot CH{:}CH\cdot CH_2\cdot CH_2\cdot CMe_2—$$

On stretching, it gives essentially the same crystalline X-ray diffraction pattern as unmodified poly*iso*butene (*L. B. Sebrell, ibid.*, 1943, **35**, 736; cf. *C. W. Bunn*, Adv. Colloid Sci., 1946, II, 125). The density is 0·91. Molecular weights approaching 100,000 have been reported. Butyl has a relatively high degree of inertness towards chemical reagents. Its vulcanisates resemble those of natural rubber reasonably well and their very low gas-permeability makes Butyl valuable in the manufacture, for example, of the inner tubes of tyres.

(e) Elastomers not based on dienes

Rubber-like properties depend essentially upon the intermolecular and intramolecular forces, and the steric factors, which operate in polymer chains. Although polymers derived from dienes have by far the greatest importance as synthetic elastomers, polymers of several other chemical types, as shown below, have come into use.

(i) Polyesters

An elastomer occurring in the seeds of *Smilax rotundifolia* is reported to be a polyester (*A. R. Kemp* and *H. Peters*, India Rubber World, 1944, **110**, 639). Some types of synthetic polyesters are rubbery (e.g. Paraplex, probably from propylene glycol and sebacic acid; see *B. S. Biggs et al.*, Ind. Eng. Chem., 1947, **39**, 1090). Certain polyester-amides (Vulcaprene, from ethylene glycol, ethanolamine and adipic acid) have also been developed as elastomers (*D. A. Harper*, Trans. Instn. Rubb. Ind., 1948, **24**, 181).

(ii) Polyacrylates

Certain polyacrylic compositions have rubbery properties. These include an interpolymer from ethyl acrylate (Vol. I, p. 631) and 2-chloroethyl vinyl ether (95 and 5% respectively), which has been developed industrially as Lactoprene EV (*W. C. Mast et al.*, Ind. Eng. Chem., 1946, **38**, 960; 1949, **41**, 703).

(iii) Polysulphides

J. C. Patrick made use of the condensation between dihalides and sodium polysulphides to obtain rubbery polymers, developed in the United States as Thiokol, e.g.

$$CH_2Cl\cdot CH_2Cl + Na_2S_4 \longrightarrow —CH_2\cdot CH_2\cdot S_4\cdot CH_2\cdot CH_2\cdot S_4\cdot CH_2\cdot CH_2—$$

(U.S.P. 1,890,191, 1932; Trans. Faraday Soc., 1936, **32**, 347; Ind. Eng. Chem., 1936, **28**, 1144).

(iv) Silicones

This large group of polymers (see *E. G. Rochow*, Chemistry of Silicones, New York, 1946) includes rubbery types. These are reported to be linear poly(dimethylsiloxanes) formed, e.g., by the process:

$$SiMe_2Cl_2 + H_2O \longrightarrow —O\cdot Si:Me_2\cdot O\cdot SiMe_2\cdot O\cdot SiMe_2—$$

(v) Polyvinyl chloride

This material (p. 406) represent a borderline type, equally well classified with plastics. In its usual plasticised condition polyvinyl chloride is a flexible, somewhat rubbery material which can be used in place of natural rubber for some surposes, such as insulation for electric cables.

Additional general bibliography

The following works are additional to those mentioned in the text.

C. O. Weber, Chemistry of India Rubber, London, 1919; *C. D. Harries*, Untersuchungen über die Natürlichen und Künstlichen Kautschukarten, Berlin, 1919; *C. W. Bedford* and *H. A. Winkelmann*, Systematic Survey of Rubber Chemistry, New York, 1923; *H. L. Fisher*, Chemistry of Rubber, Chem. Reviews, 1930, **7**, 51; *F. Marchionna*, Latex and its Applications, New York, 1933; *K. Memmler* (editor), The Science of Rubber (translated by *R. F. Dunbrook* and *V. N. Morris*), New York, 1934; *T. R. Dawson* and *B. D. Porritt*, Rubber, Physical and Chemical Properties, Croydon, England, 1935; Beilstein's Handbuch der Organischen Chemie, 1938, Vol. 30, Rubber and derivatives; *C. E. H. Bawn*, Chemistry of High Polymers, London, 1948; *R. Houwink* (editor), Elastomers and Plastomers, Their Chemistry, Physics, and Technology, 3 Vols., New York, Amsterdam, London, Brussels, 1948–1950; *G. Martin et al.*, Natural Rubber, Dict. appl. Chem. 1950, **10**, 550–578; *R. F. Dunbrook* and *H. L. Fisher*, Synthetic Rubber, *ibid.*, 1950, **10**, 578–636; *E. M. Frith* and *R. F. Tuckett*, Linear Polymers, London, 1951.

INDEX

EXPLANATORY NOTE TO THE INDEX

The explanatory note to the Index of Vol. IA has been followed as far as possible.

The following prefixes have not been counted for alphabetising:

n	*as*	*meso*	*d*-	D-	C-
iso	*s*	*cis*	*dl*-	DL-	N-
sec.	*gem.*	*trans*	*l*-	L-	O-
tert.	*vic.*				S-

In the case of ethyl esters entries have normally been cut down to "ester" or "—, ester" at the end, the repeat sign referring to the corresponding acid.

In a very small number of cases where one compound of the same name but different numbering appears in the same small section of the text, the entries have been condensed in one (plural) entry.

Optically active compounds are placed in the order *d*-, *dl*-, *l*-.

INDEX

PRINTED IN THE NETHERLANDS BY
DRUKKERIJ MEIJER, WORMERVEER AND AMSTERDAM